Finite Difference Schemes and Partial Differential Equations

$$u_t + a u_x = 0$$

$$\hat{u}_t + i a \hat{u} = 0$$

$$\frac{\hat{u}_t}{\hat{u}} = -ia$$

$$\hat{u} = \hat{u}(0)\, e^{-ia\omega t}$$

$$\hat{u}(t,\omega) = \hat{u}(0)\, e^{-iat}$$

$$\hat{u}(t+k,\omega) = \hat{u}(0)\, e^{-iat}\, e^{-iak}$$

$$= e^{-iak}\, \hat{u}(t,\omega)$$

$$\hat{u}^{n+1} = e^{-iak}\, \hat{u}^{n}$$

The Wadsworth & Brooks/Cole Mathematics Series

Finite Difference Schemes and Partial Differential Equations

John C. Strikwerda
University of Wisconsin – Madison

Wadsworth & Brooks/Cole Advanced Books & Software
Pacific Grove, California

Wadsworth & Brooks/Cole Advanced Books & Software
A Division of Wadsworth, Inc.

Printed in the United States of America
10   9   8   7   6   5   4   3

Library of Congress Cataloging-in-Publication Data

Strikwerda, John C., [date]–
    Finite difference schemes and partial differential equations /
John C. Strikwerda.
        p.   cm.
    Bibliography: p.
    Includes index.
    ISBN 0-534-09984-X :
    1. Differential equations, Partial—Numerical solutions.
2. Finite differences.   I. Title.
QA374.S88 1989
515.3'53—dc19

Sponsoring Editor: John Kimmel
Editorial Assistant: Jennifer Greenwood
Production Editor: Phyllis Larimore, Marjorie Sanders
Manuscript Editor: Linda Thompson
Cover Design: Roy Neuhaus
Art Coordinator: Lisa Torri
Printing and Binding: Arcata Graphics, Fairfield

Preface

This text presents the basic theory of finite difference schemes applied to the numerical solution of partial differential equations. It is designed to be used as an introductory graduate text for students in applied mathematics, engineering, and the sciences, and with that in mind, presents the theory of finite difference schemes in a way that is both rigorous and accessible to the typical graduate student in the course. The two aims of the text are to present the basic material necessary to do scientific computation with finite difference schemes and to present the basic theory for understanding these methods.

The text was developed for two courses: a basic introduction to finite difference schemes for partial differential equations and an upper-level graduate course on the theory related to initial value problems. Because students in these courses have diverse backgrounds in mathematics, the text presumes knowledge only through advanced calculus, although some mathematical maturity is required for the more advanced topics. Students taking an introduction to finite difference schemes are often acquainted with partial differential equations, but many have not had a formal course on the subject. For this reason, much of the necessary theory of partial differential equations is developed in the text.

The chief motivation for this text was the desire to present the material on time-dependent equations, Chapters 1 through 11, in a unified way that was accessible to students who would use the material in scientific and engineering studies. Chapters 1 through 11 contain much that is not in any other textbook, but more important, the unified treatment, using Fourier analysis, emphasizes that one can study finite difference schemes using a few powerful ideas to understand most of their properties. The material on elliptic partial differential equations, Chapters 12, 13, and 14, is intended to be only an introduction; it should enable students to progress to more advanced texts and implement the basic methods knowledgeably.

Several distinctive features of this textbook are:

- The fundamental concepts of convergence, consistency, and stability play an important role from the beginning.

- The concept of order of accuracy of a finite difference scheme is carefully presented with a single basic method of determining the order of accuracy of a scheme.
- Convergence proofs are given relating the order of accuracy of the scheme to that of the solution. A complete proof of the Lax-Richtmyer equivalence theorem, for the simple case of constant coefficient equations, is presented using methods accessible to most students in the course.
- Fourier analysis is used throughout the text to give a unified treatment of many of the important ideas.
- The basic theory of well-posed initial value problems is presented.
- The basic theory of well-posed initial-boundary value problems is presented for both partial differential equations and finite difference schemes.

A suggested one-semester introductory course can cover most of the material in Chapters 1, 2, 3, 5, 6, 7, 12, 13, and 14 and parts of Chapters 4 and 10. A more advanced course could concentrate on Chapters 9, 10, and 11.

In many textbooks on finite difference schemes, the discussion of the von Neumann stability condition does not make it clear when one may use the restricted condition and when one must use the general condition. In this text, theorems showing when the restricted condition may be used are stated and proved. The treatment given here was motivated by discussions with engineers and engineering students who were using the restricted condition when the more general condition was called for.

The treatment of accuracy of finite difference schemes is new and is an attempt to make the method for analyzing accuracy a rigorous procedure, rather than a grab-bag of quite different methods. This treatment is a result of queries from students who used textbook methods, but were confused because they employed the wrong "trick" at the wrong time. Because many applications involve inhomogeneous equations, I have included the forcing function in the analysis of accuracy.

The convergence results of Chapter 10 are unique to this textbook. Both students and practicing computational engineers are often puzzled about why second-order accurate schemes do not always produce solutions that are accurate of second order. Indeed, some texts give students the impression that solutions to finite difference schemes are always computed with the accuracy of the scheme. The important results in Chapter 10 show how the order of accuracy of the scheme is related to the accuracy of the solution and the smoothness of the solution.

The material on Schur and von Neumann polynomials in Chapter 4 also appears in a textbook for the first time. Tony Chan deserves credit for calling my attention to Miller's method, which should be more widely known. The analysis of stability for multilevel, higher-order accurate schemes is not practical without methods such as Miller's.

There are two topics that, regretfully, have been omitted from this text due to limitations of time and space. These are nonlinear hyperbolic equations and the multigrid methods for elliptic equations. Also, it would have been nice to include more material on variable grids, grid generations techniques, and other topics related to actual scientific computing. But I have decided to leave these embellishments to others or to later editions.

The numbering of the theorems, lemmas, and corollaries is done as a group. That is, the corollary after Theorem 2.2.1 is numbered 2.2.2, and the next theorem is Theorem 2.2.3. The end of each proof is marked with the symbol ▌ and the end of each example is marked with the symbol □.

Many students have offered comments on the course notes from which this book evolved and they have improved the material immensely. Special thanks go to Scott Markel, Naomi Decker, Bruce Wade, and Poon Fung for detecting many typographical errors. I also acknowledge the reviewers, William Coughran, AT&T Bell Laboratories; Max Gunzberger, Carnegie-Mellon University; Joseph Oliger, Stanford University; Nick Trefethen, Massachusetts Institute of Technology; and Bruce Wade, Cornell University, for their helpful comments.

John C. Strikwerda

Contents

APPENDICES

Chapter 1

Hyperbolic Partial Differential Equations

We begin our study of finite difference methods for partial differential equations by considering the important class of partial differential equations called hyperbolic equations. In later chapters we consider other classes of partial differential equations, especially parabolic and elliptic equations. For each of these classes of equations we consider prototypical equations, with which we illustrate the important concepts and distinguishing features associated with each class. The reader is referred to textbooks on partial differential equations for other approaches to partial differential equations, e.g., Folland [16], Garabedian [20], Weinberger [57]. After introducing each class of differential equations we consider finite difference methods for the numerical solution of equations in the class.

We begin this chapter by considering the simplest hyperbolic equation and then extend our discussion to include hyperbolic systems of equations and equations with variable coefficients. After the basic concepts have been introduced, we begin our discussion of finite difference schemes. The important concepts of convergence, consistency, and stability are presented and shown to be related by the Lax-Richtmyer equivalence theorem. The chapter concludes with a discussion of the Courant-Friedrichs-Lewy condition and related topics.

1.1 Overview of Hyperbolic Partial Differential Equations

The One-Way Wave Equation

The prototype for all hyperbolic partial differential equations is the one-way wave equation:

$$u_t + au_x = 0 \tag{1.1.1}$$

where a is a constant, t represents time, and x represents the spatial variable. The subscript denotes differentiation, i.e., $u_t = \partial u/\partial t$. We give $u(t,x)$ at the initial time, which we always take to be 0—that is, $u(0,x)$ is required to be equal to a given function $u_0(x)$ for all real numbers x—and we wish to determine the values of $u(t,x)$ for positive values of t. This is called an *initial value problem*.

1

By inspection we observe that the solution of (1.1.1) is

$$u(t, x) = u_0(x - at). \tag{1.1.2}$$

(Actually, we know only this is *a* solution; we prove later that this is the unique solution.)

The formula (1.1.2) tells us several things. First, the solution at any time t_0 is a copy of the original function, but shifted to the right, if a is positive, or left, if a is negative, by an amount $|a|t_0$. Another way to say this is that the solution at (t, x) depends only on the value of $\xi = x - at$. The lines in the (t, x) plane on which $x - at$ is constant are called *characteristics*. The parameter a has dimensions of distance divided by time and is called the speed of propagation along the characteristic. Thus the solution of (1.1.1) can be regarded as a wave that propagates with speed a without change of shape, as illustrated in Figure 1.1.

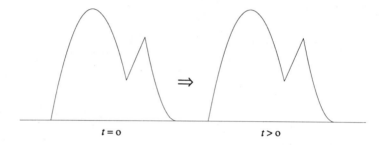

$t = 0$ $\qquad\qquad\qquad\qquad\qquad\qquad\qquad$ $t > 0$

Figure 1.1

Secondly, whereas (1.1.1) appears to make sense only if u is differentiable, (1.1.2) requires no differentiability of u_0. In general, we allow for discontinuous solutions for hyperbolic problems. An example of a discontinuous solution is a shock wave, which is a feature of solutions of nonlinear hyperbolic equations.

To illustrate further the concept of characteristics, consider the more general hyperbolic equation

$$u_t + au_x + bu = f(t, x)$$
$$u(0, x) = u_0(x) \tag{1.1.3}$$

where a and b are constants. Based on our preceding observations we change variables from (t, x) to (τ, ξ), where τ and ξ are defined by

$$\tau = t \qquad \xi = x - at.$$

The inverse transformation is then

$$t = \tau \qquad x = \xi + a\tau,$$

and we define $\tilde{u}(\tau, \xi) = u(t, x)$, where (τ, ξ) and (t, x) are related by the preceding relations. (Both u and $\tilde{u}$ represent the same function, but the tilde is needed to distinguish between the two coordinate systems for the independent variables.) Equation (1.1.3) then becomes

$$\frac{\partial \tilde{u}}{\partial \tau} = \frac{\partial t}{\partial \tau} u_t + \frac{\partial x}{\partial \tau} u_x$$

$$= u_t + a u_x = -bu + f(\tau, \xi + a\tau).$$

So we have

$$\frac{\partial \tilde{u}}{\partial \tau} = -b\tilde{u} + f(\tau, \xi + a\tau).$$

This is an ordinary differential equation in τ and the solution is

$$\tilde{u}(\tau, \xi) = u_0(\xi) e^{-b\tau} + \int_0^\tau f(\sigma, \xi + a\sigma) e^{-b(\tau - \sigma)} \, d\sigma.$$

Returning to the original variables, we obtain the representation for the solution of equation (1.1.3) as

$$u(t, x) = u_0(x - at) e^{-bt} + \int_0^t f(s, x - a(t - s)) e^{-b(t - s)} \, ds. \qquad (1.1.4)$$

We see from (1.1.4) that $u(t, x)$ depends only on values of (t', x') such that $x' - at' = x - at$, i.e., only on the values of u and f on the characteristic through (t, x) for $0 \le t' \le t$.

This method of solution of (1.1.3) is easily extended to nonlinear equations of the form

$$u_t + a u_x = f(t, x, u). \qquad (1.1.5)$$

See Exercises 1.1.1, 1.1.2, and 1.1.3.

Systems of Hyperbolic Equations

We now examine systems of hyperbolic equations with constant coefficients in one space dimension. The variable u is now a vector of dimension d.

Definition 1.1.1   *A system of the form*

$$u_t + A u_x + B u = F(t, x) \qquad (1.1.6)$$

is hyperbolic if the matrix A is diagonalizable with real eigenvalues.

By saying that the matrix A is *diagonalizable*, we mean that there is a nonsingular matrix P such that $P A P^{-1}$ is a diagonal matrix, that is,

$$P A P^{-1} = \begin{pmatrix} a_1 & & 0 \\ & \ddots & \\ 0 & & a_d \end{pmatrix} = \Lambda.$$

The eigenvalues a_i of A are the characteristic speeds of the system. Under the change of variables $w = Pu$ we have, in the case $B = 0$,

$$w_t + \Lambda\, w_x = PF(t, x) = \tilde{F}(t, x)$$

or

$$w_t^i + a_i\, w_x^i = \tilde{f}^i(t, x),$$

which is the form of (1.1.3). Thus when matrix B is zero, the one-dimensional hyperbolic system (1.1.6) reduces to a set of independent scalar hyperbolic equations. If B is not zero, then in general the resulting system of equations is coupled together, but only in the undifferentiated terms. The effect of the lower-order term, Bu, is to cause growth, decay, or oscillations in the solution, but it does not alter the primary feature of the propagation of the solution along the characteristics. The definition of hyperbolic systems in more than one space dimension is given in Chapter 9.

Example 1.1.1 As an example of a hyperbolic system we consider the system

$$u_t + 2u_x + v_x = 0$$
$$v_t + u_x + 2v_x = 0,$$

which can be written as

$$\begin{pmatrix} u \\ v \end{pmatrix}_t + \begin{pmatrix} 2 & 1 \\ 1 & 2 \end{pmatrix} \begin{pmatrix} u \\ v \end{pmatrix}_x = 0.$$

As initial data we take

$$u(x, 0) = u_0(x) = \begin{cases} 1 & \text{if } |x| \le 1, \\ 0 & \text{if } |x| > 1, \end{cases}$$
$$v(x, 0) = 0.$$

By adding and subtracting the two equations, the system can be rewritten as

$$(u + v)_t + 3(u + v)_x = 0$$
$$(u - v)_t + (u - v)_x = 0$$

or

$$w_t^1 + 3w_x^1 = 0 \qquad w^1(0, x) = u_0(x)$$
$$w_t^2 + w_x^2 = 0 \qquad w^2(0, x) = u_0(x).$$

The matrix P is $\begin{pmatrix} 1 & 1 \\ 1 & -1 \end{pmatrix}$ for this transformation. The solution is, therefore,

$$w^1(t, x) = w_0^1(x - 3t)$$
$$w^2(t, x) = w_0^2(x - t)$$

or

$$u(t, x) = \tfrac{1}{2}(w^1 + w^2) = \tfrac{1}{2}\left[u_0(x - 3t) + u_0(x - t)\right]$$

$$v(t, x) = \tfrac{1}{2}(w^1 - w^2) = \tfrac{1}{2}\left[u_0(x - 3t) - u_0(x - t)\right].$$

These formulas show that the solution consists of two independent parts, one propagating with speed 3 and one with speed 1. □

Equations with Variable Coefficients

We now examine equations for which the characteristic speed is a function of t and x. Consider the equation

$$u_t + a(t, x)u_x = 0 \qquad (1.1.7)$$

with initial condition $u(0, x) = u_0(x)$, which has the variable speed of propagation $a(t, x)$. If, as we did after equation (1.1.3), we change variables to τ and ξ, where $\tau = t$ and ξ is as yet undetermined, we have

$$\frac{\partial \tilde{u}}{\partial \tau} = \frac{\partial t}{\partial \tau} u_t + \frac{\partial x}{\partial \tau} u_x$$

$$= u_t + \frac{\partial x}{\partial \tau} u_x.$$

In analogy with the constant coefficient case, we set

$$\frac{dx}{d\tau} = a(t, x) = a(\tau, x).$$

This is an ordinary differential equation for x giving the speed along the characteristic through the point (τ, x) as $a(\tau, x)$. We set the initial value for the characteristic curve through (τ, x) to be ξ. Thus (1.1.7) is equivalent to the system of ordinary differential equations

$$\frac{d\tilde{u}}{d\tau} = 0, \qquad \tilde{u}(0, \xi) = u_0(\xi),$$

$$\frac{dx}{d\tau} = a(\tau, x), \qquad x(0) = \xi. \qquad (1.1.8)$$

As we see from the first equation in (1.1.8), u is constant along each characteristic curve, but the characteristic need not be a straight line. We now present an example to illustrate these ideas.

Example 1.1.2 Consider the equation

$$u_t + x\, u_x = 0$$

$$u(0, x) = \begin{cases} 1 & \text{if } 0 \le x \le 1, \\ 0 & \text{otherwise.} \end{cases}$$

Corresponding to (1.1.8) we have the equations

$$\frac{d\tilde{u}}{d\tau} = 0, \qquad \frac{dx}{d\tau} = x, \qquad x(0) = \xi.$$

The general solution of the differential equation for $x(\tau)$ is $x(\tau) = ce^\tau$. Because we specify that ξ is defined by $x(0) = \xi$, we have $x(\tau) = \xi e^\tau$, or $\xi = xe^{-t}$. The equation for $\tilde{u}$ shows that $\tilde{u}$ is independent of τ, so by the condition at τ equal to zero we have that

$$\tilde{u}(\tau, \xi) = u_0(\xi).$$

Thus

$$u(t, x) = \tilde{u}(\tau, \xi) = u_0(\xi) = u_0(xe^{-t}).$$

So we have, for $t > 0$,

$$u(t, x) = \begin{cases} 1 & \text{if } 0 \le x \le e^t, \\ 0 & \text{otherwise.} \end{cases} \qquad \square$$

As for equations with constant coefficients, these methods apply to nonlinear equations of the form

$$u_t + a(t, x)u_x = f(t, x, u). \tag{1.1.9}$$

See Exercise 1.1.7. Equations for which the characteristic speeds depend on u, i.e., with characteristic speed $a(t, x, u)$, require special care, since the characteristic curves may intersect.

Systems with Variable Coefficients

For systems of hyperbolic equations in one space variable with variable coefficients, we require uniform diagonalizability. (See Appendix A for a discussion of matrix norms.)

Definition 1.1.2   *The system*

$$u_t + A(t, x)\, u_x + B(t, x)u = F(t, x) \tag{1.1.10}$$

with

$$u(0, x) = u_0(x)$$

is hyperbolic if there is a matrix function $P(t, x)$ *such that*

$$P(t, x)\, A(t, x)\, P^{-1}(t, x) = \Lambda(t, x) = \begin{pmatrix} a_1(t, x) & & 0 \\ & \ddots & \\ 0 & & a_d(t, x) \end{pmatrix}$$

is diagonal with real eigenvalues and the matrix norms of $P(t,x)$ and $P^{-1}(t,x)$ are bounded in x and t for $x \in R$, $t \geq 0$.

The characteristic curves for system (1.1.10) are the solutions to the differential equations

$$\frac{dx^i}{dt} = a_i(t,x) \qquad x^i(0) = \xi^i.$$

Setting $v = P(t,x)u$ we obtain the system for v:

$$v_t + \Lambda v_x = P(t,x)\,F(t,x) + G(t,x)v$$

where

$$G = (P_t + \Lambda P_x - PB)P^{-1}.$$

In terms of directional derivatives this system is equivalent to

$$\left.\frac{dv^i}{dt}\right|_{\text{along } x^i} = \tilde{f}^i(t,x) + \sum_{j=1}^{d} g^i_j(t,x)v^j.$$

This formula is not a practical method of solution for most problems because the ordinary differential equations are often quite difficult to solve, but the formula does show the importance of characteristics for these systems.

EXERCISES 1.1

1. Show that the initial value problem for (1.1.5) is equivalent to the family of initial value problems for the ordinary differential equations

$$\frac{d\tilde{u}}{d\tau} = f(\tau, \xi + a\tau, \tilde{u})$$

with $\tilde{u}(0, \xi) = u_0(\xi)$. Show that the solution of (1.1.5), $u(t,x)$, is given by $u(t,x) = \tilde{u}(t, x - at)$.

2. Show that the solution of the initial value problem for

$$u_t + u_x = \cos^2 u$$

is given by

$$u(t,x) = \tan^{-1}\left\{\tan[u_0(x-t)] + t\right\}.$$

3. Show that all solutions to

$$u_t + a\,u_x = 1 + u^2$$

become unbounded in finite time. That is, $u(t,x)$ tends to infinity for some x as t approaches some value t^*, where t^* is finite.

4. Show that the initial value problem for the equation

$$u_t + \left(1 + x^2\right) u_x = 0$$

is not well defined. *Hint:* Consider the region covered by the characteristics originating on the x-axis.

5. Obtain the solution of the system

$$u_t + u_x + v_x = 0 \qquad u(x,0) = u_0(x)$$
$$v_t + u_x - v_x = 0 \qquad v(x,0) = v_0(x).$$

6. Solve the initial value problem for

$$u_t + \frac{1}{1 + \frac{1}{2}\cos x}\, u_x = 0.$$

Show that the solution is given by $u(t,x) = u_0(\xi)$ where ξ is the unique solution of $\xi + \frac{1}{2}\sin\xi = x + \frac{1}{2}\sin x - t$.

7. Show that the initial value problem for (1.1.9) is equivalent to the family of initial value problems for the system of ordinary differential equations

$$\frac{d\tilde{u}}{d\tau} = f(\tau, x(\tau), \tilde{u}), \qquad \tilde{u}(0, \xi) = u_0(\xi),$$
$$\frac{dx}{d\tau} = a(\tau, x(\tau)), \qquad x(0) = \xi.$$

The solution to (1.1.9) is given by $u\left(t, x(\xi)\right) = \tilde{u}(t, \xi)$.

1.2 Boundary Conditions

We now consider hyperbolic partial differential equations on a finite interval rather than on the whole real line. Most applications of partial differential equations involve domains with boundaries, and it is important to specify data correctly at these locations. The conditions relating the solution of the differential equation to data at a boundary are called boundary conditions. A more complete discussion of the theory of boundary conditions for time-dependent partial differential equations is given in Chapter 11. The problem of determining a solution to a differential equation when both initial data and boundary data are present is called an *initial-boundary value problem*. In this section we restrict the discussion to initial-boundary value problems for hyperbolic equations in one space variable.

The discussion of initial-boundary value problems serves to illustrate again the importance of the concept of characteristics. Consider the simple equation

$$u_t + a u_x = 0 \quad \text{with } 0 \le x \le 1,\ t \ge 0. \tag{1.2.1}$$

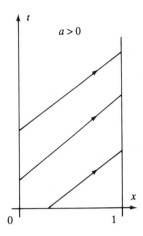
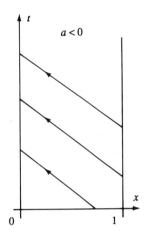

Figure 1.2
Characteristics for equation (1.2.1)

If a is positive the characteristics in this region propagate from the left to the right, as shown in Figure 1.2. By examining the characteristics in Figure 1.2, we see that the solution must be specified on the boundary at x equal to 0, in addition to the initial data, in order to be defined for all time. Moreover, no data can be supplied at the other boundary or the solution will be overdetermined.

If we specify initial data $u(0, x) = u_0(x)$ and boundary data $u(t, 0) = g(t)$, then the solution is given by

$$u(t, x) = \begin{cases} u_0(x - at) & \text{if } x - at > 0, \\ g(t - a^{-1}x) & \text{if } x - at < 0. \end{cases}$$

Along the characteristic given by $x - at = 0$, there will be a jump discontinuity in u if $u_0(0)$ is not equal to $g(0)$. If a is negative the roles of the two boundaries are reversed.

Now consider the hyperbolic system

$$\begin{pmatrix} u^1 \\ u^2 \end{pmatrix}_t + \begin{pmatrix} a & b \\ b & a \end{pmatrix} \begin{pmatrix} u^1 \\ u^2 \end{pmatrix}_x = 0 \tag{1.2.2}$$

on the interval $0 \le x \le 1$. The eigenvalues, or characteristic speeds, of the system are easily seen to be $a + b$ and $a - b$. We consider only the cases where a and b are positive. If we have $0 < b < a$, then both characteristic families propagate to the right, as shown in Figure 1.3. This means that the entire solution, both components u^1 and u^2, must be specified at x equal to 0, and no data should be specified at x equal to 1. Notice that the slope of the characteristic in these figures is the inverse of the speed. Thus the characteristics with the slower speed have the greater slope.

The most interesting case is where $0 < a < b$, since then the characteristic families propagate in opposite directions (see Figure 1.3). If system (1.2.2) is

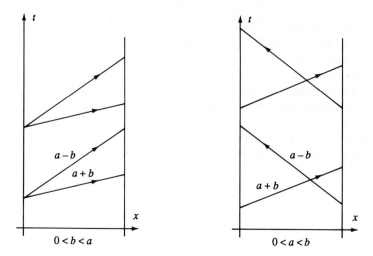

Figure 1.3
Characteristics for system (1.2.3)

put into the form (1.1.6), it is

$$\begin{pmatrix} u^1 + u^2 \\ u^1 - u^2 \end{pmatrix}_t + \begin{pmatrix} a+b & 0 \\ 0 & a-b \end{pmatrix} \begin{pmatrix} u^1 + u^2 \\ u^1 - u^2 \end{pmatrix}_x = 0. \tag{1.2.3}$$

Certainly one way to determine the solution uniquely is to specify $u^1 + u^2$ at x equal to 0 and specify $u^1 - u^2$ at x equal to 1. However, there are other possible boundary conditions; for example, any of the form

$$\begin{aligned} u^1 + u^2 &= \alpha_0(u^1 - u^2) + \beta_0(t) \quad \text{at } x = 0 \\ u^1 - u^2 &= \alpha_1(u^1 + u^2) + \beta_1(t) \quad \text{at } x = 1 \end{aligned} \tag{1.2.4}$$

will determine the solution. The coefficients α_0 and α_1 may be functions of t or constants.

As examples, we have that the boundary conditions

$$\begin{aligned} u^1(t, 0) &= \beta_0(t) \\ u^2(t, 1) &= \beta_1(t) \end{aligned}$$

can be put in the form

$$\begin{aligned} u^1(t, 0) + u^2(t, 0) &= -(u^1(t, 0) - u^2(t, 0)) + 2\beta_0(t), \\ u^1(t, 1) + u^2(t, 1) &= \quad u^1(t, 1) - u^2(t, 1) + 2\beta_1(t), \end{aligned}$$

which are equivalent to the conditions in (1.2.4) with α_0 and α_1 equal to -1 and 1, respectively.

Boundary conditions that determine a unique solution are said to be *well-posed*. For the system (1.2.3) the boundary conditions are well-posed if and only if they are equivalent to (1.2.4). The boundary conditions (1.2.4) express the value of the characteristic variable on the *incoming* characteristic in terms of the *outgoing* characteristic variable and the data. By incoming characteristic we mean a characteristic that enters the domain at the boundary under consideration; an outgoing characteristic is one that leaves the domain. We see then that specifying u^1 or u^2 at x equal to 0 is well-posed, and specifying u^1 or u^2 at x equal to 1 is also well-posed. However, specifying $u^1 - u^2$ at x equal to 0 is ill-posed, as is specifying $u^1 + u^2$ at x equal to 1.

For a hyperbolic initial-boundary value problem to be well-posed, the number of boundary conditions must be equal to the number of incoming characteristics. The procedure for determining whether or not an initial-boundary value problem is well-posed is given in Chapter 11.

Periodic Problems

Besides the initial value problem on the whole real line R, we can also consider periodic problems on an interval. For example, consider the one-way wave equation (1.1.1) on the interval $[0, 1]$, where the solution satisfies

$$u(t, 0) = u(t, 1), \qquad (1.2.5)$$

for all nonnegative values of t. Condition (1.2.5) is sometimes called the periodic boundary condition, but strictly speaking it is not a boundary condition, since for periodic problems there are no boundaries.

A periodic problem for a function $u(t, x)$ with x in the interval $[0, 1]$ is equivalent to one on the real line satisfying $u(t, x) = u(t, x + \ell)$ for every integer ℓ. Thus the function $u(t, x)$ is determined by its values of x in any interval of length 1, such as $[-\frac{1}{2}, \frac{1}{2}]$.

A periodic problem may also be regarded as being defined on a circle that is coordinatized by an interval with endpoints being identified. In this view there is a boundary in the coordinate system but not in the problem itself.

EXERCISES 1.2

1. Consider system (1.2.2) on the interval $[0, 1]$, with a equal to 0 and b equal to 1, and with the boundary conditions u^1 equal to 0 at the left and u^1 equal to 1 at the right boundary. Show that if the initial data are given by $u^1(0, x) = x$ and $u^2(0, x) = 1$, then the solution is $u^1(t, x) = x$, and $u^2(t, x) = 1 - t$, for all (t, x) with $0 \le x \le 1$ and $0 \le t$.

2. Consider system (1.2.2) on the interval $[0, 1]$, with a equal to 0 and b equal to 1 and with the boundary conditions u^1 equal to 0 at the left and u^1 equal to $1 + t$ at the right boundary. Show that if the initial data are given by

$u^1(0, x) = x$ and $u^2(0, x) = 1$, then for $0 \le x + t \le 3$ the solution is given by

$$
\begin{pmatrix} u^1(t,x) \\ u^2(t,x) \end{pmatrix} =
\begin{cases}
\begin{pmatrix} \dfrac{x}{1-t} \end{pmatrix} & \text{if } 0 \le t < 1 - x, \\[2ex]
\begin{pmatrix} 2x + t - 1 \\ 2 - x - 2t \end{pmatrix} & \text{if } 1 - x \le t < 1 + x, \\[2ex]
\begin{pmatrix} \dfrac{3x}{3(1-t)} \end{pmatrix} & \text{if } 1 + x \le t < 3 - x.
\end{cases}
$$

3.   Consider system (1.2.2) on the interval $[0, 1]$, with a equal to 0 and b equal to 1 and with the boundary conditions u^1 equal to 0 at both the left and the right boundaries. Show that if the initial data are given by $u^1(0, x) = x$ and $u^2(0, x) = 1$, then for $0 \le t \le 1$ the solution is given by

$$
\begin{pmatrix} u^1(t,x) \\ u^2(t,x) \end{pmatrix} =
\begin{cases}
\begin{pmatrix} \dfrac{x}{1-t} \end{pmatrix} & \text{if } 0 \le x < 1 - t, \\[2ex]
\begin{pmatrix} x - 1 \\ 2 - t \end{pmatrix} & \text{if } 1 - t \le x < 1.
\end{cases}
$$

4.   Show that the initial-boundary value problem of Exercise 3 has the solution for $1 \le t \le 2$ given by

$$
\begin{pmatrix} u^1(t,x) \\ u^2(t,x) \end{pmatrix} =
\begin{cases}
\begin{pmatrix} \dfrac{x}{3-t} \end{pmatrix} & \text{if } 0 \le x < t - 1, \\[2ex]
\begin{pmatrix} x - 1 \\ 2 - t \end{pmatrix} & \text{if } t - 1 < x < 1.
\end{cases}
$$

5.   Consider system (1.2.2) on the interval $[0, 1]$, with a equal to 1 and b equal to 2 and with the boundary conditions u^1 equal to 0 at the left and u^1 equal to 1 at the right boundary. Show that if the initial data are given by $u^1(0, x) = x$ and $u^2(0, x) = 1$, then for $0 \le t \le 1 + x$ the solution is given by

$$
\begin{pmatrix} u^1(t,x) \\ u^2(t,x) \end{pmatrix} =
\begin{cases}
\begin{pmatrix} \dfrac{x - t}{1 - 2t} \end{pmatrix} & \text{if } 0 \le t \le \min(\tfrac{1}{3}x, 1 - x), \\[2ex]
\begin{pmatrix} \frac{2}{3}x \\ 1 - \frac{1}{3}x - t \end{pmatrix} & \text{if } \tfrac{1}{3}x \le t \le 1 - x, \\[2ex]
\begin{pmatrix} 2x - 1 \\ 2 - x - 3t \end{pmatrix} & \text{if } 1 - x \le t \le \tfrac{1}{3}x, \\[2ex]
\begin{pmatrix} t + \frac{5}{3}x - 1 \\ 2 - 2t - \frac{4}{3}x \end{pmatrix} & \text{if } \max(\tfrac{1}{3}x, 1 - x) \le t \le \min(\tfrac{4}{3} - x, 1 + x), \\[2ex]
\begin{pmatrix} \frac{2}{3}x + \frac{1}{3} \\ \frac{2}{3} - \frac{1}{3}x - t \end{pmatrix} & \text{if } \tfrac{4}{3} - x \le t \le 1 + x.
\end{cases}
$$

1.3 Introduction to Finite Difference Schemes

We begin our discussion of finite difference schemes by defining a grid of points in the (t, x) plane. Let h and k be positive numbers; then the grid will be the points $(t_n, x_m) = (nk, mh)$ for arbitrary integers n and m. For a function v defined on the grid we write v_m^n for the value of v at the grid point (t_n, x_m). We also use the notation u_m^n for $u(t_n, x_m)$ when u is defined for continuously varying (t, x). The set of points (t_n, x_m) for a fixed value of n is called *grid level n*. We are interested in grids with small values of h and k.

The basic idea of finite difference schemes is to replace derivatives by finite differences. This can be done in many ways; as examples we have

$$\frac{\partial u}{\partial t}(nk, mh) \simeq \frac{u((n+1)k, mh) - u(nk, mh)}{k},$$

$$\simeq \frac{u((n+1)k, mh) - u((n-1)k, mh)}{2k}.$$

That these are valid approximations is seen from the formulas

$$\frac{\partial u}{\partial t}(t, x) = \lim_{\varepsilon \to 0} \frac{u(t+\varepsilon, x) - u(t, x)}{\varepsilon}$$

$$= \lim_{\varepsilon \to 0} \frac{u(t+\varepsilon, x) - u(t-\varepsilon, x)}{2\varepsilon},$$

relating the derivative to the values of u. Similar formulas approximate derivatives with respect to x.

Using these approximations we obtain the following five finite difference schemes for equation (1.1.1). Many other schemes are presented later.

$$\frac{v_m^{n+1} - v_m^n}{k} + a\frac{v_{m+1}^n - v_m^n}{h} = 0 \tag{1.3.1}$$

$$\frac{v_m^{n+1} - v_m^n}{k} + a\frac{v_m^n - v_{m-1}^n}{h} = 0 \tag{1.3.2}$$

$$\frac{v_m^{n+1} - v_m^n}{k} + a\frac{v_{m+1}^n - v_{m-1}^n}{2h} = 0 \tag{1.3.3}$$

$$\frac{v_m^{n+1} - v_m^{n-1}}{2k} + a\frac{v_{m+1}^n - v_{m-1}^n}{2h} = 0 \tag{1.3.4}$$

$$\frac{v_m^{n+1} - \frac{1}{2}\left(v_{m+1}^n + v_{m-1}^n\right)}{k} + a\frac{v_{m+1}^n - v_{m-1}^n}{2h} = 0 \tag{1.3.5}$$

We refer to scheme (1.3.1) as the forward-time forward-space scheme because forward difference approximations are used for both the time and space derivatives. Similarly (1.3.2) and (1.3.3) are referred to as the forward-time backward-space scheme and forward-time central-space scheme, respectively. The scheme

(1.3.4) is called the leapfrog scheme and (1.3.5) is called the Lax-Friedrichs scheme.

The method of deriving these five schemes is very simple. This is one of the significant features of the general method of finite differences, namely, that it is very easy to derive finite difference schemes for partial differential equations. However, the analysis of finite difference schemes to determine if they are good approximations to the differential equation requires some powerful mathematical tools. Moreover, to develop very efficient and accurate schemes requires more work than went into obtaining the schemes (1.3.1)–(1.3.5). Nonetheless, the finite difference method is notable for the great variety of schemes which can be used to approximate a given partial differential equation.

Given this short list of schemes we are naturally led to the question of which of them are useful and which are not, as indeed some are not. This is a basic question, and we spend some time and care in answering it. In fact the question can be answered on several levels. We first answer it on the most primitive level, determining which schemes have solutions that approximate solutions of the differential equation at all. Later on we determine which schemes are more accurate than others and also investigate the efficiency of the various schemes.

Each of the schemes (1.3.1)–(1.3.5) can be written expressing v_m^{n+1} as a linear combination of values of v at levels n and $n-1$. For example, scheme (1.3.1) can be written as

$$v_m^{n+1} = (1 + a\lambda) v_m^n - a\lambda v_{m+1}^n$$

where $\lambda = k/h$. The quantity λ will appear often in the study of schemes for hyperbolic equations and will always be equal to k/h. Those schemes that involve v at only two levels—e.g., $n+1$ and n—are called one-step schemes. Of the schemes just listed all except the leapfrog scheme (1.3.4) are one-step schemes. Given the initial data v_m^0, a one-step scheme can be used to evaluate v_m^n for all positive values of n.

The leapfrog scheme (1.3.4) is an example of a multistep scheme. For a multistep scheme it is not sufficient to specify the values of v_m^0 in order to determine v_m^n for all positive values of n. To specify completely the means of computing a solution to a multistep scheme we must either specify v on enough time levels so that the scheme can be employed or we must specify a procedure for computing the values of v on these initial time levels. For example, to use the leapfrog scheme we could specify the values of v_m^0 and v_m^1 for all m, or we could specify that scheme (1.3.1) would be used to compute the values of v_m^1 from the values v_m^0. In either case the leapfrog scheme (1.3.4) would be used to compute v_m^n for n greater than 1.

When we refer to the leapfrog scheme we do not always distinguish between these two ways of initializing the computation. As we show in Section 4.1, many of the properties of the leapfrog scheme are independent of the method used to initialize the solution. Since the usual practice is to use a one-step scheme to initialize the first time level, we usually assume that the initialization is done by using a one-step scheme. This is illustrated in Example 1.3.2. The subject of how to initialize schemes such as the leapfrog scheme is considered in more detail in Section 4.1.

Example 1.3.1 Before we proceed with the analysis of finite difference schemes, we present the results of some computations using two of the schemes just presented. We use the initial-boundary value problem

$$u_t + u_x = 0 \qquad \text{on} \qquad -2 \le x \le 3, 0 \le t$$

with initial data

$$u_0(x) = \begin{cases} 1 - |x| & \text{if } |x| \le 1, \\ 0 & \text{if } |x| \ge 1. \end{cases}$$

On the boundary at x equal to -2, we specify that u is zero.

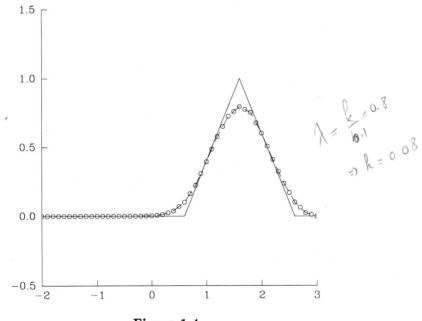

Figure 1.4

The first computation uses the Lax-Friedrichs scheme with $\lambda = 0.8$ and h equal to 0.1. At the right-hand boundary we use the condition $v_M^{n+1} = v_{M-1}^{n+1}$, where $x_M = 3$. For our initial data we take $v_m^0 = u_0(x_m)$. The computation proceeds using the formula

$$v_m^{n+1} = \tfrac{1}{2}\left(v_{m+1}^n + v_{m-1}^n\right) - \tfrac{1}{2}\lambda\left(v_{m+1}^n - v_{m-1}^n\right) \qquad (1.3.6)$$

to find the values of v_m^{n+1} for all values except those at the endpoints of the interval. A graph of the solution at $t = 1.6$ is shown in Figure 1.4. In the figure the exact solution to the differential equation is given by the solid line and

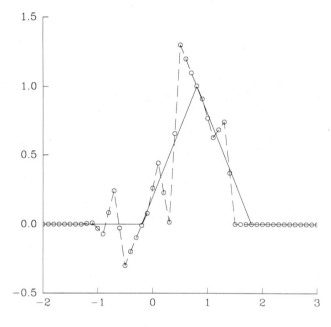

Figure 1.5

the solution of the scheme is shown as the curve with the circles. In Figure 1.4 we see that the finite difference scheme computes a reasonable solution, except that the computed solution does not maintain the sharp corners of the exact solution. A smaller value of h, with the same value of λ, improves the shape of the computed solution.

A similar calculation but using $\lambda = 1.6$ is shown in Figure 1.5 at $t = 0.8$. The figure shows that for this case the computed solution is not well-behaved. As the computation proceeds for larger values of t, the behavior becomes worse. Also, if the grid spacing is decreased, with λ fixed at 1.6, the behavior does not get better and in fact becomes worse. The explanation for this behavior is given in the next chapter. □

Example 1.3.2 The leapfrog scheme with $\lambda = 0.8$ gives much better results than does the Lax-Friedrichs scheme for the same initial-boundary value problem in Example 1.3.1. This is shown in Figure 1.6. Notice that the resolution of the peak in the solution is much better in Figure 1.6 than in Figure 1.4. The leapfrog scheme has a less smooth solution than does the Lax-Friedrichs, however, the small oscillations do not detract significantly from the accuracy. In Section 5.1 we discuss methods of removing these oscillations. At the right-hand boundary, v_M^{n+1} is computed as it was for the Lax-Friedrichs scheme.

As discussed before, the leapfrog scheme requires that another scheme be used to calculate the values at the time level with n equal to 1. For the calculations shown in Figure 1.6, the the forward-time central-space scheme (1.3.3) was used. □

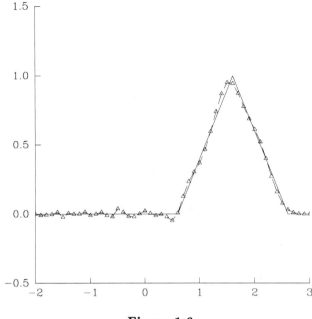

Figure 1.6

Computer Implementation of Finite Difference Schemes

To implement any of the finite difference schemes (1.3.1)–(1.3.5) or similar finite difference schemes in a computer program, values of the solution v_m^n should not be stored beyond the time steps in which they are needed. A simple way to do this is to use two one-dimensional arrays **vold** and **vnew**, each of which is indexed by the spatial grid indices. The values of **vnew(m)** and **vold(m)** correspond to v_m^{n+1} and v_m^n, respectively. For each value of n, **vnew**, corresponding to v^{n+1}, is computed using **vold**, corresponding to v^n. After **vnew** has been computed for all m, then **vold** must be reset to **vnew**, and the time step is incremented to the next value. For the leapfrog scheme the array **vnew** can be used to store both v^{n-1} and v^{n+1}.

Any values of the solution that are to be saved or plotted may be written to a file as they are computed. It is not advisable to save past values beyond the time they are needed in the computation.

A more convenient way to store the solution for schemes (1.3.1)–(1.3.5) is to use a two-dimensional array, such as **v(nmod,m)**, where **nmod** is equal to n modulo 2. The values of **v(0, ·)** are used to compute the values of **v(1, ·)**, which are used to compute **v(0, ·)**, and so on. This method avoids the need to reset arrays such as **vold**, which was set equal to **vnew** in the method described previously.

For periodic problems on the interval $[0, 1]$ with $h = 1/M$ and grid points $x_m = mh$, it is useful to store values at x_0 and at x_M, even though these values represent the same point in the periodic problem.

EXERCISES 1.3

1. For values of x in the interval $[-1, 3]$ and t in $[0, 2.4]$, solve the one-way wave equation

$$u_t + u_x = 0,$$

with the initial data

$$u(0, x) = \begin{cases} \cos^2 \pi x & \text{if } |x| \leq \frac{1}{2}, \\ 0 & \text{otherwise,} \end{cases}$$

and the boundary data $u(t, -1) = 0$.

Use the following four schemes:
  a. Forward-time backward-space with $\lambda = 0.8$ and with $h = \frac{1}{10}, \frac{1}{20}$, and $\frac{1}{40}$
  b. Forward-time central-space with $\lambda = 0.8$ and $h = \frac{1}{10}, \frac{1}{20}$, and $\frac{1}{40}$
  c. Lax-Friedrichs with $\lambda = 0.8$ and 1.6 and $h = \frac{1}{10}, \frac{1}{20}$, and $\frac{1}{40}$
  d. Leapfrog with $\lambda = 0.8$ and $h = \frac{1}{10}, \frac{1}{20}$, and $\frac{1}{40}$

For schemes (b), (c), and (d), at the right boundary use the condition $v_M^{n+1} = v_{M-1}^{n+1}$, where $x_M = 3$. For scheme (d) use scheme (b) to compute the solution at $n = 1$.

For each scheme determine whether the scheme is a useful or useless scheme. For the purposes of this exercise *only,* a scheme will be useless if $|v_m^n|$ is greater than 5 for any value of m and n. It will be regarded as a useful scheme if the solution looks like a reasonable approximation to the solution of the differential equations. Graph or plot several solutions at the last time they were computed. What do you notice about the "blow-up time" for the useless schemes as the mesh size decreases? Is there a pattern to these solutions? For the useful cases, how does the error decrease as the mesh decreases; i.e., as h decreases by $\frac{1}{2}$, by how much does the error decrease?

2. Solve the system

$$u_t + \tfrac{1}{3}(t - 2)u_x + \tfrac{2}{3}(t + 1)w_x + \tfrac{1}{3}u = 0$$
$$w_t + \tfrac{1}{3}(t + 1)u_x + \tfrac{1}{3}(2t - 1)w_x - \tfrac{1}{3}w = 0$$

by the Lax-Friedrichs scheme—that is, each time derivative is approximated as it is for the scalar equation and the spatial derivatives are approximated by central differences. The initial values are

$$u(0, x) = \max(0, 1 - |x|),$$
$$w(0, x) = \max(0, 1 - 2|x|).$$

Consider values of x in $[-3, 3]$ and t in $[0, 2]$. Take h equal to $\frac{1}{20}$ and λ equal to $\frac{1}{2}$. At each boundary set $u = 0$, and set w equal to the newly computed value one grid point in from the boundary. Describe the solution behavior for t in the range $[1.5, 2]$. You may find it convenient to plot the solution. Solve the system in the form given; do not attempt to diagonalize it.

3. Solve the system

$$u_t + \tfrac{1}{3}(t-2)u_x + \tfrac{2}{3}(t+1)w_x = 0$$
$$w_t + \tfrac{1}{3}(t+1)u_x + \tfrac{1}{3}(2t-1)w_x = 0$$

by the Lax-Friedrichs scheme as in Exercise 2, using the same initial data. An examination of the computed solution should show how to obtain the analytical solution to this problem.

1.4 Convergence and Consistency

The most basic property that a scheme must have in order to be useful is that its solutions approximate the solution of the corresponding partial differential equation and that the approximation improves as the grid spacings, h and k, tend to zero. We call such a scheme a *convergent scheme,* but before formally defining this concept it is appropriate to extend our discussion to a wider class of partial differential equations than the hyperbolic equations. We consider linear partial differential equations of the form

$$P(\partial_t, \partial_x)u = f(t, x)$$

which are of first order in the derivative with respect to t. We also assume for such equations or systems of equations that the specification of initial data, $u(0, x)$, completely determines a unique solution. More is said about this in Chapter 9. Examples of equations that are first order in time are the one-way wave equation (1.1.1) and the following three equations:

$$u_t - bu_{xx} + au_x = 0$$
$$u_t - cu_{txx} + bu_{xxxx} = 0 \qquad (1.4.1)$$
$$u_t + cu_{tx} + au_x = 0$$

Definition 1.4.1 *A one-step finite difference scheme approximating a partial differential equation is a convergent scheme if for any solution to the partial differential equation, $u(t, x)$, and solutions to the finite difference scheme, v_m^n, such that v_m^0 converges to $u_0(x)$ as mh converges to x, then v_m^n converges to $u(t, x)$ as (nk, mh) converges to (t, x) as h, k converge to 0.*

This definition is not complete until we clarify the nature of the convergence of v_m^n, defined on the grid, to $u(t, x)$ defined for continuously varying (t, x). We discuss this convergence completely in Chapter 10. For multistep schemes the definition assumes that some initializing procedure is used to compute the first several time levels necessary to employ the multistep scheme. For the case that the data are specified on these first time levels, the definition is altered to require v_m^j for $0 \leq j \leq J$ to converge to $u_0(x_m)$.

As illustrated by Figures 1.4 and 1.6, the Lax-Friedrichs scheme and the leapfrog scheme with λ equal to 0.8 are convergent schemes. These figures show that the solution of the difference scheme is a reasonable approximation to the solution of the differential equation. As h and k are decreased the solutions of the schemes become better approximations. The Lax-Friedrichs scheme with $\lambda = 1.6$ is not convergent. As h and k decrease, with λ equal to 1.6, the solution of the scheme does not approach the solution of the differential equation in any sense. As can be seen in Figure 1.5, the behavior of a nonconvergent scheme can be quite poor.

Proving that a given scheme is convergent is not easy in general, if attempted in a direct manner. However, there are two related concepts that are easy to check, consistency and stability. First, we define consistency.

Definition 1.4.2   *Given a partial differential equation $Pu = f$ and a finite difference scheme, $P_{k,h}v = f$, we say the finite difference scheme is consistent with the partial differential equation if for any smooth function $\phi(t,x)$*

$$P\phi - P_{k,h}\phi \to 0 \quad \text{as} \quad k, h \to 0,$$

the convergence being pointwise convergence at each grid point.

For some schemes we may have to restrict the manner in which k and h tend to zero in order for it to be consistent (see Example 1.4.2). When we refer to a smooth function we mean one that is sufficiently differentiable for the context.

We demonstrate the use of this definition and the notation by presenting two examples, showing that two of the schemes in the above list are consistent with the equation (1.1.1).

Example 1.4.1 The Forward-time Forward-space Scheme   For the one-way wave equation (1.1.1), the operator P is $\dfrac{\partial}{\partial t} + a\dfrac{\partial}{\partial x}$ so that

$$P\phi = \phi_t + a\phi_x.$$

For the forward-time forward-space scheme (1.3.1), the difference operator $P_{k,h}$ is given by

$$P_{k,h}\phi = \frac{\phi_m^{n+1} - \phi_m^n}{k} + a\frac{\phi_{m+1}^n - \phi_m^n}{h},$$

where

$$\phi_m^n = \phi(nk, mh).$$

We begin with the Taylor series of the function ϕ in t and x about (t_n, x_m). We have that

$$\phi_m^{n+1} = \phi_m^n + k\phi_t + \tfrac{1}{2}k^2\phi_{tt} + O(k^3),$$

$$\phi_{m+1}^n = \phi_m^n + h\phi_x + \tfrac{1}{2}h^2\phi_{xx} + O(h^3),$$

where the derivatives on the right-hand side are all evaluated at (t_n, x_m), and so

$$P_{k,h}\phi = \phi_t + a\phi_x + \tfrac{1}{2}k\phi_{tt} + \tfrac{1}{2}ah\phi_{xx} + O(k^2) + O(h^2).$$

Thus

$$P\phi - P_{k,h}\phi = -\tfrac{1}{2}k\phi_{tt} - \tfrac{1}{2}ah\phi_{xx} + O(k^2) + O(h^2)$$
$$\rightarrow 0 \quad \text{as} \quad (k,h) \rightarrow 0.$$

Therefore, this scheme is consistent. □

When analyzing consistency it is convenient to use the "big oh" and "little oh" notation, as we have done in the preceding example. In general, if F and G are functions of some parameter α, we write

$$F = O(G) \quad \text{as} \quad \alpha \rightarrow 0,$$

if

$$\left| \frac{F}{G} \right| \leq K$$

for some constant K and all α sufficiently small. We write

$$F = o(G) \quad \text{as} \quad \alpha \rightarrow 0,$$

if F/G converges to zero as α tends to zero. In particular, a quantity is $O(h^r)$ if it is bounded by a constant multiple of h^r for small h. A quantity is $o(1)$ if it converges to zero at an unspecified rate.

Example 1.4.2 The Lax-Friedrichs Scheme For the Lax-Friedrichs scheme,

$$P_{k,h}\phi = \frac{\phi_m^{n+1} - \tfrac{1}{2}\left(\phi_{m+1}^n + \phi_{m-1}^n\right)}{k} + a\frac{\phi_{m+1}^n - \phi_{m-1}^n}{2h},$$

we use the Taylor series

$$\phi_{m\pm1}^n = \phi_m^n \pm h\phi_x + \tfrac{1}{2}h^2\,\phi_{xx} \pm \tfrac{1}{6}h^3\phi_{xxx} + O(h^4),$$

where, as before, the derivatives are evaluated at (t_n, x_m). Using the Taylor series we have

$$\tfrac{1}{2}\left(\phi_{m+1}^n + \phi_{m-1}^n\right) = \phi_m^n + \tfrac{1}{2}h^2\,\phi_{xx} + O(h^4),$$

and

$$\frac{\phi_{m+1}^n - \phi_{m-1}^n}{2h} = \phi_x + \tfrac{1}{6}h^2\,\phi_{xxx} + O(h^4).$$

Substituting these expressions in the scheme, we obtain

$$P_{k,h}\phi = \phi_t + a\,\phi_x + \tfrac{1}{2}k\,\phi_{tt} - \tfrac{1}{2}k^{-1}h^2\,\phi_{xx}$$
$$+ \tfrac{1}{6}ah^2\,\phi_{xxx} + O\left(h^4 + k^{-1}h^4 + k^2\right)$$

So $P_{k,h}\phi - P\phi \rightarrow 0$ as $h, k \rightarrow 0$; i.e., it is consistent as long as $k^{-1}h^2 \rightarrow 0$. □

Consistency implies that the solution of the partial differential equation, if it is smooth, is an approximate solution of the finite difference scheme. Similarly, convergence means that a solution of the finite difference scheme approximates a solution of the partial differential equation. It is natural to consider whether consistency is sufficient for a scheme to be convergent. Consistency is certainly necessary for convergence, but as the following example shows, a scheme may be consistent but not convergent.

Example 1.4.3 Consider the partial differential equation $u_t + u_x = 0$ with the forward-time forward-space scheme,

$$\frac{v_m^{n+1} - v_m^n}{k} + \frac{v_{m+1}^n - v_m^n}{h} = 0.$$

The scheme may be rewritten as

$$v_m^{n+1} = v_m^n - \frac{k}{h}\left(v_{m+1}^n - v_m^n\right)$$

$$= (1 + \lambda)\, v_m^n - \lambda\, v_{m+1}^n$$

(1.4.2)

where we have set $\lambda = k/h$ as usual. In Example 1.4.1 this scheme was shown to be consistent. As initial conditions for the differential equation we take

$$u_0(x) = \begin{cases} 1 & \text{if } -1 \leq x \leq 0, \\ 0 & \text{elsewhere.} \end{cases}$$

The solution of the partial differential equation is a shift of u_0 to the right by t. In particular, for t greater than 0, there are positive values of x for which $u(t, x)$ is nonzero.

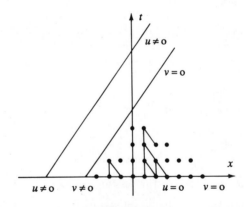

Figure 1.7

For the difference scheme take the initial data

$$v_m^0 = \begin{cases} 1 & \text{if } -1 \leq mh \leq 0, \\ 0 & \text{elsewhere.} \end{cases}$$

As equation (1.4.2) shows, the solution at (t_n, x_m) depends only on $x_{m'}$ for $m' \geq m$ at previous times. Thus we conclude that

$$v_m^n = 0 \qquad \text{for } m > 0, n \geq 0.$$

This is illustrated in Figure 1.7. Therefore, v_m^n can not converge to $u(t, x)$, since for positive t and x, the function u is not identically zero, yet v_m^n is zero. Notice that we conclude that the scheme is nonconvergent without specifying the type of convergence, but clearly, a sequence of functions that are all zero—that is, the v_m^n for $m > 0$—cannot converge, under any reasonable definition of convergence, to the nonzero function u. □

EXERCISES 1.4

1. Show that the forward-time central-space scheme (1.3.3) is consistent with equation (1.1.1).

2. Show that the leapfrog scheme (1.3.4) is consistent with the one-way wave equation (1.1.1).

3. Show that the following scheme is consistent with the one-way wave equation (1.1.1).

$$\frac{v_m^{n+1} - v_m^n}{k} + \frac{a}{2}\left(\frac{v_{m+1}^{n+1} - v_m^{n+1}}{h} + \frac{v_m^n - v_{m-1}^n}{h}\right) = f_m^n \qquad (1.4.3)$$

4. Show that the following scheme is consistent with the equation $u_t + cu_{tx} + au_x = f$.

$$\frac{v_m^{n+1} - v_m^n}{k} + c\frac{v_{m+1}^{n+1} - v_{m-1}^{n+1} - v_{m+1}^n + v_{m-1}^n}{2kh} + a\frac{v_{m+1}^n - v_{m-1}^n}{2h} = f_m^n \qquad (1.4.4)$$

5. Interpret the results of Exercise 1.3.1 in light of the definition of convergence. Based on the cases run in that exercise, decide which of the schemes are convergent.

1.5 Stability

Example 1.4.3 shows that a scheme must satisfy other conditions besides consistency before we can conclude that it is convergent. The important property that is required is stability. To introduce this concept we note that if a scheme is convergent, then as v_m^n converges to $u(t, x)$, certainly v_m^n is bounded in some sense. This is the essence of stability. The following definition of stability is for the homogeneous initial value problem, that is, one in which the right-hand-side function f is 0.

Definition 1.5.1   *A finite difference scheme $P_{k,h}v_m^n = 0$ for a first-order equation is stable in a stability region Λ if there is an integer J such that for any positive time T, there is a constant C_T such that*

$$h \sum_{m=-\infty}^{\infty} |v_m^n|^2 \leq C_T h \sum_{j=0}^{J} \sum_{m=-\infty}^{\infty} |v_m^j|^2 \qquad (1.5.1)$$

for $0 \leq nk \leq T$, with $(k,h) \in \Lambda$.

Before proceeding with our discussion of stability, we introduce some notation that will be of use in understanding inequality (1.5.1). We first introduce the notation

$$\|w\|_h = \left(h \sum_{m=-\infty}^{\infty} |w_m|^2 \right)^{1/2}, \qquad (1.5.2)$$

for any grid function w. The quantity $\|w\|_h$ is called the L^2 norm of the grid function w and is a measure of the size of the solution (see Appendix B for a discussion of function norms). In many problems the L^2 norm is a measure of a physically significant quantity such as the energy of the system. With this notation the inequality (1.5.1) can be written as

$$\|v^n\|_h \leq \left(C_T \sum_{j=0}^{J} \|v^j\|_h^2 \right)^{1/2},$$

which is equivalent to

$$\|v^n\|_h \leq C_T^* \sum_{j=0}^{J} \|v^j\|_h, \qquad (1.5.3)$$

for some constant C_T^*. Inequalities (1.5.1) and (1.5.3) express the idea that the norm of the solution at any time t, with $0 \leq t \leq T$, is limited in the amount of growth that can occur. The growth is at most a constant multiple of the sum of the norms of the solution on the first $J+1$ steps.

We may take J equal to zero for one-step schemes and also for multistep schemes incorporating an initializing procedure for computing the solution for the first several time steps, as discussed earlier in this section. We include the possibility of J being positive to include multistep schemes with data specified on the first $J+1$ levels. It will be shown that the stability of a multistep scheme is not dependent on the method of initialization.

A stability region is any bounded nonempty region of the first quadrant of R^2 that has the origin as an accumulation point. That is, a stability region must contain a sequence (k_ν, h_ν) that converges to the origin as ν tends to infinity. A common example is a region of the form $\{(k,h) : 0 < k \leq ch \leq C\}$ for some positive constants c and C.

To demonstrate whether or not the estimate (1.5.1) holds for a particular scheme can be quite formidable unless we use methods from Fourier analysis, which is discussed in the next chapter. In Section 2.2 a relatively simple procedure, von Neumann analysis, is presented for determining the stability of difference schemes.

For certain rather simple schemes we can determine sufficient conditions that ensure that the scheme is stable. This is done by establishing the stability estimate (1.5.1) directly.

Example 1.5.1 We will prove a sufficient condition for stability for the forward-time forward-space scheme (1.3.1) by considering schemes of the form

$$v_m^{n+1} = \alpha v_m^n + \beta v_{m+1}^n,$$

of which the forward-time forward-space scheme is a special case. We will show that the scheme is stable if $|\alpha| + |\beta| \leq 1$. The analysis is similar for the forward-time backward-space scheme (1.3.2). We have

$$\sum_{m=-\infty}^{\infty} |v_m^{n+1}|^2 = \sum_{m=-\infty}^{\infty} |\alpha v_m^n + \beta v_{m+1}^n|^2$$

$$\leq \sum_{m=-\infty}^{\infty} |\alpha|^2 |v_m^n|^2 + 2|\alpha||\beta||v_m^n||v_{m+1}^n| + |\beta|^2 |v_{m+1}^n|^2$$

$$\leq \sum_{m=-\infty}^{\infty} |\alpha|^2 |v_m^n|^2 + |\alpha||\beta|(|v_m^n|^2 + |v_{m+1}^n|^2) + |\beta|^2 |v_{m+1}^n|^2$$

$$= \sum_{m=-\infty}^{\infty} (|\alpha|^2 + 2|\alpha||\beta| + |\beta|^2) |v_m^n|^2$$

$$= (|\alpha| + |\beta|)^2 \sum_{m=-\infty}^{\infty} |v_m^n|^2,$$

where we have used the inequality $2xy \leq x^2 + y^2$. Thus the scheme is stable if $|\alpha| + |\beta| \leq 1$. For the forward-time forward-space scheme (1.3.1) the condition $|\alpha| + |\beta| \leq 1$ is that $|1 + a\lambda| + |a\lambda|$ is at most 1. Thus we see that this scheme is stable if $-1 \leq a\lambda \leq 0$. In Section 2.2 we show that this is also a necessary condition. $\square$

The concept of stability for finite difference schemes is closely related to the concept of well-posedness for initial value problems for partial differential equations. As before we restrict our discussion to equations $Pu = f$ that are of first order with respect to differentiation in time.

Definition 1.5.2 *The initial value problem for the first-order partial differential equation $Pu = 0$ is well-posed if for any time $T \geq 0$, there is a constant C_T such that any solution $u(t, x)$ satisfies*

$$\int_{-\infty}^{\infty} |u(t, x)|^2 \, dx \leq C_T \int_{-\infty}^{\infty} |u(0, x)|^2 \, dx, \quad \text{for} \quad 0 \leq t \leq T. \tag{1.5.4}$$

$$\| u(t, x) \|_2^2 \leq C_T \| u(0, x) \|_2^2$$

A discussion of the concept of a well-posed initial value problem is given in Chapter 9. It is shown that only well-posed initial value problems can be used to model the evolution of physical processes. The methods of Fourier analysis that are introduced in the next chapter will be useful in the study of well-posed initial value problems.

In Chapter 9 we discuss stability and well-posedness for the inhomogeneous problems, $P_{k,h}v = f$ and $Pu = f$, respectively. As we show, the inhomogeneous equations can be treated using the estimates (1.5.1) and (1.5.4) by use of Duhamel's principle. Thus a scheme is stable for the equation $P_{k,h}v = f$ if it is stable for the equation $P_{k,h}v = 0$.

The Lax-Richtmyer Equivalence Theorem

The importance of the concepts of consistency and stability is seen in the Lax-Richtmyer equivalence theorem, which is the fundamental theorem in the theory of finite difference schemes for initial value problems.

Theorem 1.5.1   The Lax-Richtmyer Equivalence Theorem. *A consistent finite difference scheme for a partial differential equation for which the initial value problem is well-posed is convergent if and only if it is stable.*

A proof of this theorem is given in Chapter 10. The Lax-Richtmyer equivalence theorem is a very useful theorem, since it provides a simple characterization of convergent schemes. As discussed earlier, determining whether a scheme is convergent or nonconvergent can be difficult if we attempt to verify Definition 1.4.1 in a rather direct way. However, the determination of the consistency of a scheme is quite simple, as we have seen, and determining the stability of a scheme is also quite easy, as we show in Section 2.2. Thus the more difficult result—convergence—is replaced by the equivalent and easily verifiable conditions of consistency and stability. It is also significant that the determination of the consistency and stability of schemes involves essentially algebraic manipulations. A computerized symbolic manipulation language can be useful in determining consistency and stability. By contrast, a direct proof of convergence would rely on concepts in analysis. Such a proof would have to begin by considering any solution u of the differential equation and then it would have to be shown that given any ε, there exist h and k small enough that the solution of the scheme is within ε of u. The Lax-Richtmyer theorem allows us to dispense with all this analysis.

The preceding discussion of Theorem 1.5.1 has focused on the half of the theorem that states that consistency and stability imply convergence. The theorem is useful the other direction also. It states that we should not consider any unstable schemes, since none of these will be convergent. Thus the class of reasonable schemes is precisely delimited as those that are consistent and stable; no other schemes are worthy of consideration.

The Lax-Richtmyer equivalence theorem is an example of the best type of mathematical theorem. It relates an important concept that is difficult to establish directly with other concepts that are relatively easy to verify and establishes this relationship very precisely. Notice that if we had only the half of the theorem that showed that consistency and stability implied convergence, then it would be conceivable that there were unstable schemes that were also convergent. If we had only the other half of the theorem, stating that a consistent convergent scheme is stable, then we would not know if a stable consistent scheme is convergent. The usefulness of the Lax-Richtmyer theorem arises both from the ease of verifying consistency and stability and from the precise relationship established between these concepts and the concept of convergence.

EXERCISES 1.5

1. Show that schemes of the form

$$v_m^{n+1} = \alpha v_{m+1}^n + \beta v_{m-1}^n$$

are stable if $|\alpha| + |\beta|$ is less than or equal to 1. Conclude that the Lax-Friedrichs scheme (1.3.5) is stable if $|a\lambda|$ is less than or equal to 1.

2. By multiplying the leapfrog scheme (1.3.4) by $v_m^{n+1} + v_m^{n-1}$ and summing over all values of m, obtain the relation

$$\sum_{m=-\infty}^{\infty} |v_m^{n+1}|^2 + |v_m^n|^2 + a\lambda(v_m^{n+1}v_{m+1}^n - v_{m+1}^{n+1}v_m^n)$$

$$= \sum_{m=-\infty}^{\infty} |v_m^n|^2 + |v_m^{n-1}|^2 + a\lambda(v_m^n v_{m+1}^{n-1} - v_{m+1}^n v_m^{n-1})$$

$$= \sum_{m=-\infty}^{\infty} |v_m^1|^2 + |v_m^0|^2 + a\lambda(v_m^1 v_{m+1}^0 - v_{m+1}^1 v_m^0).$$

Using the inequality $-\frac{1}{2}(x^2 + y^2) \le xy \le \frac{1}{2}(x^2 + y^2)$, show that

$$(1 - |a\lambda|) \sum_{m=-\infty}^{\infty} |v_m^{n+1}|^2 + |v_m^n|^2 \le (1 + |a\lambda|) \sum_{m=-\infty}^{\infty} |v_m^1|^2 + |v_m^0|^2$$

and conclude that the scheme is stable for $|a\lambda| < 1$.

3. By multiplying scheme (1.4.3), with f_m^n equal to 0, by $v_m^{n+1} + v_m^n$ and summing over all values of m, obtain the relation

$$\sum_{m=-\infty}^{\infty} \left(1 - \frac{a\lambda}{2}\right) |v_m^{n+1}|^2 + \frac{a\lambda}{2} v_m^{n+1} v_{m+1}^{n+1}$$

$$= \sum_{m=-\infty}^{\infty} \left(1 - \frac{a\lambda}{2}\right) |v_m^n|^2 + \frac{a\lambda}{2} v_m^n v_{m+1}^n.$$

Conclude that the scheme is stable for $a\lambda < 1$.

4.   By multiplying scheme (1.4.3), with f_m^n equal to 0, by $v_{m+1}^{n+1} + v_{m-1}^n$ and summing over all values of m, obtain the relation

$$\sum_{m=-\infty}^{\infty} \frac{a\lambda}{2}|v_m^{n+1}|^2 + \left(1 - \frac{a\lambda}{2}\right) v_m^{n+1} v_{m+1}^{n+1}$$

$$= \sum_{m=-\infty}^{\infty} \frac{a\lambda}{2}|v_m^n|^2 + \left(1 - \frac{a\lambda}{2}\right) v_m^n v_{m+1}^n$$

$$= \sum_{m=-\infty}^{\infty} \frac{a\lambda}{2}|v_m^0|^2 + \left(1 - \frac{a\lambda}{2}\right) v_m^0 v_{m+1}^0.$$

Conclude that the scheme is stable for $a\lambda > 1$.

1.6 The Courant-Friedrichs-Lewy Condition

The condition that the magnitude of $a\lambda$ be at most 1 is the stability condition for many finite difference schemes for hyperbolic systems in one space dimension when λ is a constant. This has been the stability condition for the Lax-Friedrichs scheme (1.3.5) (see Exercise 1.5.1) and for the forward-time forward-space scheme (1.3.1) when a is negative and the forward-time backward-space scheme (1.3.2) when a is positive (see Example 1.5.1). We now show that this condition is a necessary condition for stability for many explicit schemes for the equation (1.1.1).

An explicit finite difference scheme is any scheme that can be written in the form

$$v_m^{n+1} = \text{a } finite \text{ sum of } v_{m'}^{n'} \text{ with } n' \le n.$$

All the schemes we considered so far are explicit; we examine implicit (that is, nonexplicit) schemes later. We now prove the following result, which covers all the one-step schemes we have discussed.

Theorem 1.6.1   *For an explicit scheme for the hyperbolic equation (1.1.1) of the form $v_m^{n+1} = \alpha v_{m-1}^n + \beta v_m^n + \gamma v_{m+1}^n$ with $k/h = \lambda$ held constant, a necessary condition for stability is the Courant-Friedrichs-Lewy (CFL) condition,*

$$|a\lambda| \le 1.$$

For systems of equations for which v is a vector and $\alpha, \beta,$ and γ are matrices, we must have $|a_i\lambda| \le 1$ for all eigenvalues a_i of the matrix A.

Proof   First consider the case of a single equation. If $|a\lambda| > 1$, then by considering the point $(t, x) = (1, 0)$ we see that the solution to the partial differential equation depends on the values of $u_0(x)$ at $x = \pm a$, (actually only at one or the other of $+a$ or $-a$). But the finite difference scheme will have

v_0^n depend on v_m^0 only for $m \le n$, by the form of the scheme. See Figure 1.8. Since $h = \lambda^{-1}k$, we have $mh \le \lambda^{-1}kn = \lambda^{-1}$, since $kn = 1$. So v_0^n depends on x only for $|x| \le \lambda^{-1} < |a|$. Thus v_0^n cannot converge to $u(1,0)$ as $h \to 0$, with $h/k = 1$. This proves the theorem in this case.

For the case of a system of equations, we have that $u(1, x)$ depends on $u_0(x)$ for x in the interval $[-a, a]$, where a is the maximum magnitude of the characteristic speeds a_i. If $|a_i \lambda| > 1$ for some characteristic speed a_i, then we can take initial data that are zero in $[-\lambda^{-1}, \lambda^{-1}]$ but not zero near a_i. Then $u(1, x)$ will not be zero, in general, and yet v_0^n with $nk = 1$ will be zero. Thus v^n cannot converge to $u(1, \cdot)$, and the theorem is proved. ∎

A similar argument can be used to show that there is no explicit, consistent scheme for hyperbolic partial differential equations that is stable for all values of λ (with λ constant as $h, k \to 0$). We obtain the following theorem; first proved by Courant, Friedrichs, and Lewy [9].

Theorem 1.6.2 *There are no explicit, unconditionally stable, consistent finite difference schemes for hyperbolic systems of partial differential equations.*

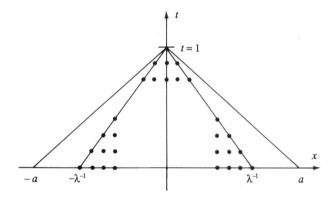

Figure 1.8

We now present two implicit schemes for the one-way wave equation (1.1.1). These schemes are consistent and stable for all values of λ, and thus illustrate that Theorem 1.6.2 does not extend to implicit schemes. The two schemes are the backward-time central-space scheme

$$\frac{v_m^{n+1} - v_m^n}{k} + a \frac{v_{m+1}^{n+1} - v_{m-1}^{n+1}}{2h} = 0 \tag{1.6.1}$$

and the backward-time backward-space scheme

$$\frac{v_m^{n+1} - v_m^n}{k} + a \frac{v_m^{n+1} - v_{m-1}^{n+1}}{h} = 0. \tag{1.6.2}$$

We are not concerned at this point with how to solve for the values v_m^{n+1} given the values at time level n; this topic is considered in Section 3.4. It is easy to check that both of these schemes are consistent schemes for (1.1.1). In Section 2.2 we show that the scheme (1.6.1) is stable for all values of a and λ.

Example 1.6.1 We now show that the backward-time backward-space scheme (1.6.2) is stable when a is positive and λ is any positive number. This shows that Theorem 1.6.2 does not extend to implicit schemes.

We first write the scheme (1.6.2) as

$$(1 + a\lambda)v_m^{n+1} = v_m^n + a\lambda\, v_{m-1}^{n+1}$$

If we take the square of both sides, we obtain

$$(1 + a\lambda)^2|v_m^{n+1}|^2 \le |v_m^n|^2 + 2a\lambda|v_m^n|\,|v_{m-1}^{n+1}| + (a\lambda)^2|v_{m-1}^{n+1}|^2$$

$$\le (1 + a\lambda)|v_m^n|^2 + (a\lambda + (a\lambda)^2)|v_{m-1}^{n+1}|^2.$$

Taking the sum over all values of m, we obtain

$$(1 + a\lambda)^2 \sum_{m=-\infty}^{\infty} |v_m^{n+1}|^2 \le (1 + a\lambda) \sum_{m=-\infty}^{\infty} |v_m^n|^2 + (a\lambda + (a\lambda)^2) \sum_{m=-\infty}^{\infty} |v_m^{n+1}|^2,$$

which easily gives the estimate

$$\sum_{m=-\infty}^{\infty} |v_m^{n+1}|^2 \le \sum_{m=-\infty}^{\infty} |v_m^n|^2 \, ,$$

and this shows that the scheme is stable for every value of λ when a is positive. $\square$

Notice that even though we can choose λ arbitrarily large for scheme (1.6.2) and still have a stable scheme, the solution will not be accurate unless λ is restricted to reasonable values. We discuss the accuracy of solutions in Chapter 3, and in Section 5.2 we show that there are advantages to choosing $|a\lambda|$ small.

EXERCISES 1.6

1.   Show that the following modified Lax-Friedrichs scheme for the one-way wave equation, $u_t + au_x = f$, given by

$$v_m^{n+1} = \tfrac{1}{2}\left(v_{m+1}^n + v_{m-1}^n\right) - \frac{a\lambda}{1 + (a\lambda)^2}(v_{m+1}^n - v_{m-1}^n) + kf_m^n$$

is stable for all values of λ. Discuss the relation of this explicit and unconditionally stable scheme to Theorem 1.6.2.

2.   Modify the proof of Theorem 1.6.1 to cover the leapfrog scheme.

3. Show that schemes of the form

$$\alpha v_{m+1}^{n+1} + \beta v_{m-1}^{n+1} = v_m^n$$

are stable if $\Big| |\alpha| - |\beta| \Big|$ is greater than or equal to 1. Conclude that the reverse Lax-Friedrichs scheme,

$$\frac{\frac{1}{2}\left(v_{m+1}^{n+1} + v_{m-1}^{n+1}\right) - v_m^n}{k} + a\frac{v_{m+1}^{n+1} - v_{m-1}^{n+1}}{2h} = 0$$

is stable if $|a\lambda|$ is greater than or equal to 1.

Chapter 2

Analysis of Finite Difference Schemes

In this chapter we present and develop the important tool of Fourier analysis, with which we shall analyze finite difference schemes and their solutions. In this and subsequent chapters these tools are used to study many important properties of finite difference schemes and their solutions. We use Fourier analysis throughout this text to study both finite difference schemes and partial differential equations.

2.1 Fourier Analysis

The tool that we will use most extensively in our study of stability and well-posedness is Fourier analysis. We will use Fourier analysis both on both the real line R and on the grid of integers, Z or hZ, which is defined by $hZ = \{hm : m \in Z\}$. For a function $u(x)$ defined on the real line R, its Fourier transform $\hat{u}(\omega)$ is defined by

$$\hat{u}(\omega) = \frac{1}{\sqrt{2\pi}} \int_{-\infty}^{\infty} e^{-i\omega x} u(x) \, dx. \qquad (2.1.1)$$

The Fourier transform of u is a function of the real variable ω and is uniquely defined by u. The function $\hat{u}$ is an alternative representation of the function u. Information about certain properties of u can be inferred from the properties of $\hat{u}$. For example, the rate at which $\hat{u}$ decays for large values of ω is related to the number of derivatives that u has.

The Fourier inversion formula, given by

$$u(x) = \frac{1}{\sqrt{2\pi}} \int_{-\infty}^{\infty} e^{i\omega x} \, \hat{u}(\omega) \, d\omega, \qquad (2.1.2)$$

shows how u can be recovered from $\hat{u}$. The Fourier inversion formula expresses the function u as a superposition of waves, given by $e^{i\omega x}$, with different amplitudes $\hat{u}(\omega)$. We will postpone for now the discussion of what conditions $u(x)$ must satisfy so that (2.1.1) and (2.1.2) are well defined. Notice that $\hat{u}(\omega)$ may be complex valued even if $u(x)$ is real valued.

In a similar fashion, if v is a grid function defined for all integers m, its Fourier transform is given by

$$\hat{v}(\xi) = \frac{1}{\sqrt{2\pi}} \sum_{m=-\infty}^{\infty} e^{-im\xi} v_m \qquad (2.1.3)$$

for $\xi \in [-\pi, \pi]$, and $\hat{v}(-\pi) = \hat{v}(\pi)$. The Fourier inversion formula is given by

$$v_m = \frac{1}{\sqrt{2\pi}} \int_{-\pi}^{\pi} e^{im\xi}\, \hat{v}(\xi)\, d\xi. \tag{2.1.4}$$

Fourier analysis on Z is the same as the study of Fourier series representations of functions defined on an interval. From the perspective of Fourier series one usually starts with a function $\hat{v}(\xi)$ defined on the interval $[-\pi, \pi]$ and shows that it can be represented as a series such as (2.1.3) with coefficients v_m given by (2.1.4). In our study of finite difference schemes it is more natural to start with the grid functions v_m and regard the formula (2.1.4) as a representation of the grid function. The two approaches are mathematically equivalent. The Fourier inversion formula (2.1.4) has an interpretation, analogous to (2.1.2), as expressing v as a superposition of waves.

If the spacing between the grid points is h, we can change variables and define the transform by

$$\hat{v}(\xi) = \frac{1}{\sqrt{2\pi}} \sum_{m=-\infty}^{\infty} e^{-imh\xi} v_m\, h \tag{2.1.5}$$

for $\xi \in [-\pi/h, \pi/h]$, and then the inversion formula is

$$v_m = \frac{1}{\sqrt{2\pi}} \int_{-\pi/h}^{\pi/h} e^{imh\xi}\, \hat{v}(\xi)\, d\xi. \tag{2.1.6}$$

An important consequence of the preceding definitions is that the L^2 norm of u, which is

$$\|u\|_2 = \left(\int_{-\infty}^{\infty} |u(x)|^2\, dx \right)^{1/2},$$

is the same as the L^2 norm of $\hat{u}(\omega)$, i.e.,

$$\|u\|^2 = \int_{-\infty}^{\infty} |u(x)|^2\, dx = \int_{-\infty}^{\infty} |\hat{u}(\omega)|^2\, d\omega = \|\hat{u}\|^2 \tag{2.1.7}$$

(See Appendix B for a discussion of function norms.) Also, for the discrete transform we have equality for the L^2 norm of v, as defined in (1.5.2), and the L^2 norm of $\hat{v}$, that is,

$$\|\hat{v}\|_h^2 = \int_{-\pi/h}^{\pi/h} |\hat{v}(\xi)|^2\, d\xi = \sum_{-\infty}^{\infty} |v_m|^2\, h = \|v\|_h^2. \tag{2.1.8}$$

The relations (2.1.7) and (2.1.8) are called Parseval's relations. Using Parseval's relations one can show that the Fourier transform is defined for all functions in $L^2(R)$ and $L^2(hZ)$. For proofs of Parseval's relation for functions in $L^2(R)$

the reader is referred to texts on Fourier analysis, such as Titchmarsh [50], and Goldberg [21].

We can give an indication of the proof for Parseval's relation for functions in $L^2(hZ)$ quite easily. Starting with the left-hand side of equation (2.1.8) and using the definition of the transform, we have

$$\|\hat{v}\|_h^2 = \int_{-\pi/h}^{\pi/h} |\hat{v}(\xi)|^2 \, d\xi = \int_{-\pi/h}^{\pi/h} \overline{\hat{v}(\xi)} \frac{1}{\sqrt{2\pi}} \sum_{m=-\infty}^{\infty} e^{-imh\xi} v_m \, h \, d\xi$$

$$= \frac{1}{\sqrt{2\pi}} \sum_{m=-\infty}^{\infty} \int_{-\pi/h}^{\pi/h} e^{-imh\xi} \overline{\hat{v}(\xi)} \, d\xi \, v_m \, h$$

$$= \sum_{m=-\infty}^{\infty} \overline{\frac{1}{\sqrt{2\pi}} \int_{-\pi/h}^{\pi/h} e^{imh\xi} \hat{v}(\xi) \, d\xi} \, v_m \, h$$

$$= \sum_{m=-\infty}^{\infty} \overline{v_m} v_m \, h = \|v\|_h^2.$$

The only step in this derivation that needs justification is the interchange of the integration and summation operations. This is not difficult, and readers familiar with real analysis can easily fill in the details.

Parseval's relation will be used extensively in our study of stability. It allows us to replace the stability estimates (1.5.1) and (1.5.3) by the equivalent inequality

$$\|v^n\|_h \leq C_T^* \sum_{j=0}^{J} \|v^j\|_h, \tag{2.1.9}$$

for the transform of the grid function. In the next section we study the stability of schemes by examining the effect of the scheme on the transform of the solution.

It should also be pointed out that there is not a relation equivalent to Parseval's relation if the norm is the maximum norm (see Exercise 2.1.6). Because there is no such relation, the Lax-Richtmyer theorem is not valid in the maximum norm, at least in a straightforward way, as is shown in Section 10.5 (see Exercise 10.5.2).

We now present some examples of functions and their Fourier transforms.

Example 2.1.1 We take the grid function given by

$$v_m = \begin{cases} 1 & \text{if } |x_m| < 1, \\ \frac{1}{2} & \text{if } |x_m| = 1, \\ 0 & \text{if } |x_m| > 1, \end{cases}$$

on a grid with spacing h. For the case where $h = M^{-1}$ for some integer M, we have by (2.1.3)

$$\hat{v}(\xi) = \frac{h}{\sqrt{2\pi}} \left(\frac{1}{2} e^{-iMh\xi} + \frac{1}{2} e^{-iMh\xi} \right) + \frac{h}{\sqrt{2\pi}} \sum_{m=-(M-1)}^{M-1} e^{-imh\xi}$$

$$= \frac{h}{\sqrt{2\pi}} \cos\xi + \frac{h}{\sqrt{2\pi}} \frac{\sin(M - \frac{1}{2})h\xi}{\sin \frac{1}{2}h\xi}$$

$$= \frac{h}{\sqrt{2\pi}} \cos\xi + \frac{h}{\sqrt{2\pi}} \frac{\sin Mh\xi \cos \frac{1}{2}h\xi - \cos Mh\xi \sin \frac{1}{2}h\xi}{\sin \frac{1}{2}h\xi}$$

$$= \frac{h}{\sqrt{2\pi}} \sin\xi \, \cot \frac{1}{2}h\xi.$$

Parseval's relation then asserts that

$$2 - \frac{1}{2}h = 2h \left(\frac{1}{2} \right)^2 + h \sum_{m=-(M-1)}^{M-1} 1$$

$$= \frac{h^2}{2\pi} \int_{-\pi/h}^{\pi/h} \sin^2\xi \cot^2 \tfrac{1}{2}h\xi \, d\xi,$$

as can also be verified by direct evaluation of the integral. $\square$

Example 2.1.2 For our second example we take the grid function given by

$$v_m = e^{-\alpha|m|h}$$

for any positive constant α. We have for the transform

$$\hat{v}(\xi) = \frac{1}{\sqrt{2\pi}} \sum_{m=-\infty}^{\infty} e^{-imh\xi} e^{-\alpha|m|h} \, h$$

$$= \frac{h}{\sqrt{2\pi}} \left(1 + \sum_{m=1}^{\infty} e^{-imh\xi} e^{-\alpha|m|h} + \sum_{m=-1}^{-\infty} e^{-imh\xi} e^{-\alpha|m|h} \right)$$

$$= \frac{h}{\sqrt{2\pi}} \left(1 + \frac{e^{-(\alpha-i\xi)h}}{1 - e^{-(\alpha-i\xi)h}} + \frac{e^{-(\alpha+i\xi)h}}{1 - e^{-(\alpha+i\xi)h}} \right)$$

$$= \frac{h}{\sqrt{2\pi}} \frac{1 - e^{-2\alpha h}}{(1 - 2e^{-\alpha h} \cos h\xi + e^{-2\alpha h})}.$$

By Parseval's relation we have that

$$\|v\|_h^2 = h\frac{1 + e^{-2\alpha h}}{1 - e^{-2\alpha h}}$$

$$= \|\hat{v}\|_h^2 = \frac{h^2}{2\pi}\int_{-\pi/h}^{\pi/h}\left(\frac{1 - e^{-2\alpha h}}{1 - 2e^{-\alpha h}\cos h\xi + e^{-2\alpha h}}\right)^2 d\xi,$$

which can be verified by direct evaluation of the integral. $\square$

Fourier Analysis and Partial Differential Equations

We conclude this section by using the tools of Fourier analysis to study partial differential equations. In the next sections we use similar tools to study the stability of finite difference schemes. If we differentiate the Fourier inversion formula (2.1.2) we obtain

$$\frac{\partial u}{\partial x}(x) = \frac{1}{\sqrt{2\pi}}\int_{-\infty}^{\infty}e^{i\omega x}i\omega\,\hat{u}(\omega)\,d\omega$$

and from this we conclude by (2.1.1) that

$$\left(\widehat{\frac{\partial u}{\partial x}}\right)(\omega) = i\omega\,\hat{u}(\omega). \tag{2.1.10}$$

The relation (2.1.10) shows the real power of the Fourier transform; under the transform the operation of differentiation is converted into the operation of multiplication. The coupling of calculus—i.e., differentiation—with algebra—i.e., multiplication—gives us machinery to solve more easily many difficult problems in the theory of differential equations and difference schemes. The important results of the next section on stability and of Chapter 9 on well-posedness use the Fourier transform to reduce questions about schemes and differential equations to questions in algebra; for example, we show in Section 4.3 that a multistep scheme is stable if the roots of a certain polynomial are all inside the unit circle.

An important consequence of (2.1.10) is that, by Parseval's relations, $u(x)$ has L^2 integrable derivatives of order through r if and only if

$$\int_{-\infty}^{\infty}(1 + |\omega|^2)^r\,|\hat{u}(\omega)|^2\,d\omega < \infty. \tag{2.1.11}$$

We define the space of functions H^r, for each nonnegative value of r, as the set of functions in $L^2(R)$ such that the norm

$$\|u\|_{H^r} = \left(\int_{-\infty}^{\infty}(1 + |\omega|^2)^r\,|\hat{u}(\omega)|^2\,d\omega\right)^{1/2}$$

is finite. Notice that the norm on H^0 is the same as the L^2 norm.

We also define the expression $\|D^r u\|$ by

$$\|D^r u\|^2 = \int_{-\infty}^{\infty} \left| \frac{\partial^r}{\partial x^r} u(x) \right|^2 dx$$

$$= \int_{-\infty}^{\infty} |\omega|^{2r} |\hat{u}(\omega)|^2 d\omega$$

where the integral over x is defined only when r is an integer, but we define $\|D^r u\|$ by the last integral when r is not an integer.

We now apply Fourier analysis to the initial value problem for the one-way wave equation (1.1.1). We begin by transforming only in the spatial variable. We obtain for $\hat{u}(t, \omega)$ the equation

$$\hat{u}_t = -ia\omega\, \hat{u}, \tag{2.1.12}$$

which is an ordinary differential equation in t. This equation is easily solved, using the initial data, giving the solution as

$$\hat{u}(t, \omega) = e^{-ia\omega t} \hat{u}_0(\omega).$$

By the use of Parseval's relation, we immediately obtain, using $|e^{-ia\omega t}| = 1$,

$$\int_{-\infty}^{\infty} |u(t, x)|^2\, dx = \int_{-\infty}^{\infty} |\hat{u}(t, \omega)|^2\, d\omega$$

$$= \int_{-\infty}^{\infty} |e^{-ia\omega t} \hat{u}_0(\omega)|^2\, d\omega = \int_{-\infty}^{\infty} |\hat{u}_0(\omega)|^2\, d\omega = \int_{-\infty}^{\infty} |u_0(x)|^2\, dx, \tag{2.1.13}$$

which shows that the initial value problem for (1.1.1) is well-posed according to Definition 1.5.2. The equality of the first and last integrals in (2.1.13) can be easily established by the solution formula (1.1.2), however, the method of (2.1.13) can be used to prove results for more general partial differential equations. A more general discussion of well-posed initial value problems is in Chapter 9.

The Fourier Transform in Higher Dimensions

The Fourier transform is defined for higher dimensions by the formula

$$\hat{u}(\omega) = \frac{1}{(2\pi)^{N/2}} \int_{R^N} e^{-i\omega \cdot x} u(x)\, dx \tag{2.1.14}$$

where both x and ω are variables in R^N. The inner product $\omega \cdot x$ is the usual inner product in R^N. The inversion formula is given by

$$u(x) = \frac{1}{(2\pi)^{N/2}} \int_{R^N} e^{i\omega \cdot x} \hat{u}(\omega)\, d\omega. \tag{2.1.15}$$

Similar formulas hold for the discrete transforms; they are

$$\hat{v}(\xi) = \frac{1}{(2\pi)^{N/2}} \sum_{m \in Z^N} e^{-ihm\cdot\xi} v_m \, h^N \tag{2.1.16}$$

for $\xi \in [-\pi/h, \pi/h]^N$, and the inversion formula is

$$v_m = \frac{1}{(2\pi)^{N/2}} \int_{[-\pi/h,\pi/h]^N} e^{ihm\cdot\xi} \hat{v}(\xi) \, d\xi. \tag{2.1.17}$$

Parseval's relation also holds for higher dimensions.

Almost all the techniques we use for one-dimensional problems carry over to higher dimensions without much difficulty. We restrict much of our analysis to the one-dimensional case for simplicity, leaving the higher-dimensional cases to the exercises.

EXERCISES 2.1

1. Show that if u is in H^r, then $\dfrac{du}{dx}$ is in H^{r-1}.

2. Check the following list of transforms and determine for which values of r they are in H^r.

$u(x)$	$\hat{u}(\omega)$
$e^{-\|x\|}$	$\sqrt{\dfrac{2}{\pi}}\dfrac{1}{1+\omega^2}$
$e^{-ax^2/2}$	$\dfrac{1}{\sqrt{a}}e^{-\omega^2/2a}$
$xe^{-\|x\|}$	$-2i\sqrt{\dfrac{2}{\pi}}\dfrac{\omega}{(1+\omega^2)^2}$
$\|x\|e^{-\|x\|}$	$\sqrt{\dfrac{2}{\pi}}\dfrac{1-\omega^2}{(1+\omega^2)^2}$
$u(x) = \begin{cases} x^\alpha e^{-x} & \text{if } x \geq 0, \\ 0 & \text{if } x < 0. \end{cases}$	$\dfrac{1}{\sqrt{2\pi}}\dfrac{\Gamma(1+\alpha)}{(1+i\omega)^{1+\alpha}}$

3. Use an argument similar to that used in (2.1.13) to show that the initial value problem for the equation $u_t = u_{xxx}$ is well-posed.

4. Use an argument similar to that used in (2.1.13) to show that the initial value problem for the equation $u_t + u_x + bu = 0$ is well-posed.

5. Show that if the function $u(x)$ is in $L^2(R)$ and its transform satisfies

$$|\hat{u}(\omega)| \leq \frac{C}{1 + \omega^4},$$

for some constant C, then the first and second derivatives of u exist and are bounded functions.

6. Show that if $u(x)$ is in $L^1(R)$ then $\hat{u}(\omega)$ is a continuous function on R. Show that $\|\hat{u}\|_\infty \leq (2\pi)^{-1/2}\|u\|_1$. (See Appendix B for the notation.) Prove an equivalent relation for grid functions.

7. The Schwartz class $\mathcal{S}$ is defined as the set of all C^∞ functions f on R such that for each pair of integers (α, β) the function $(1 + |x|^\alpha) \left(\dfrac{d}{dx} \right)^\beta f(x)$ is bounded. Show that the Fourier transform of a function in $\mathcal{S}$ is also in $\mathcal{S}$.

8. **(Finite Fourier Transforms)** For a function v_m defined on the integers, $m = 0, 1, \ldots, M - 1$, we can define the Fourier transform as

$$\hat{v}_\ell = \sum_{m=0}^{M-1} e^{-2i\pi \ell m/M} v_m \quad \text{for } \ell = 0, \ldots, M - 1.$$

For this transform prove the Fourier inversion formula

$$v_m = \frac{1}{M} \sum_{\ell=0}^{M-1} e^{2i\pi \ell m/M} \hat{v}_\ell,$$

and the Parseval's relation

$$\sum_{m=0}^{M-1} |v_m|^2 = M \sum_{\ell=0}^{M-1} |\hat{v}_\ell|^2.$$

Note that v_m and $\hat{v}_\ell$ can be defined for all integers by making them periodic with period M.

9. **(Finite Fourier Transforms)** If M is a even integer, one can define the cosine and sine transforms of a function v_m defined for the integers $m = 0, 1, \ldots, M - 1$ by defining

$$\hat{v}_\ell^c = \sum_{m=0}^{M-1} \cos\left(\frac{2\pi \ell m}{M}\right) v_m \quad \text{for } \ell = 0, \ldots, \frac{M}{2},$$

$$\hat{v}_\ell^s = \sum_{m=0}^{M-1} \sin\left(\frac{2\pi \ell m}{M}\right) v_m \quad \text{for } \ell = 1, \ldots, \frac{M}{2} - 1.$$

Show that $\hat{v}_\ell$ as defined in Exercise 8 satisfies

$$\hat{v}_\ell = \hat{v}_\ell^c - i\hat{v}_\ell^s \quad \text{for } l = 0, \ldots, \frac{M}{2}$$

$$\hat{v}_\ell = \hat{v}_\ell^c + i\hat{v}_\ell^s \quad \text{for } l = \frac{M}{2} + 1, \ldots, M - 1,$$

and then show that

$$v_m = \frac{1}{M}(\hat{v}_0^c + (-1)^m \hat{v}_{M/2}^c) + \frac{2}{M} \sum_{\ell=1}^{M/2-1} \cos\left(\frac{2\pi\ell m}{M}\right) \hat{v}_\ell^c + \sin\left(\frac{2\pi\ell m}{M}\right) \hat{v}_\ell^s,$$

for $m = 0, \ldots, M - 1$.

10. Use the multidimensional Fourier transform (2.1.14) to prove that the initial value problem for the equation

$$u_t + au_x + bu_y = 0$$

is well-posed. (See (2.1.13).)

11. Prove the "uncertainty principle" inequality:

$$\int_{-\infty}^{\infty} |f(x)|^2 \, dx \int_{-\infty}^{\infty} |\hat{f}(\omega)|^2 \, d\omega \leq 4 \int_{-\infty}^{\infty} x^2 |f(x)|^2 \, dx \int_{-\infty}^{\infty} \omega^2 |\hat{f}(\omega)|^2 \, d\omega$$

2.2 Von Neumann Analysis

An important application of Fourier analysis is the von Neumann analysis of stability of finite difference schemes. With the use of Fourier analysis we can give necessary and sufficient conditions for the stability of finite difference schemes. The resulting method is easier to apply and is more generally applicable than are the methods used in the examples at the end of Chapter 1.

We illustrate the method by considering a particular example and then discuss the method in general. Through the use of the Fourier transform the determination of the stability of a scheme is reduced to relatively simple algebraic considerations. We begin by studying the forward-time backward-space scheme

$$\frac{v_m^{n+1} - v_m^n}{k} + a\frac{v_m^n - v_{m-1}^n}{h} = 0, \tag{2.2.1}$$

which can be rewritten as

$$v_m^{n+1} = (1 - a\lambda)v_m^n + a\lambda \, v_{m-1}^n, \tag{2.2.2}$$

where $\lambda = k/h$. Using the Fourier inversion formula (2.1.6) for v^n, we have

$$v_m^n = \frac{1}{\sqrt{2\pi}} \int_{-\pi/h}^{\pi/h} e^{imh\xi} \, \hat{v}^n(\xi) \, d\xi$$

and substituting this in (2.2.2) for v_m^n and v_{m-1}^n, we obtain

$$v_m^{n+1} = \frac{1}{\sqrt{2\pi}} \int_{-\pi/h}^{\pi/h} e^{imh\xi} \big[(1 - a\lambda) + a\lambda e^{-ih\xi}\big] \hat{v}^n(\xi) \, d\xi. \qquad (2.2.3)$$

Comparing this formula with the Fourier inversion formula

$$v_m^{n+1} = \frac{1}{\sqrt{2\pi}} \int_{-\pi/h}^{\pi/h} e^{imh\xi} \, \hat{v}^{n+1}(\xi) \, d\xi$$

and using the fact that the Fourier transform is unique, we deduce that the integrand of (2.2.3) is the same as that in the inversion formula. We then have that

$$\hat{v}^{n+1}(\xi) = \big[(1 - a\lambda) + a\lambda e^{-ih\xi}\big] \hat{v}^n(\xi)$$
$$= g(h\xi) \, \hat{v}^n(\xi), \qquad (2.2.4)$$

where

$$g(h\xi) = (1 - a\lambda) + a\lambda e^{-ih\xi}.$$

The formula (2.2.4) shows that advancing the solution of the scheme by one time step is equivalent to multiplying the Fourier transform of the solution by the *amplification factor* $g(h\xi)$. The amplification factor is so called because its magnitude is the amount that the amplitude of each frequency in the solution, given by $\hat{v}^n(\xi)$, is amplified in advancing the solution one time step. From (2.2.4) we obtain the important formula

$$\hat{v}^n(\xi) = g(h\xi)^n \hat{v}^0(\xi). \qquad (2.2.5)$$

Note that the superscript on $\hat{v}$ is an index of the time level, while on g it is a power.

By means of the Fourier transform every one-step scheme can be put in the form (2.2.5). We use this representation of schemes to study their stability and accuracy. The use of the Fourier transform provides a standard method to study the wide variety of schemes. The amplification factor of a scheme contains all of the information about the scheme and, as we will see, it is easy to extract very important information from it.

We now use formula (2.2.5) to study the stability of scheme (2.2.1). This analysis is analogous to that displayed in equation (2.1.13) to study the well-posedness of the initial value problem for equation (2.1.12). By Parseval's relation, (2.1.8), and (2.2.5),

$$h \sum_{m=-\infty}^{\infty} |v_m^n|^2 = \int_{-\pi/h}^{\pi/h} |\hat{v}^n(\xi)|^2 \, d\xi$$

$$= \int_{-\pi/h}^{\pi/h} |g(h\xi)|^{2n} |\hat{v}^0(\xi)|^2 \, d\xi.$$

Thus we see that the stability inequality (1.5.1) will hold, with $J = 0$, if $|g(h\xi)|^{2n}$ is suitably bounded. We now evaluate $|g(h\xi)|$. Setting $\theta = h\xi$, we have

$$|g(\theta)|^2 = \left|(1 - a\lambda) + a\lambda e^{-i\theta}\right|^2 = (1 - a\lambda + a\lambda\cos\theta)^2 + a^2\lambda^2\sin^2\theta$$

$$= (1 - 2a\lambda\sin^2\tfrac{1}{2}\theta)^2 + 4\,a^2\lambda^2\sin^2\tfrac{1}{2}\theta\cos^2\tfrac{1}{2}\theta$$

$$= 1 - 4a\lambda\sin^2\tfrac{1}{2}\theta + 4a^2\lambda^2\sin^4\tfrac{1}{2}\theta + 4a^2\lambda^2\sin^2\tfrac{1}{2}\theta\cos^2\tfrac{1}{2}\theta$$

$$= 1 - 4a\lambda(1 - a\lambda)\sin^2\tfrac{1}{2}\theta.$$

We see that $|g(\theta)|$ is bounded by 1 if $0 \leq a\lambda \leq 1$; thus by (2.2.5)

$$h\sum_{m=-\infty}^{\infty}|v_m^n|^2 \leq \int_{-\pi/h}^{\pi/h}\left|\hat{v}^0(\xi)\right|^2\,d\xi$$

$$= h\sum_{m=-\infty}^{\infty}\left|v_m^0\right|^2,$$

and the scheme is stable by Definition 1.5.1.

However, if $a\lambda$ is not between 0 and 1 and λ is fixed as h and k tend to zero, then $|g(\theta)|$ is greater than 1 for some values of θ, and the scheme is unstable, as we show next.

The Stability Condition

The exact condition for stability of constant coefficient one-step schemes is given in the next theorem. Although in the example we have just considered the amplification factor, g, was a function only of $\theta = h\xi$, in general g will also depend on h and k. Also, we have considered schemes only for equation (1.1.1), and yet our definition of stability applies to more general partial differential equations that are first order in the differentiation with respect to time. To allow for more general equations, we have to allow the magnitude of the amplification factor to exceed 1 by a small amount.

Theorem 2.2.1   *A one-step finite difference scheme (with constant coefficients) is stable if and only if there is a constant K (independent of θ, k, and h) and some positive grid spacings k_0 and h_0 such that*

$$|g(\theta, k, h)| \leq 1 + Kk \tag{2.2.6}$$

for all θ, $0 < k \leq k_0$, and $0 < h \leq h_0$. If $g(\theta, k, h)$ is independent of h and k, the stability condition (2.2.6) can be replaced with

$$|g(\theta)| \leq 1. \tag{2.2.7}$$

This theorem shows that to determine the stability of a finite difference scheme we need consider only the amplification factor $g(h\xi)$. This observation is due to von Neumann, and because of that, this analysis is usually called von Neumann analysis.

Before proceeding with the proof of this theorem, we consider some examples that use the special condition (2.2.7).

Example 2.2.1 We consider the forward-time forward-space scheme (1.3.1), for which
$$g(h\xi) = 1 + a\lambda - a\lambda e^{ih\xi}$$
where a is positive and λ is constant. This formula is obtained in the same fashion as (2.2.4); we have that
$$|g|^2 = 1 + 4a\lambda(1 + a\lambda)\sin^2 \tfrac{1}{2}\theta.$$
If λ is constant, then we may use the restricted stability condition (2.2.7), and we see that $|g|$ is greater than 1 for θ not equal to 0, and therefore this scheme is unstable. Recall that by Example 1.4.3 we know that this scheme is not convergent. $\square$

We needn't write out the integrals (2.1.6) and obtain expressions such as (2.2.3) to obtain the amplification factor g. A simpler and equivalent procedure is to replace v_m^n in the scheme by $g^n e^{im\theta}$ for each value of n and m. The resulting equation can then be solved for the amplification factor.

Example 2.2.2 We use the forward-time central-space scheme (1.3.3)
$$\frac{v_m^{n+1} - v_m^n}{k} + a\frac{v_{m+1}^n - v_{m-1}^n}{2h} = 0$$
to illustrate this procedure. Replacing v_m^n by $g^n e^{imh\xi}$ the preceding expression is transformed to
$$\frac{g^{n+1}e^{im\theta} - g^n e^{im\theta}}{k} + a\frac{g^n e^{i(m+1)\theta} - g^n e^{i(m-1)\theta}}{2h}$$
$$= g^n e^{im\theta}\left(\frac{g-1}{k} + a\frac{e^{i\theta} - e^{-i\theta}}{2h}\right) = 0$$
which gives the amplification factor as
$$g = 1 - ia\lambda\sin\theta$$
with $\lambda = k/h$. This method of obtaining the amplification factor is certainly easier than the earlier analysis.

If λ is constant, then g is independent of h and k and
$$|g(\theta)|^2 = 1 + a^2\lambda^2\sin^2\theta.$$
Since $|g(\theta)|$ is greater than 1 for θ not equal to 0 or π, by Theorem 2.2.1 this scheme is unstable. $\square$

The determination of the amplification factor by replacing v_m^n by $g^n e^{im\theta}$ is not to be regarded as merely looking for solutions of the difference scheme that have the form $v_m^n = g^n e^{im\theta}$. The replacement of v_m^n by $g^n e^{im\theta}$ is a shortcut in the method used at the beginning of the section, in which we *proved* that all solutions of the one-step difference scheme were given by formula (2.2.5) and this proof gave the form of the amplification factor. That same procedure can be applied to any one-step scheme to determine the form of the amplification factor. A rearrangement of the manipulations used to determine the amplification factor shows that the two procedures are equivalent in determining the form of the amplification factor.

Example 2.2.3   As an example of a scheme that requires the more general condition (2.2.6), we consider the modified Lax-Friedrichs scheme for

$$u_t + a\, u_x - u = 0, \tag{2.2.8}$$

given by

$$\frac{v_m^{n+1} - \frac{1}{2}\left(v_{m+1}^n + v_{m-1}^n\right)}{k} + a\frac{v_{m+1}^n - v_{m-1}^n}{2h} - v_m^n = 0.$$

This scheme has the amplification factor

$$g(\theta, k, h) = \cos\theta - ia\lambda\sin\theta + k$$

and

$$|g|^2 = (\cos\theta + k)^2 + a^2\lambda^2 \sin^2\theta$$

$$\leq (1 + k)^2$$

if $|a\lambda| \leq 1$. Notice that since (2.2.8) has solutions that grow with t, (see Section 1.1), any consistent, stable scheme for (2.2.8) must have $|g|$ larger than 1 for some values of θ. □

As the examples show, the amplification factor $g(\theta, k, h)$ is an algebraic function of $e^{i\theta}$, and it is a continuous function of all of its arguments. We will always assume that $g(\theta, k, h)$ is a smooth function of all of its arguments.

Proof of Theorem 2.2.1   We have, by Parseval's relation and the definition of g, that

$$\|v^n\|_h^2 = \int_{-\pi/h}^{\pi/h} |g(h\xi, k, h)|^{2n} \left|\hat{v}^0(\xi)\right|^2 \, d\xi.$$

If $|g(h\xi, k, h)| \leq 1 + Kk$, we have

$$\|v^n\|_h^2 \leq \int_{-\pi/h}^{\pi/h} (1 + Kk)^{2n} \left|\hat{v}^0(\xi)\right|^2 \, d\xi$$

$$= (1 + Kk)^{2n} \|v^0\|_h^2.$$

Now $n \leq T/k$, so

$$(1 + Kk)^n \leq (1 + Kk)^{T/k} \leq e^{KT}.$$

Therefore, $\|v^n\|_h \leq e^{KT}\|v^0\|_h$, which is (1.5.1), and thus the scheme is stable.

We now prove that if inequality (2.2.6) cannot be satisfied for any value of K, then the scheme is not stable. To do this we show that we can achieve any amount of growth in the solution, that is, we show that the stability inequality (1.5.1) cannot hold.

If for some positive value C there is an interval of θ's, $\theta \in [\theta_1, \theta_2]$ and $h \in (0, h_0]$ and $k \in (0, k_0]$ with $|g(\theta, k, h)| \geq 1 + Ck$, then we construct a function v_m^0 as

$$\hat{v}^0(\xi) = \begin{cases} 0 & \text{if } h\xi \notin [\theta_1, \theta_2], \\ \sqrt{h(\theta_2 - \theta_1)^{-1}} & \text{if } h\xi \in [\theta_1, \theta_2]. \end{cases}$$

Then

$$\|v^n\|_h^2 = \int_{-\pi/h}^{\pi/h} |g(h\xi, k, h)|^{2n} |\hat{v}^0(\xi)|^2 \, d\xi$$

$$= \int_{\theta_1/h}^{\theta_2/h} |g(h\xi, k, h)|^{2n} \frac{h}{\theta_2 - \theta_1} \, d\xi$$

$$\geq (1 + Ck)^{2n}$$

$$\geq \frac{1}{2} e^{2TC} \|v^0\|_h^2$$

for n near T/k. This shows the scheme to be unstable if C can be arbitrarily large. The proof of condition (2.2.7) is very easy and is similar to the proof of Theorem 2.2.3, so we omit the proof here. ∎

Corollary 2.2.2 *If a scheme as in Theorem 2.2.1 is modified so that the modifications result only in the addition to the amplification factor of terms that are $O(k)$ uniformly in ξ, then the modified scheme is stable if and only if the original scheme is stable.*

Proof If g is the amplification factor for the scheme and satisfies $|g| \leq 1 + Kk$, then the amplification factor of the modified scheme, g', satisfies

$$|g'| = |g + O(k)| \leq 1 + Kk + Ck = 1 + K'k.$$

Hence the modified scheme is stable if the original scheme is stable, and vice versa. ∎

The use of Theorem 2.2.1 and Corollary 2.2.2 allow one to determine the stability of all the schemes we have discussed so far, with the exception of the leapfrog scheme, which is not a one-step scheme. Stability for multistep schemes such as the leapfrog scheme is discussed in Chapter 4.

The following theorem shows how to reduce further algebraic manipulation in evaluating $|g|$ and determining the stability of a scheme.

Theorem 2.2.3 *A consistent one-step scheme for the equation*

$$u_t + au_x + bu = 0$$

is stable if and only if it is stable for this equation when b is equal to 0. Moreover, when $k = \lambda h$ and λ is a constant, the stability condition on $g(h\xi, k, h)$ is

$$|g(\theta, 0, 0)| \leq 1. \tag{2.2.9}$$

Proof Because of consistency it is easy to see that the lower-order term bu contributes to the expression for g only terms that are proportional to k. By Corollary 2.2.2 the removal of these terms does not affect the stability of the scheme.

Using the Taylor series in k and h, we must have

$$g(\theta, k, h) = g(\theta, 0, 0) + O(h) + O(k),$$

and if $h = \lambda^{-1}k$, then the terms that are $O(h)$ are also $O(k)$. Moreover, since θ is restricted to the compact set $[-\pi, \pi]$, the $O(k)$ terms are uniformly bounded. Thus by Corollary 2.2.2 the stability condition is

$$|g(\theta, 0, 0)| \leq 1 + Kk,$$

for some constant K. But the left-hand side of this relation is independent of k, and the inequality must hold for all small positive values of k. We have, therefore, that the preceding estimate holds if and only if

$$|g(\theta, 0, 0)| \leq 1.$$

This same reasoning proves the last assertion of Theorem 2.2.1. ∎

Because of Theorem 2.2.3 we usually write g as a function only of $h\xi$, i.e., $g(h\xi)$, and do not display the dependence on h and k. It is important to realize that the stability condition (2.2.9) cannot be used in all cases.

Note that the stability condition (2.2.6) is equivalent to

$$|g|^2 \leq 1 + K'k \tag{2.2.10}$$

for some constant K'. If (2.2.6) holds, then

$$|g|^2 \leq 1 + 2Kk + k^2 \leq 1 + (2K + k_0)k.$$

Similarly, if (2.2.10) holds, then

$$|g| \leq (1 + K'k)^{1/2} \leq 1 + \tfrac{1}{2}K'k.$$

For many schemes it is easier to work with $|g|^2$ rather than with $|g|$ itself.

We now present several examples to illustrate the various ideas discussed in this section.

Example 2.2.4 We perform von Neumann analysis for the Lax-Friedrichs scheme of Example 2.2.3. The scheme is stable if and only if the scheme is stable without the undifferentiated term. For this case

$$g(\theta) = \cos\theta - ia\lambda \sin\theta,$$

and

$$|g|^2 = \cos^2\theta + a^2\lambda^2 \sin^2\theta.$$

We see that $|g(\theta)|$ is less than or equal to 1 if and only if $|a\lambda| \le 1$. Thus the Lax-Friedrichs scheme with λ constant is stable if and only if $|a\lambda| \le 1$. As shown in Example 1.4.2, the Lax-Friedrichs scheme is consistent only if $k^{-1}h^2$ tends to zero with k and h. We have that $k^{-1}h^2 = k\lambda^{-2}$, and thus if λ is constant and $|a\lambda| \le 1$, the scheme is both stable and consistent. $\square$

Example 2.2.5 Some schemes are easier to understand or implement if they are written as two separate steps. We now give an example of this, using the forward-time central-space scheme with a smoothing operator for the one-way wave equation. The scheme is

$$\tilde{v}_m^{n+1} = v_m^n - \tfrac{1}{2}a\lambda(v_{m+1}^n - v_{m-1}^n) + kf_m^n$$
$$v_m^{n+1} = \tfrac{1}{4}(\tilde{v}_{m+1}^{n+1} + 2\tilde{v}_m^{n+1} + \tilde{v}_{m-1}^{n+1}).$$

(2.2.11)

To apply von Neumann analysis to this scheme, we could eliminate all reference to the intermediate quantity $\tilde{v}$, obtaining an equation for v_m^{n+1} in terms of $v_{m'}^n$ for m' ranging from $m-2$ to $m+2$. We use an equivalent and simpler procedure, which is to replace all occurrences of $\tilde{v}_m^{n+1}$ by $\tilde{g}g^n e^{im\theta}$ as well as the usual replacement of v_m^n by $g^n e^{im\theta}$. We obtain

$$\tilde{g} = 1 - ia\lambda \sin\theta$$

and

$$g = \frac{1}{2}(1 + \cos\theta)\tilde{g} = \tilde{g}\cos^2\tfrac{1}{2}\theta.$$

We then obtain

$$|g|^2 = |\tilde{g}|^2 \cos^4\tfrac{1}{2}\theta = (1 + a^2\lambda^2 \sin^2\theta)\cos^4\tfrac{1}{2}\theta .$$

If we take λ to be constant, then the stability requirement is that g have magnitude at most 1. For stability we must satisfy

$$(1 + a^2\lambda^2 \sin^2\theta)\cos^4\tfrac{1}{2}\theta \le 1$$

or

$$(1 + 4a^2\lambda^2 \sin^2\tfrac{1}{2}\theta\cos^2\tfrac{1}{2}\theta)\cos^4\tfrac{1}{2}\theta \le 1,$$

which is equivalent to

$$4a^2\lambda^2 \sin^2 \tfrac{1}{2}\theta \cos^2 \tfrac{1}{2}\theta \cos^4 \tfrac{1}{2}\theta \le 1 - \cos^4 \tfrac{1}{2}\theta$$

$$= (1 - \cos^2 \tfrac{1}{2}\theta)(1 + \cos^2 \tfrac{1}{2}\theta)$$

$$= \sin^2 \tfrac{1}{2}\theta(1 + \cos^2 \tfrac{1}{2}\theta).$$

Canceling the common nonnegative factor of $\sin^2 \tfrac{1}{2}\theta$, we obtain the condition

$$4a^2\lambda^2 \cos^6 \tfrac{1}{2}\theta \le 1 + \cos^2 \tfrac{1}{2}\theta,$$

which must hold for all values of θ. We first consider the particular case of θ equal to 0, obtaining the necessary condition that

$$a^2\lambda^2 \le \tfrac{1}{2}. \tag{2.2.12}$$

We now show that this condition is also sufficient, that is, θ equal to 0 is the "worst case." Assuming that (2.2.12) holds, and using that $\cos^2 \tfrac{1}{2}\theta$ is at most 1, we have

$$4a^2\lambda^2 \cos^6 \tfrac{1}{2}\theta \le 2\cos^2 \tfrac{1}{2}\theta \le 1 + \cos^2 \tfrac{1}{2}\theta .$$

Thus the forward-time central-space scheme with the smoother (2.2.11) is stable if and only if

$$|a\lambda| \le \frac{1}{\sqrt{2}}.$$

This scheme is not recommended for use in actual computation. For example, it requires more work per time step than does the Lax-Friedrichs scheme, and the time-step limitation is more severe. The forward-time central-space scheme (1.3.3), without the smoother, is unstable; see Example 2.2.2. □

Example 2.2.6 An interesting example of the relation between consistency to stability is a scheme for the equation

$$u_t + au_{xxx} = f \tag{2.2.13}$$

obtained by applying the ideas of the Lax-Friedrichs scheme (1.3.5). The scheme is

$$v_m^{n+1} = \tfrac{1}{2}(v_{m+1}^n + v_{m-1}^n) - \tfrac{1}{2}akh^{-3}(v_{m+2}^n - 2v_{m+1}^n + 2v_{m-1}^n - v_{m-2}^n) + kf_m^n. \tag{2.2.14}$$

This scheme is consistent with equation (2.2.13) if $k^{-1}h^2$ tends to zero as h and k tend to zero; see Exercise 2.2.3. This is similar to the result for the Lax-Friedrichs scheme as discussed in Example 1.4.2.

The amplification factor for the scheme (2.2.14) is

$$g(\theta) = \cos\theta + 4akh^{-3}i\sin\theta \sin^2 \tfrac{1}{2}\theta,$$

and it is easily shown (see Exercise 2.2.3) that the scheme is stable only if

$$4|a|kh^{-3}$$

is bounded.

The consistency condition, that $k^{-1}h^2$ tend to zero, and the stability condition, that $4akh^{-3}$ be bounded as k and h tend to zero, cannot both be satisfied. Thus this scheme is not a convergent scheme, since it can not be both consistent and stable. $\square$

EXERCISES 2.2

1. Show that the backward-time central-space scheme (1.6.1) is consistent with equation (1.1.1) and is unconditionally stable.

2. Show that if one takes $\lambda = k^{1/2}$, i.e., $k = h^2$, then the forward-time central-space scheme (1.3.3) is stable and consistent with equation (1.1.1). (See Example 2.2.2.)

3. Verify the consistency and stability conditions of scheme (2.2.14) as given in Example 2.2.6.

4. Show that the box scheme

$$\frac{1}{2k}\left[(v_m^{n+1} + v_{m+1}^{n+1}) - (v_m^n + v_{m+1}^n)\right] + \frac{a}{2h}\left[(v_{m+1}^{n+1} - v_m^{n+1}) + (v_{m+1}^n - v_m^n)\right] = f_m^n$$

is consistent with the one-way wave equation $u_t + au_x = f$ and is stable for all values of λ.

5. Show that the scheme

$$\frac{v_m^{n+1} - v_m^n}{k} + a\frac{v_{m+2}^n - 3v_{m+1}^n + 3v_m^n - v_{m-1}^n}{h^3} = f_m^n$$

is consistent with the equation (2.2.13) and, if $\nu = kh^{-3}$ is constant, then it is stable when $0 \le a\nu \le \frac{1}{4}$.

6. Determine the stability of the following scheme, sometimes called the Euler backward scheme, for $u_t + au_x = f$.

$$v_m^{n+1/2} = v_m^n - \frac{a\lambda}{2}(v_{m+1}^n - v_{m-1}^n) + kf_m^n$$

$$v_m^{n+1} = v_m^n - \frac{a\lambda}{2}(v_{m+1}^{n+1/2} - v_{m-1}^{n+1/2}) + kf_m^{n+1}$$

The variable $v^{n+1/2}$ is a temporary variable, as is $\tilde{v}$ in Example 2.2.5.

7. Using von Neumann analysis, show that the reverse Lax-Friedrichs scheme of Exercise 1.6.3 is stable for $|a\lambda|$ greater than or equal to 1.

2.3 Comments on Instability and Stability

An examination of the solutions of unstable finite difference schemes shows that instability is related to high-frequency oscillations. An example is seen in Figure 1.5 for the Lax-Friedrichs scheme applied to the one-way wave equation with $a\lambda$ equal to 1.6. The amplification factor for this scheme has magnitude given by $|g(\theta)|^2 = \cos^2\theta + a^2\lambda^2\sin^2\theta$. The maximum value of $|g(\theta)|$ is attained at θ equal to $\pi/2$, where $|g|$ is 1.6. An examination of the ratios of the norms $\|v^{n+1}\|_h/\|v^n\|_h$ or of the ratio of the maximum magnitudes of v^n shows that these ratios are close to 1.6.

Moreover, the pattern of the instability in Figure 1.5 shows the strong presence of the frequency $h^{-1}\pi/2$ associated with θ equal to $\pi/2$. Notice that θ equal to $\pi/2$ represents waves such as $\tilde{v}_m = \varepsilon\sin m\pi/2$, which have a wavelength of $4h$ on a finite difference grid. The forward-time central-space scheme (1.3.3) shows a similar pattern, since it also has the maximum of $|g(\theta)|$ attained at θ equal to $\pi/2$.

The forward-time forward-space scheme (1.3.1) is unstable for a positive, and it attains the maximum value of $|g(\theta)|$ at θ equal to π; see Example 2.2.1. The pattern of the instability associated with this scheme is different than that associated with the two other schemes just mentioned; see Exercise 2.3.1. The instability is represented by disturbances of the form $\tilde{v}_m = \varepsilon(-1)^m = \varepsilon\cos m\pi$, with a wavelength on the grid of $2h$.

Instability is seen to be the rapid growth of high frequency modes in the solution of the finite difference solution. It follows then that instability is evident sooner with initial data that contains larger amplitudes for its high frequencies. Based on the properties of the Fourier transform in Section 2.1, we conclude that instability will be evident sooner with initial data that is not smooth. This is indeed the case, as is easily demonstrated (see Exercise 2.3.2).

An important point that is related to the previous discussion is that instability is essentially a local phenomenon. This can be seen somewhat in Figure 1.5 where the oscillations arise at the points where the derivative of the solution is discontinuous. Of course, the oscillations caused by the instability propagate to other regions, which can ultimately make the disturbance seem to be global in extent.

The proof that instability is first seen at points of discontinuity requires a good understanding of Fourier analysis. It is also somewhat difficult to define the problem correctly. Since this topic is not germane to our goal of understanding convergent and stable schemes, we will not pursue it.

Understanding the nature of instabilities can help distinguish between the effects of a programming error and an instability of a finite difference scheme. The effects of a programming error can be quite global and not confined to regions in which there is a discontinuity. The effects of instability will be oscillatory and will be most noticeable in regions where the solution is least smooth.

Stability Conditions for Variable Coefficients

The analysis of stability as done in the previous section does not apply directly to problems with variable coefficients. Nonetheless, the stability conditions obtained for constant coefficient schemes can be used to give stability conditions for the same scheme applied to equations with variable coefficients. For example, the Lax-Friedrichs scheme applied to $u_t + a(t, x)u_x = 0$ is

$$v_m^{n+1} = \tfrac{1}{2}(v_{m+1}^n + v_{m-1}^n) - \tfrac{1}{2}a(t_n, x_m)\lambda(v_{m+1}^n - v_{m-1}^n). \tag{2.3.1}$$

The stability condition for this scheme is that $|a(t_n, x_m)|\lambda \leq 1$ be satisfied for all values of (t_n, x_m) in the domain of computation.

The general procedure is that one considers each of the *frozen coefficient problems* arising from the scheme. The frozen coefficient problems are the constant coefficient problems obtained by fixing the coefficients at their values attained at each point in the domain of the computation. If each frozen coefficient problem is stable, then the variable coefficient problem is also stable. The proof of this result is beyond the scope of this text; the interested reader may wish to refer to the works of Kreiss [26], Lax and Nirenberg [30], Michelson [34], Shintani and Toemeda [45], Yamaguti and Nogi [59], and Wade [56].

If the stability condition as obtained from the frozen coefficient problems is violated in a small region, the instability phenomena that arise will originate in that area and will not grow outside that area; see Exercise 2.3.3.

Numerical Stability and Dynamic Stability

The term *stability* is used in a number of contexts in applied mathematics and engineering, and it is important to distinguish between the several uses of this term. The stability of Definition 1.5.1 can be called the *numerical stability* of finite difference schemes. In applied mathematics it is common to study *dynamic stability,* which refers to the property of a system in which small variations from a reference state will decay, or at least not grow, with time. Dynamic stability refers to the behavior of solutions as time extends to infinity, whereas the numerical stability of a scheme always refers to the behavior of solutions over a finite interval of time as the grid is refined.

To compare these two concepts, consider the equation

$$u_t + au_x + bu = 0 \tag{2.3.2}$$

for x in R and $t > 0$. If the value of b is positive, then the equation can be said to be dynamically stable since any solution will decay as t increases. If b is negative, then it is dynamically unstable, since solutions grow without bound as t increases. (See the discussion relating to equation (1.1.4) to verify these assertions.) For a finite difference scheme for (2.3.2), the numerical stability is independent of the value of b, as shown by Theorem 2.2.3. One can use any convergent scheme to compute solutions to (2.3.2) for any value of b; however, a numerically unstable scheme applied to a dynamically stable equation will not compute convergent solutions.

EXERCISES 2.3

1.   Use the unstable forward-time forward-space scheme (1.3.1) for $u_t + u_x = 0$ with the initial data

$$u_0(x) = \begin{cases} 1 - |x| & \text{if } |x| \leq 1, \\ 0 & \text{otherwise,} \end{cases}$$

on the interval $[-1, 3]$ for $0 \leq t \leq 1$. Use a grid spacing of 0.1 and λ equal to 0.8. Demonstrate that the instability grows by approximately $|g(\pi)|$ per time step. Comment on the appearance of the graph of v_m^n as a function of m. Use the boundary condition $u(t, -1) = 0$, at the left and use $v_M^{n+1} = v_{M-1}^{n+1}$ at the right boundary.

2.   Use the unstable forward-time central-space scheme (1.3.3) for $u_t + u_x = 0$ with the following two sets of initial data on the interval $[-1, 3]$ for $0 \leq t \leq 4$:

(a) $u_0(x) = \begin{cases} 1 - |x| & \text{if } |x| \leq 1, \\ 0 & \text{otherwise.} \end{cases}$

(b) $u_0(x) = \sin x$

Use a grid spacing of 0.1 and λ equal to 0.8. Demonstrate that the instability is evident sooner with the less smooth initial data (a) than it is for the smooth data (b). Show that the growth in the instability for each case is approximately $|g(\pi/2)|$. For (a) use the boundary condition $u(t, -1) = 0$, and for (b) use the boundary condition $u(t, -1) = -\sin(1 + t)$. Use $v_M^{n+1} = v_{M-1}^{n+1}$ at the right boundary.

3.   Solve the equation

$$u_t + (1 + \alpha x)u_x = 0$$

on the interval $[-3, 3]$ and $0 \leq t \leq 2$ with the Lax-Friedrichs scheme (2.3.1) with $\alpha = -0.5$ and λ equal to 1. Demonstrate that the instability phenomena occur where $|(1 + \alpha x_m)\lambda|$ is greater than 1. Use the same initial data as in Exercise 1. Specify the solution to be 0 at both boundaries.

Chapter 3

Order of Accuracy of
Finite Difference Schemes

3.1 Order of Accuracy

In the previous two chapters we classified schemes as acceptable or nonacceptable only on the basis of whether or not they are convergent. This, via the Lax-Richtmyer equivalence theorem, led us to consider stability and consistency. However, two convergent schemes may differ considerably in how well their solutions approximate the solution of the differential equation. This may be seen by comparing Figures 1.4 and 1.6, which show solutions computed with the Lax-Friedrichs and leapfrog schemes. Both of these schemes are convergent for λ equal to 0.8, yet the leapfrog scheme has a solution that is closer to the solution of the differential equation than does the Lax-Friedrichs scheme. In this section we define the order of accuracy of a scheme, which can be regarded as an extension of the definition of consistency. The leapfrog scheme has a higher order of accuracy than does the Lax-Friedrichs scheme, and thus, in general, its solutions will be more accurate than those of the Lax-Friedrichs scheme. The proof that schemes with higher order of accuracy generally produce more accurate solutions is in Chapter 10.

Before defining the order of accuracy of a scheme, we introduce two schemes, which, as we will show, are more accurate than most of the schemes we have presented so far. We will also have to pay more attention to the way the forcing function, $f(t,x)$, is incorporated into the scheme.

The Lax-Wendroff Scheme

To derive the Lax-Wendroff scheme (see [31]) we begin by using the Taylor series in time for $u(t+k,x)$, where u is a solution to the inhomogeneous one-way wave equation

$$u(t+k,x) = u(t,x) + ku_t(t,x) + \frac{k^2}{2}u_{tt}(t,x) + O(k^3).$$

We now use the differential equation that u satisfies,

$$u_t = -au_x + f$$

and the relation

$$u_{tt} = -au_{tx} + f_t = a^2 u_{xx} - af_x + f_t,$$

to obtain

$$u(t+k,x) = u(t,x) - ak\, u_x\,(t,x) + \frac{a^2 k^2}{2} u_{xx}\,(t,x) + kf - \frac{ak^2}{2} f_x + \frac{k^2}{2} f_t + O(k^3).$$

Replacing the derivatives in x by second-order accurate differences and f_t by a forward difference, we obtain

$$u(t+k,x) = u(t,x) - ak\frac{u(t,x+h) - u(t,x-h)}{2h}$$

$$+ \frac{a^2 k^2}{2}\frac{u(t,x+h) - 2u(t,x) + u(t,x-h)}{h^2}$$

$$+ \frac{k}{2}\left[f(t+k,x) + f(t,x)\right] - \frac{ak^2}{2}\frac{\left[f(t,x+h) - f(t,x-h)\right]}{2h}$$

$$+ O(kh^2) + O(k^3).$$

This gives the Lax-Wendroff scheme

$$\frac{v_m^{n+1} - v_m^n}{k} + a\frac{v_{m+1}^n - v_{m-1}^n}{2h} - \frac{a^2 k}{2}\frac{(v_{m+1}^n - 2v_m^n + v_{m-1}^n)}{h^2}$$

$$= \tfrac{1}{2}(f_m^{n+1} + f_m^n) - \frac{ak}{4h}(f_{m+1}^n - f_{m-1}^n), \tag{3.1.1}$$

or, equivalently,

$$v_m^{n+1} = v_m^n - \frac{a\lambda}{2}(v_{m+1}^n - v_{m-1}^n) + \frac{a^2 \lambda^2}{2}(v_{m+1}^n - 2v_m^n + v_{m-1}^n)$$

$$+ \frac{k}{2}(f_m^{n+1} + f_m^n) - \frac{ak\lambda}{4}(f_{m+1}^n - f_{m-1}^n) \tag{3.1.2}$$

where $f_m^n = f(t_n, x_m)$.

The Crank-Nicolson Scheme

To derive the Crank-Nicolson scheme we begin with the formula

$$u_t = \frac{u(t+k,x) - u(t,x)}{k} + O(k^2)$$

for u_t evaluated at $(t + \frac{1}{2}k, x)$. We also use the relation

$$u_x\left(t + \frac{1}{2}k, x\right) = \frac{u_x(t + k, x) + u_x(t, x)}{2} + O(k^2)$$

$$= \frac{1}{2}\left[\frac{u(t + k, x + h) - u(t + k, x - h)}{2h} + \frac{u(t, x + h) - u(t, x - h)}{2h}\right]$$

$$+ O(k^2) + O(h^2).$$

Using these approximations for $u_t + au_x = f$ about $(t + \frac{1}{2}k, x)$, we obtain

$$\frac{v_m^{n+1} - v_m^n}{k} + a\frac{v_{m+1}^{n+1} - v_{m-1}^{n+1} + v_{m+1}^n - v_{m-1}^n}{4h} = \frac{f_m^{n+1} + f_m^n}{2} \tag{3.1.3}$$

or, equivalently,

$$\frac{a\lambda}{4}v_{m+1}^{n+1} + v_m^{n+1} - \frac{a\lambda}{4}v_{m-1}^{n+1} = -\frac{a\lambda}{4}v_{m+1}^n + v_m^n + \frac{a\lambda}{4}v_{m-1}^n + \frac{k}{2}(f_m^{n+1} + f_m^n). \tag{3.1.4}$$

As we see from these two schemes, a scheme for the partial differential equation $Pu = f$ can be written in general as $P_{k,h}v = R_{k,h}f$ in a natural way, where each expression $P_{k,h}v$ and $R_{k,h}f$ evaluated at a grid point (t_n, x_m), involves only a finite sum of terms $v_{m'}^{n'}$ or $f_{m'}^{n'}$, respectively. We are now able to give our first definition of the order of accuracy of a scheme.

Definition 3.1.1 *A scheme $P_{k,h}v = R_{k,h}f$ that is consistent with the differential equation $Pu = f$ is accurate of order p in time and order q in space if for any smooth function $\phi(t, x)$*

$$P_{k,h}\phi - R_{k,h}P\phi = O(k^p) + O(h^q). \tag{3.1.5}$$

We will say that this scheme is accurate of order (p, q).

If we compare this definition with Definition 1.4.2, we see that consistency requires only that $P_{k,h}\phi - P\phi$ be $o(1)$, whereas Definition 3.1.1 takes into consideration the more detailed information on this convergence. The operator $R_{k,h}$ is required to be an approximation of the identity operator by the requirement that $P_{k,h}$ be consistent with P. The quantity $P_{k,h}\phi - R_{k,h}P\phi$ is called the *truncation error* of the scheme.

We now illustrate this definition by showing that the Lax-Wendroff scheme (3.1.1) is accurate of order $(2, 2)$. We use the Taylor series, as before, for the left-hand side of (3.1.1) evaluated at (t_n, x_m) to obtain

$$\phi_t + \frac{k}{2}\phi_{tt} + a\phi_x - \frac{a^2 k}{2}\phi_{xx} + O(k^2) + O(h^2). \tag{3.1.6}$$

For a smooth function $f(t, x)$, the right-hand side of (3.1.1) becomes

$$f + \frac{k}{2}f_t - \frac{ak}{2}f_x + O(k^2) + O(h^2)$$

and if $f = \phi_t + a\phi_x = P\phi$, this is

$$\phi_t + a\phi_x + \frac{k}{2}\phi_{tt} + \frac{k}{2}a\phi_{xt} - \frac{ak}{2}\phi_{xt} - \frac{a^2 k}{2}\phi_{xx} + O(k^2) + O(h^2)$$

which agrees with (3.1.6) to $O(k^2) + O(h^2)$. Hence the scheme (3.1.1) is accurate of order $(2,2)$.

We also see from this analysis that the Lax-Wendroff scheme with $R_{k,h}f^n_m = f^n_m$, i.e.,

$$v^{n+1}_m = v^n_m - \frac{a\lambda}{2}\left(v^n_{m+1} - v^n_{m-1}\right) + \frac{a^2\lambda^2}{2}\left(v^n_{m+1} - 2v^n_m + v^n_{m-1}\right) + k f^n_m, \quad (3.1.7)$$

is accurate of order $(1,2)$.

Notice that to determine the order of accuracy we use the form (3.1.1) of the Lax-Wendroff scheme rather than (3.1.2), which is derived by multiplying by k and rearranging the terms. Without an appropriate normalization, in this case demanding that $P_{k,h}u$ be consistent with Pu, we can get incorrect results by multiplying the scheme by powers of k or h.

Definition 3.1.1 is not completely satisfactory. For example, it cannot be applied to the Lax-Friedrichs scheme, which contains the term $k^{-1}h^2\phi_{xx}$ in the Taylor series expansion of $P_{k,h}\phi$. We therefore give the following definition, which is more generally applicable. We assume that the time step is chosen as a function of the space step, i.e., $k = \Lambda(h)$, where Λ is a smooth function of h and $\Lambda(0) = 0$.

Definition 3.1.2   *A scheme $P_{k,h}v = R_{k,h}f$ with $k = \Lambda(h)$ that is consistent with the differential equation $Pu = f$ is accurate of order r if for any smooth function $\phi(t,x)$,*

$$P_{k,h}\phi - R_{k,h}P\phi = O(h^r). \quad (3.1.8)$$

If we take $\Lambda(h) = \lambda h$, then the Lax-Friedrichs scheme (1.3.5) is consistent with the one-way wave equation according to Definition 3.1.2.

Symbols of Difference Schemes

Another useful way of checking for the accuracy of a scheme is by comparing the symbols of the difference scheme to the symbol of the differential operator. Using the symbol is often a more convenient method than is that given in Definitions 3.1.1 and 3.1.2.

Definition 3.1.3   *The symbol $p_{k,h}(s,\xi)$ of a difference operator $P_{k,h}$ is defined by*

$$P_{k,h}(e^{skn}e^{imh\xi}) = p_{k,h}(s,\xi)e^{skn}e^{imh\xi}.$$

That is, the symbol is the quantity multiplying the grid function $e^{skn}e^{imh\xi}$ after operating on this function with the difference operator.

As an example, for the Lax-Wendroff operator we have

$$p_{k,h}(s,\xi) = \frac{e^{sk}-1}{k} + \frac{ia}{h}\sin h\xi + 2\frac{a^2k}{h^2}\sin^2 \tfrac{1}{2}h\xi$$

and

$$r_{k,h}(s,\xi) = \frac{1}{2}(e^{sk}+1) - \frac{iak}{2h}\sin h\xi.$$

Definition 3.1.4 *The symbol $p(s,\xi)$ of the differential operator P is defined by*

$$P(e^{st}e^{i\xi x}) = p(s,\xi)e^{st}e^{i\xi x}.$$

That is, the symbol is the quantity multiplying the function $e^{st}e^{ix\xi}$ after operating on this function with the differential operator.

In checking the accuracy of a scheme by using Taylor series and Definition 3.1.1, it is seen that the derivatives of ϕ serve primarily as arbitrary coefficients for the polynomials in h and k. The powers of the dual variables s and ξ can also serve as the coefficients of h and k in the definition of accuracy, as the following theorem states.

Theorem 3.1.1 *A scheme $P_{k,h}v = R_{k,h}f$ that is consistent with $Pu = f$ is accurate of order (p,q) if and only if for each value of s and ξ,*

$$\frac{p_{k,h}(s,\xi)}{r_{k,h}(s,\xi)} - p(s,\xi) = O(k^p) + O(h^q). \tag{3.1.9}$$

Proof By consistency we have for each smooth function ϕ that

$$P_{k,h}\phi - P\phi$$

tends to zero as h and k tend to zero; see Definition 1.3.2. Taking

$$\phi(t,x) = e^{st}e^{i\xi x}$$

we have that

$$p_{k,h}(s,\xi) - p(s,\xi) = o(1) \tag{3.1.10}$$

for each (s,ξ).

From Definition 3.1.1 for the order of accuracy and using $\phi(t,x)$ as before, we have—by the definition of the symbol—that

$$p_{k,h}(s,\xi) - r_{k,h}(s,\xi)p(s,\xi) = O(k^p) + O(h^q). \tag{3.1.11}$$

Hence from (3.1.10) and (3.1.11) we have that

$$r_{k,h}(s,\xi) = 1 + o(1), \tag{3.1.12}$$

and by dividing (3.1.11) by $r_{k,h}(s,\xi)$, we obtain (3.1.9).

To show that (3.1.9) implies (3.1.5), we again have by consistency that (3.1.12) holds, and hence (3.1.11) holds also. To obtain the Taylor series expansion for $P_{k,h}\phi$, we note that if

$$p_{k,h}(s,\xi) = \sum_{\ell,j \geq 0} A_{\ell,j}(k,h)s^{\ell}(i\xi)^j$$

then

$$P_{k,h}\phi = \sum_{\ell,j \geq 0} A_{\ell,j}(k,h)\frac{\partial^{\ell+j}\phi}{\partial t^{\ell}\partial x^j}.$$

Therefore, (3.1.5) follows from (3.1.9). ∎

Corollary 3.1.2   *A scheme $P_{k,h}v = R_{k,h}f$ with $k = \Lambda(h)$ that is consistent with $Pu = f$ is accurate of order r if and only if for each value of s and ξ*

$$\frac{p_{k,h}(s,\xi)}{r_{k,h}(s,\xi)} - p(s,\xi) = O(h^r). \tag{3.1.13}$$

In practice the form (3.1.11) is often more convenient than is (3.1.9) or (3.1.13) to show the order of accuracy.

In Chapter 10 we show that if a scheme is accurate of order r, then the finite difference solution converges to the solution of the differential equation with the same order provided that the initial data are sufficiently smooth.

Example 3.1.1   As an example of using Theorem 3.1.1, we prove that the Crank-Nicolson scheme (3.1.3) is accurate of order $(2,2)$. From (3.1.3) we have that

$$p_{k,h}(s,\xi) = \frac{e^{sk} - 1}{k} + ia\frac{e^{sk} + 1}{2}\frac{\sin h\xi}{h}$$

and

$$r_{k,h}(s,\xi) = \frac{e^{sk} + 1}{2}.$$

The left-hand side of (3.1.11) for this case is

$$\frac{e^{sk} - 1}{k} + ia\frac{e^{sk} + 1}{2}\frac{\sin h\xi}{h} - \frac{e^{sk} + 1}{2}(s + ia\xi). \tag{3.1.14}$$

We could use Taylor series expansions on this expression, but the work is reduced if we first multiply (3.1.14) by $e^{-sk/2}$. Since $e^{-sk/2}$ is $O(1)$, multiplying by it will not affect the determination of accuracy. We then have

$$\frac{e^{sk/2} - e^{-sk/2}}{k} + ia\frac{e^{sk/2} + e^{-sk/2}}{2}\frac{\sin h\xi}{h} - \frac{e^{sk/2} + e^{-sk/2}}{2}(s + ia\xi). \tag{3.1.15}$$

The Taylor series expansions of the different expressions are then

$$\frac{e^{sk/2} - e^{-sk/2}}{k} = s + \frac{s^3 k^2}{24} + O\left(k^4\right),$$

$$\frac{e^{sk/2} + e^{-sk/2}}{2} = 1 + \frac{s^2 k^2}{8} + O\left(k^4\right),$$

and

$$\frac{\sin h\xi}{h} = \xi - \frac{\xi^3 h^2}{6} + O\left(h^4\right).$$

Substituting these expansions in (3.1.15) we obtain

$$s + ia\xi + \frac{s^3 k^2}{24} + ia\frac{s^2 \xi k^2}{8} - ia\frac{\xi^3 h^2}{6}$$

$$- \left(1 + \frac{s^2 k^2}{8}\right)(s + ia\xi) + O\left(k^4 + h^4 + k^2 h^2\right)$$

$$= -\frac{k^2 s^3}{12} - ia\frac{\xi^3 h^2}{6} + O\left(k^4 + h^4 + k^2 h^2\right)$$

$$= O\left(k^2\right) + O\left(h^2\right).$$

Thus, the Crank-Nicolson scheme is accurate of order $(2, 2)$.

Using Taylor series expansions directly on (3.1.14) instead of (3.1.15) would have resulted in terms of order h and k in the expansion. These terms would have all canceled out, giving the same order of accuracy. Working with equation (3.1.15) greatly reduces the amount of algebraic manipulation that must be done to check the order of accuracy. Similar techniques can be used on other schemes.

□

We use symbols to prove the following theorem about schemes for the one-way wave equation and other hyperbolic equations.

Theorem 3.1.3 *An explicit one-step scheme for hyperbolic equations that has the form*

$$v_m^{n+1} = \sum_{\ell=-\infty}^{\infty} \alpha_\ell \, v_{m+\ell}^n \tag{3.1.16}$$

for homogeneous problems can be at most first-order accurate if all the coefficients α_ℓ are nonnegative, except for the trivial schemes for the one-way wave equation with $|a\lambda| = \ell$, where ℓ is an integer, given by

$$v_m^{n+1} = v_{m-\ell}^n. \tag{3.1.17}$$

Proof We prove the theorem only for the one-way wave equation (1.1.1). As shown in the discussion of Section 1.1, this is sufficient for the general case. The symbol of the scheme (3.1.16) is

$$p_{k,h}(s, \xi) = \frac{e^{sk} - \sum \alpha_\ell e^{i\ell h\xi}}{k}.$$

If we allow for a right-hand side symbol $r_{k,h}(s, \xi) = 1 + O(k) + O(h)$, the accuracy of the scheme is determined by considering the expression

$$\frac{e^{sk} - \sum \alpha_\ell \, e^{i\ell h\xi}}{k} - (1 + O(k) + O(h))(s + ia\xi).$$

If this expression is to be bounded as k tends to 0, we must have

$$\sum_{\ell=-\infty}^{\infty} \alpha_\ell = 1. \tag{3.1.18}$$

The terms in s to the first power agree, and the coefficients of ks^2 will cancel only if $r_{k,h} = 1 + \frac{1}{2}sk + O(\xi k) + O(h)$. The only occurrence of terms with the monomial $s\xi$ occur in the product of $r_{k,h}$ with $s + ia\xi$, and these will cancel only if $r_{k,h} = 1 + \frac{1}{2}k(s - ia\xi) + O(h)$. Moreover, the term $O(h)$ must be actually $O(h^2)$, since there is no term of the form sh coming from the symbol of the scheme. The terms to the first power of ξ are

$$-i\frac{h}{k} \sum_{\ell=-\infty}^{\infty} \alpha_\ell \ell - ia,$$

and this expression must be zero if the scheme is to be first-order accurate. This gives the relation

$$\sum_{\ell=-\infty}^{\infty} \alpha_\ell \, \ell = -a\lambda. \tag{3.1.19}$$

Next consider the terms that are the coefficients of ξ^2. They are

$$-\frac{h^2}{2k} \sum_{\ell=-\infty}^{\infty} \alpha_\ell \ell^2 + \frac{ka^2}{2}.$$

To have second-order accuracy this expression must also be zero, giving

$$\sum_{\ell=-\infty}^{\infty} \alpha_\ell \, \ell^2 = a^2\lambda^2. \tag{3.1.20}$$

We now use the Cauchy-Schwarz inequality on these three relations for the coefficients of the scheme. We have

$$|a\lambda| = \left| \sum_{\ell=-\infty}^{\infty} \alpha_\ell \ell \right| = \left| \sum_{\ell=-\infty}^{\infty} \sqrt{\alpha_\ell} \sqrt{\alpha_\ell} \ell \right|$$

$$\leq \left(\sum_{\ell=-\infty}^{\infty} \alpha_\ell \right)^{\frac{1}{2}} \left(\sum_{\ell=-\infty}^{\infty} \alpha_\ell \ell^2 \right)^{\frac{1}{2}} = |a\lambda|.$$

Since the first and last expressions in this string of inequalities and equalities are the same, it follows that all the expressions are equal. However, the Cauchy-Schwarz inequality is an equality only if all the terms with same index are proportional. This means there must be a constant c such that

$$\sqrt{\alpha_\ell} \, \ell = c\sqrt{\alpha_\ell} \quad \text{for all } \ell, \tag{3.1.21}$$

and this implies that at most one α_ℓ is nonzero. It is then easy to check that the only way these relations can be satisfied is if $|a\lambda|$ is an integer, and the resulting schemes are the trivial schemes (3.1.17). This proves the theorem. ∎

An examination of equations (3.1.18), (3.1.19), and (3.1.20) shows that the Lax-Wendroff scheme is the explicit one-step second-order accurate scheme that uses the fewest number of grid points. (See Exercise 3.1.9.)

Order of Accuracy for Homogeneous Equations

For many initial value problems one is concerned only with the homogeneous equation $Pu = 0$ rather than the inhomogeneous equation $Pu = f$. In this case one can determine the order of accuracy without explicit knowledge of the operator $R_{k,h}$. We now show how this is done. It is important to make sure that our treatment of this topic applies to schemes for systems of differential equations as well as to single equations.

We begin by extending the set of symbols we have been using. Thus far we have considered symbols of finite difference schemes and symbols of partial differential operators, but we will find it convenient to extend the class of symbols.

Definition 3.1.5 *A symbol $a(s,\xi)$ is an infinitely differentiable function defined for complex values of s with Re $s \geq c$ for some constant c and for all real values of ξ.*

This definition includes as symbols not only the symbols of differential operators and finite difference operators, but also many other functions. Symbols of differential operators are polynomials in s and ξ, and symbols of difference operators are polynomials in e^{ks} with coefficients that are either polynomials or rational functions of $e^{ih\xi}$.

Definition 3.1.6   *A symbol $a(s,\xi)$ is congruent to zero modulo a symbol $p(s,\xi)$, written*

$$a(s,\xi) \equiv 0 \bmod p(s,\xi),$$

if there is a symbol $b(s,\xi)$ such that

$$a(s,\xi) = b(s,\xi)\,p(s,\xi).$$

We also write

$$a(s,\xi) \equiv c(s,\xi) \bmod p(s,\xi)$$

if

$$a(s,\xi) - c(s,\xi) \equiv 0 \bmod p(s,\xi).$$

We can now define the order of accuracy for homogeneous equations.

Theorem 3.1.4   *A scheme $P_{k,h}v = 0$, with $k = \Lambda(h)$, that is consistent with the equation $Pu = 0$ is accurate of order r if*

$$p_{k,h}(s,\xi) \equiv O(h^r) \bmod p(s,\xi). \tag{3.1.22}$$

Proof   By Definition 3.1.6 the relation (3.1.22) holds if and only if there is a symbol $\tilde{r}_{k,h}(s,\xi)$ such that

$$p_{k,h}(s,\xi) - \tilde{r}_{k,h}(s,\xi)p(s,\xi) = O(h^r).$$

Since $p(s,\xi)$ is a linear polynomial in s with coefficients that are polynomials in ξ and since $p_{k,h}(s,\xi)$ is essentially a polynomial in e^{sk} with coefficients that are rational functions of $e^{ih\xi}$, it is not difficult to show that there is a symbol $r_{k,h}(s,\xi)$ such that

$$r_{k,h}(s,\xi) \equiv \tilde{r}_{k,h}(s,\xi) + O(h^r)$$

and $r_{k,h}(s,\xi)$ is a polynomial in e^{sk} with coefficients that are rational functions of $e^{ih\xi}$. The replacement of $\tilde{r}_{k,h}(s,\xi)$ by $r_{k,h}(s,\xi)$ is not strictly necessary for the proof, but it is important from the point of view of constructing an actual difference operator $R_{k,h}$ whose symbol is $r_{k,h}(s,\xi)$ and that can actually be used in computation. ∎

If we wish to use the Taylor series method of Definition 3.1.1 for checking the accuracy of homogeneous equations, then we can proceed in a way analogous to Definition 3.1.6 and Theorem 3.1.4. Equivalently, we can show that if

$$P_{k,h}\phi = O(h^r)$$

for each formal solution to $P\phi = 0$, then the scheme is accurate of order r. By saying a *formal solution* we emphasize that we do not require knowledge of the existence of solutions nor about the smoothness of the solution, we merely use the relation $P\phi = 0$ in evaluating $P_{k,h}\phi$. As an example, for the Lax-Wendroff scheme for the homogeneous equation (1.1.1), we have

$$\phi(t + k, x) = \phi(t, x) + k\phi_t(t, x) + \frac{k^2}{2}\phi_{tt}(t, x) + O(k^3)$$

$$= \phi(t, x) + k\left[-a\phi_x(t, x)\right] + \frac{k^2}{2}\left(a^2\phi_{xx}\right) + O(k^3)$$

$$= \phi(t, x) - \frac{a\lambda}{2}\left[\phi(t, x + h) - \phi(t, x - h)\right]$$

$$+ \frac{a^2\lambda^2}{2}\left[\phi(t, x + h) - 2\phi(t, x) + \phi(t, x - h)\right] + O(k^3) + O(kh^2).$$

In this derivation we have used the relations

$$\phi_t = -a\phi_x$$

and

$$\phi_{tt} = -a\phi_{xt} = a^2\phi_{xx}.$$

From the preceding expression we obtain the scheme (3.1.2) without the terms involving f.

As is seen in Chapter 10, even for the homogeneous initial value problem it is important to know that the symbol $r_{k,h}(s, \xi)$ exists in order to prove that the proper order of convergence is attained.

Order of Accuracy of the Solution

We have spent some time on rigorously defining the order of accuracy of finite difference schemes, and the importance of this concept is that it relates directly to the accuracy of the solutions that are computed using these schemes. The order of accuracy of the solution of a finite difference scheme is a quantity that can be determined by computation. For our purposes here and in the exercises, it is sufficient to define the order of accuracy of the solution of a finite difference scheme as follows. If we have an initial value problem for a partial differential equation with solution $u(t, x)$ and a finite difference scheme, we use the initial data of the differential equation evaluated at the grid points as initial data for the scheme, i.e., $v_m^0 = u(0, x_m)$. We also assume that the time step is a function of the space step, i.e., $k = \Lambda(h)$. We then determine the error at time $t = nk$ by

$$\text{Error}(t) = \|u(t, \cdot) - v^n\|_h$$

$$= \left(h \sum_m |u(t, x_m) - v_m^n|^2\right)^{1/2},$$

where the sum is over all grid points. The order of accuracy of the solution is defined to be that number r, if it exists, such that

$$\text{Error}(t) = O(h^r).$$

In Chapter 10 it is shown that for smooth initial data, the order of accuracy of the solution is equal to the order of accuracy of the scheme. Moreover, for those cases in which the data are not smooth enough for the accuracy of the solution to equal that of the scheme, it is shown how the order of accuracy of the solution depends on both the order of accuracy of the scheme and the smoothness of the initial data.

The order of accuracy of the solution, as given here, is dependent on the way the initial data for the scheme is chosen and on the norm. For example, if the error is measured as the maximum value of $|u(t, x_m) - v_m^n|$, then the order of accuracy of the solution can be different than, and usually less than, the order obtained by the preceding definition. This topic is discussed in more detail in Chapter 10.

Stability of the Lax-Wendroff and Crank-Nicolson Schemes for Hyperbolic Equations

We conclude this section by demonstrating the stability of the Lax-Wendroff and Crank-Nicolson schemes.

The Lax-Wendroff scheme for $u_t + au_x = 0$ is

$$v_m^{n+1} = v_m^n - \frac{a\lambda}{2}\left(v_{m+1}^n - v_{m-1}^n\right) + \frac{a^2\lambda^2}{2}\left(v_{m+1}^n - 2v_m^n + v_{m-1}^n\right),$$

and so the amplification factor is

$$g(\theta) = 1 - \frac{a\lambda}{2}(e^{i\theta} - e^{-i\theta}) + \frac{a^2\lambda^2}{2}(e^{i\theta} - 2 + e^{-i\theta})$$

$$= 1 - ia\lambda\sin\theta - a^2\lambda^2(1 - \cos\theta)$$

$$= 1 - 2a^2\lambda^2\sin^2\tfrac{1}{2}\theta - ia\lambda\sin\theta.$$

The magnitude of $g(\theta)$ is given by

$$|g(\theta)|^2 = \left(1 - 2a^2\lambda^2\sin^2\tfrac{1}{2}\theta\right)^2 + \left(2a\lambda\sin\tfrac{1}{2}\theta\cos\tfrac{1}{2}\theta\right)^2$$

$$= 1 - 4a^2\lambda^2\sin^2\tfrac{1}{2}\theta + 4a^4\lambda^4\sin^4\tfrac{1}{2}\theta + 4a^2\lambda^2\sin^2\tfrac{1}{2}\theta\cos^2\tfrac{1}{2}\theta$$

$$= 1 - 4a^2\lambda^2\left(1 - a^2\lambda^2\right)\sin^4\tfrac{1}{2}\theta.$$

We have $|g(\theta)| \leq 1$, that is, the scheme is stable if and only if $|a\lambda| \leq 1$.

For the Crank-Nicolson scheme we obtain

$$g(\theta) = \frac{1 - i\frac{1}{2}a\lambda \sin \theta}{1 + i\frac{1}{2}a\lambda \sin \theta}$$

so

$$|g(\theta)|^2 = \frac{1 + (\frac{1}{2}a\lambda \sin \theta)^2}{1 + (\frac{1}{2}a\lambda \sin \theta)^2} = 1.$$

This scheme is stable for any value of λ; it is said to be *unconditionally stable*.

EXERCISES 3.1

1. Show that the (forward-backward) MacCormack scheme

$$\tilde{v}_m^{n+1} = v_m^n - a\lambda(v_{m+1}^n - v_m^n) + kf_m^n$$

$$v_m^{n+1} = \frac{1}{2}(v_m^n + \tilde{v}_m^{n+1} - a\lambda(\tilde{v}_m^{n+1} - \tilde{v}_{m-1}^{n+1}) + kf_m^{n+1})$$

is a second-order accurate scheme for the one-way wave equation (1.1.1). Show that for $f = 0$ it is identical with the Lax-Wendroff scheme (3.1.2).

2. Solve $u_t + u_x = 0$, $-1 \le x \le 1$, $0 \le t \le 1.2$ with $u(0, x) = \sin 2\pi x$ and periodic boundary conditions, i.e., $u(t, 1) = u(t, -1)$. Use two methods:

(a) Forward-time backward-space with $\lambda = 0.8$
(b) Lax-Wendroff with $\lambda = 0.8$

Demonstrate the first-order accuracy of the solution of (a) and the second-order accuracy of the solution of (b) using $h = \frac{1}{10}, \frac{1}{20}, \frac{1}{40}$, and $\frac{1}{80}$. Measure the error in the L^2 norm and maximum norm. The L^2 norm is

$$\left(h \sum_m |v_m^n - u(t_n, x_m)|^2 \right)^{1/2},$$

where the sum is over all the grid points. (Do not sum both the grid point at $x = -1$ and $x = 1$ as separate points.)

3. Show that the box scheme

$$\frac{1}{2k}\left[(v_m^{n+1} + v_{m+1}^{n+1}) - (v_m^n + v_{m+1}^n)\right]$$

$$+ \frac{a}{2h}\left[(v_{m+1}^{n+1} - v_m^{n+1}) + (v_{m+1}^n - v_m^n)\right] \qquad (3.1.23)$$

$$= \frac{1}{4}\left(f_{m+1}^{n+1} + f_m^{n+1} + f_{m+1}^n + f_m^n\right)$$

is an approximation to the one-way wave equation $u_t + au_x = f$ that is accurate of order $(2, 2)$ and is stable for all values of λ.

4. Using the box scheme (3.1.23), solve the one-way wave equation $u_t + u_x = \sin(x - t)$ on the interval $[0, 1]$ for $0 \le t \le 1.2$ with $u(0, x) = \sin x$ and with $u(t, 0) = -(1 + t) \sin t$ as the boundary condition.

Demonstrate the second-order accuracy of the solution using $\lambda = 1.2$ and $h = \frac{1}{10}, \frac{1}{20}, \frac{1}{40}$, and $\frac{1}{80}$. Measure the error in the L^2 norm and maximum norm. The L^2 norm is

$$\left(h \sum_m |v_m^n - u(t_n, x_m)|^2 \right)^{1/2},$$

where the sum is over all the grid points.

Demonstrate that the box scheme of Exercise 2.2.4 is only first-order accurate. To implement the box scheme note that v_0^{n+1} is given by the boundary data, and then each value of v_{m+1}^{n+1} can be determined from v_m^{n+1} and the other values.

5. Solve the equation

$$u_t + u_x = \cos^2 u$$

with the scheme (3.1.7), treating the $\cos^2 u$ term as $f(t, x)$. Show that the scheme is first-order accurate. The exact solution is given by

$$\tan [u(t, x)] = \tan [u_0(x - t)] + t.$$

Use a smooth function, such as $\sin(x - t)$, as initial data and boundary data.

6.   Modify the scheme of Exercise 5 to be second-order accurate and explicit. There are several ways to do this. One way uses $\cos^2 v_m^{n+1} = \cos^2 v_m^n - \sin 2v_m^n \left(v_m^{n+1} - v_m^n \right) + O\left(k^2 \right)$. Another way is to evaluate explicitly the f_t term in the derivation of the Lax-Wendroff scheme and eliminate all derivatives with respect to t using the equation.

7. Determine the order of accuracy of the Euler backward scheme in Exercise 2.2.6.

8. Determine the accuracy and stability of the following scheme for $u_t + u_{tx} + au_x = f$.

$$v_m^{n+1} + \left(1 + \frac{ka}{2} \right) \frac{v_{m+1}^{n+1} - v_{m-1}^{n+1}}{2h} = v_m^n + \left(1 - \frac{ka}{2} \right) \frac{v_{m+1}^n - v_{m-1}^n}{2h} + \frac{k}{2} (f_m^{n+1} + f_m^n)$$

Hint: This scheme is somewhat symmetric about time level $n + \frac{1}{2}$, much like the Crank-Nicolson scheme.

9. Using equations (3.1.18), (3.1.19), and (3.1.20), show that the Lax-Wendroff scheme is the only explicit one-step second-order accurate scheme that uses only the grid points x_{m-1}, x_m, and x_{m+1} to compute the solution at x_m for the next time step.

10. Show that the scheme discussed in Example 2.2.6 has the symbol

$$\frac{e^{sk} - \cos h\xi}{k} + 4ai\frac{\sin^2 \frac{1}{2}h\xi \sin h\xi}{h^3}$$

and discuss the accuracy of the scheme.

3.2 Difference Notation and the Difference Calculus

To assist in our analysis and discussion of schemes we introduce some notation for finite differences. The forward and backward difference operators are defined by

$$\delta_+ v_m = \frac{v_{m+1} - v_m}{h} \tag{3.2.1}$$

and

$$\delta_- v_m = \frac{v_m - v_{m-1}}{h}, \tag{3.2.2}$$

respectively. We will occasionally use the notation δ_{x+} and δ_{x-} for these operators and define

$$\delta_{t+} v_m^n = \frac{v_m^{n+1} - v_m^n}{k}$$

for the forward difference in t; we similarly define δ_{t-}.

The central (first) difference operator δ_0, or δ_{x0}, is defined by

$$\delta_0 v_m = \tfrac{1}{2}(\delta_+ v_m + \delta_- v_m),$$

or, more succinctly,

$$\delta_0 = \tfrac{1}{2}(\delta_+ + \delta_-).$$

The central second difference operator is $\delta_+\delta_-$, which we also denote by δ^2. We have

$$\delta^2 v_m = \frac{v_{m+1} - 2v_m + v_{m-1}}{h^2},$$

and also

$$\delta^2 = (\delta_+ \cdot \delta_-)/h.$$

We now demonstrate the use of this notation in deriving fourth-order accurate approximations to the first and second derivative operators. By Taylor series we have

$$\delta_0 u = \frac{du}{dx} + \frac{h^2}{6}\frac{d^3 u}{dx^3} + O(h^4) = \left(1 + \frac{h^2}{6}\frac{d^2}{dx^2}\right)\frac{du}{dx} + O(h^4)$$

$$= \left(1 + \frac{h^2}{6}\delta^2\right)\frac{du}{dx} + O(h^4), \tag{3.2.3}$$

where we have used

$$\frac{d^2 f}{dx^2} = \delta^2 f + O(h^2).$$

We may rewrite the formula for $\delta_0 u$ as

$$\frac{du}{dx} = \left(1 + \frac{h^2}{6}\delta^2\right)^{-1} \delta_0 u + O(h^4). \tag{3.2.4}$$

The inverse of the operator $1 + \frac{h^2}{6}\delta^2$ is used only in a symbolic sense. In practice the inverse is always eliminated by operating on both sides of the expression with $1 + \frac{h^2}{6}\delta^2$. Applying this formula to the simple equation

$$\frac{du}{dx} = f, \tag{3.2.5}$$

we have the equation

$$\left(1 + \frac{h^2}{6}\delta^2\right)^{-1} \delta_0 u(x_m) = f(x_m)$$

to fourth order. From this we have

$$\delta_0 u(x_m) = \left(1 + \frac{h^2}{6}\delta^2\right) f(x_m)$$

or

$$\frac{v_{m+1} - v_{m-1}}{2h} = f_m + \frac{1}{6}(f_{m+1} - 2f_m + f_{m-1})$$
$$= \frac{1}{6}(f_{m+1} + 4f_m + f_{m-1}).$$

Another fourth-order difference formula may be derived by using the formula

$$\delta_0 u = \frac{du}{dx} + \frac{h^2}{6}\delta^2 \delta_0 u + O(h^4)$$

which may be rewritten as

$$\left(1 - \frac{h^2}{6}\delta^2\right)\delta_0 u = \frac{du}{dx} + O(h^4). \tag{3.2.6}$$

Applied to (3.2.5) we obtain the fourth-order approximation

$$\left(1 - \frac{h^2}{6}\delta^2\right)\delta_0 v_m = f_m$$

or

$$\frac{-v_{m+2} + 8v_{m+1} - 8v_{m-1} + v_{m-2}}{12h} = f_m.$$

For the second-order derivative we have the two formulas

$$\frac{d^2}{dx^2} = \left(1 + \frac{h^2}{12}\delta^2\right)^{-1}\delta^2 + O(h^4), \tag{3.2.7}$$

and

$$\frac{d^2}{dx^2} = \left(1 - \frac{h^2}{12}\delta^2\right)\delta^2 + O(h^4). \tag{3.2.8}$$

It is of some use to develop the formalism relating differences to derivatives. Let $\partial = \partial_x = \dfrac{d}{dx}$, then by Taylor series

$$u(x + h) = \sum_{j=0}^{\infty} \frac{h^j}{j!}\,\partial^j u(x)$$

$$= e^{h\partial}u(x). \tag{3.2.9}$$

This formalism may be regarded as a purely symbolic operation to obtain difference equations. If we adopt this view then we should always check the accuracy of the formulas by the methods of Section 3.1. We may also regard this formalism as a shorthand notation for general Taylor series methods. For example, we can write out the expressions in (3.2.3) without writing down the symbol u. If we use this shorthand notation properly, the results will be consistent with the methods of Section 3.1, and there is no need to perform additional checks on the accuracy of schemes derived by this formalism. Therefore, we may express formulas (3.2.1) and (3.2.2) as

$$\delta_+ = \frac{e^{h\partial} - 1}{h}$$

and

$$\delta_- = \frac{1 - e^{-h\partial}}{h}.$$

Also

$$\delta_0 = \tfrac{1}{2}(\delta_+ + \delta_-) = \frac{e^{h\partial} - e^{-h\partial}}{2h} = \frac{\sinh h\partial}{h} \tag{3.2.10}$$

and

$$\delta^2 = \delta_+\delta_- = h^{-2}(e^{h\partial} - 1)(1 - e^{-h\partial})$$

$$= \left[h^{-1}(e^{h\partial/2} - e^{-h\partial/2})\right]^2 \tag{3.2.11}$$

$$= \left(\frac{\sinh \frac{1}{2}h\partial}{\frac{1}{2}h}\right)^2.$$

Notice that to obtain the symbols of these operators according to Definitions 3.1.3 and 3.1.4 we need only replace ∂ by $i\xi$.

We may generalize formula (3.2.4) as follows. From (3.2.10) we have

$$\delta_0 = \frac{\sinh h\partial}{h} = \frac{\sinh h\partial}{h\partial}\partial \tag{3.2.12}$$

and from (3.2.11) we have

$$h\delta = 2\sinh \tfrac{1}{2}h\partial \tag{3.2.13}$$

where δ is defined by this relation. Thus

$$h\partial = 2\sinh^{-1}\tfrac{1}{2}h\delta$$

or

$$\partial = \frac{\sinh^{-1}\tfrac{1}{2}h\delta}{\tfrac{1}{2}h} \tag{3.2.14}$$

and so, from (3.2.12),

$$\delta_0 = \frac{\sinh[2\sinh^{-1}(\tfrac{1}{2}h\delta)]}{2\sinh^{-1}\tfrac{1}{2}h\delta}\partial$$

or

$$\partial = \frac{2\sinh^{-1}(\tfrac{1}{2}h\delta)}{\sinh[2\sinh^{-1}(\tfrac{1}{2}h\delta)]}\delta_0$$

$$= \left[1 + \left(\frac{h\delta}{2}\right)^2\right]^{-1/2} \frac{\sinh^{-1}\tfrac{1}{2}h\delta}{\tfrac{1}{2}h\delta}\delta_0. \tag{3.2.15}$$

One may use the expression (3.2.15) to substitute for the derivatives with respect to x in differential equations and similarly use the square of (3.2.14) to substitute for the second derivative. By expanding the Taylor series to high enough powers of h approximations to any order accuracy can be obtained.

It is important to realize that not all schemes arise by a straight forward application of these formulas. The Lax-Wendroff scheme is a good example of a scheme relying on clever manipulations to obtain second-order accuracy in time, even though the scheme is a one-step scheme. Other examples of higher-order accuracy schemes using similar ideas are given in Chapter 4.

Derivation of Schemes Using the Symbolic Calculus

To illustrate the use of the symbolic calculus, we derive two higher-order accurate schemes.

Example 3.2.1 We first derive a $(4,4)$ scheme for the one-way wave equation. The starting point for the derivation is the Taylor series expansion for a solution of $u_t + au_x = f$,

$$\frac{u_m^{n+2} - u_m^{n-2}}{4k} = u_t + \frac{2k^2}{3} u_{ttt} + O(k^4)$$

$$= \left(1 + \frac{2k^2}{3} \delta_t^2\right) u_t + O(k^4)$$

$$= \left(1 + \frac{2k^2}{3} \delta_t^2\right) (-au_x + f) + O(k^4)$$

$$= -\left(1 + \frac{2k^2}{3} \delta_t^2\right) a(1 - \frac{h^2 \delta^2}{6}) \delta_0 u$$

$$+ \left(1 + \frac{2k^2}{3} \delta_t^2\right) f + O(k^4) + O(h^4)$$

$$= (-a(1 - \frac{h^2 \delta^2}{6}) \delta_0 \left(\frac{2u_m^{n+1} - u_m^n + 2u_m^{n-1}}{3}\right)$$

$$+ \left(\frac{2f_m^{n+1} - f_m^n + 2f_m^{n-1}}{3}\right) + O(k^4) + O(h^4).$$

This gives the $(4,4)$ scheme

$$\frac{v_m^{n+2} - v_m^{n-2}}{4k} + a(1 - \frac{h^2 \delta^2}{6}) \delta_0 \left(\frac{2v_m^{n+1} - v_m^n + 2v_m^{n-1}}{3}\right) = \frac{2f_m^{n+1} - f_m^n + 2f_m^{n-1}}{3}.$$

In Chapter 4 we present methods to show that this scheme is stable for

$$|a\lambda| < \frac{\sqrt{3}}{4} \frac{1}{(1 + \sqrt{6})(\sqrt{6} - 3/2)^{1/2}},$$

(see Exercise 4.3.5). $\square$

Example 3.2.2 As a second example we derive a scheme that is a hybrid between the Lax-Wendroff scheme (3.1.1) and the Crank-Nicolson scheme (3.1.3) for the one-way wave equation. We begin by considering $u(t_{n+1/3}, x)$.

$$\frac{u^{n+1} - u^n}{k} = u_t^{n+1/3} + \frac{k}{6} u_{tt}^{n+1/3} + O(k^2)$$

$$= u_t^{n+1/3} + \frac{k}{6} (a^2 u_{xx}^{n+1/3} + (f_t^{n+1/3} - af_x^{n+1/3}) + O(k^2)$$

and using the relation $\varphi^{n+1/3} = (\varphi^{n+1} + 2\varphi^n)/3 + O(k^2)$, we obtain

$$\frac{v_m^{n+1} - v_m^n}{k} + a\delta_0 \left(\frac{v_m^{n+1} + 2v_m^n}{3} \right) - \frac{k}{6} a^2 \delta^2 \left(\frac{v_m^{n+1} + 2v_m^n}{3} \right)$$

$$= \frac{f_m^{n+1} + f_m^n}{2} - \frac{ak}{6} \delta_0 \left(\frac{f_m^{n+1} + 2f_m^n}{3} \right). \tag{3.2.16}$$

This scheme is a $(2, 2)$ scheme and is stable for $|a\lambda| \leq 3$. See Exercise 3.2.9. $\square$

Example 3.2.3 For our last example we derive an implicit $(2, 2)$ scheme for the one-way wave equation. We have from (3.2.2) that

$$\partial_t v^{n+1} = -k^{-1} \ln(1 - k\delta_-) v^{n+1} \tag{3.2.17}$$

and by (3.2.9)

$$\partial_t u^{n+2/3} = e^{-k\partial_t/3} \partial_t u^{n+1}$$

$$= -\left(1 - \frac{1}{3} k\delta_- \right) k^{-1} \ln(1 - k\delta_-) u^{n+1} + O(k^2)$$

$$= \left(1 - \frac{1}{3} k\delta_- \right) (\delta_- + \frac{1}{2} k\delta_-^2) u^{n+1} + O(k^2)$$

$$= \left(\delta_- + \frac{1}{6} k\delta_-^2 \right) u^{n+1} + O(k^2)$$

$$= \frac{7u^{n+1} - 8u^n + u^{n-1}}{6k} + O(k^2).$$

Using this relation with $u_x^{n+2/3} = (2u_x^{n+1} + u_x^n)/3 + O(k^2)$ we obtain

$$\frac{7v_m^{n+1} - 8v_m^n + v_m^{n-1}}{6k} + a\delta_0 \left(\frac{2v_m^{n+1} + v_m^n}{3} \right) = f_m^{n+2/3}. \tag{3.2.18}$$

In Example 4.3.1 it is shown that this scheme is unconditionally stable. $\square$

EXERCISES 3.2

1. Derive (3.2.7) and (3.2.8).

2. Obtain (3.2.4) directly from (3.2.15).

3. Obtain (3.2.8) from $\partial^2 = \frac{4}{h^2} \left(\sinh^{-1} \frac{1}{2} h\delta \right)^2$, which is equivalent to (3.2.14).

4. Show that the following modified box scheme scheme for $u_t + au_x = f$ is accurate of order $(2, 4)$ and is unconditionally stable. The scheme is

$$\frac{1}{16}(-v_{m+2}^{n+1} + 9v_{m+1}^{n+1} + 9v_m^{n+1} - v_{m-1}^{n+1})$$

$$+ \frac{a\lambda}{48}(-v_{m+2}^{n+1} + 27v_{m+1}^{n+1} - 27v_m^{n+1} + v_{m-1}^{n+1})$$

$$= \frac{1}{16}(-v_{m+2}^{n} + 9v_{m+1}^{n} + 9v_m^{n} - v_{m-1}^{n})$$

$$- \frac{a\lambda}{48}(-v_{m+2}^{n} + 27v_{m+1}^{n} - 27v_m^{n} + v_{m-1}^{n})$$

$$+ \frac{k}{32}(-f_{m+2}^{n+1} + 9f_{m+1}^{n+1} + 9f_m^{n+1} - f_{m-1}^{n+1}$$

$$- f_{m+2}^{n} + 9f_{m+1}^{n} + 9f_m^{n} - f_{m-1}^{n}).$$

5. Determine the stability and accuracy of the following scheme, a modification of the Lax-Wendroff scheme, for $u_t + au_x = f$. For the stability analysis, but not the accuracy analysis, assume that λ is a constant.

$$\frac{1}{6}(v_{m+1}^{n+1} + 4v_m^{n+1} + v_{m-1}^{n+1}) = \frac{1}{6}(v_{m+1}^{n} + 4v_m^{n} + v_{m-1}^{n}) - \frac{1}{2}a\lambda(v_{m+1}^{n} - v_{m-1}^{n})$$

$$+ \frac{1}{2}a^2\lambda^2(v_{m+1}^{n} - 2v_m^{n} + v_{m-1}^{n})$$

$$+ \frac{k}{12}(f_{m+1}^{n+1} + 4f_m^{n+1} + f_{m-1}^{n+1} + f_{m+1}^{n} + 4f_m^{n} + f_{m-1}^{n})$$

$$- \frac{k}{4}a\lambda(f_{m+1}^{n} - f_{m-1}^{n})$$

6. Show that the scheme for $u_t + u_x = f$ given by

$$v_m^{n+1} = v_m^{n} - ak\left(1 - \frac{h^2\delta^2}{6}\right)\delta_0 v_m^{n}$$

$$+ \frac{a^2 k^2}{2}\left[\left(\frac{4}{3} + a^2\lambda^2\right)\delta^2 v_m^{n} - \left(\frac{1}{3} + a^2\lambda^2\right)\delta_0^2 v_m^{n}\right]$$

$$+ \frac{k}{2}(f_m^{n+1} + f_m^{n}) - \frac{ak^2}{2}\delta_0 f_m^{n}$$

is accurate of order $(2, 4)$ and stable if

$$|a\lambda| \le \left(\frac{\sqrt{17} - 1}{6}\right)^{1/2}.$$

Note that $O(kh^2) \le O(k^2) + O(h^4)$. *Hint:* The computation of $|g|^2$ can be done similarly to that of the Lax-Wendroff scheme.

7. Show that the improved Crank-Nicolson scheme for $u_t + au_x = f$ is accurate of order $(2,4)$ and is unconditionally stable. The scheme is

$$\frac{1}{6}v_{m+1}^{n+1} + \frac{2}{3}v_m^{n+1} + \frac{1}{6}v_{m-1}^{n+1} + \frac{a\lambda}{4}(v_{m+1}^{n+1} - v_{m-1}^{n+1})$$

$$= \frac{1}{6}v_{m+1}^n + \frac{2}{3}v_m^n + \frac{1}{6}v_{m-1}^n - \frac{a\lambda}{4}(v_{m+1}^n - v_{m-1}^n)$$

$$+ \frac{k}{12}(f_{m+1}^{n+1} + 4f_m^{n+1} + f_{m-1}^{n+1} + f_{m+1}^n + 4f_m^n + f_{m-1}^n).$$

8. Show that the scheme derived in Example 3.2.2,

$$\frac{v_m^{n+1} - v_m^n}{k} + a\delta_0\left(\frac{v_m^{n+1} + 2v_m^n}{3}\right) - \frac{k}{6}a^2\delta^2\left(\frac{v_m^{n+1} + 2v_m^n}{3}\right)$$

$$= \frac{f_m^{n+1} + f_m^n}{2} - \frac{ak}{6}\delta_0\left(\frac{f_m^{n+1} + 2f_m^n}{3}\right),$$

is stable for $|a\lambda| \leq 3$.

9. Use the relationship $\partial = \ln(1 + h\delta_+)$ to derive the second-order accurate one-sided approximation

$$\frac{du}{dx}(x_0) \approx \frac{-3u(x_0) + 4u(x_1) - u(x_2)}{2h}.$$

3.3 Boundary Conditions for Finite Difference Schemes

In solving initial-boundary value problems such as (1.2.1) by finite difference schemes, we must use the boundary conditions required by the partial differential equation in order to determine the finite difference solution. Many schemes also require additional boundary conditions, called *numerical boundary conditions*, to determine the solution uniquely. We introduce our study of numerical boundary conditions by considering the Lax-Wendroff scheme applied to the initial-boundary value problem (1.2.1). In Chapter 11 we discuss the theory of boundary conditions in more detail.

When we use the Lax-Wendroff scheme on equation (1.2.1), the scheme can be applied only at the interior grid points and not at the boundary points. This is because the scheme requires grid points to the left and right of (t_n, x_m) when computing v_m^{n+1}, and at the boundaries either x_{m-1} or x_{m+1} is not a grid point. Assuming that a is positive, the value of v_0^n is supplied by the boundary data as required by the differential equation. At x_M, where x_M is the last grid point on the right, we must use some means other than the scheme to compute v_M^{n+1}. This additional condition is a numerical boundary condition. Numerical boundary conditions should be some form of extrapolation that determines the solution on the boundary in terms of the solution in the interior. For example, each of the following are numerical boundary conditions for (1.2.1).

$$v_M^{n+1} = v_{M-1}^{n+1} \qquad (3.3.1a)$$

$$v_M^{n+1} = 2v_{M-1}^{n+1} - v_{M-2}^{n+1} \qquad (3.3.1b)$$

$$v_M^{n+1} = v_{M-1}^{n} \qquad (3.3.1c)$$

$$v_M^{n+1} = 2v_{M-1}^{n} - v_{M-2}^{n-1} \qquad (3.3.1d)$$

Formulas (3.3.1a) and (b) are simple extrapolations of the solution at interior grid points to the boundary. Formulas (3.3.1c) and (d) are sometimes called *quasi-characteristic extrapolation,* since the extrapolation is done from points near the characteristics.

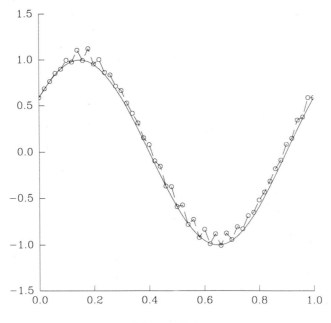

Figure 3.1

Numerical boundary conditions often take the form of one-sided differences. For example, rather than formulas (3.3.1) we might use

$$v_M^{n+1} = v_M^{n} - a\lambda(v_M^{n} - v_{M-1}^{n}). \qquad (3.3.2)$$

However, we can easily see that (3.3.2) is the result of using the Lax-Wendroff scheme for v_M^{n+1} where v_{M+1}^n is determined by

$$v_{M+1}^n = 2v_M^n - v_{M-1}^n.$$

This example also illustrates the use of extra points beyond the boundary to aid in the determination of the boundary values.

It is often easier to use extrapolation formulas such as (3.3.1) than to use extra points or one-sided differences. Moreover, the extrapolations can give as accurate answers as the other methods. The one-sided differences and extra points are occasionally justified by ad hoc physical arguments, which can be more confusing than useful.

There is one difficulty with numerical boundary conditions, which we do not have space to discuss in detail in this chapter—namely, that the numerical boundary condition coupled with a particular scheme can be unstable. This topic is discussed further in Chapter 11. For example, (3.3.1a) and (3.3.1b) together with the leapfrog scheme are unstable, whereas (3.3.1c) and (3.3.1d) are stable. For the Crank-Nicolson scheme conditions (3.3.1c) and (3.3.1d) are unstable when $a\lambda$ is larger than 2, but (3.3.1a) and (3.3.1b) are stable. The proofs that these boundary conditions are stable or unstable, as the case may be, are given in Chapter 11.

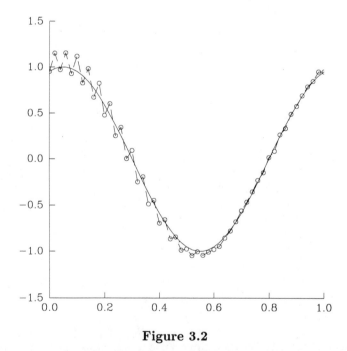

Figure 3.2

The analysis of the stability of a problem involving both initial data and boundary conditions is done by considering the several parts. First, the scheme must be stable for the initial value problem considered on an unbounded domain. This is done with von Neumann analysis. The stability of the boundary conditions is done for each boundary separately. Conditions at one boundary can not have a significantly ameliorating effect on an unstable boundary condition at the other boundary. As the preceding examples show, a boundary condition may be stable or unstable depending on the scheme with which it is being used.

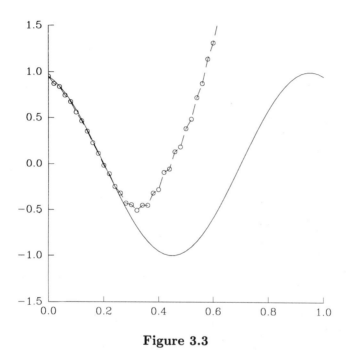

Figure 3.3

An example of an unstable boundary condition is given in Figures 3.1, 3.2, and 3.3. The leapfrog scheme is used with equation (1.2.1), with a equal to 1. The grid spacing is 0.02 and λ is equal to 0.9. At the left boundary, where x equals 0, u is specified to be the exact solution $\sin \pi(x - t)$. At the right boundary, where x is 1, (3.3.1a) is used. The figures show the effect at the times 0.9, 1.8, and 2.7. In practice, if we suspect that there is a numerical boundary condition instability, the easiest thing to do is to change to a different form of extrapolation to eliminate it. There is an analytical means of checking for these instabilities, but the algebraic manipulations are often quite involved, as will be seen in Chapter 11. If a computer program using a finite difference scheme is being used to solve a system of equations, it is usually easier to implement other boundary conditions than it is to analyze the original conditions to determine their stability.

One final comment should be made on this topic. In solving initial-boundary value problems by finite differences, it is best to distinguish clearly between those boundary conditions required by the partial differential equation and the numerical boundary conditions. By making this distinction, we can avoid solving overdetermined or underdetermined partial differential equation initial-boundary value problems.

EXERCISE 3.3

1.   Solve the initial-boundary value problem (1.2.1) with the leapfrog scheme and the following boundary conditions. Use $a = 1$. Only (d) should give good results. Why?

      a. At $x = 0$, u specified; at $x = 1$, use (3.3.1b).
      b. At $x = 0$, u specified; at $x = 1, u = 0$.
      c. At $x = 0$, (3.3.1b); at $x = 1$, use (3.3.1c).
      d. At $x = 0$, u specified; at $x = 1$, use (3.3.1c).

3.4 Solving Tridiagonal Systems

To use the Crank-Nicolson scheme and many other implicit schemes such as (1.6.1), we must know how to solve tridiagonal systems of linear equations. We now present a convenient algorithm, called the *Thomas algorithm,* to solve tridiagonal systems that arise in finite difference schemes.

Consider the system of equations

$$a_i w_{i-1} + b_i w_i + c_i w_{i+1} = d_i, \quad i = 1, \ldots, m-1 \tag{3.4.1}$$

with

$$w_0 = \beta_0 \quad \text{and} \quad w_m = \beta_m. \tag{3.4.2}$$

We will solve this system by Gaussian elimination without partial pivoting. It reduces to this: We want to replace (3.4.1) by relationships of the form

$$w_i = p_{i+1} w_{i+1} + q_{i+1}, \quad i = 0, 1, 2, \ldots, m-1, \tag{3.4.3}$$

where the values of p_{i+1} and q_{i+1} are to be determined. For (3.4.3) to be consistent with (3.4.1), we substitute (3.4.3) into (3.4.1) for w_{i-1} and examine the resulting relation between w_i and w_{i+1} :

$$a_i(p_i w_i + q_i) + b_i w_i + c_i w_{i+1} = d_i$$

or

$$w_i = -(a_i p_i + b_i)^{-1} c_i w_{i+1} + (a_i p_i + b_i)^{-1}(d_i - a_i q_i).$$

Comparing this expression with (3.4.3) we must have

$$\begin{aligned} p_{i+1} &= -(a_i p_i + b_i)^{-1} c_i \\ q_{i+1} &= (a_i p_i + b_i)^{-1}(d_i - a_i q_i), \end{aligned} \tag{3.4.4}$$

for consistency of the formulas. Thus if we know p_1 and q_1, then we can compute p_i and q_i for i greater than 1. The values of p_1 and q_1 are obtained from the boundary condition (3.4.2). At i equal to 0 we have the two formulas $w_0 = p_1 w_1 + q_1$ and $w_0 = \beta_0$. These conditions are consistent if $p_1 = 0$ and $q_1 = \beta_0$. With these initial values for p_1 and q_1, formulas (3.4.4) then give all the values of p_i and q_i up to i equal to m. To get the values of w_i we use (3.4.3) starting with w_m, which is given.

We now consider other boundary conditions. If we have

$$w_0 = w_1 + \beta_0$$

then we set $p_1 = 1$ and $q_1 = \beta_0$. If we have the boundary conditions

$$w_m = w_{m-1} + \beta_m,$$

then the relation

$$w_{m-1} = p_m w_m + q_m$$

also holds, and we combine these to obtain

$$w_m = (1 - p_m)^{-1} (q_m + \beta_m).$$

If $p_m = 1$, then w_m cannot be defined and the system with this boundary condition is singular.

In general, the values of p_1 and q_1 are determined by the boundary condition at i equal to 0 and the value of w_m is determined by the boundary condition at i equal to m, together with the relation (3.4.3) if necessary.

For the Thomas algorithm to be well-conditioned, we should have

$$|p_i| \leq 1. \tag{3.4.5}$$

This is equivalent to having the multipliers in Gaussian elimination be at most 1 in magnitude. From (3.4.3) we see that the error in w_{i+1} is multiplied by p_{i+1} to contribute to the error in w_i. If (3.4.5) is violated for several values of i, then there will be an increase in the error. This error growth is due to ill-conditioning in the Thomas algorithm, and using Gaussian elimination with partial pivoting should remove this error magnification. Condition (3.4.5) has nothing to do with the stability or instability of the scheme.

There are two cases where (3.4.5) holds.

1. Diagonal dominance, i.e., $\quad |a_i| + |c_i| \leq |b_i|$
2. $0 \leq -c_i \leq b_i$, $0 \leq a_i$ with $0 \leq p_1 \leq 1$

   or $0 \leq -a_i$, $0 \leq c_i \leq b_i$ with $-1 \leq p_1 \leq 0$.

Whenever the Thomas algorithm is used, the values of the p_i should be examined to see if condition (3.4.5) holds.

The formulas for tridiagonal systems can be extended to block tridiagonal systems in which the a_i, b_i, and c_i are square matrices and the unknown w_i are vectors. In this case the p_i are also matrices and the q_i are vectors. The method also extends to pentadiagonal systems.

Periodic Tridiagonal Systems

If we use the Crank-Nicolson scheme or a similar scheme to solve a problem with periodic solutions, then we obtain periodic tridiagonal systems. These can be solved by an extension of the previous algorithm.

Consider the system

$$a_i w_{i-1} + b_i w_i + c_i w_{i+1} = d_i, \quad i = 1, \ldots, m \tag{3.4.6}$$

with $w_0 = w_m$ and $w_{m+1} = w_1$. This periodic system can be solved as follows. Solve three systems as for the nonperiodic case, each for $i = 1, \ldots, m$:

$$a_i x_{i-1} + b_i x_i + c_i x_{i+1} = d_i \tag{3.4.7}$$

with $x_0 = 0$ and $x_{m+1} = 0$,

$$a_i y_{i-1} + b_i y_i + c_i y_{i+1} = 0 \tag{3.4.8}$$

with $y_0 = 1$ and $y_{m+1} = 0$, and

$$a_i z_{i-1} + b_i z_i + c_i z_{i+1} = 0 \tag{3.4.9}$$

with $z_0 = 0$ and $z_{m+1} = 1$.

Since these systems have the same matrix but different data, they use the same p_i's but different q_i's. (For (3.4.9), $q_i = 0$.)

Then we construct w_i as

$$w_i = x_i + r y_i + s z_i. \tag{3.4.10}$$

It is easy to see that (3.4.10) satisfies (3.4.6) for $i = 1, \ldots, m$. We choose r and s to guarantee the periodicity. The relationship $w_0 = w_m$ becomes

$$r = r y_0 = x_m + r y_m + s z_m$$

and $w_{m+1} = w_1$ becomes

$$s = s z_{m+1} = x_1 + r y_1 + s z_1$$

These are two equations in the two unknowns r and s. The solution is

$$r = \frac{x_m(1 - z_1) + x_1 z_m}{D}$$

$$s = \frac{x_m y_1 + x_1(1 - y_m)}{D}$$

with

$$D = (1 - y_m)(1 - z_1) - y_1 z_m.$$

These formulas for solving periodic tridiagonal systems as well as the formula in Exercise 3.4.3 are special cases of the Sherman-Morrison formula for computing the inverse of a matrix given the inverse of a rank 1 modification of the matrix.

EXERCISES 3.4

1. Show that the condition (3.4.5) is violated for the Crank-Nicolson scheme (3.1.4) when $p_0 = 0$ and $a\lambda > 4$.

2. Show that the second-order differential equation

$$a(x)\frac{d^2u}{dx^2} + b(x)\frac{du}{dx} + c(x)u = d(x)$$

for $\alpha \leq x \leq \beta$ with $u(\alpha) = A$ and $u(\beta) = B$ can be solved by an algorithm similar to the Thomas algorithm. Set

$$\frac{du}{dx} = p(x)u + q(x)$$

and determine equations for $p(x)$ and $q(x)$. Discuss how $p \geq 0$ is the analogue to (3.4.5).

3. Show that the following algorithm also solves the periodic tridiagonal system (3.4.6).

1. Solve $a_ix_{i-1} + b_ix_i + c_ix_{i+1} = d_i$, $i = 1, \ldots, m$, with $x_0 = \sigma x_1$ and $x_{m+1} = \sigma x_m$ and where $\sigma = sign(a_1b_1)$.

2. Solve $a_iy_{i-1} + b_iy_i + c_iy_{i+1} = 0$, $i = 1, \ldots, m$, with $y_0 = \sigma y_1 + 1$ and $y_m = \sigma y_{m+1} + 1$.

3. The solution w_i is then obtained as $w_i = x_i - ry_i$ where $r = \dfrac{x_i - x_m}{y_i - y_m}$.

4. In the algorithm of Exercise 3, why shouldn't we take $\sigma = 1$ when a_1 and b_1 have opposite signs?

5. Verify the following formula, which is called the Sherman-Morrison formula. If $Ay = b$ and $Az = u$, then $(A + uv^T)x = b$ has the solution

$$x = y - \frac{v^Ty}{(1 + v^Tz)}z.$$

This formula is useful to compute the solution x, of $(A + uv^T)x = b$ if we have a convenient method of solving equations of the form $Ay = b$.

Chapter 4

Stability for Multistep Schemes

In Section 2.2 we gave necessary and sufficient conditions for the stability of one-step schemes. In the first section of this chapter we examine the leapfrog scheme and give necessary and sufficient conditions for the stability of this scheme. In the second section we present the stability analysis for general multistep schemes. In the last section we present the theory of Schur and von Neumann polynomials, which gives an algorithm for determining the stability criteria for multistep schemes.

4.1 Stability for the Leapfrog Scheme

We begin by analyzing the stability of the leapfrog scheme (1.3.4) for the one-way wave equation (1.1.1), which is

$$\frac{v_m^{n+1} - v_m^{n-1}}{2k} + a \frac{v_{m+1}^n - v_{m-1}^n}{2h} = 0.$$

By using the Fourier inversion formula for v^{n-1}, v^n, and v^{n+1}, we obtain the equation

$$\int_{-\pi/h}^{\pi/h} e^{imh\xi} \left(\hat{v}^{n+1}(\xi) + 2ia\lambda \sin(h\xi)\, \hat{v}^n(\xi) - \hat{v}^{n-1}(\xi) \right)\, d\xi = 0,$$

in a manner similar to the method used to obtain equation (2.2.3). By the uniqueness of the Fourier transform, we conclude that the integrand in this integral must be zero, giving the relationship

$$\hat{v}^{n+1}(\xi) + 2ia\lambda \sin(h\xi)\, \hat{v}^n(\xi) - \hat{v}^{n-1}(\xi) = 0. \tag{4.1.1}$$

To solve this three-term recurrence relation in $\hat{v}^n$, we set $\hat{v}^n = g^n$, where the superscript on $\hat{v}$ is an index and on g represents the power. We then obtain, after canceling g^{n-1},

$$g^2 + 2ia\lambda \sin(h\xi)g - 1 = 0.$$

There are two roots to this equation, given by

$$g_\pm = -ia\lambda \sin(h\xi) \pm \sqrt{1 - (a\lambda)^2 \sin^2(h\xi)}. \tag{4.1.2}$$

When g_+ and g_- are not equal, the solution for $\hat{v}^n$ in (4.1.1) is given by

$$\hat{v}^n(\xi) = A(\xi)g_+(h\xi)^n + B(\xi)\left[\frac{g_-(h\xi)^n - g_+(h\xi)^n}{g_-(h\xi) \ - g_+(h\xi)}\right] \tag{4.1.3}$$

for functions $A(\xi)$ and $B(\xi)$, which are determined by the initial conditions. When g_+ and g_- are equal, then the solution is

$$\hat{v}^n(\xi) = A(\xi)g(h\xi)^n + B(\xi)ng(h\xi)^{n-1},$$

where $g_+ = g_- = g$. The functions $A(\xi)$ and $B(\xi)$ are related to $\hat{v}^0(\xi)$ and $\hat{v}^1(\xi)$ by

$$A(\xi) = \hat{v}^0(\xi) \tag{4.1.4}$$

and

$$B(\xi) = \hat{v}^1(\xi) - \hat{v}^0(\xi)g_+(h\xi). \tag{4.1.5}$$

We now consider the stability of the leapfrog scheme using Definition 1.5.1 with J equal to 1. We first consider the case where g_+ and g_- are not equal, and we choose the initial data v^0 and v^1 so that $B(\xi)$ is identically zero. Then from (4.1.3) we have

$$|\hat{v}^n(\xi)| \ = \ |A(\xi)| \, |g_+(h\xi)|^n.$$

As with the one-step schemes, we see that it is necessary that $g_+(h\xi)$ satisfies the inequality

$$|g_+(h\xi)| \leq 1 + Kk,$$

just as for the amplification factor of a one-step scheme. Obviously, $g_-(h\xi)$ must also satisfy such an estimate. If we take λ to be a constant, then we may employ the restricted condition

$$|g_\pm(h\xi)| \leq 1, \tag{4.1.6}$$

to determine the stability. From (4.1.2) with $|a\lambda| \leq 1$ we have that

$$|g_+|^2 = |g_-|^2 = 1 - (a\lambda)^2 \sin^2\theta + (a\lambda\sin\theta)^2 = 1.$$

If $|a\lambda|$ is greater than 1, then for θ equal to $\pi/2$ we have $|g_-| = |a\lambda| + \sqrt{(a\lambda)^2 - 1} > 1$, which shows that the scheme is unstable in this case. From this we see that the stability condition is $|a\lambda| \leq 1$, except that we must examine what happens when g_+ and g_- are equal.

It is easy to see from (4.1.2) that g_+ can be equal to g_- only when $|a\lambda\sin\theta| = 1$. Since we know already that $|a\lambda|$ must be at most 1, we need consider only $|a\lambda| \leq 1$. But then $g_+ = g_-$ only when $|a\lambda| = 1$ and $\theta = \pm\pi/2$, and we then have $g_+ = g_- = \pm i$. The solution for $\hat{v}^n$ is then

$$\hat{v}^n = A\left(\pm\frac{\pi}{2h}\right)(\pm i)^n + B\left(\pm\frac{\pi}{2h}\right)n(\pm i)^{n-1},$$

and in general $\hat{v}^n(\pm\pi/2h)$ will grow linearly in n.

Since $\hat{v}^n$ for θ equal to $\pm\,\pi/2$ behaves this way—that is, has a growth that is linear in n—we can show that there are solutions to the finite difference scheme whose norm grows very nearly linearly in n, and therefore the leapfrog scheme is unstable if $|a\lambda| = 1$. Hence the leapfrog scheme is stable only if $|a\lambda|$ is strictly less than 1. Thus the necessary and sufficient condition for the stability of the leapfrog scheme (1.3.4) is

$$|a\lambda| < 1. \tag{4.1.7}$$

The instability that occurs for $|a\lambda| = 1$ is much milder than that which occurs for $|a\lambda| > 1$; nonetheless, it is an instability.

Initializing the Leapfrog Scheme

The leapfrog scheme and other three-level schemes require a one-step scheme to get started. We can use any one-step scheme, even an unstable scheme, to initialize a multistep scheme. A consistent unstable scheme that is used for only the first several time steps will produce a small growth in the solution. This growth is small because of consistency. The stability of the leapfrog scheme or other multistep schemes will keep this small initial growth from being amplified. Also, as is shown in Chapter 10, if λ is a constant, then the initialization scheme can be accurate of order one less than that of the scheme without degrading the overall accuracy of the scheme. Thus our use of the forward-time central-space scheme (1.3.3) to initialize the leapfrog scheme does not affect the stability or accuracy of the leapfrog scheme, as shown in Figure 1.6.

We now take a closer look at the solution of the leapfrog scheme. As (4.1.3) shows, the solution to the leapfrog scheme consists of two parts, one associated with g_+ and the other with g_-. We are interested in how these two parts behave and how they contribute to the total solution. For definiteness we take the case where for the first time-step the forward-time central-space scheme is used. That is, $\hat{v}^1$ is given by

$$\hat{v}^1(\xi) = (1 - ia\lambda \sin h\xi)\,\hat{v}^0(\xi). \tag{4.1.8}$$

Using this relation and the expansions

$$g_+ = 1 - ia\lambda \sin h\xi - \tfrac{1}{2}a^2\lambda^2 \sin^2 h\xi + O(h\xi)^4$$

$$g_- = -1 - ia\lambda \sin h\xi + \tfrac{1}{2}a^2\lambda^2 \sin^2 h\xi + O(h\xi)^4$$

we have, from (4.1.5), that

$$B(\xi) = \left[\tfrac{1}{2}a^2\lambda^2 \sin^2 h\xi + O(h\xi)^4\right]\hat{v}^0(\xi).$$

This formula shows that $B(\xi)$ is small, i.e., $O(h\xi)^2$ for $|h\xi|$ small. Thus for these values of $h\xi$, the scheme behaves like a one-step scheme with amplification factor g_+. For larger values of $|h\xi|$, the magnitude of $B(\xi)$ need not be small.

The portion of the solution associated with g_- is called the *parasitic mode*. Since at ξ equal to 0 the value of g_- is -1, we see that this parasitic mode oscillates rapidly in time. As is shown in Chapter 5 the parasitic mode also travels in the wrong direction. That is, when a is positive, the parasitic mode travels to the left.

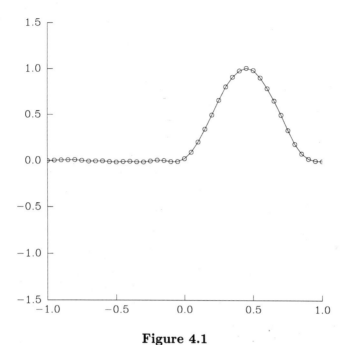

Figure 4.1

Example 4.1.1 An interesting way to see the parasitic mode and also to illustrate the effect of inconsistent boundary conditions is shown in Figures 4.1–4.3. The figures show the solution computed by the leapfrog scheme with initial data as a pulse given by

$$v_m^0 = \begin{cases} \cos^2 \pi x_m & \text{if } |x_m| \leq \frac{1}{2}, \\ 0 & \text{otherwise.} \end{cases}$$

The value of a is 1, λ is 0.9, and x is in the interval $[-1, 1]$. At both boundaries the values of v^n are fixed at zero. At the right boundary this is inconsistent with the differential equation (see Section 1.2). This inconsistency will serve our purpose of generating a substantial parasitic mode in the solution.

Figure 4.1 shows the solution at t equal to 0.45, with the pulse moving to the right, and Figure 4.2 shows the solution at t equal to 1.80 and moving to the left. The inconsistent boundary condition has generated a solution having a significant parasitic mode, as indicated by the oscillatory nature of the pulse and its "wrong" direction of travel. Figure 4.3 shows the solution at t equal to 3.6 with the original pulse shape nearly restored. The parasitic mode has

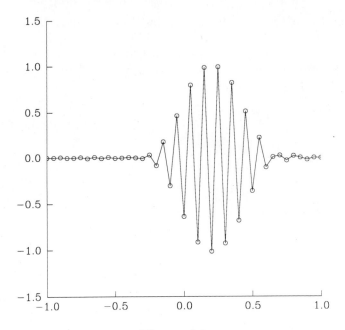

Figure 4.2

been converted to the nonparasitic mode by the boundary condition at the left endpoint of the interval. The scheme was initialized using the forward-time central-space scheme (1.3.3), but the phenomena displayed in these figures are not dependent on the initialization. □

In any calculation with multistep schemes, as opposed to one-step schemes, there will be parasitic modes. These parasitic modes usually cause only minor difficulty, but in some cases they must be reduced or removed. We can reduce the effect of the parasitic modes by the use of dissipation, which is discussed in the next chapter.

Example 4.1.2 As a further illustration of the stability of multistep schemes we consider the $(2, 4)$ leapfrog scheme

$$\frac{v_m^{n+1} - v_m^{n-1}}{2k} + a \left(1 - \frac{h^2 \delta^2}{6}\right) \delta_0 v_m^n = f_m^n, \qquad (4.1.9)$$

which uses the fourth-order difference formula (3.2.6). The equation for the amplification factor is

$$g^2 + 2g\, ia\lambda \left(1 + \frac{2}{3} \sin^2 \frac{1}{2}\theta\right) \sin\theta - 1 = 0,$$

or

$$g^2 + 2g\, ia\lambda \left(\frac{4 - \cos\theta}{3}\right) \sin\theta - 1 = 0,$$

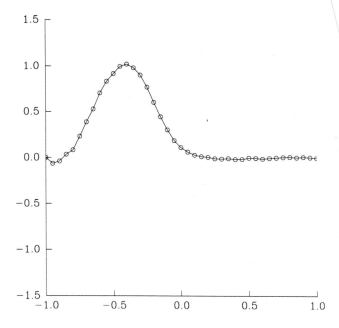

Figure 4.3

and the amplification factors are

$$g_{\pm} = -ia\lambda \frac{4 - \cos\theta}{3} \sin\theta \pm \sqrt{1 - a^2\lambda^2 \left(\frac{4 - \cos\theta}{3}\right)^2 \sin^2\theta}.$$

The condition that g_+ and g_- have magnitude at most 1 and that they not be equal is easily seen to be that

$$|a\lambda| \left(\frac{4 - \cos\theta}{3}\right) |\sin\theta| < 1 \qquad (4.1.10)$$

for all values of θ. To determine the extrema of $(4 - \cos\theta)\sin\theta$, we have at the extrema

$$\frac{d}{d\theta}(4 - \cos\theta)\sin\theta = 1 + 4\cos\theta - 2\cos^2\theta = 0.$$

This quadratic equation in $\cos\theta$ has one root for real θ, given by

$$\cos\theta = 1 - \sqrt{\frac{3}{2}}.$$

Substituting this in (4.1.10), we obtain that the necessary and sufficient condition for stability is that

$$|a\lambda| < \left(1 + \frac{1}{\sqrt{6}}\right)^{-1} \left(\sqrt{6} - \frac{3}{2}\right)^{-1/2}. \quad \square \qquad (4.1.11)$$

The value of the right-hand side of (4.1.11) is approximately 0.7208 and, because this constraint is more severe than that for the usual $(2,2)$ leapfrog scheme (1.3.3), we might judge this scheme to be less efficient in some sense. However, quite the opposite is true. Because the scheme (4.1.9) is fourth-order accurate in space but only second-order accurate in time, we should take $|a\lambda|$ smaller than the limit given by (4.1.11)—for example 0.25—to improve the temporal accuracy. As a consequence of the fourth-order accuracy we can either take the spatial grid spacing larger for the $(2,4)$ scheme (4.1.9) than we would for the $(2,2)$ scheme (1.3.4) without sacrificing accuracy in the solution, or we can use the same spatial grid spacing with (4.1.9) as we would for (1.3.4) and use the smaller time step to attain higher accuracy without much more effort. Either way it is seen that the constraint (4.1.11) is not a severe limitation on the scheme.

EXERCISES 4.1

1. Show that the implicit $(2,4)$ leapfrog scheme

$$\frac{v_m^{n+1} - v_m^{n-1}}{2k} + a\left(1 + \frac{h^2}{6}\delta^2\right)^{-1}\delta_0 v_m^n = f_m^n$$

for the one-way wave equation with λ constant is stable if and only if

$$|a\lambda| < \frac{1}{\sqrt{3}}.$$

2. Show that the $(2,2)$ leapfrog scheme for $u_t + au_{xxx} = f$ (see (2.2.13)) given by

$$\frac{v_m^{n+1} - v_m^{n-1}}{2k} + a\delta^2\delta_0 v_m^n = f_m^n,$$

with $\nu = k/h^3$ constant, is stable if and only if

$$|a\nu| < \frac{2}{3^{3/2}}.$$

3. Show that the leapfrog scheme

$$\frac{v_m^{n+1} - v_m^{n-1}}{2k} + a\left(1 - \frac{h^2}{6}\delta^2 + \frac{h^4}{30}\delta^4\right)\delta_0 v_m^n = f_m^n$$

for the one-way wave equation is accurate of order $(2,6)$ and, if λ is constant, is stable if and only if

$$|a\lambda| < \frac{3}{[2(\frac{2}{5})^{1/3} - 1]^{1/2}[(\frac{5}{2})^{2/3} + 3(\frac{5}{2})^{1/3} + 1]}.$$

Hint: The critical value of θ is for $\cos\theta$ equal to $1 - (\frac{5}{2})^{1/3}$.

4. Show that the $(2, \infty)$ leapfrog scheme for the one-way wave equation

$$\frac{v_m^{n+1} - v_m^{n-1}}{2k} + \left[1 + \left(\frac{h\delta}{2}\right)^2\right]^{-1/2} \frac{\sinh^{-1}\frac{1}{2}h\delta}{\frac{1}{2}h\delta}\delta_0 v_m^n = f_m^n$$

is stable, if λ is constant, if and only if $|a\lambda| < 1/\pi$. See equation (3.2.15).

4.2 Stability for General Multistep Schemes

We now discuss the stability conditions for a general multistep scheme. As for one-step schemes, we assume that the differential equation is of first order in the differentiation with respect to t.

The stability of the multistep scheme

$$P_{k,h}v = R_{k,h}f \tag{4.2.1}$$

is determined by considering the roots of the amplification polynomial $\Phi(g, \theta)$ given by

$$\Phi(g, \theta) = k\, p_{k,h}\left(\frac{\ln g}{k}, \theta h^{-1}\right)$$

or, equivalently,

$$\Phi\left(e^{sk}, h\xi\right) = k\, p_{k,h}\left(s, \xi\right).$$

Alternatively, Φ can be obtained by requiring that

$$v_m^n = g^n e^{im\theta} \tag{4.2.2}$$

is a solution to the equation (4.2.1) with $f = 0$. $\Phi(g, \theta)$ is the polynomial of which g must be a root so that (4.2.2) can be a solution of (4.2.1). We assume that the scheme involves $\sigma + 1$ time levels, so that Φ is a polynomial of order σ. Note that J in Definition 1.5.1 will be taken to be σ.

Since we are primarily concerned with the roots of this polynomial, there is no difficulty in dealing with a scalar multiple of $\Phi(g, \theta)$ rather than $\Phi(g, \theta)$ itself. However, the relationship between $\Phi(g, \theta)$ and the symbol $p(s, \xi)$ is important in proving convergence results for multistep schemes in Chapter 10.

Example 4.2.1 Consider the multistep scheme for the one-way wave equation given by

$$\frac{3v_m^{n+1} - 4v_m^n + v_m^{n-1}}{2k} + a\frac{v_{m+1}^{n+1} - v_{m-1}^{n+1}}{2h} = f_m^{n+1}. \tag{4.2.3}$$

For this scheme the amplification polynomial is

$$\Phi(g, \theta) = \frac{1}{2}(3 + 2ia\lambda\sin\theta)g^2 - 2g + \frac{1}{2}.$$

The analysis of the stability of this scheme is not as easy as that of the leapfrog scheme, and therefore we postpone the analysis until the next section, in which we present a general method for analyzing the stability of multistep schemes. This scheme is accurate of order $(2, 2)$ and unconditionally stable; see Exercise 4.3.3. □

For a one-step scheme $\Phi(g,\theta)$ is a linear polynomial in g, and the general solution of the homogeneous difference equation is given by (2.2.5). For a multistep scheme in which Φ is a polynomial of degree σ, there are two cases to consider. First, if Φ has distinct roots, $g_\nu(\theta)$, the general solution to the homogeneous difference scheme is given by

$$\hat{v}^n(\xi) = \sum_{\nu=1}^{\sigma} g_\nu(h\xi)^n A_\nu(\xi). \tag{4.2.4}$$

The coefficients $A_\nu(\xi)$ are determined by the data on the time levels for n from 0 to $\sigma-1$. If the roots $g_\nu(h\xi)$ are bounded away from each other, independently of k and h, then the values of A_ν are bounded by the sum

$$C \sum_{j=0}^{\sigma-1} |v^j(\xi)| \tag{4.2.5}$$

for some constant C (see Exercise 4.2.1). As with one-step schemes, it is then easily shown that the stability condition is

$$|g_\nu(h\xi)| \leq 1 + Kk, \qquad \text{for } \nu = 1, \ldots, \sigma \tag{4.2.6}$$

for each root of Φ. In the cases that $\Phi(g,\theta)$ is independent of k and h, the restricted condition

$$|g_\nu(h\xi)| \leq 1, \qquad \text{for } \nu = 1, \ldots, \sigma \tag{4.2.7}$$

holds.

We now consider the situation in which $\Phi(g,\theta)$ has multiple roots. For simplicity we assume that the restricted condition (4.2.7) can be used. (The general case is handled in the exercises.) Suppose that $g_0(\theta_0)$ is a multiple root of the amplification polynomial Φ at θ_0; then the function

$$\hat{v}_m^n = \left[g_0(\theta_0)^n B_0 + n g_0(\theta_0)^{n-1} B_1 \right] e^{im\theta_0}$$

is a solution of the difference equation for any values of B_0 and B_1. If B_0 equals 0, then the magnitude of $\hat{v}_m^n$ is

$$n \, |g_0(\theta_0)|^{n-1} \, |B_1|. \tag{4.2.8}$$

If $|g_0(\theta_0)|$ is less than 1, then this quantity is bounded by

$$\left(|g_0(\theta_0)| \log |g_0(\theta_0)|^{-1} \right)^{-1} |B_1| \tag{4.2.9}$$

(see Exercise 4.2.2). However if $|g_0(\theta_0)|$ is equal to 1, then the quantity (4.2.8) cannot be bounded independently of n. As in the proof of Theorem 2.2.1, we can construct a solution to the finite difference scheme that is not bounded, as

required by Definition 1.5.1, the definition of stability. We state thi.
the next theorem. A root that is not a multiple root is called a simple

Theorem 4.2.1 *If the amplification polynomial* $\Phi(g, \theta)$ *is explicitly*
dent of h and k, then the necessary and sufficient condition for the fi.
ference scheme to be stable is that all roots, $g_\nu(\theta)$, *satisfy*
 a. $|g_\nu(\theta)| \leq 1$ *and*
 b. *If* $|g_\nu(\theta)| = 1$, *then* $g_\nu(\theta)$ *must be a simple root.*

Notice in particular that there is at most one root $g_0(\theta)$ such that $g_0(0) = 1$.
For completeness we state the general theorem as well.

Theorem 4.2.2 *A finite difference scheme for a scalar equation is stable if and*
only if all the roots, $g_\nu(\theta)$, *of the amplification polynomial* $\Phi(\theta, k, h)$ *satisfy the*
following conditions.
 a. *There is a constant K such that* $|g_\nu| \leq 1 + Kk$.
 b. *There are positive constants c_0 and c_1 such that if* $c_0 \leq |g_\nu| \leq 1 + Kk$,
  then g_ν *is a simple root, and for any other root g_μ the relation*

$$|g_\nu - g_\mu| \geq c_1$$

holds for h and k sufficiently small.

The proofs of these theorems are similar to that of Theorem 2.2.1 and are
left as exercises.

EXERCISES 4.2

1. Verify that the values of $A_\nu(\xi)$ in equation (4.2.4) can be bounded by the
quantity (4.2.5) if the roots $g_\nu(\theta)$ are bounded away from each other. *Hint:*
The matrix to be inverted is a Vandemonde matrix.

2. Verify the estimate (4.2.9).

3. Prove Theorem 4.2.1.

4. Prove Theorem 4.2.2.

4.3 The Theory of Schur and von Neumann Polynomials

The application of Theorem 4.2.1 to a particular scheme requires us to determine
the location of roots of amplification polynomials, and in this section we present
an algorithm for checking the roots of such polynomials. We first present some
examples on which to apply the theory. At the end of this section we determine
the stability conditions for each of these schemes.

Example 4.3.1 The second-order accurate scheme for the one-way wave equation (1.1.1)

$$\frac{7v_m^{n+1} - 8v_m^n + v_m^{n-1}}{6k} + a\delta_0 \left(\frac{2v_m^{n+1} + v_m^n}{3} \right) = f_m^{n+2/3}, \qquad (4.3.1)$$

which was derived in Example 3.2.3, has the amplification polynomial

$$\Phi(z) = (7 + 4i\beta) z^2 - (8 - 2i\beta) z + 1 \qquad (4.3.2)$$

where $\beta = a\lambda \sin\theta$. $\square$

Example 4.3.2 The second scheme we consider, also for (1.1.1), is a $(3, 4)$ accurate scheme

$$\frac{23v_m^{n+1} - 21v_m^n - 3v_m^{n-1} + v_m^{n-2}}{24k}$$

$$+ \left(1 + \frac{h^2}{6}\delta^2 \right)^{-1} \left[a\delta_0 \left(\frac{v_m^{n+1} + v_m^n}{2} \right) + \frac{k^2 a^2}{8} \delta^2 \left(\frac{v_m^{n+1} - v_m^n}{k} \right) \right] = f_m^{n+1/2}.$$

$$(4.3.3)$$

This scheme has the amplification polynomial

$$(23 - 12\alpha + 12i\beta)z^3 - (21 - 12\alpha - 12i\beta)z^2 - 3z + 1 \qquad (4.3.4)$$

where

$$\alpha = \frac{a^2\lambda^2 \sin^2 \frac{1}{2}\theta}{1 - \frac{2}{3} \sin^2 \frac{1}{2}\theta} \qquad (4.3.5)$$

and

$$\beta = \frac{a\lambda \sin\theta}{1 - \frac{2}{3} \sin^2 \frac{1}{2}\theta}. \quad \square \qquad (4.3.6)$$

Example 4.3.3 The third example is the $(4, 4)$ accurate scheme for the one-way wave equation (1.1.1)

$$\frac{v_m^{n+2} - v_m^{n-2}}{4k} + a \left(1 + \frac{h^2}{6}\delta^2 \right)^{-1} \delta_0 \left(\frac{2v_m^{n+1} - v_m^n + 2v_m^{n-1}}{3} \right)$$

$$(4.3.7)$$

$$= \frac{2f_m^{n+1} - f_m^n + 2f_m^{n-1}}{3}$$

which has the amplification polynomial

$$z^4 + \frac{4}{3}i\beta \left(2z^3 - z^2 + 2z \right) - 1, \qquad (4.3.8)$$

where β is as in (4.3.6). The derivation of this scheme is similar to the derivation in Example 3.2.1. $\square$

A direct determination of the roots of these polynomials is a formidable task. Fortunately there is a well-developed theory and algorithm for checking whether these polynomials satisfy the conditions of Theorem 4.2.1. We begin with some definitions and notations. These definitions and the following discussion are based on the paper of Miller [35]. Let $\varphi(z)$ be a polynomial of degree d,

$$\varphi(z) = a_d z^d + \cdots + a_0 = \sum_{\ell=0}^{d} a_\ell z^\ell.$$

We say that φ is of exact degree d if a_d is not zero.

Definition 4.3.1   *The polynomial φ is a Schur polynomial if all its roots, r_ν, satisfy*

$$|r_\nu| < 1.$$

Definition 4.3.2   *The polynomial φ is a von Neumann polynomial if all its roots, r_ν, satisfy*

$$|r_\nu| \le 1.$$

Definition 4.3.3   *The polynomial φ is a simple von Neumann polynomial if φ is a von Neumann polynomial and its roots on the unit circle are simple roots.*

Definition 4.3.4   *The polynomial φ is a conservative polynomial if all its roots lie on the unit circle, i.e., $|r_\nu| = 1$ for all roots r_ν.*

For any polynomial φ we define the polynomial φ^* by

$$\varphi^*(z) = \sum_{\ell=0}^{d} \bar{a}_{d-\ell} z^\ell$$

where the bar on the coefficients of φ denotes the complex conjugate. Note that

$$\varphi^*(z) = \overline{\varphi(\bar{z}^{-1})} z^d.$$

Finally, for a polynomial $\varphi_0(z)$ we define recursively the polynomial

$$\varphi_{j+1}(z) = \frac{\varphi_j^*(0)\varphi_j(z) - \varphi_j(0)\varphi_j^*(z)}{z}. \tag{4.3.9}$$

It is easy to see that the degree of φ_{j+1} is less than that of φ_j. The next two theorems give recursive tests for Schur polynomials and simple von Neumann polynomials.

Theorem 4.3.1   *φ_j is a Schur polynomial of exact degree d if and only if φ_{j+1} is a Schur polynomial of exact degree $d-1$ and $|\varphi_j(0)| < |\varphi_j^*(0)|$.*

Theorem 4.3.2 φ_j *is a simple von Neumann polynomial if and only if either* $|\varphi_j(0)| < |\varphi_j^*(0)|$ *and* φ_{j+1} *is a simple von Neumann polynomial or* φ_{j+1} *is identically zero and* φ_j' *is a Schur polynomial.*

The proofs of these theorems depend on Rouché's theorem from complex analysis.

Theorem 4.3.3   Rouché's Theorem. *Let the functions* φ *and* ψ *be analytic within and on a simple closed curve* C, *and suppose*

$$|\varphi(z) - \psi(z)| < |\varphi(z)| \tag{4.3.10}$$

on the curve C. *Then* φ *and* ψ *have the same number of zeros in the interior of* C.

The proof of Rouché's theorem rests on the observation that the number of zeros of φ inside the curve C is equal to the number of times the image of C under φ winds around the origin. Inequality (4.3.10) constrains the image of C under ψ to wind around the origin the same number of times as φ does. Rouché's theorem has been called the "walk-the-dog theorem" to emphasize the geometric nature of the theorem. The "dog," $\psi(z)$, must go around the origin exactly as many times as its "master," $\varphi(z)$, as long as the "leash," $\varphi(z) - \psi(z)$, is shorter than the distance of the master from the origin. The proof of Rouché's theorem is given in standard introductory texts on complex analysis.

Proof of Theorem 4.3.1   First assume that $|\varphi_j(0)| < |\varphi_j^*(0)|$ and that φ_{j+1} is a Schur polynomial of degree $d-1$. If we let $\psi(z) = z\varphi_{j+1}(z)/\varphi_j^*(0)$, we have, by the definition of φ_{j+1},

$$|\varphi_j(z) - \psi(z)| = \left| \frac{\varphi_j(0)}{\varphi_j^*(0)} \varphi_j^*(z) \right| < |\varphi_j^*(z)|.$$

On the unit circle we also have that

$$|\varphi_j^*(z)| = |\varphi_j(\bar{z}^{-1})| = |\varphi_j(z)|$$

since $\bar{z}^{-1} = z$ on the unit circle. Thus by Rouché's theorem, φ_j has as many zeros inside the unit circle as does $z\varphi_{j+1}$. Hence φ_j is a Schur polynomial.

Now assume that φ_j is a Schur polynomial of degree d. Then the product of the roots of φ_j is a_0/a_d, and this quantity must have a magnitude less than 1. This is equivalent to $|\varphi_j(0)| < |\varphi_j^*(0)|$. Rouché's theorem then shows that $z\varphi_{j+1}$ also is a Schur polynomial; hence φ_{j+1} is a Schur polynomial. ∎

Proof of Theorem 4.3.2   We begin the proof by observing that a von Neumann polynomial can be written as

$$\varphi_j(z) = \prod_{\nu=1}^{\ell} (z - \alpha_\nu) \, \tilde{\varphi}_j(z)$$

where $|\alpha_\nu| = 1$ for $1 \leq \nu \leq \ell$ and $\tilde{\varphi}_j(z)$ is a Schur polynomial or a constant. (In case $\ell = 0$, the theorem follows from Theorem 4.3.1.) If $\tilde{\varphi}_j(z)$ is not a constant, then it is easily checked that

$$\varphi_{j+1}(z) = \prod_{\nu=1}^{\ell} (z - \alpha_\nu) \tilde{\varphi}_{j+1}(z)$$

and the theorem is proved in the case that φ_{j+1} is not identically zero. We also see that φ_{j+1} is identically zero only if all the roots of φ_j lie on the unit circle, i.e., φ_j is a conservative polynomial.

In the case φ_j is a conservative polynomial of degree d, we consider the polynomials

$$\varphi_j^\varepsilon(z) = \varphi_j(z) + \varepsilon z \varphi_j'(z) \tag{4.3.11}$$

for small positive values of ε. It is easily checked that the simple roots r_ν^ε of φ_j^ε are given by

$$r_\nu^\varepsilon = r_\nu(1 + \varepsilon)^{-1} + O(\varepsilon^2).$$

Thus, for small positive values of ε, φ_j^ε is a Schur polynomial. Theorem 4.3.1 then implies that $\varphi_{j+1}^\varepsilon$ is also a Schur polynomial, and it is easy to check that

$$\varphi_{j+1}^\varepsilon(z) = \varepsilon(2 + d\varepsilon)\varphi_j^*(0)\varphi_j'(z). \tag{4.3.12}$$

Hence $\varphi_j'(z)$ is a Schur polynomial. The argument in the other direction follows easily. ∎

For completeness we state the following three theorems without proof.

Theorem 4.3.4 *φ_j is a von Neumann polynomial of degree d if and only if either φ_{j+1} is a von Neumann polynomial of degree $d-1$ and $|\varphi_j(0)| < |\varphi_j^*(0)|$ or φ_{j+1} is identically zero and φ_j' is a von Neumann polynomial.*

Theorem 4.3.5 *φ_j is a conservative polynomial if and only if φ_{j+1} is identically zero and φ_j' is a von Neumann polynomial.*

Theorem 4.3.6 *φ_j is a simple conservative polynomial if and only if φ_{j+1} is identically zero and φ_j' is a Schur polynomial.*

We now apply this theory to the examples given at the beginning of this section. In applying this theory it is very helpful to use a computerized symbol manipulation language to assist in the algebraic transformations.

Example 4.3.1, continued We analyze the scheme (4.3.1) using Theorem 4.3.2 and begin by setting

$$\varphi_0(z) = (7 + 4i\beta)z^2 - (8 - 2i\beta)z + 1,$$

which is polynomial (4.3.2). The scheme will be stable precisely when $\varphi_0(z)$ is a simple von Neumann polynomial. We make repeated use of Theorem 4.3.2. We first check that $|\varphi_0^*(0)| = |7 - 4i\beta| > 1 = |\varphi_0(0)|$ and then, using (4.3.9), we obtain

$$\varphi_1(z) = 4(12 + 4\beta^2)z - 4(12 - 2\beta^2 - 12i\beta).$$

φ_1 is a simple von Neumann polynomial if and only if

$$\left(12 + 4\beta^2\right)^2 \geq \left(12 - 2\beta^2\right)^2 + 12^2\beta^2$$

and this inequality always holds, with equality only if β is zero. Thus the scheme (4.3.1) is unconditionally stable. $\square$

Example 4.3.2, continued For scheme (4.3.3) with φ_0 equal to the amplification polynomial (4.3.4), we have that

$$|\varphi_0^*(0)|^2 - |\varphi_0(0)|^2 = 24(2 - \alpha)(11 - 6\alpha) + 12^2\beta^2$$

and this expression is nonnegative for $0 \leq \alpha \leq \frac{11}{6}$. (Since α, given by (4.3.5), depends on θ and vanishes for θ equal to zero, we need not consider the case of α greater than 2, nor need we consider negative α.) Again, we make repeated use of Theorem 4.3.2.

The polynomial φ_1, after dividing by 24, is

$$\varphi_1(z) = \left[(11 - 6\alpha)(2 - \alpha) + 6\beta^2\right]z^2$$

$$- 2\left[(2 - \alpha)(5 - 3\alpha) - 3\beta^2 - (11 - 6\alpha)i\beta\right]z$$

$$- (2 - \alpha - 2i\beta).$$

We have

$$|\varphi_1^*(0)|^2 - |\varphi_1(0)|^2 = 4(5 - 3\alpha)\left[3(2 - \alpha)^3 + \beta^2(13 - 6\alpha)\right] + 36\beta^4.$$

Thus for stability we must have

$$0 \leq \alpha \leq \frac{5}{3} < \frac{11}{6}.$$

This places a more severe requirement on α. Finally

$$\varphi_2(z) = \left[120 - 252\alpha + 198\alpha^2 - 69\alpha^3 + 9\alpha^4 + (18\alpha^2 - 69\alpha + 65)\beta^2 + 9\beta^4\right]z$$

$$+ 9\beta^4 + 6(5 - 3\alpha)i\beta^3 + (3\alpha - 5)\beta^2$$

$$- \left(18\alpha^3 + 102\alpha^2 + 192\alpha - 120\right)i\beta$$

$$- 9\alpha^4 + 69\alpha^3 - 198\alpha^2 + 252\alpha - 120.$$

We have that the one root of φ_2 is within or on the unit circle when

$$|\varphi_2^*(0)|^2 - |\varphi_2(0)|^2$$

is nonnegative. This quantity is

$$12\beta^4(5 - 3\alpha)\left[6\beta^2 + (11 - 6\alpha)(2 - \alpha)\right],$$

and is nonnegative when α is at most $\frac{5}{3}$. Thus the stability condition for (4.3.3) is

$$\alpha = |a\lambda|^2 \frac{\sin^2 \frac{1}{2}\theta}{1 - \frac{2}{3}\sin^2 \frac{1}{2}\theta} \le \frac{5}{3}.$$

The maximum value of the left hand side of this inequality is achieved at θ equal to π. Thus the scheme (4.3.3) is stable if and only if

$$|a\lambda| \le \frac{\sqrt{5}}{3}.$$

Notice that (4.3.3) is an implicit scheme but is not unconditionally stable. □

Example 4.3.3, continued To complete our final example we consider the implicit $(4, 4)$ scheme (4.3.7) with amplification polynomial $\varphi_0(z)$ given by (4.3.8). Using (4.3.9) we find that $\varphi_1(z)$ is identically zero, so by Theorem 4.3.2, $\varphi_0(z)$ is a simple von Neumann polynomial if and only if

$$\psi_1(z) = \tfrac{3}{4}\varphi_0'(z) = 3z^3 + i\beta(6z^2 - 2z + 2)$$

is a Schur polynomial. By checking that $|\psi_1(0)| < |\psi_1^*(0)|$, i.e., $|2\beta| < 3$, we see that ψ_1 is a Schur polynomial only if $|\beta| < \frac{3}{2}$.

Proceeding with the algorithm given by Theorem 4.3.2 and (4.3.9), we have

$$\psi_2(z) = (9 - 4\beta^2)z^2 + (4\beta^2 + 18i\beta)z - 12\beta^2 - 6i\beta.$$

This is a Schur polynomial only if

$$(9 - 4\beta^2)^2 > (12\beta^2)^2 + (6\beta)^2 \qquad\qquad (4.3.13)$$

which is equivalent to

$$\beta^2 < \frac{9(\sqrt{41} - 3)}{64},$$

and is a more severe restriction than that $|\beta|$ be less than $\frac{3}{2}$. We next obtain

$$\psi_3(z) = \left(81 - 108\beta^2 - 128\beta^4\right)z + 32\beta^4 - 264i\beta^3 + 144\beta^2 + 162i\beta.$$

The one root of ψ_3 is inside the unit circle only if

$$\left(81 - 108\beta^2 - 128\beta^4\right)^2 - \left(32\beta^4 + 144\beta^2\right)^2 - \left(264\beta^3 - 162\beta\right)^2$$

is nonnegative. This expression factors as

$$3 \left(9 - 4\beta^2\right) \left(3 - 16\beta^2\right) \left(80\beta^4 - 72\beta^2 + 81\right).$$

The last factor is always positive, and we deduce that ψ_3 is a Schur polynomial for

$$\beta^2 < \frac{3}{16} < \frac{9(\sqrt{41} - 3)}{64}.$$

We obtain that the stability condition for the scheme (4.3.7) is

$$|\beta| = \frac{|a\lambda \sin\theta|}{1 - \frac{2}{3}\sin^2\frac{1}{2}\theta} < \frac{\sqrt{3}}{4}.$$

The maximum of $|\beta|$ as a function of θ occurs when $\cos\theta$ is $-\frac{1}{2}$. Thus the scheme is stable when

$$|a\lambda| < \tfrac{1}{4}.$$

Notice that when $|a\lambda|$ is $\frac{1}{4}$, the polynomial $\varphi_0(z)$ has a double root on the unit circle. Since $\varphi_1(z)$ vanishes identically, we have that $\varphi_0(z)$ is a conservative polynomial; that is, all the amplification factors of the scheme (4.3.7) satisfy

$$|g_\nu(\theta)| \equiv 1.$$

Even though this scheme is implicit it is not unconditionally stable. $\square$

EXERCISES 4.3

1. Verify the accuracy of the schemes (4.3.1), (4.3.3), and (4.3.7).

2. Verify that formula (4.3.12) follows from (4.3.9) for the polynomials (4.3.11).

3. Using the methods of this section verify that the scheme (4.2.3) is unconditionally stable.

4. Show that if $\varphi_1(z)$, as defined by (4.3.9), is identically zero, then if α is a root of $\varphi_0(z)$, so is $\bar{\alpha}^{-1}$.

5. Show that the explicit $(4,4)$ scheme for (1.1.1) derived in Example 3.2.1,

$$\frac{v_m^{n+2} - v_m^{n-2}}{4k} + a\left(1 - \frac{h^2}{6}\delta^2\right)\delta_0\left(\frac{2v_m^{n+1} - v_m^n + 2v_m^{n-1}}{3}\right)$$

$$= \frac{2f_m^{n+1} - f_m^n + 2f_m^{n-1}}{3},$$

is stable for

$$|a\lambda| < \frac{\sqrt{3}}{4}\frac{1}{(1 + \sqrt{6})(\sqrt{6} - 3/2)^{1/2}}.$$

Hint: The amplification polynomial for this scheme is very similar to (4.3.8).

6. Use the methods of this section to show that the leapfrog scheme (1.3.4) is stable if and only if $|a\lambda|$ is less than 1.

7. Show that the following scheme for $u_t + au_x = f$ is accurate of order $(3,4)$ and is unstable for all values of λ.

$$\frac{11v_m^{n+1} - 18v_m^n + 9v_m^{n-1} - 2v_m^{n-2}}{6k} + a\left(1 + \frac{h^2}{6}\delta^2\right)^{-1}\delta_0 v_m^{n+1} = f_m^{n+1}.$$

8. Show that the scheme

$$\frac{v_m^{n+2} + v_m^{n+1} - v_m^{n-1} - v_m^{n-2}}{6k} + a\left(1 - \frac{h^2\delta^2}{6}\right)\delta_0 v_m^n = f_m^n$$

is a $(2,4)$ accurate scheme for $u_t + au_x = f$ and is stable for

$$|a\lambda| < \frac{\sqrt{69 - 11\sqrt{33}}}{8(\sqrt{6}+1)(\sqrt{6}-3/2)^{1/2}}.$$

9. Show that the scheme

$$\frac{v_m^{n+2} + v_m^{n+1} - v_m^{n-1} - v_m^{n-2}}{6k} + a\left(1 + \frac{h^2\delta^2}{6}\right)^{-1}\delta_0 \frac{v_m^{n+1} + v_m^{n-1}}{2} = f_m^n$$

is a $(2,4)$ accurate scheme for $u_t + au_x = f$ and is stable for

$$|a\lambda| < \tfrac{1}{3}\left(2^{1/3} - 1\right).$$

Hint: The real root of $1 - 15x + 3x^2 - x^3$ is $\left(2^{1/3} - 1\right)^2$.

10. Show that the scheme

$$\frac{2v_m^{n+1} + 3v_m^n - 6v_m^{n-1} + v_m^{n-2}}{6k} + a\left(1 + \frac{h^2\delta^2}{6}\right)^{-1}\delta_0 v_m^n = 0$$

is a $(3,4)$ accurate scheme for the one-way wave equation $u_t + au_x = 0$ and is unstable for all values of λ.

11. A Hurwitz polynomial is a polynomial $f(z)$, all of whose roots are in the left complex half-plane, i.e., Re $z < 0$. If f has the coefficients a_j we define

$$f^*(z) = \sum_{\ell=0}^{d} \bar{a}_\ell(-z)^\ell.$$

Given a polynomial f_0 we recursively define

$$f_{j+1} = \frac{f_j(z)f_j^*(-1) - f_j^*(z)f_j(-1)}{z+1}.$$

Prove that f_j is a Hurwitz polynomial of exact degree d if and only if f_{j+1} is a Hurwitz polynomial of exact degree $d-1$ and $|f_j(-1)| < |f_j^*(-1)|$. *Hint:* $|f_j(-1)|$ is a constant multiple of the distance of the roots from -1. The proof is similar to that of Theorem 4.3.1.

Chapter 5

Dissipation and Dispersion

5.1 Dissipation

In Section 1.3 we noted that the leapfrog scheme was more accurate than the Lax-Friedrichs scheme, as illustrated by Figures 1.4 and 1.6. However, the solution computed with the leapfrog scheme contains small oscillations that detract from the appearance of the solutions. In this section we discuss a way of removing, or at least reducing, the amplitude of this "noise." For many calculations, especially for nonlinear equations, these small, high-frequency oscillations can have a significant role in reducing the accuracy of the solution.

To consider the method of propagation of these oscillations, consider the leapfrog scheme (1.3.4) with initial data given by

$$v_m^n = (-1)^{n+m}\varepsilon, \quad \text{for} \quad m \in Z \qquad (5.1.1)$$

for n equal to 0 and 1. It is easy to see that (5.1.1) is then the solution for all values of n. This shows that the leapfrog scheme (1.3.4) propagates these disturbances without damping them. A more striking illustration of propagation without damping was seen in Figures 4.1–4.3, in which the solution in Figure 4.3 was "reconstructed" as the reflection of the solution in Figure 4.2. This propagation without damping is a consequence of the amplification factors $g_+(\theta)$ and $g_-(\theta)$ having magnitude equal to 1. (See formula (4.1.2).)

Next consider the Lax-Wendroff scheme (3.1.1) with $|a\lambda|$ less than 1 and with data (5.1.1) for $n = 0$. Because of the repetition of the data, the solution here satisfies

$$v_m^{n+1} = (1 - 2a^2\lambda^2)v_m^n.$$

Since $|1 - 2a^2\lambda^2|$ is less than 1, the oscillation decreases in size each step. This decreasing of high-frequency oscillations is called *dissipation*.

The definition of dissipation is usually given under the assumption that the lower-order terms have been removed. This is also assumed in the definition of dissipation given next. Also note that we include both one-step schemes and multistep schemes in the definition.

Definition 5.1.1 *A scheme is dissipative of order $2r$ if there exists a positive constant c, independent of h and k, such that each amplification factor $g_\nu(\theta)$ satisfies*

$$|g_\nu(\theta)| \le 1 - c \sin^{2r} \tfrac{1}{2}\theta. \qquad (5.1.2)$$

A scheme that is dissipative of order $2r$ is also said to have dissipation of order $2r$. Similar to the observation at the end of Section 2.2, we note that (5.1.2) is equivalent to

$$|g_\nu(\theta)|^2 \le 1 - c' \sin^{2r} \tfrac{1}{2}\theta. \tag{5.1.3}$$

We also note that for the most general case, in which we cannot use the restricted stability condition (2.2.7) but must use the general condition of (2.2.6), the estimate (5.1.2) must be replaced by

$$|g_\nu(\theta)| \le \left(1 - c \sin^{2r} \tfrac{1}{2}\theta\right)(1 + Kk), \tag{5.1.4}$$

and similarly for (5.1.3).

As the definition shows, to decide if a given scheme is dissipative, we need consider only $|g(\theta)|$. For the Lax-Wendroff scheme we have

$$|g(\theta)|^2 = 1 - 4a^2\lambda^2 \left(1 - a^2\lambda^2\right) \sin^4 \tfrac{1}{2}\theta.$$

So for $|a\lambda| = 1$ we have $|g(\theta)| = 1$, but for $0 < |a\lambda| < 1$ the scheme is dissipative of order 4. In fact, for $\theta = \pi$, we have $g(\theta) = 1 - 2a^2\lambda^2$, as our example showed.

Many texts give the definition of dissipation by replacing the expression $\sin^{2r}\theta$ in (5.1.2) by $|\theta|^{2r}$, with θ restricted in magnitude to less than π. The definitions are equivalent; we prefer the form (5.1.2), since that is the form that actually occurs in evaluating $|g(\theta)|$ for most schemes.

The leapfrog scheme (1.3.4) and the Crank-Nicolson scheme (3.1.3) are called *strictly* nondissipative schemes because their amplification factors are identically 1 in magnitude. The Lax-Friedrichs scheme (1.3.5) and the backward-time central-space scheme (1.6.1) and the $(2,2)$ implicit scheme (4.2.3) are nondissipative but not strictly nondissipative. For each of these schemes $|g(\pi)|$ and $|g(0)|$ are 1, but $|g(\theta)|$ is less than 1 for all other values of θ. These schemes reduce the magnitude of most frequencies but not the highest frequency on the grid.

Dissipation can be added to any nondissipative scheme, as we will show, and this provides us with some control over the properties of the scheme. In adding dissipation to a nondissipative scheme, we must be careful not to affect the order of accuracy adversely. For example, the modified leapfrog scheme

$$\frac{v_m^{n+1} - v_m^{n-1}}{2k} + a\delta_0 v_m^n + \frac{\varepsilon}{2k}\left(\tfrac{1}{2}h\delta\right)^4 v_m^{n-1} = f_m^n \tag{5.1.5}$$

is a second-order accurate scheme for $u_t + au_x = f$ for small values of ε. The amplification factors are

$$g_\pm = -ia\lambda\sin\theta \pm \sqrt{1 - a^2\lambda^2 \sin^2\theta - \varepsilon\sin^4 \tfrac{1}{2}\theta}.$$

If ε is not greater than $1 - a^2\lambda^2$, the scheme is stable and dissipative of order 4 (see Exercise 5.1.2). Note that $\sin^{2r} \tfrac{1}{2}\theta$ is the symbol of $\left(\tfrac{1}{2}ih\delta\right)^{2r}$. Similarly, the Crank-Nicolson scheme (3.1.3) can be modified as

$$\frac{v_m^{n+1} - v_m^n}{k} + \frac{a}{2}\delta_0\left(v_m^{n+1} + v_m^n\right) + \frac{\varepsilon}{k}\left(\tfrac{1}{2}h\delta\right)^4 v_m^n = \frac{1}{2}\left(f_m^{n+1} + f_m^n\right). \tag{5.1.6}$$

This scheme is second-order accurate and dissipative of order 4 for small values of ε.

To show that any scheme can have dissipation added to it, we consider the amplification polynomial and modify it as in formula (4.3.11). To be more precise the scheme corresponding to

$$\Phi^\varepsilon(g, \theta) = \Phi(g, \theta) + \varepsilon \sin^{2r} \tfrac{1}{2}\theta \, g\Phi'(g, \theta) \qquad (5.1.7)$$

will have all roots inside the unit circle except at θ equal to 0. ($\Phi'(g, \theta)$ is the derivative of Φ with respect to g.) Another choice for a dissipative scheme is

$$\Phi^\varepsilon(g, \theta) = \Phi(g, \theta) + \varepsilon \sin^{2r} \tfrac{1}{2}\theta \, [g\Phi'(g, \theta) - n\Phi(g, \theta)] . \qquad (5.1.8)$$

The preceding general procedures are not always advisable to use, but it does give one guidance in adding dissipation to a scheme (see Exercises 5.1.3 and 5.1.4).

If we use the methods of Section 4.3, then we can determine if the scheme is dissipative by checking if the amplification polynomial is a Schur polynomial for values of θ other than θ equal to 0. For a dissipative scheme the amplification polynomial is a Schur polynomial for θ not equal to zero.

EXERCISES 5.1

1. Show that the scheme (5.1.6) is dissipative of order 4 and stable if $0 < \varepsilon < 2$.

2. Show that the modified leapfrog scheme (5.1.5) is stable for ε satisfying

$$0 < \varepsilon \le 1 \quad \text{if} \quad 0 < a^2\lambda^2 \le \tfrac{1}{2}$$

and

$$0 < \varepsilon \le 4a^2\lambda^2 \left(1 - a^2\lambda^2\right) \quad \text{if} \quad \tfrac{1}{2} \le a^2\lambda^2 < 1.$$

3. Construct the modified scheme corresponding to formula (5.1.7) using the multistep scheme (4.2.3). Compare this scheme with

$$\frac{3v_m^{n+1} - 4v_m^n + v_m^{n-1}}{2k} + a\delta_0 v_m^{n+1} = \frac{\varepsilon}{2k} \left(\frac{i}{2}h\delta\right)^{2r} v_m^{n-1}.$$

4. Construct the leapfrog scheme with added dissipation using the method given by formula (5.1.8). Compare this scheme with the scheme (5.1.5).

5. Construct the Crank-Nicolson scheme with added dissipation using the method given by formulas (5.1.7) and (5.1.8). Compare these schemes with each other and with the scheme (5.1.6).

6. Show that the scheme of Exercise 3.2.6 is dissipative of order 6 for

$$0 < |a\lambda| < \left(\frac{\sqrt{17} - 1}{6}\right)^{1/2}.$$

7. Show that the scheme (3.2.16) is dissipative of order 4 if $0 < |a\lambda| < 3$.

5.2 Dispersion

To introduce the idea of dispersion we look again at equation (1.1.1) and notice that we can write the solution as

$$u(t, x) = \frac{1}{\sqrt{2\pi}} \int_{-\infty}^{\infty} e^{i\omega x} e^{-i\omega at} \hat{u}_0(\omega) \, d\omega. \tag{5.2.1}$$

From this we conclude that

$$\hat{u}(t + k, \omega) = e^{-i\omega ak} \hat{u}(t, \omega). \tag{5.2.2}$$

If we consider a one-step finite difference scheme, we have, from (2.2.5), that

$$\hat{v}^{n+1} = g(h\xi)\hat{v}^n, \tag{5.2.3}$$

and by comparing (5.2.2) and (5.2.3) we see that we should expect that $g(h\xi)$ should be a good approximation to $e^{-i\xi ak}$.

To emphasize the similarity between $e^{-i\xi ak}$ and $g(h\xi)$, we write

$$g(h\xi) = |g(h\xi)| e^{-i\xi\alpha(h\xi)k}. \tag{5.2.4}$$

The quantity $\alpha(h\xi)$ is called the *phase speed* and is the speed at which waves of frequency ξ are propagated by the finite difference scheme. If $\alpha(h\xi)$ were equal to a for all ξ, then waves would propagate with the correct speed, but this is not the case for any finite difference scheme except in trivial cases. The speed $\alpha(h\xi)$ is only an approximation to a.

The phenomenon of waves of different frequencies traveling with different speeds is called *dispersion*. In studying dispersion for finite difference schemes it is convenient to define the *phase error* as $a - \alpha(h\xi)$.

The effect of dispersion can easily be seen in computing the solution to (1.1.1) with initial data that is a square pulse, i.e., $u = 1$ only for $0 \le x \le 1$. For the partial differential equation the shape is preserved; it is only translated. For the finite difference scheme the shape is not preserved because the different frequencies that make up the square pulse are moved with different speeds.

Example 5.2.1 We consider the Lax-Wendroff scheme to study its dispersion. We have

$$g = 1 - 2(a\lambda)^2 \sin^2 \tfrac{1}{2} h\xi - ia\lambda \sin h\xi$$

and so

$$\tan[\alpha(h\xi)\xi k] = \frac{a\lambda \sin h\xi}{1 - 2(a\lambda)^2 \sin^2 \tfrac{1}{2} h\xi}. \tag{5.2.5}$$

Since this formula does not give too much insight into the behavior of $\alpha(h\xi)$, we study the Taylor series of $\alpha(h\xi)$ around $\xi = 0$. We use the formulas

$$\sin x = x \left[1 - \tfrac{1}{6}x^2 + O(x^4)\right]$$

$$\tan x = x \left[1 + \tfrac{1}{3}x^2 + O(x^4)\right]$$

$$\tan^{-1} y = y \left[1 - \tfrac{1}{3}y^2 + O(y^4)\right].$$

Using the series for $\sin x$ in (5.2.5) we obtain, after some work,

$$\tan\left[\alpha(h\xi)\xi k\right] = a\lambda h\xi\left\{1 - (h\xi)^2 \left[\tfrac{1}{6} - \tfrac{1}{2}(a\lambda)^2\right] + O(h\xi)^4\right\}.$$

From the formula for $\tan^{-1} y$ we obtain

$$\alpha(h\xi) = a\left\{1 - \tfrac{1}{6}(h\xi)^2 \left[1 - (a\lambda)^2\right] + O(h\xi)^4\right\}. \tag{5.2.6}$$

We see that for $h\xi$ small and $|a\lambda| < 1$, $\alpha(h\xi)$ is less than a. Also we see that if $|a\lambda|$ is close to 1, then the dispersion will be less.

To deduce the behavior of $\alpha(h\xi)$ for larger values of ξ, we refer to the formula for g and (5.2.5). We find that for ξ equal to $h^{-1}\pi$, g has the value $1 - 2a^2\lambda^2$. If $a^2\lambda^2$ is greater than $\tfrac{1}{2}$, then g is negative, and so $\alpha(\pi)h^{-1}\pi k$ is equal to π. Thus $\alpha(\pi)$ is λ^{-1}. However, if $a^2\lambda^2$ is less than $\tfrac{1}{2}$ then g is positive and so $\alpha(\pi)$ is 0. By consistency, $\alpha(h\xi)$ will always be close to a for small values of ξ, and, in particular, $\alpha(0)$ is equal to a. This is proved in Chapter 10. □

For the leapfrog scheme and other multistep schemes, the phase error is defined by considering the one amplification factor $g_0(h\xi)$ for which

$$g_0(0) = 1.$$

As we showed in Section 4.2, there is only one such amplification factor. For the leapfrog scheme (1.3.4) we see that the phase speed is given by

$$\sin[k\alpha(h\xi)\xi] = a\lambda \sin h\xi, \tag{5.2.7}$$

or, equivalently,

$$\sin[\alpha(\theta)\lambda\theta] = a\lambda \sin\theta.$$

(This is obtained most easily from (4.1.2) by noting that since $|g_+| = 1$, the imaginary part of g_+ must be $-a\lambda \sin h\xi$.) The expansion of $\alpha(h\xi)$ for small values of ξ results in the same formula as for the Lax-Wendroff scheme up to $O(h\xi)^4$; see Exercise 5.2.1. Note also that $\alpha(\pi)$ is 0 for the leapfrog scheme.

One can also study the propagation velocities of parasitic modes for multistep schemes. For the leapfrog scheme it is seen that $\alpha_-(0) = \alpha_-(\pi) = \lambda^{-1}$

for the parasitic mode. (The subscript is included to distinguish this speed from the $\alpha(h\xi)$ of (5.2.7).) Thus for the leapfrog scheme the fastest phase speeds are associated with the parasitic modes.

As a general principle, for hyperbolic partial differential equations it is best to take $|a\lambda|$ close to the stability limit to keep the dispersion and dissipation small. If we are interested in a particular frequency, say ξ_0, then we should choose h so that $h\xi_0$ is much less than π to get accurate results, both in the speed of the wave (dispersion) and in the amplitude (dissipation). For the leapfrog and Lax-Wendroff schemes for (1.1.1) with $a\lambda$ equal to 1 the schemes have no dispersion error. These are exceptional cases, and this does not happen for variable coefficient equations or nontrivial systems.

EXERCISES 5.2

1. Show that the formula (5.2.6) is also true for the leapfrog scheme, where $\alpha(h\xi)$ is given by (5.2.7).

2. For the backward-time central-space scheme (1.6.1), show that the phase speed is given by

$$\tan\left[k\alpha(h\xi)\xi\right] = a\lambda \sin h\xi$$

and satisfies

$$\alpha(h\xi) = a\left[1 - \frac{(h\xi)^2}{6}\left(1 + 2a^2\lambda^2\right) + O\left(h\xi\right)^4\right].$$

3. Show that the phase speed for the Crank-Nicolson scheme (3.1.3) is given by

$$\tan\left[\tfrac{1}{2}k\alpha(h\xi)\xi\right] = \tfrac{1}{2}a\lambda \sin h\xi$$

and satisfies

$$\alpha(h\xi) = a\left[1 - \frac{(h\xi)^2}{6}\left(1 + \tfrac{1}{2}a^2\lambda^2\right) + O\left(h\xi\right)^4\right].$$

4. Show that for the multistep scheme (4.2.3), the amplification factor $g_+(\theta)$ satisfying $g_+(0) = 1$ can be expanded as

$$g_+(\theta)^{-1} = 2 - \sqrt{1 - 2ia\lambda \sin\theta}$$

$$= 1 + ia\lambda \sin\theta - \frac{1}{2}(a\lambda \sin\theta)^2 - \frac{i}{2}(a\lambda \sin\theta)^3 + O(\theta)^4$$

and thus

$$\tan\left[k\alpha(h\xi)\xi\right] = a\lambda \sin h\xi \left(1 + O(h\xi)^4\right),$$

and conclude that $\alpha(h\xi)$ is the same as for the scheme of Exercise 2 to within $O(h\xi)^4$.

5. Show that the $(2,4)$ Crank-Nicolson scheme

$$\frac{v_m^{n+1} - v_m^n}{k} + a\left(1 + \frac{h^2}{6}\delta^2\right)^{-1}\delta_0\left(\frac{v_m^{n+1} + v_m^n}{2}\right) = 0 \qquad (5.2.8)$$

has phase speed given by

$$\tan[\tfrac{1}{2}k\alpha(h\xi)\xi] = \frac{3}{2}\frac{a\lambda\sin h\xi}{2 + \cos h\xi}$$

$$= \frac{1}{2}ak\xi\left[1 + O(h\xi)^4\right].$$

and thus

$$\alpha(h\xi) = a\left[1 - \frac{1}{3}a^2(k\xi)^2 + O(k\xi)^4\right]\left(1 + O(h\xi)^4\right).$$

6. Show that the phase speed for the $(2,4)$ Lax-Wendroff scheme of Exercise 5.1.6 satisfies

$$\tan k\alpha(h\xi)\xi = \frac{ak\xi\left(1 + O(h\xi)^4\right)}{1 - \frac{1}{2}a^2(k\xi)^2\left[1 + O(h\xi)^4\right]}$$

and therefore

$$\alpha(h\xi) = a\left[1 + \frac{1}{6}a^2(k\xi)^2\right]\left(1 + O(h\xi)^4\right).$$

5.3 Group Velocity and the Propagation of Wave Packets

The study of wave packets introduces another interesting aspect of dispersion, that of group velocity; see also Trefethen [51] and Vichnevetsky and Bowles [54]. We consider the one-way wave equation (1.1.1) with initial data of the form

$$u(0, x) = e^{i\xi_0 x}p(x) \qquad (5.3.1)$$

where $p(x)$ is a relatively smooth function decaying rapidly with $|x|$. The solution for the initial condition (5.3.1) is

$$u(t, x) = e^{i\xi_0(x - at)}p(x - at). \qquad (5.3.2)$$

We call a function of the form (5.3.2) a *wave packet*. We refer to the function $p(x)$ as the *envelope* of the packet and the frequency ξ_0 as the *frequency* of the wave packet.

As a particular case, we will use the function

$$u(0, x) = \begin{cases} \cos\xi_0 x \, \cos^2\frac{1}{2}\pi x & \text{if } |x| \le 1, \\ 0 & \text{otherwise,} \end{cases} \qquad (5.3.3)$$

in our numerical illustrations. In this case we use $\cos \xi_0 x$, the real part of $e^{i\xi_0 x}$, instead of $e^{i\xi_0 x}$ itself.

For a finite difference scheme we know that dispersion will cause the pure wave with frequency ξ_0 to travel with the phase velocity $\alpha(h\xi_0)$, but it is not evident what will be the speed or speeds associated to a wave packet. As we will show, a strictly nondissipative finite difference scheme with a wave packet as initial data will have a solution that is approximately

$$v^*(t, x) = e^{i\xi_0(x - \alpha(h\xi_0)t)} p(x - \gamma(h\xi_0)t) \tag{5.3.4}$$

where $\alpha(h\xi_0)$ is the phase velocity of the scheme and $\gamma(h\xi_0)$ is the group velocity. The group velocity is given by

$$\gamma(\theta) = \frac{d\theta\alpha(\theta)}{d\theta} = \alpha(\theta) + \theta\alpha'(\theta). \tag{5.3.5}$$

Notice that since $\alpha(h\xi)$ tends to a as h tends to zero, we have that $\gamma(h\xi)$ also tends to a; that is, as h tends to zero the function v^*, which approximates v_m^n, tends to the exact solution (5.3.2).

Example 5.3.1 The concept of group velocity is illustrated in Figure 5.1. The computation uses the leapfrog scheme to solve the one-way wave equation $u_t + u_x = 0$ on the interval $[-2, 2]$ with periodicity. The grid spacing is 0.05 with $\lambda = 0.95$. The initial condition is (5.3.3) with ξ_0 equal to 5π.

Figure 5.1 displays the computed solution in solid lines and also the graph of the envelope, not the solution itself, at time 19.8. It is immediately seen that the envelope at the computed solution does not correspond to that of the exact solution, so the wave packet has traveled with a speed that is less than 1. The group velocity for ξ_0 equal to 5π is approximately 0.9545, and a wave packet traveling with this velocity would be centered at -1.093. This location is marked by the dagger in the figure. It is seen that this is a very good approximation to the center of the computed solution wave packet.

To show that the high-frequency mode of the wave packet travels with the phase velocity rather than the group velocity, two other points are marked with square boxes in the figure. These points mark the location of the points closest to 0 at which the initial solution is zero but propagated with the phase velocity $\alpha(5\pi h)$, which is approximately 0.9872. These points correspond to those in the initial condition at $-1/10$ and $1/10$, i.e., those two points x closest to 0 such that $u(0, x)$ is 0.

Finally, the graph of v^* is shown with a dashed line. It is seen that the approximation of v_m^n by $v^*(t_n, x_m)$ is a good approximation, better than the approximation of $u(t, x)$ by v_m^n. $\square$

We now justify the claim that v^* approximates the solution of the scheme. The initial data (5.3.1) has the Fourier transform $\hat{p}(\xi - \xi_0)$, and thus the solution of the finite difference scheme is

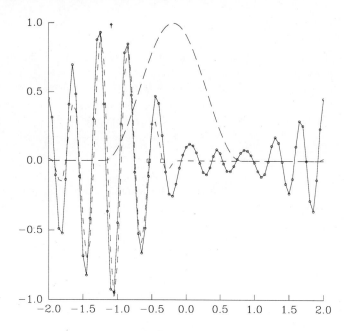

Figure 5.1

$$v_m^n = \frac{1}{\sqrt{2\pi}} \int_{-\pi/h}^{\pi/h} e^{i\xi x_m} e^{-i\xi\alpha(h\xi)t_n} \hat{p}_h(\xi - \xi_0)\, d\xi \qquad (5.3.6)$$

where $p_{h,m}$ is the discrete function given by evaluating p at the grid points x_m. We show in Section 10.2 that $\hat{p}_h(\xi)$ is approximately $\hat{p}(\xi)$ for $|\xi|$ much less than $h^{-1}\pi$. For now we may disregard the distinction between $\hat{p}(\xi - \xi_0)$ and $\hat{p}_h(\xi - \xi_0)$.

We change the variable of integration in (5.3.6) by replacing ξ by $\omega + \xi_0$. We obtain, since all the functions are periodic with period $2\pi h^{-1}$,

$$v_m^n = \frac{1}{\sqrt{2\pi}} \int_{-\pi/h}^{\pi/h} e^{i(\omega+\xi_0)x_m} e^{-i(\omega+\xi_0)\alpha(h\omega+h\xi_0)t_n} \hat{p}_h(\omega)\, d\omega, \qquad (5.3.7)$$

and define $\tilde{v}(t,x)$ by replacing $\hat{p}_h(\omega)$ by $\hat{p}(\omega)$ and by extending the range of integration to the whole real line, obtaining

$$\tilde{v}(t,x) = \frac{1}{\sqrt{2\pi}} \int_{-\infty}^{\infty} e^{i(\omega+\xi_0)x} e^{-i(\omega+\xi_0)\alpha(h\omega+h\xi_0)t} \hat{p}(\omega)\, d\omega \qquad (5.3.8)$$

It can be shown by the methods of Chapter 10 that the replacement of $\hat{p}_h(\omega)$ by $\hat{p}(\omega)$ and the extension of the limits of integration to $(-\infty, \infty)$ do not cause significant errors in the approximation; see Exercise 10.2.6.

We write $\tilde{v}(t,x)$ as

$$\tilde{v}(t,x) = e^{i\xi_0\left(x - \alpha(h\xi_0)t\right)} \frac{1}{\sqrt{2\pi}} \int_{-\infty}^{\infty} e^{i\omega(x - \tilde{\gamma}t)} \hat{p}(\omega)\, d\omega, \qquad (5.3.9)$$

with

$$\tilde{\gamma}(h\omega) = \frac{(\omega + \xi_0)\alpha(h\omega + h\xi_0) - \xi_0\alpha(h\xi_0)}{\omega}$$

$$= \frac{(\varphi + \theta_0)\alpha(\varphi + \theta_0) - \theta_0\alpha(\theta_0)}{\varphi}$$

with $\theta_0 = h\xi_0$ and $\varphi = h\omega$. The use of Taylor series on $\alpha(\varphi)$ about θ_0 results in

$$\tilde{\gamma}(\varphi) = \left.\frac{d(\theta\alpha(\theta))}{d\theta}\right|_{\theta=\theta_0} + \varphi\frac{1}{2}\left.\frac{d^2\theta\alpha(\theta)}{d\theta^2}\right|_{\theta=\theta^*}$$

for some value of θ^* between θ_0 and $\theta_0 + \varphi$. Writing this in terms of ω and ξ_0, we have

$$\tilde{\gamma}(h\omega) = \left.\frac{d(\xi\alpha(h\xi))}{d\xi}\right|_{\xi=\xi_0} + h\frac{1}{2}\omega\left.\frac{d^2(\theta\alpha(\theta))}{d\theta^2}\right|_{\theta=h\xi^*}$$

for some value of ξ^* between ξ_0 and $\xi_0 + \omega$. We see that $\tilde{\gamma}(h\omega)$ is equal to the group velocity $\gamma(h\xi_0)$ to within an error on the order of h. Rewriting (5.3.9) we have

$$\tilde{v}(t,x) = e^{i\xi_0\left[x - \alpha(h\xi_0)t\right]} \frac{1}{\sqrt{2\pi}} \int_{-\infty}^{\infty} e^{i\omega\left[x - \gamma(h\xi_0)t\right]} e^{ihtr(\omega)} \hat{p}(\omega)\, d\omega \qquad (5.3.10)$$

where we have written $r(\omega)$ for the term $\frac{1}{2}\omega^2\, d^2\theta\alpha(\theta)/d\theta^2$.

If we replace the factor $e^{ihtr(\omega)}$ by 1 in the expression for $\tilde{v}(t,x)$, we obtain $v^*(t,x)$

$$v^*(t,x) = e^{i\xi_0\left[x - \alpha(h\xi_0)t\right]} \frac{1}{\sqrt{2\pi}} \int_{-\infty}^{\infty} e^{i\omega\left[x - \gamma(h\xi_0)t\right]} \hat{p}(\omega)\, d\omega$$

$$= e^{i\xi_0\left[x - \alpha(h\xi_0)t\right]} p\big(x - \gamma(h\xi_0)t\big). \qquad (5.3.11)$$

Since $e^{ihtr(\omega)} = 1 + O(h\omega)$, it is shown in Section 10.2 that the difference between $\tilde{v}(t,x)$ and $v^*(t,x)$ is also $O(h)$, provided that $p(x)$ is smooth enough (see Exercise 10.2.6). This shows (up to the details deferred to Chapter 10) that the solution to the finite difference scheme is approximated to within $O(h)$ by $v^*(t,x)$. If ξ_0 is such that the quantity $\xi_0\big[a - \alpha(h\xi_0)\big]t$ is $O(1)$, then v_m^n also differs from the exact solution, $u(t,x)$, by $O(1)$, as we discussed earlier in the analysis of the phase error. In this case the approximation of v_m^n by $v^*(t,x)$ can be much better than the approximation of $u(t,x)$ by v_m^n when t is large. This is well illustrated in Figure 5.1.

Group velocity can be used to explain some rather striking behavior of schemes (see Exercise 5.3.9). Even in the presence of dissipation the propagation of waves is governed by the phase and group velocity, as Exercise 5.3.6 demonstrates. Group velocity has been used by Trefethen to explain instability caused by boundary conditions; see [52].

EXERCISES 5.3

1. Show that the group velocity for the Lax-Wendroff scheme is given by
$$\gamma(h\xi) = a\frac{1 - 2(1 - a^2\lambda^2)\sin^2 \frac{1}{2}h\xi}{1 - 4a^2\lambda^2(1 - a^2\lambda^2)\sin^4 \frac{1}{2}h\xi}.$$

2. Show that the group velocity for the leapfrog scheme (1.3.4) is given by
$$\gamma(h\xi) = a\frac{\cos h\xi}{\sqrt{1 - a^2\lambda^2 \sin^2 h\xi}}.$$
Compare the phase speed and group velocity at $\xi = h^{-1}\pi$.

3. Show that the group velocity for the Crank-Nicolson scheme (3.1.3) is given by
$$\gamma(\theta) = a\frac{\cos\theta}{1 + \frac{1}{4}a^2\lambda^2 \sin^2\theta}.$$

4. Show that the group velocity for the box scheme (3.1.23) is given by
$$\gamma(\theta) = a\frac{\sec^2 \frac{1}{2}\theta}{1 + a^2\lambda^2 \tan^2 \frac{1}{2}\theta}.$$

5. Repeat the calculation of Example 5.3.1 using the leapfrog scheme but on the interval $[-1, 9]$ for $0 \le t \le 7.5$. Specify the solution at the left boundary to be 0, and at the right boundary use quasi-characteristic extrapolation (3.3.1c). Demonstrate that the wave packet moves with the group velocity and that the high-frequency mode travels with the phase velocity. Show that the conclusions of Example 5.3.1 are valid in this case also. Study the effect of small amounts of dissipation using the scheme (5.1.5).

6. Repeat the calculation of Example 5.3.1 using the Lax-Wendroff scheme. Demonstrate that the wave packet moves with the group velocity and that the high-frequency mode travels with the phase velocity. In this exercise you will, of course, also see the effect of dissipation on the solution.

7. Repeat the calculation of Example 5.3.1 using the Crank-Nicolson scheme but using ξ_0 equal to 3π and λ equal to 1. Demonstrate that the wave packet moves with the group velocity and that the high-frequency mode travels with the phase velocity. Note that the Crank-Nicolson scheme is highly dispersive; that is, because the phase speed is not as good an approximation to a as it is for the leapfrog scheme, the wave packet will be significantly distorted. This exercise will require you to solve a periodic tridiagonal system; see Section 3.4.

8. Solve the one-way wave equation $u_t + u_x = 0$ on the interval $[-3, 9]$ for $0 \le t \le 7.5$. Use the Crank-Nicolson scheme with grid spacing of 0.05 and λ equal to 1. For initial data use the wave packet (5.3.3) with ξ equal to 3. Demonstrate that the wave packet moves with the group velocity and that the high-frequency mode travels with the phase velocity. Note that the Crank-Nicolson scheme is highly dispersive; that is, because the phase speed is not as good an approximation to a as it is for the leapfrog scheme, the wave packet will be significantly distorted.

9. Solve the one-way wave equation $u_t + u_x = 0$ on the interval $[-3, 3]$ for $0 \le t \le 1.45$. Use the leapfrog scheme with grid spacing of 0.1 and λ equal to 0.9. For initial data use the wave packet (5.3.3) with ξ equal to 9π. To compute the values of the solution at the first step, use two different methods to initialize, the Lax-Friedrichs scheme and the forward-time, central-space scheme. The difference between the two solutions is quite dramatic. It can be explained by considering the amplitude associated with the parasitic mode for each case and noting that for the Lax-Friedrichs scheme $g(\pi) = -1$, whereas for the forward-time, central-space scheme $g(\pi) = 1$. Also, for the leapfrog scheme $\gamma(\pi)$ is -1, but for the parasitic mode $\gamma_-(\pi)$ is 1.

Chapter 6

Parabolic Partial Differential Equations

6.1 Overview of Parabolic Partial Differential Equations

The simplest parabolic equation is the one-dimensional heat equation,

$$u_t = b u_{xx} \tag{6.1.1}$$

where b is a positive number. This equation arises in the study of heat transfer, in which case the function $u(t, x)$ gives the temperature at time t and location x resulting from the initial temperature distribution. Equations similar to (6.1.1) arise in many other applications, including viscous fluid flow and diffusion processes. As for the one-way wave equation (1.1.1), we are interested in the initial value problem for the heat equation (6.1.1); that is, we wish to determine the solution $u(t, x)$ for t positive, given the initial condition that $u(0, x) = u_0(x)$ for some function u_0.

We can obtain a formula for the solution to (6.1.1) by using the Fourier transform of (6.1.1) in space to obtain the equation

$$\hat{u}_t = -b\omega^2 \hat{u}.$$

Using the initial values, this equation has the solution

$$\hat{u}(t, \omega) = e^{-b\omega^2 t} \hat{u}_0(\omega),$$

and thus by the Fourier inversion formula

$$u(t, x) = \frac{1}{\sqrt{2\pi}} \int_{-\infty}^{\infty} e^{i\omega x} e^{-b\omega^2 t} \hat{u}_0(\omega) \, d\omega. \tag{6.1.2}$$

Formula (6.1.2) shows that u at time t is obtained from u_0 by damping the high-frequency modes of u_0. It also shows why the solution operator for a parabolic equation is called a dissipative operator, since all high-frequencies are dissipated.

112

A second formula can be obtained by using the definition of $\hat{u}_0$ in (6.1.2) and interchanging the order of integration. We have

$$u(t,x) = \frac{1}{\sqrt{2\pi}} \int_{-\infty}^{\infty} e^{i\omega x} e^{-b\omega^2 t} \left[\frac{1}{\sqrt{2\pi}} \int_{-\infty}^{\infty} e^{-i\omega y} u_0(y)\, dy \right] d\omega$$

$$= \frac{1}{\sqrt{4\pi}} \int_{-\infty}^{\infty} \left(\frac{1}{\sqrt{\pi}} \int_{-\infty}^{\infty} e^{i\omega(x-y)} e^{-b\omega^2 t}\, d\omega \right) u_0(y)\, dy$$

$$= \frac{1}{\sqrt{4\pi bt}} \int_{-\infty}^{\infty} e^{-(x-y)^2/4bt} u_0(y)\, dy.$$

(See Exercise 6.1.4 for the evaluation of the integral in the parentheses.)

The formula

$$u(t,x) = \frac{1}{\sqrt{4\pi bt}} \int_{-\infty}^{\infty} e^{-(x-y)^2/4bt} u_0(y)\, dy. \tag{6.1.3}$$

expresses $u(t,x)$ as a weighted average of u_0. For small t the weighting function multiplying $u_0(y)$ is very peaked about $y = x$, whereas for larger t the weighting function is much wider.

There are several important things to learn from the representations (6.1.2) and (6.1.3). First, the solution to (6.1.1) is an infinitely differentiable function of t and x for any positive value of t. This is easily seen by differentiating the representation (6.1.2), obtaining

$$\frac{\partial^{\ell+m} u(t,x)}{\partial t^\ell \partial x^m} = \frac{1}{\sqrt{2\pi}} \int_{-\infty}^{\infty} e^{i\omega x} (i\omega)^m (-b\omega^2)^\ell e^{-b\omega^2 t} \hat{u}_0(\omega)\, d\omega.$$

Since the quantity $(i\omega)^m(-b\omega^2)^\ell e^{-b\omega^2 t}$ is in $L^2(R)$ for positive values of t, we obtain, by the Cauchy-Schwarz inequality,

$$\left| \frac{\partial^{\ell+m} u(t,x)}{\partial t^\ell \partial x^m} \right| \le C_{t,\ell,m} \|u_0\| \tag{6.1.4}$$

for some constant $C_{t,\ell,m}$. Secondly, we see from (6.1.3) that if u_0 is nonnegative and not identically zero, then $u(t,x)$ will be positive for all (t,x) with t positive. This is in accord with our physical intuition that shows that heat will distribute itself rapidly and that temperatures colder than the initial temperatures will not occur in an isolated system.

In the remainder of this section we discuss two topics, the convection-diffusion equation and Fokker-Planck equations. These topics are not essential for the material that follows but are included to give the reader a better understanding of parabolic equations and how they arise in applications.

The Convection-Diffusion Equation

We briefly consider the convection-diffusion equation

$$u_t + au_x = bu_{xx}, \tag{6.1.5}$$

which obviously has similarities to hyperbolic and parabolic equations. We study it further in Section 6.4. To solve (6.1.5) let $y = x - at$ and set

$$w(t, y) = u(t, y + at).$$

Then

$$w_t = u_t + au_x = bu_{xx}$$

and

$$w_y = u_x, \quad w_{yy} = u_{xx},$$

so

$$w_t = bw_{yy}. \tag{6.1.6}$$

Since $u(t, x) = w(t, x - at)$, we see that the solution of (6.1.5), when examined from a coordinate system moving with speed a, is (6.1.6). Thus the solution of (6.1.5) travels with speed a (convection) and is dissipated with strength b (diffusion).

Fokker-Planck Equations

Many of the applications of parabolic equations arise as macroscopic descriptions of processes whose microscopic description is essentially probabilistic. Heat flow is related to the random motion of electrons and atoms; viscous fluid forces are related to molecular forces. Parabolic equations are also used in economic models to give a macroeconomic description of market behavior.

We present a simple illustration of the relation between random processes and parabolic equations. The resulting equation is an example of a Fokker-Planck equation.

Consider a discrete process with states identified by $x_i = \eta i$ for $i = 0, \pm 1, \pm 2, \ldots$, where η is some positive number. Suppose that transitions occur only between neighboring states between the discrete times $t_n = \tau n, n = 0, 1, 2, \ldots$. Let p_i^n be the probability that a transition from state i to $i + 1$ occurs in one time unit starting at t_n, and let q_i^n be the probability that a transition from state i to $i - 1$ occurs in one time unit starting at t_n. One may think of this process as describing a collection of objects such as atoms, electrons, insects, or computer jobs, which change their position or state every τ time units. Those at x_i will move to x_{i+1} with probability p_i^n and to x_{i-1} with probability q_i^n; they will stay put with probability $1 - p_i^n - q_i^n$. Let u_i^n be the probability density function at time t_n, that is, u_i^n is the probability that an object is at x_i at time t_n. Then we have the relationship

$$u_i^{n+1} = p_{i-1}^n u_{i-1}^n + q_{i+1}^n u_{i+1}^n + (1 - p_i^n - q_i^n)\, u_i^n, \tag{6.1.7}$$

that is, at time $t_{n+1} = t_n + \tau$, a object could be at x_i only if it came from x_{i-1}, from x_{i+1}, or x_i at the time t_n; this formula expresses the effect on u_i^{n+1} of each possibility. This equation is called the *Chapman-Kolmogorov* equation for the process.

Now we will take the limit as τ and η tend to zero, but we first rewrite the preceding equation as

$$u_i^{n+1} - u_i^n = \tfrac{1}{2}\left(p_{i-1}^n - q_{i-1}^n\right)u_{i-1}^n - \tfrac{1}{2}\left(p_{i+1}^n - q_{i+1}^n\right)u_{i+1}^n$$

$$+ \tfrac{1}{2}\left[\left(p_{i-1}^n + q_{i-1}^n\right)u_{i-1}^n - 2\left(p_i^n + q_i^n\right)u_i^n + \left(p_{i+1}^n + q_{i+1}^n\right)u_{i+1}^n\right].$$

We define functions $u(t,x)$, $c(t,x)$ and $d(t,x)$ as limits as η and τ tend to zero, given by

$$\sum_{a \le x_i \le b} u_i^n \rightarrow \int_a^b u(t,x)\,dx, \quad \text{for } t = n\tau,$$

$$\frac{p_i^n - q_i^n}{\tau}\eta \rightarrow c(t,x), \quad \text{and} \quad \frac{p_i^n + q_i^n}{2\tau}\eta^2 \rightarrow d(t,x).$$

We will assume that these limits exist in an appropriate sense. We then obtain

$$\frac{\partial u}{\partial t} = -\frac{\partial}{\partial x}\left[c(t,x)u\right] + \frac{\partial^2}{\partial x^2}\left[d(t,x)u\right]. \tag{6.1.8}$$

This is called the *Fokker-Planck* equation for the continuous process, which is the limit of the discrete process.

From (6.1.8) we see that $c(t,x)$ being positive corresponds to having p_i^n greater than q_i^n, which means objects will tend to move to the right. Similarly, $c(t,x)$ being negative means objects will tend to move to the left. Also, a larger value of $d(t,x)$ corresponds to larger values of $p_i^n + q_i^n$, which is the probability that an object will move. The solution $u(t,x)$ of (6.1.8) is a probability density function and satisfies

$$\int_{-\infty}^{\infty} u(t,x)\,dx = 1.$$

Fokker-Planck equations are applicable to many physical systems for which there is an underlying randomness. Specific examples of Fokker-Planck equations are the equation for the probability distribution for velocity in one-dimensional Brownian motion, which is

$$u_t = (vu)_v + u_{vv}, \tag{6.1.9}$$

and the energy in three-dimensional Brownian motion, which is

$$w_t = 2\left[\left(e - \frac{3}{2}\right)w\right]_e + 2(ew)_{ee}. \tag{6.1.10}$$

In (6.1.9) the probability density function u is a function of the velocity v and the time t. The probability that a particle at time t has a velocity between a and b is $\int_a^b u(t,v)\,dv$.

It is worth noting that often a discrete process involving many states or objects can be better modeled by an accurate difference scheme for the differential equation describing the limiting continuous process than by approximations of the discrete process itself. That is, we can approximate a discrete process involving a great many states either by simulating the discrete process using (6.1.7) with fewer states, so as to make it computationally feasible, or by considering the limiting continuous process described by (6.1.8). The continuous process may have to be further approximated by a numerical method. As an example, we could study heat flow by examining the motion of the molecules in a solid. The limiting continuous process would be that described by the heat equation, or some variation of it. For most applications the numerical solution of the heat equation is more accurate, and certainly more efficient, than a simulation of the molecular motion.

EXERCISES 6.1

1. Determine the behavior of the quantity $C_{t,\ell,m}$ in (6.1.4) as a function of t. In particular, show that $C_{t,\ell,m}$ is unbounded as t approaches 0 for $(\ell, m) \neq 0$. Show that $C_{t,\ell,m}$ can be defined by the maximum value of $(i\omega)^m(-b\omega^2)^\ell e^{-b\omega^2 t}$ as a function of ω.

2. Use the representation (6.1.3) to verify the following estimates on the norms of $u(t, x)$.

$$\|u(t, \cdot)\|_1 \leq \|u_0\|_1$$

$$\|u(t, \cdot)\|_\infty \leq \|u_0\|_\infty$$

Show that if u_0 is nonnegative, then

$$\|u(t, \cdot)\|_1 = \|u_0\|_1.$$

3. Show that if the three functions $u_1(t, v_1)$, $u_2(t, v_2)$, and $u_3(t, v_3)$ each satisfy the one-dimensional equation (6.1.9), then the probability density function $w(t, e)$ satisfies equation (6.1.10) where

$$e = \tfrac{1}{2}\left(v_1^2 + v_2^2 + v_3^2\right)$$

and

$$\int_0^E w(t, e)\, de = \iiint_{v_1^2 + v_2^2 + v_3^2 \leq 2E} u_1(t, v_1)u_2(t, v_2)u_3(t, v_3)\, dv_1\, dv_2\, dv_3.$$

4. Evaluate the integral

$$\frac{1}{\sqrt{\pi}} \int_{-\infty}^\infty e^{i\omega(x-y)} e^{-b\omega^2 t}\, d\omega,$$

which appears in the derivation of equation (6.1.3), by considering the function

$$F(\alpha) = \frac{1}{\sqrt{\pi}} \int_{-\infty}^\infty e^{i\omega\alpha} e^{-\omega^2}\, d\omega.$$

Hint: Show that $F(0) = 1$ and that $F'(\alpha) = -\tfrac{1}{2}\alpha F(\alpha)$.

6.2 Parabolic Systems and Boundary Conditions

We now discuss general parabolic equations in one space dimension. A more complete discussion is contained in Chapter 9. We consider parabolic systems in which the solution u is a vector function with d components. A system of the form

$$u_t = Bu_{xx} + Au_x + Cu + F(t,x) \tag{6.2.1}$$

is parabolic, or Petrovskii parabolic, if the eigenvalues of B all have positive real parts. A common special case is when B is positive definite, but in general the eigenvalues need not be real, nor does B have to be diagonalizable. Notice that no restrictions are placed on the matrices A and C.

Theorem 6.2.1 *The initial value problem for the system (6.2.1) is well-posed in the sense of Definition 1.5.2, and actually a stronger estimate holds. For each $T > 0$ there is a constant C_T such that*

$$\int_{-\infty}^{\infty} |u(t,x)|^2 \, dx + \int_0^t \int_{-\infty}^{\infty} |u_x(s,x)|^2 \, dx \, ds$$
$$\leq C_T \left(\int_{-\infty}^{\infty} |u(0,x)|^2 \, dx + \int_0^t \int_{-\infty}^{\infty} |F(s,x)|^2 \, dx \, ds \right) \tag{6.2.2}$$

for $0 \leq t \leq T$.

Note that estimate (6.2.2) is stronger than estimate (1.3.4) for hyperbolic systems, since it gives a bound on the derivative of u with respect to x in addition to a bound for u. The bound on u_x in (6.2.2) implies that the solution to the system (6.2.1) is infinitely differentiable for positive t.

Proof We prove Theorem 6.2.1 only for the case when the equation is homogeneous, that is, when $F(t,x)$ is zero. We begin by considering the Fourier transform of equation (6.2.1), which is,

$$\hat{u}_t = (-\omega^2 B + i\omega A + C)\hat{u} \tag{6.2.3}$$

For large values of $|\omega|$ the eigenvalues of the matrix

$$-\omega^2 B + i\omega A + C$$

must have real parts that are less than $-b\omega^2$ for some positive value b. Indeed,

$$-\omega^2 B + i\omega A + C = -\omega^2 \left[B - i(\omega)^{-1} A - (\omega)^{-2} C \right],$$

and because the eigenvalues of a matrix are continuous functions of the matrix, the eigenvalues of $B - i(\omega)^{-1}A - (\omega)^{-2}C$ must be close to those of B itself. Considering all values of ω we deduce that the eigenvalues have real parts bounded by $a - b\omega^2$ for some positive value of b and some value a. The solution of the differential equation (6.2.3) is given by

$$\hat{u}(t,\omega) = e^{(-\omega^2 B + i\omega A + C)t} \hat{u}_0(\omega).$$

Using results on the matrix norm (see Appendix A, Proposition A.10), we have

$$|\hat{u}(t,\omega)| \leq K e^{(a-b\omega^2)t} |\hat{u}_0(\omega)|.$$

From this we easily obtain

$$\int_{-\infty}^{\infty} |\hat{u}(t,\omega)|^2 \, d\omega \leq K_t \int_{-\infty}^{\infty} |\hat{u}_0(\omega)|^2 \, d\omega$$

and

$$\int_0^t \int_{-\infty}^{\infty} \omega^2 |\hat{u}(s,\omega)|^2 \, d\omega ds \leq K_t \int_{-\infty}^{\infty} |\hat{u}_0(\omega)|^2 \, d\omega,$$

from which (6.2.2) easily follows by Parseval's relation. ∎

Boundary Conditions for Parabolic Systems

A parabolic system such as (6.2.1) with d equations and defined on a finite interval requires d boundary conditions at each boundary. The most commonly occurring boundary conditions for parabolic systems involve both the unknown functions and their first derivatives with respect to x. The general form of such boundary conditions is

$$T_0 u = b_0$$
$$T_1 \frac{\partial u}{\partial x} + T_2 u = b_1 \tag{6.2.4}$$

where T_0 is a $d_0 \times d$ matrix and T_1 and T_2 are $(d-d_0) \times d$ matrices. We may assume that T_1 has full row rank if it is nonzero. Boundary conditions are said to be well-posed if the solution of the differential equation depends continuously on the boundary data. The theory of well-posed boundary conditions is discussed in Chapter 11. The condition for the boundary conditions to be well-posed is that the $d \times d$ matrix

$$T = \begin{bmatrix} T_0 \\ T_1 B^{-1/2} \end{bmatrix}, \tag{6.2.5}$$

consisting of the d_0 rows of T_0 and the $d - d_0$ rows of $T_1 B^{-1/2}$, is invertible. The matrix $B^{-1/2}$ is that square root of B^{-1} whose eigenvalues all have positive real part (see Appendix A). The matrix T_2 is a lower-order term and does not affect the well-posedness.

Two important boundary conditions are when T_0 is the identity matrix, which is called the Dirichlet boundary condition for the system, and when T_1 is the identity matrix with T_2 being zero, which is called the Neumann boundary condition. These are easily seen to satisfy the condition that (6.2.5) be nonsingular.

EXERCISES 6.2

1. Prove the estimate (6.2.2) for the scalar equation (6.1.1) by the energy method, i.e., multiply (6.1.1) by $u(t, x)$ and integrate by parts in t and x.

2. Prove the estimate (6.2.2) for the scalar equation (6.1.1) from the Fourier representation.

3. Modify the proof of the estimate (6.2.2) given in the text to include the case in which $F(t, x)$ is not zero.

4. Prove estimate (6.2.2) by the energy method for the system

$$\begin{pmatrix} u^1 \\ u^2 \end{pmatrix}_t = \begin{pmatrix} 1 & 4 \\ -1 & 1 \end{pmatrix} \begin{pmatrix} u^1 \\ u^2 \end{pmatrix}_{xx}.$$

6.3 Finite Difference Schemes for Parabolic Equations

In this section we begin our study of finite difference schemes for parabolic equations. The definitions of convergence, consistency, stability, and accuracy of finite difference schemes given in Sections 1.4, 1.5, and 3.1 were given in sufficient generality that they apply to schemes for parabolic equations. The methods we use to study the schemes are also much the same.

We begin by considering the forward-time central-space scheme for the heat equation (6.1.1)

$$\frac{v_m^{n+1} - v_m^n}{k} = b \frac{v_{m+1}^n - 2v_m^n + v_{m-1}^n}{h^2}, \tag{6.3.1}$$

or

$$v_m^{n+1} = (1 - 2b\mu) v_m^n + b\mu \left(v_{m+1}^n + v_{m-1}^n \right),$$

where $\mu = kh^{-2}$. The parameter μ plays a role for parabolic equations similar to the role of λ for hyperbolic equations. The scheme (6.3.1) is easily seen to be first-order accurate in time and second-order in space. The stability analysis is similar to what we did for hyperbolic equations, i.e., replace v_m^n by $g^n e^{im\theta}$. The amplification factor for the scheme (6.3.1) satisfies

$$\frac{g - 1}{k} = b \frac{e^{i\theta} - 2 + e^{-i\theta}}{h^2},$$

or

$$g = 1 + b \frac{k}{h^2} \left(e^{i\theta} + e^{-i\theta} - 2 \right),$$

and, finally,

$$g = 1 - 4b\mu \sin^2 \tfrac{1}{2}\theta.$$

Since g is a real quantity, the condition $|g| \leq 1$ is equivalent to

$$-1 \leq g \leq 1, \quad \text{or} \quad 4b\mu \sin^2 \tfrac{1}{2}\theta \leq 2,$$

which is true for all θ if and only if

$$b\mu \leq \tfrac{1}{2}. \tag{6.3.2}$$

Scheme (6.3.1) is dissipative of order 2 as long as $b\mu$ is strictly less than $\tfrac{1}{2}$ and positive.   Therefore, we usually take $b\mu < \tfrac{1}{2}$ so that the scheme will be dissipative. Dissipativity is a desirable property for schemes for parabolic equations to have, since then the finite difference solution will become smoother in time, as does the solution of the differential equation. As we will show later (e.g., Theorem 6.3.2) dissipative schemes for (6.1.1) satisfy estimates analogous to (6.2.2) and are often more accurate for nonsmooth initial data. See Section 10.4 and Exercise 6.3.10.

The stability condition (6.3.2) means the time-step k is at most $(2b)^{-1}h^2$, which means that when the spatial accuracy is increased by reducing h in half, then k, the time-step, must be reduced by one-fourth. This restriction on k can be quite severe for practical computation, and other schemes are usually more efficient. Notice that even though the scheme is accurate of order $(1,2)$, because of the stability condition the scheme (6.3.1) is second-order accurate if μ is constant.

We now list some other schemes and their properties. We will give the schemes for the inhomogeneous heat equation

$$u_t = bu_{xx} + f(t,x), \tag{6.3.3}$$

and we will assume that b is positive.

The Backward-Time Central-Space Scheme

The backward-time central-space scheme is

$$\frac{v_m^{n+1} - v_m^n}{k} = b\frac{v_{m+1}^{n+1} - 2v_m^{n+1} + v_{m-1}^{n+1}}{h^2} + f_m^n. \tag{6.3.4}$$

This scheme is implicit and unconditionally stable. It is accurate of order $(1,2)$, and is dissipative when μ is bounded away from 0.

The Crank-Nicolson Scheme

The Crank-Nicolson scheme (see [10]) is given by

$$\begin{aligned}
\frac{v_m^{n+1} - v_m^n}{k} = &\frac{1}{2}b\frac{v_{m+1}^{n+1} - 2v_m^{n+1} + v_{m-1}^{n+1}}{h^2}\\
&+ \frac{1}{2}b\frac{v_{m+1}^n - 2v_m^n + v_{m-1}^n}{h^2} + \frac{1}{2}(f_m^{n+1} + f_m^n).
\end{aligned} \tag{6.3.5}$$

The Crank-Nicolson scheme is implicit, unconditionally stable, and second-order accurate, i.e., accurate of order $(2,2)$. It is dissipative of order 2 if μ is constant, but not dissipative if λ is constant. Even though the Crank-Nicolson scheme (6.3.5) is second-order accurate, whereas the scheme (6.3.4) is only first-order accurate, with nonsmooth initial data and with λ held constant, the dissipative scheme (6.3.4) may be more accurate than the Crank-Nicolson scheme, which is not dissipative when λ is constant (also see Exercise 6.3.10). This is discussed further and illustrated in Section 10.4.

The Leapfrog Scheme

The leapfrog scheme is

$$\frac{v_m^{n+1} - v_m^{n-1}}{2k} = b\frac{v_{m+1}^n - 2v_m^n + v_{m-1}^n}{h^2} + f_m^n, \tag{6.3.6}$$

and this scheme is unstable for all values of μ.

The Du Fort–Frankel Scheme

The Du Fort–Frankel scheme may be viewed as a modification of the leapfrog scheme. It is

$$\frac{v_m^{n+1} - v_m^{n-1}}{2k} = b\frac{v_{m+1}^n - \left(v_m^{n+1} + v_m^{n-1}\right) + v_{m-1}^n}{h^2} + f_m^n. \tag{6.3.7}$$

This scheme is explicit and yet unconditionally stable. The order of accuracy is given by $O\left(h^2\right) + O\left(k^2\right) + O\left(k^{-2}h^2\right)$. The scheme is nondissipative, and this limits its usefulness.

The Du Fort–Frankel scheme is distinctive in that it is both explicit and unconditionally stable. It can be rewritten as

$$(1 + 2b\mu)\, v_m^{n+1} = 2b\mu \left(v_{m+1}^n + v_{m-1}^n\right) + (1 - 2b\mu)\, v_m^{n-1}.$$

To determine the stability we must solve for the roots of the amplification polynomial equation (see Section 4.2):

$$(1 + 2b\mu)\, g^2 - 4b\mu \cos\theta \, g - (1 - 2b\mu) = 0.$$

The two solutions of this equation are

$$g_\pm = \frac{2b\mu \cos\theta \pm \sqrt{1 - 4b^2\mu^2 \sin^2\theta}}{1 + 2b\mu}.$$

If $1 - 4b^2\mu^2 \sin^2\theta$ is nonnegative, then we have

$$|g_\pm| \le \frac{2b\mu |\cos\theta| + \sqrt{1 - 4b^2\mu^2 \sin^2\theta}}{1 + 2b\mu} \le \frac{2b\mu + 1}{1 + 2b\mu} = 1.$$

and if $1 - 4b^2\mu^2\sin^2\theta$ is negative, then

$$|g_\pm|^2 = \frac{(2b\mu\cos\theta)^2 + 4b^2\mu^2\sin^2\theta - 1}{(1+2b\mu)^2}$$

$$= \frac{4b^2\mu^2 - 1}{4b^2\mu^2 + 4b\mu + 1} < 1.$$

Thus for any value of μ or θ, we have that both g_+ and g_- are bounded by 1 in magnitude. Moreover, when g_+ and g_- are equal, they both have magnitude less than 1, and so this introduces no constraint on the stability (see Section 4.2). Thus the scheme is stable for all values of μ.

Even though the Du Fort–Frankel scheme is both explicit and unconditionally stable, it is consistent only if k/h tends to zero with h and k (see Exercise 6.3.2.). Theorem 1.6.2, which states that there are no explicit unconditionally stable schemes for hyperbolic equations, does not extend directly to parabolic equations. However, the proper analog of the results of Section 1.6 for parabolic equations is the following theorem.

Theorem 6.3.1   *An explicit, consistent scheme for the parabolic system (6.2.1) is convergent only if k/h tends to zero as k and h tend to zero.*

The proof of this theorem is similar in spirit to that of Theorem 1.6.2. It does require one result that is beyond this text: If $u(t,x)$ is a solution to (6.2.1) and u is zero for positive x when t is between 0 and 1, then u is identically zero for negative x as well (see Proposition C.4). The proof of Theorem 6.3.1 for the special case of equation (6.1.1) is left as an exercise (see Exercise 6.3.3).

Lower-Order Terms and Stability

For schemes for hyperbolic equations, we have Corollary 2.2.2 and Theorem 2.2.3 showing that lower-order terms can be ignored in determining stability. These results do not always apply directly to parabolic equations because the contribution to the amplification factor from first derivative terms are often $O\left(k^{1/2}\right)$. For example, for the forward-time central-space scheme for $u_t = bu_{xx} - au_x + cu$ we have

$$g = 1 - 4b\mu\sin^2\tfrac{1}{2}\theta - ia\lambda\sin\theta + ck.$$

For the stability analysis, the term ck can be dropped by Corollary 2.2.2. However, for the first derivative term $\lambda = k^{1/2}\mu^{1/2}$ and if μ is fixed, Corollary 2.2.2 cannot be applied. Nonetheless, we have

$$|g|^2 = \left(1 - 4b\mu\sin^2\tfrac{1}{2}\theta\right)^2 + a^2k\mu\sin^2\theta$$

and since the first derivative term gives an $O(k)$ contribution to $|g|^2$, it does not affect the stability. Similar results hold for other schemes, in particular, for the Crank-Nicolson scheme (6.3.5) and the backward-time central-space scheme (6.3.4).

Dissipativity and Smoothness of Solutions

We now show that a dissipative one-step scheme for a parabolic equation has solutions that become smoother as t increases, provided μ is constant.

Theorem 6.3.2 *A one-step scheme, consistent with (6.1.1), that is dissipative of order 2 with μ constant satisfies*

$$\|v^{n+1}\|_h^2 + ck \sum_{\nu=1}^{n} \|\delta_+ v^\nu\|_h^2 \leq \|v^0\|_h^2 \tag{6.3.8}$$

for all initial data v^0 and $n \geq 0$.

Proof Let c_0 be such that

$$|g|^2 \leq 1 - c_0 \sin^2 \tfrac{1}{2} h\xi.$$

Then by

$$\hat{v}^{\nu+1}(\xi) = g\hat{v}^\nu(\xi),$$

we have

$$|\hat{v}^{\nu+1}|^2 = |g|^2 |\hat{v}^\nu|^2 \leq |\hat{v}^\nu|^2 - c_0 \sin^2 \tfrac{1}{2} h\xi |\hat{v}^\nu|^2.$$

By adding this inequality for $\nu = 0, \ldots, n$ we obtain, using $\mu = k\,h^{-2}$,

$$|\hat{v}^{n+1}|^2 + \mu^{-1} c_0 k \sum_{\nu=0}^{n} |h^{-1} \sin \tfrac{1}{2} \xi h \hat{v}^\nu|^2 \leq |\hat{v}^0|^2.$$

Since

$$\left| \frac{2 \sin \tfrac{1}{2} h\xi}{h} \hat{v}^\nu \right| = \left| \frac{e^{ih\xi} - 1}{h} \hat{v}^\nu \right| = |\widehat{\delta_+ v^\nu}|,$$

we have

$$|\hat{v}^{n+1}|^2 + c\,k \sum_{\nu=0}^{n} |\widehat{\delta_+ v^\nu}|^2 \leq |\hat{v}^0|^2$$

and integrating over ξ, by Parseval's relation, we obtain

$$\|v^{n+1}\|_h^2 + ck \sum_{\nu=0}^{n} \|\delta_+ v^\nu\|_h^2 \leq \|v^0\|_h^2,$$

which is inequality (6.3.8). ∎

We now use Theorem 6.3.2 to show that the solutions become smoother with time, that is, that the norms of the high-order differences are bounded and in fact tend to zero at a rate that is faster than that of the norm of u. Since $|g| \leq 1$, we have

$$\|v^{\nu+1}\|_h \leq \|v^\nu\|_h.$$

In addition, since δ_+v is also a solution of the scheme, we have

$$\|\delta_+v^{\nu+1}\|_h \le \|\delta_+v^\nu\|_h.$$

Therefore, from (6.3.8)

$$\|v^{n+1}\|_h^2 + ct\|\delta_+v^n\|_h^2 \le \|v^0\|_h^2$$

which shows for $nk = t > 0$ that $\|\delta_+v^n\|_h$ is bounded. In fact, we have

$$\|\delta_+v^n\|_h^2 \le Ct^{-1}\|v^0\|_h^2,$$

which shows that the norm of the difference δ_+v^n decays to zero as t increases.

Since δ_+v^n also satisfies the difference equation, we find for $nk = t > 0$ and any integer r, that $\|\delta_+^r v^n\|_h$ is bounded. Thus the solution of the difference scheme, as is true for the solution to the differential equation, becomes smoother as t increases.

The preceding argument can be modified to show that if v_m^n converges to $u(t_n, x_m)$ with order of accuracy p, then $\delta_+^r v^n$ also converges to $\delta_+^r u(t_n, x)$ with order of accuracy p. Thus if D^r is a difference approximation to ∂_x^r with order of accuracy p, then $D^r v^n$ converges to $\partial_x^r u(t_n, \cdot)$ with order of accuracy p. These results hold if the scheme is dissipative; similar statements do not hold if the scheme is nondissipative (see Exercise 6.3.10).

Boundary Conditions for Parabolic Difference Schemes

Since a parabolic equation requires one boundary condition at each boundary point, there is less need for numerical boundary conditions for difference schemes for parabolic equations than there is for schemes for hyperbolic equations.

There is no difficulty implementing the Dirichlet boundary condition; the values of the solution are specified at the grid points at the ends of the interval.

There is more variability in implementing the Neumann boundary condition. A common method is to approximate the derivative at the endpoint by the one-sided approximation

$$\frac{\partial u}{\partial x}(t_n, x_0) \approx \frac{v_1^n - v_0^n}{h}. \tag{6.3.9}$$

This approximation is only first-order accurate and will degrade the accuracy of second-order accurate schemes, such as the Crank-Nicolson scheme (6.3.5) and the forward-time central-space scheme (6.3.1) (which is second-order accurate under the stability condition (6.3.2)). A better approximation is the second-order accurate one-sided approximation (see Exercise 3.2.10)

$$\frac{\partial u}{\partial x}(t_n, x_0) \approx \frac{-3v_0^n + 4v_1^n - v_2^n}{2h}, \tag{6.3.10}$$

which maintains the second-order accuracy of these schemes.

We can also use the second-order approximation

$$\frac{\partial u}{\partial x}(t_n, x_0) \approx \frac{v_1^n - v_{-1}^n}{2h}$$

together with the scheme applied at x_0 to eliminate the value of v_{-1}^n. As an example, this boundary condition, together with the forward-time central-space scheme (6.3.1), gives the formula

$$v_0^{n+1} = (1 - 2b\mu) v_0^n + 2b\mu v_1^n. \tag{6.3.11}$$

The overall method is then second-order accurate.

Analysis of an Explicit Scheme

The scheme

$$v_m^{n+1} = e^{-2b\mu} v_m^n + \tfrac{1}{2}(1 - e^{-2b\mu})(v_{m+1}^n + v_{m-1}^n) \tag{6.3.12}$$

is sometimes advocated as an unconditionally stable scheme for (6.1.1). This scheme has been derived in various ways. Each derivation attempts to show that this scheme has better properties than does (6.3.1). As we will show however, for this scheme to be accurate it must be less efficient than is (6.3.1). Since (6.3.1) is generally regarded as being not very efficient, due to the stability constraint on the time-step, the use of scheme (6.3.12) is rarely justified. Scheme (6.3.12) is indeed unconditionally stable, but as we will show it is not convergent unless μ tends to zero with h. Thus it is less efficient than the forward-time central-space scheme (6.3.1), and perhaps less accurate. Notice that the requirement that μ tends to zero with h is more restrictive than the requirement of Theorem 6.3.1 that λ must tend to zero with h.

To study the scheme (6.3.12) define μ' by

$$e^{-2b\mu} = 1 - 2b\mu'.$$

Then the solution v_m^n to (6.3.12) is also the solution to (6.3.1) with an effective time-step $k' = \mu' h^2$. Thus, since (6.3.1) is accurate of order $(1, 2)$, we have

$$v_m^n - u(nk', x_m) = O(k') + O(h^2).$$

The solution to (6.3.12) is convergent only if

$$v_m^n - u(nk, x_m)$$

tends to zero as h and k tend to zero. Thus to be convergent we must have

$$u(nk', x_m) - u(nk, x_m)$$

tend to zero as h and k tend to zero with nk fixed, and therefore $n(k - k')$ must tend to zero for $nk = t$ fixed. We then have

$$n(k - k') = t\left(1 - \frac{k'}{k}\right)$$

$$= t\left(1 - \frac{\mu'}{\mu}\right).$$

Thus $1 - \mu'/\mu$ must tend to zero for the scheme to be convergent. But

$$1 - \frac{\mu'}{\mu} = \frac{e^{-2b\mu} - (1 - 2b\mu)}{2b\mu} = O(b\mu)$$

as μ tends to zero. This shows that scheme (6.3.12) is convergent only if μ tends to zero with h and k. This makes this scheme less efficient than the standard forward-central scheme (6.3.1). In fact, for explicit second-order accurate schemes, the forward-central scheme is essentially optimal.

EXERCISES 6.3

1.   Justify the claims about the stability and accuracy of schemes (6.3.4), (6.3.5), and (6.3.6).

2.   Show that if $\lambda = k/h$ is a constant, then the Du Fort–Frankel scheme is consistent with

$$b\lambda^2 u_{tt} + u_t = bu_{xx} + f(t, x).$$

3. Prove Theorem 6.3.1 for the equation (6.1.1). *Hint:* If u_0 is nonnegative and not identically zero, then $u(t, x)$ will be positive for all x when t is positive.

4. Show that scheme (6.3.12) with μ held constant as h and k tends to zero is consistent with

$$u_t = b' u_{xx}$$

where b' is defined by

$$e^{-2b\mu} = 1 - 2b'\mu.$$

5.   Show that a scheme for (6.1.1) of the form

$$v_m^{n+1} = \alpha v_m^n + \frac{1 - \alpha}{2}\left(v_{m+1}^n + v_{m-1}^n\right),$$

with α constant as h and k tend to zero, is consistent with the heat equation (6.1.1) only if

$$\alpha = 1 - 2b\mu.$$

6. Consider the following two schemes for (6.1.1).

$$\tilde{v}_m^{n+1/2} = v_m^n + \tfrac{1}{2}kb\delta^2 v_m^n$$

$$v_m^{n+1} = v_m^n + kb\delta^2 \tilde{v}^{n+1/2} \tag{6.3.13}$$

$$\tilde{v}_m^{n+1} = v_m^n + kb\delta^2 v_m^n$$

$$v_m^{n+1} = v_m^n + \tfrac{1}{2}k\left(\delta^2 \tilde{v}_m^{n+1} + \delta^2 v_m^n\right) \tag{6.3.14}$$

a. Show that the two schemes are in fact two different implementations of the same scheme.

b. Show that this scheme is accurate of order $(2,2)$.

c. Show that this scheme is stable if $b\mu \le \tfrac{1}{2}$, and show that $\tfrac{1}{2} \le g \le 1$.

d. Discuss the advantages and disadvantages of this scheme compared to the forward-time central-space scheme (6.3.1).

7. Show that the scheme

$$\tilde{v}_m^{n+1/4} = v_m^n + \tfrac{1}{4}k\, b\, \delta^2 v_m^n$$

$$v_m^{n+1} = v_m^n + k\, b\, \delta^2 \tilde{v}^{n+1/4}$$

for (6.1.1) is stable for $b\mu \le 1$ and accurate of order $(1,2)$, and show that it is accurate of order 2 if μ is constant. Show also that $0 \le g \le 1$. Compare this scheme with (6.3.1) in terms of accuracy and efficiency. (Notice that this scheme requires more work per time-step than does (6.3.1) but allows for a larger time-step.)

8. Show that the scheme

$$\tilde{v}^{n+1/8} = v_m^n + \tfrac{1}{8}k\, b\, \delta^2 v_m^n$$

$$v_m^{n+1} = v_m^n + k\, b\, \delta^2 \tilde{v}_m^{n+1/8}$$

for (6.1.1) is stable for $b\mu \le 2$ and accurate of order $(1,2)$, and show that it is accurate of order 2 if μ is constant. Compare it with the scheme (6.3.1) in terms of accuracy and efficiency.

9. Consider a scheme for (6.1.1) of the form

$$v_m^{n+1} = (1 - 2\alpha_1 - 2\alpha_2)v_m^n + \alpha_1(v_{m+1}^n + v_{m-1}^n) + \alpha_2(v_{m+2}^n + v_{m-2}^n).$$

Show that when μ is constant, as k and h tend to zero, that the scheme is inconsistent unless

$$\alpha_1 + 4\alpha_2 = b\mu.$$

Show that the scheme is fourth-order accurate in x if $\alpha_2 = -\alpha_1/16$.

10. Solve the initial-boundary value problem for (6.1.1) on $-1 \leq x \leq 1$ with initial data given by

$$u_0(x) = \begin{cases} 1 & \text{if } |x| < \frac{1}{2}, \\ \frac{1}{2} & \text{if } |x| = \frac{1}{2}, \\ 0 & \text{if } |x| > \frac{1}{2}. \end{cases}$$

Solve up to $t = \frac{1}{2}$. The boundary data and the exact solution are given by

$$u(t, x) = \frac{1}{2} + 2 \sum_{\ell=0}^{\infty} (-1)^{\ell} \frac{\cos \pi (2\ell + 1) x}{\pi (2\ell + 1)} e^{-\pi^2 (2\ell+1)^2 t}.$$

Use the Crank-Nicolson scheme (6.3.5) with $h = \frac{1}{10}, \frac{1}{20}, \frac{1}{40}$. Compare the accuracy and efficiency when $\lambda = 1$ and also when $\mu = 10$.

Demonstrate by the computations that when λ is constant, the error in the solution does not decrease when measured in the supremum norm, but it does decrease in the L^2 norm.

11.   a. Show that the scheme for (6.1.1) given by

$$\left(1 - \frac{kb}{2}\delta^2\right) \left(\frac{v_m^{n+1} - v_m^n}{k}\right) = b\delta^2 v_m^n$$

is the Crank-Nicolson scheme (6.3.5).

   b. Show that the implicit scheme

$$\left(1 - \frac{kb}{2}\delta^2\right) \left(\frac{v_m^{n+1} - v_m^n}{k}\right) = b\left(1 - \frac{h^2}{12}\delta^2\right) \delta^2 v_m^n$$

is accurate of order $(2, 4)$ and stable if $b\mu \leq \frac{3}{2}$.

12.   Maximum Norm Stability   Show that the forward-time central-space scheme satisfies the estimate

$$\|v^{n+1}\|_\infty \leq \|v^n\|_\infty$$

for all solutions if and only if $2b\mu \leq 1$.

13.   Maximum Norm Stability   Show that the Crank-Nicolson scheme satisfies the estimate

$$\|v^{n+1}\|_\infty \leq \|v^n\|_\infty$$

for all solutions if $b\mu \leq 1$. *Hint:* Show that if $v_{m'}^{n+1}$ is the largest value of v_m^{n+1}, then

$$v_{m'}^{n+1} \leq -\frac{b\mu}{2} v_{m'-1}^{n+1} + (1 + b\mu) v_{m'}^{n+1} - \frac{b\mu}{2} v_{m'+1}^{n+1}$$

$$\leq \|v^n\|_\infty.$$

6.4 The Convection-Diffusion Equation

We now consider finite difference schemes for the convection-diffusion equation

$$u_t + au_x = bu_{xx}, \tag{6.4.1}$$

which is discussed briefly in Section 6.1. We begin our discussion of this equation by considering the forward-time central-space scheme,

$$\frac{v_m^{n+1} - v_m^n}{k} + a\frac{v_{m+1}^n - v_{m-1}^n}{2h} = b\frac{v_{m+1}^n - 2v_m^n + v_{m-1}^n}{h^2}. \tag{6.4.2}$$

This is obviously first-order accurate in time, second-order accurate in space, and second-order accurate overall because of the stability requirement

$$b\mu \leq \tfrac{1}{2},$$

as shown in Section 6.3. The scheme is equivalent to

$$v_m^{n+1} = (1 - 2b\mu)\, v_m^n + b\mu\, (1 - \alpha)\, v_{m+1}^n + b\mu\, (1 + \alpha)\, v_{m-1}^n, \tag{6.4.3}$$

where

$$\mu = \frac{k}{h^2} \quad \text{and} \quad \alpha = \frac{ha}{2b} = \frac{a\lambda}{2b\mu}.$$

For convenience we assume that a is positive; the case when a is negative is very similar. Of course, b must be positive.

Based on the discussion in Section 6.1, we see that one property of the parabolic differential equation (6.4.1) is that

$$\sup_x |u(t, x)| \leq \sup_x |u(t', x)| \quad \text{if} \quad t > t'.$$

That is, the maximum value of $|u(t, x)|$ will not increase as t increases. From (6.4.3) we see that the scheme will have a similar property if and only if

$$\alpha \leq 1. \tag{6.4.4}$$

That is, if this condition on α is satisfied as well as the stability condition, then from (6.4.3) we have

$$|v_m^{n+1}| \leq (1 - 2b\mu)\, |v_m^n| + b\mu(1 - \alpha)\, |v_{m+1}^n| + b\mu(1 + \alpha)\, |v_{m-1}^n|$$

$$\leq \max_m |v_m^n|,$$

and thus

$$\max_m |v_m^{n+1}| \leq \max_m |v_m^n|. \tag{6.4.5}$$

If α is larger than 1, then inequality (6.4.5) will not be satisfied in general. For example, if the initial solution is given by

$$v_m^0 = 1 \quad \text{for} \quad m \le 0 \qquad \text{and} \qquad v_m^0 = -1 \quad \text{for} \quad m > 0,$$

then the solution at the first time-step with m equal to 0 is given by

$$v_0^1 = 1 - 2b\mu(1 - \alpha) = 1 + 2b\mu(\alpha - 1).$$

We can show that for α greater than 1, the solution will be oscillatory. We now discuss the interpretation of these oscillations and what can be done to avoid them.

The condition (6.4.4) can be rewritten as

$$h \le \frac{2b}{a} . \tag{6.4.6}$$

which is a restriction on the spatial mesh spacing. The quantity a/b corresponds to the Reynolds number in fluid flow or the Peclet number in heat flow and the quantity α, or twice α, is often called the *cell Reynolds number* or *cell Peclet number* of the scheme. Condition (6.4.4) or (6.4.6) is a condition on the mesh spacing that must be satisfied in order for the solution to the scheme to behave qualitatively like that of the parabolic differential equation. Notice that it is not a stability condition, since stability only deals with the limit as h and k tend to zero, and (6.4.6) is always satisfied for h small enough. The oscillations that occur when (6.4.6) is violated are not the result of instability. They do not grow excessively; they are only the result of inadequate resolution.

One way of avoiding the restriction (6.4.6) is to use *upwind differencing* of the convection term. The scheme is then

$$\frac{v_m^{n+1} - v_m^n}{k} + a\frac{v_m^n - v_{m-1}^n}{h} = b\frac{v_{m+1}^n - 2v_m^n + v_{m-1}^n}{h^2} \tag{6.4.7}$$

or

$$v_m^{n+1} = [1 - 2b\mu(1 + \alpha)] v_m^n + b\mu v_{m+1}^n + b\mu (1 + 2\alpha) v_{m-1}^n.$$

If $1 - 2b\mu(1 + \alpha)$ is positive, this scheme satisfies (6.4.5), as may easily be seen. The oscillations have been eliminated at the expense of being only first-order accurate in space. The condition that $1 - 2b\mu (1 + \alpha)$ be nonnegative is

$$2b\mu + a\lambda \le 1.$$

When b is small and a is large, this condition is less restrictive than (6.4.4). Notice however that (6.4.7) can be rewritten as

$$\frac{v_m^{n+1} - v_m^n}{k} + a\frac{v_{m+1}^n - v_{m-1}^n}{2h} = \left(b + \frac{ah}{2}\right) \left(\frac{v_{m+1}^n - 2v_m^n + v_{m-1}^n}{h^2}\right). \tag{6.4.8}$$

Thus (6.4.7) is equivalent to solving (6.4.1) by (6.4.2) after replacing b by the larger value $b' = b(1 + \alpha)$. The term $ba\alpha u_{xx}$ can be regarded as the *artificial viscosity* that has been added to (6.4.1) to make (6.4.2) have nonoscillatory solutions.

There have been many discussions about the consequences of using an upwind scheme such as (6.4.7) instead of a scheme like (6.4.2). Many of these discussions address only imprecisely stated questions and make ambiguous conclusions. Let us restrict ourselves to an example to consider these two schemes.

Example 6.4.1 Consider (6.4.1) with $b = 0.1$, $a = 10$, and we choose a grid spacing $h = 0.04$ so that α has the value 2. Scheme (6.4.2) will have oscillations and will not be a good approximation to the true solution. Solving by scheme (6.4.7) is equivalent to solving (6.4.1) with b replaced by b', which has the value 0.3, a 200% change in the value of b. Is the solution to (6.4.7) a good approximation to the solution of (6.4.1)? If it is, then presumably replacing b by zero, only a 100% change from the true value, and using a scheme for hyperbolic equations will also give a good solution.

If α is larger than 1, then none of these schemes will give a good approximation to the solution of (6.4.1). We must then ask what we hope to learn or need to learn by solving the problem. If we need only qualitative information on the general form of the solution, then perhaps (6.4.7) is good enough. The solution of (6.4.7) will have the same qualitative properties as the solution of (6.4.1), and the solution (6.4.7) will overly smooth any gradients in the solution. In this case, however, the solution to the hyperbolic equation, obtained by setting b to 0, should also be a good approximation to the true solution. However, if we need to know precise information about the solution of (6.4.1), then neither (6.4.2) nor (6.4.7) will be adequate if α is too large. We are forced to make h smaller or to try other methods, such as perturbation methods, to extract the necessary information. A good feature of (6.4.2) is that the oscillations are an indicator of the scheme's inability to resolve the gradients in the solution. Scheme (6.4.7) has no such indicator.

There is no answer to the question of which scheme is better, but it is to be hoped that this discussion clarifies some of the questions that should be asked when solving a parabolic differential equation like (6.4.1). □

To draw reasonable conclusions from this discussion, it must be remembered that most real applications involving equations like (6.4.1) are for more complex systems than the constant coefficient equation. The conclusions we should draw are these. First, there is a grid spacing limitation. If the grid spacing is too coarse, then the scheme will not compute a qualitatively correct solution. Secondly, if we need precise information about the solution and it is not cost-effective to use a small grid spacing, then other methods should be investigated to obtain this information.

In recent years a number of methods have been advocated for increasing local grid refinement only in those places where the solution is changing rapidly. Equation (6.4.1) is often used as a test problem for such methods.

EXERCISES 6.4

1.   Show that scheme (6.4.2) satisfies the condition $|g| \leq 1$ if and only if $k \leq 2b/a^2$. Discuss this condition in relation to the condition (6.4.6).

2. Show that scheme (6.4.2) has phase speed given by

$$\tan \alpha k \xi = \frac{a\lambda \sinh \xi}{1 - 4b\mu \sin^2 \frac{1}{2} h\xi}$$

and

$$\alpha(\xi) = a \left[1 - h^2\xi^2\left(\frac{1}{6} - b\mu + \frac{a^2\lambda^2}{3}\right) + O(h\xi)^4\right].$$

3.   Consider the following scheme for equation (6.4.1), which is derived in the same way as was the Lax-Wendroff scheme of Section 3.1.

$$v_m^{n+1} = v_m^n - ka\delta_0 v_m^n + kb\delta^2 v_m^n + \frac{k^2}{2}\left(a^2\delta^2 v_m^n - 2ab\delta^2\delta_0 v_m^n + b^2\delta^4 v_m^n\right).$$

Show that this scheme is stable if $b\mu \leq \frac{1}{2}$. Also show that

$$|g|^2 \leq 1 + Kk^2$$

if $b\mu \leq \frac{1}{2}$.

4.   Consider the nonlinear equation

$$u_t + \tfrac{1}{2}(u^2)_x = bu_{xx}$$

on an interval such as $-1 \leq x \leq 1$. This equation has as a solution the function

$$u(t, x) = a - c\tanh\left[\frac{c}{2b}(x - at)\right],$$

which represents a "front" moving to the right with speed a. The front has an increase in u of $2c$ as it moves past any point, and the average value of u is a. Consider only positive values for a and c. Based on the analysis of the convection-diffusion equation, it seems likely that there will be resolution restrictions on the grid spacing, h, which place upper bounds on the quantities

$$\frac{hc}{2b} \quad \text{or} \quad \frac{ha}{2b}$$

in order to get a "qualitatively correct" solution. Notice that the maximum magnitude of the slope of the front divided by the total change in u is $c/4b$.

Using any one scheme, investigate this equation and one of these resolution conditions. Justify your conclusions with a few well chosen calculations. Fix values of a and c and vary b, or fix a and b and vary c, or fix a, b, and c and vary the grid spacing and time-step.

6.5 An Approximate Integral Method

In this section we discuss a method that is similar to finite difference methods but is arrived at by a different approach. The method has been proposed by a number of researchers and called by various names. The method has been advertised as being better than finite differences methods; however, we shall see that it is no better than the simplest finite difference methods. Nonetheless, the analysis of this method is a good illustration of the use of the methods we have been discussing.

The approximate integral method begins with formula (6.1.3) for the heat equation or a similar equation for the solution of the parabolic differential equation being solved. Formula (6.1.3) can be rewritten as

$$u(t + k, x) = \frac{1}{\sqrt{4\pi bk}} \int_{-\infty}^{\infty} e^{-(x-y)^2/4bk} u(t, y) \, dy. \tag{6.5.1}$$

which gives the solution at time $t + k$ in terms of the solution at time t. Next, consider an approximation to $u(t_n, x)$, which is a piecewise constant function of x given by

$$v(t_n, x) = v_m^n \quad \text{if} \quad |x - mh| < \tfrac{1}{2} h.$$

Replacing $u(t, x)$ by $v(t_n, x)$ in (6.5.1), we obtain

$$v_m^{n+1} = \sum_{\ell=-\infty}^{\infty} \frac{1}{\sqrt{4\pi bk}} \int_{x_\ell - h/2}^{x_\ell + h/2} e^{-(mh-y)^2/4bk} \, dy \, v_\ell^n. \tag{6.5.2}$$

The integral terms in the sum can be evaluated as

$$\frac{1}{\sqrt{4\pi bk}} \int_{(\ell-1/2)h}^{(\ell+1/2)h} e^{-(mh-y)^2/4bk} \, dy = \frac{1}{\sqrt{4\pi bk}} \int_{(\ell-m-1/2)h}^{(\ell-m+1/2)h} e^{-z^2/4bk} \, dz$$

$$= \frac{1}{\sqrt{\pi}} \int_{(\ell-m-1/2)/\sqrt{4b\mu}}^{(\ell-m+1/2)/\sqrt{4b\mu}} e^{-\eta^2} \, d\eta$$

$$= \frac{1}{2} \left(\text{erf}\left(\frac{\ell-m+1/2}{2\sqrt{b\mu}} \right) - \text{erf}\left(\frac{\ell-m-1/2}{2\sqrt{b\mu}} \right) \right)$$

$$= K_{\ell-m} = K_{m-\ell},$$

where $\text{erf}(\cdot)$ is the error function.

We can then rewrite (6.5.2) as

$$v_m^{n+1} = \sum_{\ell=-\infty}^{\infty} K_{m-\ell} \, v_\ell^n. \tag{6.5.3}$$

We now consider the error that has been introduced by replacing (6.5.1) by (6.5.3). The use of the piecewise constant approximation is $O(h)$, but coupled with the integration it is $O\left(h^2\right)$. Alternatively, (6.5.3) can be regarded as a weighted rectangle rule, which is second-order accurate, as is the usual rectangle rule. Since the error in one step of the method is $O\left(h^2\right)$, the global error for the method is $O\left(k^{-1}h^2\right)$ or $O\left(\mu^{-1}\right)$.

Because each of the coefficients K_j is positive, the method is easily seen to be unconditionally stable. At this point, then, we see that μ should be taken as large as possible for best accuracy.

But to use this method, the formula (6.5.3) must be truncated; that is, we use

$$
v_m^{n+1} = \sum_{\ell=m-p}^{m+p} K_{m-\ell}\, v_\ell^n
$$

$$
= \sum_{j=-p}^{p} K_j v_{m-j}^n .
$$

(6.5.4)

The index p should be chosen so that K_p is quite small. We have

$$
K_p = \frac{1}{2}\left[\operatorname{erf}\left(\frac{p+\frac{1}{2}}{2\sqrt{b\mu}}\right) - \operatorname{erf}\left(\frac{p-\frac{1}{2}}{2\sqrt{b\mu}}\right)\right]
$$

$$
\approx \frac{1}{2}\frac{d}{dx}\operatorname{erf}\left(\frac{x}{2\sqrt{b\mu}}\right)\Big|_{x=p}
$$

$$
= \frac{1}{\sqrt{4\pi b\mu}}e^{-p^2/4b\mu} .
$$

For a fixed value of p, the value of K_p will be small if $\mu \le C_0 p^2$, where C_0 is some constant that determines the meaning of small. But this restriction on μ is of the same form as other explicit schemes. On the other hand, the accuracy is $O\left(\mu^{-1}\right)$ or $O\left(p^{-2}\right)$.

If we use this method, then μ must not be made too small or the approximation error in (6.5.3) will be large, nor can μ be too large or the truncation error, due to the choice of p, will be large. An additional complication is that as p increases, the treatment of the equations at the boundaries involves more work. In numerical tests, the method performed quite poorly in terms of accuracy and efficiency, in fact, worse than any finite difference scheme that was tested.

EXERCISE 6.5

1.   What is the effect of using a method like Simpson's rule in place of the rectangle rule?

Chapter 7

Systems of Partial Differential Equations in Higher Dimensions

In this chapter we show how to extend the results of the previous chapters to systems of equations and to equations and systems in two and three spatial dimensions. The concepts of convergence, consistency, and stability carry over without change, as does the definition of order of accuracy; the main change has to do with the increase in complexity of the schemes, especially for implicit schemes for systems of equations. There are many schemes for multidimensional systems that arise from various applications, such as aircraft flow analysis in aeronautical engineering, numerical weather prediction in meteorology, and oil reservoir simulation in geology. We are not able to present particular schemes for these applications, but the ideas that we introduce are useful in each of these areas.

We begin by discussing stability for systems of equations, both for hyperbolic and parabolic systems, and then discuss equations and systems in two and three dimensions. In Section 7.3 we introduce the alternating direction implicit method, which is among the most useful of the methods for multidimensional problems.

7.1 Stability of Finite Difference Schemes for Systems of Equations

We have discussed the one-way wave equation (1.1.1) and the heat equation (6.1.1) quite extensively, and we now show how much of what we had to say carries over to systems of the form

$$u_t + Au_x = 0 \tag{7.1.1}$$

and

$$u_t = Bu_{xx}. \tag{7.1.2}$$

where u is a vector of functions of dimension d and A and B are $d \times d$ matrices. For system (7.1.1) to be hyperbolic the matrix A must be diagonalizable with real eigenvalues (see Section 1.1), and for (7.1.2) to be parabolic all the eigenvalues of the matrix B must have positive real part (see Section 6.2). Almost all of what we have done for scalar equations extends readily to systems

135

of equations. For example, the derivations of the Lax-Wendroff scheme for the one-way wave equation and the Crank-Nicolson schemes for both the one-way wave equation and the heat equation require no change when applied to systems other than replacing a with A or b with B, respectively. The main difference is in the test for stability.

In testing the stability of one-step schemes for systems we obtain not a scalar amplification factor, but an amplification matrix G. The amplification matrix is obtained by making the substitution of $G^n e^{im\theta}$ for v_m^n. The condition for stability is that for each $T > 0$, there is a constant C_T such that for $0 \le nk \le T$, we have

$$\|G^n\| \le C_T. \tag{7.1.3}$$

One great simplification to help analyze (7.1.3) for hyperbolic systems occurs when the scheme has G as a polynomial or rational function of the matrix A (e.g., the Lax-Wendroff or Crank-Nicolson schemes). Then the same matrix that diagonalizes matrix A in (7.1.1) diagonalizes G, and the stability of the scheme depends only on the stability of the scalar equations

$$w_t + a_i w_x = 0 \tag{7.1.4}$$

where a_i is an eigenvalue of A. For the Lax-Wendroff scheme, the stability condition for (7.1.1) is $|a_i \lambda| \le 1$ for $i = 1, \ldots, d$.

Similar methods can be applied to parabolic systems, especially for dissipative schemes with μ constant. The matrix that transforms the matrix B to upper triangular form can also be used to convert G to upper triangular form. The methods of Chapter 9 can be used to obtain estimates of the powers of G.

For each of these cases, if $G = U \tilde{G} U^{-1}$, then $G^n = U \tilde{G}^n U^{-1}$ and so

$$\|G^n\| \le \|U\| \|U^{-1}\| \|\tilde{G}^n\|.$$

This implies that estimate (7.1.3) will be satisfied for G if a similar estimate holds for $\tilde{G}$.

For general schemes the situation is not as nice. A necessary condition for stability is

$$|g_\nu| \le 1 + Kk \tag{7.1.5}$$

for each eigenvalue g_ν of G, but this is not sufficient in general.

Example 7.1.1 A somewhat artificial example in which the condition (7.1.5) is not sufficient for stability is obtained by considering the system

$$u_t^1 = 0$$

$$u_t^2 = 0$$

with the first-order accurate scheme

$$v_m^{1\,n+1} = v_m^{1\,n} - c(v_{m+1}^{2\,n} - 2v_m^{2\,n} + v_{m-1}^{2\,n})$$

$$v_m^{2\,n+1} = v_m^{2\,n}.$$

The amplification matrix is

$$G = \begin{pmatrix} 1 & 4c\sin^2 \frac{1}{2}\theta \\ 0 & 1 \end{pmatrix}$$

and so

$$G^n = \begin{pmatrix} 1 & 4nc\sin^2 \frac{1}{2}\theta \\ 0 & 1 \end{pmatrix}.$$

Since $\|G^n\|$ for θ equal to π is unbounded, we conclude that this scheme is unstable. $\square$

As for single equations, it can be shown that lower-order terms do not affect the stability of systems. This is proved in Exercise 7.1.5.

Multistep Schemes as Systems

We can analyze the stability of multistep schemes by converting them to the form of a system. For example, a scheme that can be transformed to the form

$$\hat{v}^{n+1}(\xi) = \sum_{\nu=0}^{K} a_\nu(\xi)\hat{v}^{n-\nu}(\xi)$$

can be written as

$$\hat{V}^{n+1}(\xi) = G(h\xi)\hat{V}^n(\xi)$$

where $\hat{V}^n(\xi)$ is the column vector $\left(\hat{v}^n(\xi), \hat{v}^{n-1}(\xi), \ldots, \hat{v}^{n-K}(\xi)\right)^T$. The matrix $G(h\xi)$ is the companion matrix of the polynomial with coefficients $-a_\nu(\xi)$, given by

$$G(h\xi) = \begin{pmatrix} a_0 & a_1 & \cdots & a_{K-1} & a_K \\ I & 0 & \cdots & 0 & 0 \\ 0 & I & \cdots & 0 & 0 \\ \vdots & \vdots & \ddots & \vdots & \vdots \\ 0 & 0 & \cdots & I & 0 \end{pmatrix}.$$

To determine stability of scalar finite difference schemes, the methods of Section 4.3 are usually easier to apply than the verification of estimate (7.1.3). For multistep schemes applied to systems, there is no good analogue of the theory of Schur polynomials, and so the conversion to a system is often the best way to analyze the stability of schemes.

EXERCISES 7.1

1. Prove that condition (7.1.5) is a necessary condition for stability of a system.

2.   Prove that a scheme for a parabolic system is stable if the amplification matrix G is upper triangular and is dissipative of order 2. That is, there are constants c and C such that for μ constant

$$|g_{ii}(\theta)| \le 1 - c \sin^2 \tfrac{1}{2}\theta$$

and moreover, for $j > i$,

$$|g_{ij}(\theta)| \le C \sin^2 \tfrac{1}{2}\theta,$$

and $g_{ij}(\theta) = 0$ for $j < i$. You may wish to use techniques from Sections 6.3 and 9.2.

3.   Analyze the stability of the leapfrog scheme (1.3.4) as a system. Show that this analysis gives the same conclusion as obtained in Section 4.1.

4.   Show that the Lax-Friedrichs scheme applied to the system

$$\begin{pmatrix} u \\ v \end{pmatrix}_t + \begin{pmatrix} 1 & 1 \\ 0 & 1 \end{pmatrix} \begin{pmatrix} u \\ v \end{pmatrix}_x = 0$$

is unstable. The scheme is the same as (1.3.5) with the matrix $\begin{pmatrix} 1 & 1 \\ 0 & 1 \end{pmatrix}$ replacing a. (This equation is a weakly hyperbolic system; see Section 9.2.)

5.   Use the matrix factorization (A.7) of Appendix A to prove the extension of Corollary 2.2.2 to systems of equations. Let G be the amplification factor of a stable scheme, with $\|G^n\| \le C_T$ for $0 \le nk \le T$. Also, let $\tilde{G}$ be the amplification factor of a scheme with $\|G - \tilde{G}\| \le c_0 k$. Assuming that $\|\tilde{G}\| \le c_1$ with $c_1 \ge 1$, use (A.7) to establish by induction that

$$\|\tilde{G}^n\| \le C_T (1 + kc_0 c_1)^n.$$

7.2 Finite Difference Schemes in Two and Three Dimensions

In this section we consider finite difference schemes in two and three spatial dimensions. The basic definitions of convergence, consistency, and stability given in Sections 1.4 and 1.5 readily extend to two and three dimensions. One difficulty associated with schemes in more than one dimension is that the von Neumann stability analysis can become quite formidable, as we illustrate in the next two examples.

Example 7.2.1 We begin by considering the standard leapfrog scheme for the system

$$u_t + Au_x + Bu_y = 0, \tag{7.2.1}$$

where A and B are $d \times d$ matrices. The scheme may be written

$$\frac{v_{\ell,m}^{n+1} - v_{\ell,m}^{n-1}}{2k} + A\delta_{0x}v_{\ell,m}^n + B\delta_{0y}v_{\ell,m}^n = 0. \tag{7.2.2}$$

The Fourier transform of the solution, $\hat{v}^n(\xi) = \hat{v}^n(\xi_1, \xi_2)$, satisfies the recursion relation

$$\hat{v}^{n+1}(\xi) + 2i(\lambda_1 A \sin h\xi_1 + \lambda_2 B \sin h\xi_2)\hat{v}^n(\xi) - \hat{v}^{n-1}(\xi) = 0 \tag{7.2.3}$$

where $\lambda_1 = k/h_1$ and $\lambda_2 = k/h_2$.

The stability of this scheme can be analyzed using the methods introduced in the previous section. The scheme can be written as a one-step scheme and the condition (7.1.3) has to be checked. However, it is difficult to obtain reasonable conditions without making some assumptions about the matrices A and B.

The most common assumption is that A and B are *simultaneously diagonalizable*. This means that there exists a matrix P such that both PAP^{-1} and PBP^{-1} are diagonal matrices. If we set $w = P\hat{v}$, then relation (7.2.3) can be reduced to the form

$$w_\nu^{n+1}(\xi) + 2i(\lambda_1\alpha_\nu \sin\theta_1 + \lambda_2\beta_\nu \sin\theta_2)w_\nu^n(\xi) - w_\nu^{n-1}(\xi) = 0 \tag{7.2.4}$$

for $\nu = 1, ..., d$, where α_ν and β_ν are the νth entries in PAP^{-1} and PBP^{-1}, respectively. Analyzing scheme (7.2.4) is similar to the analysis done on the one-dimensional scalar leapfrog scheme in Section 4.1. We conclude that scheme (7.2.2) is stable if and only if

$$\lambda_1|\alpha_\nu| + \lambda_2|\beta_\nu| < 1$$

for all values of ν. $\square$

Example 7.2.2 A modification of the leapfrog scheme (7.2.2) allowing larger time-steps has been given by Abarbanel and Gottlieb [1]. The scheme is

$$\frac{v_{\ell,m}^{n+1} - v_{\ell,m}^{n-1}}{2k} + A\delta_{0x}\left(\frac{v_{\ell,m+1}^n + v_{\ell,m-1}^n)}{2}\right) + B\delta_{0y}\left(\frac{v_{\ell+1,m}^n + v_{\ell-1,m}^n)}{2}\right) = 0. \tag{7.2.5}$$

Assuming that A and B are simultaneously diagonalizable, the stability analysis leads easily to the condition that

$$|\lambda_1\alpha_\nu \sin\theta_1 \cos\theta_2 + \lambda_2\beta_\nu \sin\theta_2 \cos\theta_1| < 1$$

must hold for all values of θ_1, θ_2, and ν. We have, using the Cauchy-Schwarz inequality,

$$|\lambda_1 \alpha_\nu \sin \theta_1 \cos \theta_2 + \lambda_2 \beta_\nu \sin \theta_2 \cos \theta_1|$$

$$\leq \max\{\lambda_1 |\alpha_\nu|, \lambda_2 |\beta_\nu|\}(|\sin \theta_1||\cos \theta_2| + |\sin \theta_2||\cos \theta_1|)$$

$$\leq \max\{\lambda_1 |\alpha_\nu|, \lambda_2 |\beta_\nu|\}(\sin^2 \theta_1 + \cos^2 \theta_1)^{1/2}(\cos^2 \theta_2 + \sin^2 \theta_2)^{1/2}$$

$$= \max\{\lambda_1 |\alpha_\nu|, \lambda_2 |\beta_\nu|\}.$$

Thus we see that the two conditions $\lambda_1 |\alpha_\nu| < 1$ and $\lambda_2 |\beta_\nu| < 1$ for all values of ν are sufficient for stability, and it is easy to see, by taking appropriate choices of θ_1 and θ_2, that these conditions are also necessary. Thus the modified scheme (7.2.5) allows for a much larger time-step than does the standard leapfrog (7.2.2). The extra computation per time-step required by (7.2.5) is more than offset by the larger time-step making it more efficient than the standard scheme (7.2.2) (see [1]). □

Time Split Schemes

Time splitting is a general method for reducing multidimensional problems to a sequence of one-dimensional problems (see e.g., Yanenko [60]). Consider an equation of the form

$$u_t + A_1 u + A_2 u = 0 \tag{7.2.6}$$

where A_1 and A_2 are linear operators, such as $A_1 = A \partial/\partial x$ and $A_2 = B \partial/\partial y$. The operators A_1 and A_2 need not be associated with a particular dimension, but this is the most usual case. To advance the solution of (7.2.6) from a time t_0 to the time $t_0 + k$, we approximate (7.2.6) with the equations

$$u_t + 2A_1 u = 0 \quad \text{for } t_0 \leq t \leq t_0 + \tfrac{1}{2}k \tag{7.2.7a}$$

and

$$u_t + 2A_2 u = 0 \quad \text{for } t_0 + \tfrac{1}{2}k \leq t \leq t_0 + k. \tag{7.2.7b}$$

That is, each of the operators acts with twice its usual effect for half of the time.

We can then use one-step finite difference schemes to approximate (7.2.7a) and (7.2.7b). If we use second-order accurate schemes to approximate both (7.2.7a) and (7.2.7b), then the overall scheme will be second-order accurate only if the order of the splitting is reversed on alternate time-steps (see Gottlieb [22] and Strang [46]).

Stability for time split schemes does not necessarily follow from the stability of each of the steps unless the amplification factors commute with each other.

A significant difficulty associated with time split schemes is in determining the appropriate boundary conditions for each of the steps. Improper boundary conditions can seriously degrade the accuracy of the solution. A method for deriving boundary conditions for time split schemes has been given by LeVeque and Oliger [32].

Example 7.2.3 A time split scheme popular in computational fluid dynamics is the time split MacCormack scheme [33]; see also Exercise 3.1.1. For system (7.2.1) with $\Delta x = \Delta y = h$, the forward-backward MacCormack scheme is

$$\tilde{v}_{\ell,m}^{n+1/2} = v_{\ell,m}^n - A\lambda(v_{\ell+1,m}^n - v_{\ell,m}^n)$$

$$v_{\ell,m}^{n+1/2} = \tfrac{1}{2}[v_{\ell,m}^n + \tilde{v}_{\ell,m}^{n+1/2} - A\lambda(\tilde{v}_{\ell,m}^{n+1/2} - \tilde{v}_{\ell-1,m}^{n+1/2})]$$

$$\tilde{v}_{\ell,m}^{n+1} = v_{\ell,m}^{n+1/2} - B\lambda(v_{\ell,m+1}^{n+1/2} - v_{\ell,m}^{n+1/2})$$

$$v_{\ell,m}^{n+1} = \tfrac{1}{2}[v_{\ell,m}^{n+1/2} + \tilde{v}_{\ell,m}^{n+1} - B\lambda(\tilde{v}_{\ell,m}^{n+1} - \tilde{v}_{\ell,m-1}^{n+1})].$$

An advantage of this scheme is that each of the four stages is very easy to program, making it suitable for use on high speed vector or parallel processors.

□

EXERCISES 7.2

1. Show that the scheme

$$\frac{v_{\ell,m}^{n+1} - \tfrac{1}{4}(v_{\ell+1,m}^n + v_{\ell-1,m}^n + v_{\ell,m+1}^n + v_{\ell,m-1}^n)}{k} + a\delta_{0x}v_{\ell,m}^n + b\delta_{0y}v_{\ell,m}^n = 0$$

for the equation $u_t + au_x + bu_y = 0$, with $\Delta x = \Delta y = h$, is stable if and only if $(|a|^2 + |b|^2)\lambda^2 \le 1/2$.

2. Show that the scheme

$$\frac{v_{\ell,m}^{n+1} - \tfrac{1}{4}(v_{\ell+1,m+1}^n + v_{\ell-1,m+1}^n + v_{\ell+1,m-1}^n + v_{\ell-1,m-1}^n)}{k} + a\delta_{0x}v_{\ell,m}^n + b\delta_{0y}v_{\ell,m}^n = 0$$

for the equation $u_t + au_x + bu_y = 0$, with $\Delta x = \Delta y = h$, is stable if and only if $(|a| + |b|)\lambda \le 1$.

3. Show that the two-dimensional Du Fort–Frankel scheme for the equation $u_t = b(u_{xx} + u_{yy}) + f$ given by

$$\frac{v_{\ell,m}^{n+1} - v_{\ell,m}^{n-1}}{2k} = b\frac{v_{\ell+1,m}^n + v_{\ell-1,m}^n + v_{\ell,m+1}^n + v_{\ell,m-1}^n - 2\left(v_{\ell,m}^{n+1} + v_{\ell,m}^{n-1}\right)}{h^2} + f_m^n,$$

where $\Delta x = \Delta y = h$, is unconditionally stable.

4. Show that the scheme given by the two-step algorithm

$$\tilde{v}_{\ell+1/2,m+1/2}^{n+1/2} = \frac{1}{4}\left(v_{\ell+1,m+1}^n + v_{\ell,m+1}^n + v_{\ell+1,m}^n + v_{\ell,m}^n\right)$$

$$-\frac{a\lambda}{4}\left(v_{\ell+1,m+1}^n + v_{\ell+1,m}^n - v_{\ell,m+1}^n - v_{\ell,m}^n\right)$$

$$-\frac{b\lambda}{4}\left(v_{\ell+1,m+1}^n + v_{\ell,m+1}^n - v_{\ell+1,m}^n - v_{\ell,m}^n\right)$$

$$v_{\ell,m}^{n+1} = v_{\ell,m}^{n} - \frac{a\lambda}{2}\left(\tilde{v}_{\ell+1/2,m+1/2}^{n+1/2} + \tilde{v}_{\ell+1/2,m-1/2}^{n+1/2} - \tilde{v}_{\ell-1/2,m+1/2}^{n+1/2} - \tilde{v}_{\ell-1/2,m-1/2}^{n+1/2}\right)$$

$$- \frac{b\lambda}{2}\left(\tilde{v}_{\ell+1/2,m+1/2}^{n+1/2} + \tilde{v}_{\ell-1/2,m+1/2}^{n+1/2} - \tilde{v}_{\ell+1/2,m-1/2}^{n+1/2} - \tilde{v}_{\ell-1/2,m-1/2}^{n+1/2}\right)$$

for the equation $u_t + au_x + bu_y = 0$, with $\Delta x = \Delta y = h$, is second-order accurate and stable if and only if $(|a|^2 + |b|^2)\lambda^2 \le 1$.

5. Prove that if the two steps of a time split scheme have amplification factors which commute with each other, then the time split scheme is stable if each step is stable.

7.3 The Alternating Direction Implicit (ADI) Method

In this section we examine a very powerful method that is especially useful for solving parabolic equations on rectangular domains. It is also useful for equations of other types and on more general domains, although it can then become quite complex. This method is called the *alternating direction implicit,* or ADI, method. We discuss the derivation of the name and show that the method can be applied quite generally.

We begin by defining a parabolic equation in two spatial dimensions. The general definition is given in Section 9.2. The equation in two spatial variables

$$u_t = b_{11}u_{xx} + 2b_{12}u_{xy} + b_{22}u_{yy} \tag{7.3.1}$$

is parabolic if

$$b_{11}, b_{22} > 0 \quad \text{and} \quad b_{12}^2 < b_{11}b_{22}.$$

The most common example is the two-dimensional heat equation

$$u_t = b(u_{xx} + u_{yy}),$$

which governs heat flow in two dimensions. Parabolic equations arise in many other two- and three-dimensional problems, including the study of flows in porous media and modeling of economic processes. We introduce the ADI method using the two-dimensional heat equation as our primary example.

The ADI Method on a Square

Consider

$$u_t = b_1 u_{xx} + b_2 u_{yy} \tag{7.3.2}$$

on a square. Note that there is no term with a mixed derivative, i.e., there is no u_{xy} term. The ADI method applies most simply to parabolic equations of the form (7.3.2). Later in this section we consider how to modify the basic method in order to include the mixed derivative terms.

If we were to use a scheme similar to the Crank-Nicolson scheme for (7.3.2), with discretization of both spatial derivatives, the scheme would be unconditionally stable, but the matrix to be inverted at each time-step would be much more difficult to invert than were the tridiagonal matrices encountered in one-dimensional problems. The ADI method, which we now derive, is a way of reducing two-dimensional problems to a succession of many one-dimensional problems.

Let A_1 and A_2 be linear operators, which can be quite general, but for convenience think of

$$A_1 u = b_1 u_{xx}$$

$$A_2 u = b_2 u_{yy}.$$

In general we assume that we have convenient methods to solve the equations

$$w_t = A_1 w$$

and

$$w_t = A_2 w$$

by the Crank-Nicolson scheme or a similar scheme. The ADI method gives us a way to use these schemes to solve the combined equation

$$u_t = A_1 u + A_2 u \tag{7.3.3}$$

using the methods for the simpler "one-dimensional" problems.

We begin by using the same idea as used in the Crank-Nicolson scheme, that of centering the difference scheme about $t = \left(n + \frac{1}{2}\right) k$. By the Taylor series, (7.3.3) becomes

$$\frac{u^{n+1} - u^n}{k} = \frac{1}{2} \left(A_1 u^{n+1} + A_1 u^n\right) + \frac{1}{2} \left(A_2 u^{n+1} + A_2 u^n\right) + O\left(k^2\right)$$

or

$$\left(I - \frac{k}{2} A_1 - \frac{k}{2} A_2\right) u^{n+1} = \left(I + \frac{k}{2} A_1 + \frac{k}{2} A_2\right) u^n + O\left(k^3\right). \tag{7.3.4}$$

As noted before, if we discretize the operators A_1 and A_2 with respect to the spatial variable at this stage, then the matrix corresponding to the left-hand side will be difficult to invert. We now note the formula

$$(1 \pm a_1)(1 \pm a_2) = 1 \pm a_1 \pm a_2 + a_1 a_2$$

and, based on this, add $k^2 A_1 A_2 u^{n+1}/4$ to both sides of equation (7.3.4) and then write it as

$$\left(I - \frac{k}{2} A_1 - \frac{k}{2} A_2 + \frac{k^2}{4} A_1 A_2\right) u^{n+1} = \left(I + \frac{k}{2} A_1 + \frac{k}{2} A_2 + \frac{k^2}{4} A_1 A_2\right) u^n$$

$$+ \frac{k^2}{4} A_1 A_2 \left(u^{n+1} - u^n\right) + O\left(k^3\right), \tag{7.3.5}$$

which can be factored as

$$\left(I - \frac{k}{2}A_1\right)\left(I - \frac{k}{2}A_2\right)u^{n+1} = \left(I + \frac{k}{2}A_1\right)\left(I + \frac{k}{2}A_2\right)u^n$$

$$+ \frac{k^2}{4}A_1 A_2 \left(u^{n+1} - u^n\right) + O\left(k^3\right).$$

Consider first the second term on the right-hand side. We have

$$u^{n+1} = u^n + O(k)$$

so with the k^2 factor this second term is $O(k^3)$, which is the same order as the errors already introduced. So we have

$$\left(I - \frac{k}{2}A_1\right)\left(I - \frac{k}{2}A_2\right)u^{n+1} = \left(I + \frac{k}{2}A_1\right)\left(I + \frac{k}{2}A_2\right)u^n + O\left(k^3\right). \quad (7.3.6)$$

If we discretize this equation, then we have a more convenient method. In the case that $A_1 = b_1 u_{xx}$ and $A_2 = b_2 u_{yy}$, the matrices corresponding to $I - \frac{k}{2}A_i$ will be tridiagonal and can be solved conveniently with the Thomas algorithm; see Section 3.4. Let A_{1h} and A_{2h} be second-order approximations to A_1 and A_2, respectively. We obtain

$$\left(I - \frac{k}{2}A_{1h}\right)\left(I - \frac{k}{2}A_{2h}\right)u^{n+1} = \left(I + \frac{k}{2}A_{1h}\right)\left(I + \frac{k}{2}A_{2h}\right)u^n$$

$$+ O\left(k^3\right) + O\left(kh^2\right)$$

or

$$\left(I - \frac{k}{2}A_{1h}\right)\left(I - \frac{k}{2}A_{2h}\right)v^{n+1} = \left(I + \frac{k}{2}A_{1h}\right)\left(I + \frac{k}{2}A_{2h}\right)v^n. \quad (7.3.7)$$

The Peaceman-Rachford Algorithm

To solve (7.3.7) Peaceman and Rachford [41] used

$$\left(I - \frac{k}{2}A_{1h}\right)\tilde{v}^{n+1/2} = \left(I + \frac{k}{2}A_{2h}\right)v^n \quad (7.3.8a)$$

$$\left(I - \frac{k}{2}A_{2h}\right)v^{n+1} = \left(I + \frac{k}{2}A_{1h}\right)\tilde{v}^{n+1/2}. \quad (7.3.8b)$$

Formulas (7.3.8) shows the origin of the name *alternating direction implicit method*. The two steps alternate which direction is implicit and which is explicit. More generally the term ADI applies to any method that involves the reduction of the problem to one-dimensional implicit problems by factoring the scheme.

We now show that formulas (7.3.8) are equivalent to formula (7.3.7). If we start with equation (7.3.8b), operate with $\left(I - \frac{k}{2}A_{1h}\right)$, and then use (7.3.8a), we obtain

$$\left(I - \frac{k}{2}A_{1h}\right)\left(I - \frac{k}{2}A_{2h}\right)v^{n+1} = \left(I - \frac{k}{2}A_{1h}\right)\left(I + \frac{k}{2}A_{1h}\right)\tilde{v}^{n+1/2}$$

$$= \left(I + \frac{k}{2}A_{1h}\right)\left(I - \frac{k}{2}A_{1h}\right)\tilde{v}^{n+1/2} = \left(I + \frac{k}{2}A_{1h}\right)\left(I + \frac{k}{2}A_{2h}\right)v^{n}.$$

Notice that the equivalence of (7.3.8) to (7.3.7) does not require that the operators A_{1h} and A_{2h} commute with each other. Some ADI methods similar to (7.3.8) require that some of the operators commute with each other; see Exercise 7.3.14.

The D'Yakonov scheme for (7.3.7) is

$$\left(I - \frac{k}{2}A_{1h}\right)\bar{v}^{n+1/2} = \left(I + \frac{k}{2}A_{1h}\right)\left(I + \frac{k}{2}A_{2h}\right)v^{n}$$

$$\left(I - \frac{k}{2}A_{2h}\right)v^{n+1} = \bar{v}^{n+1/2}.$$

(7.3.9)

The variables $\tilde{v}^{n+1/2}$ in (7.3.8) and $\bar{v}^{n+1/2}$ in (7.3.9) should be thought of as intermediate or temporary variables in the calculation and not as approximations to $u(t, x)$ at any time t. By consistency such variables in ADI methods are usually first-order approximations to the solution, but this is of little significance.

The Douglas-Rachford Method

Other ADI schemes can be derived starting with other basic schemes. Starting with the backward-time central-space scheme for (7.3.3), we have

$$(I - kA_1 - kA_2)u^{n+1} = u^n + O\left(k^2\right)$$

or

$$\left(I - kA_1 - kA_2 + k^2 A_1 A_2\right)u^{n+1} = u^n + k^2 A_1 A_2 u^n + k^2 A_1 A_2\left(u^{n+1} - u^n\right)$$

$$+ O\left(k^2\right),$$

which gives the scheme

$$(I - kA_{1h})(I - kA_{2h})v^{n+1} = \left(I + k^2 A_{1h} A_{2h}\right)v^n.$$

The Douglas-Rachford method [11] for this scheme is

$$(I - kA_{1h})\tilde{v}^{n+1/2} = (I + kA_{2h})v^n$$

$$(I - kA_{2h})v^{n+1} = \tilde{v}^{n+1/2} - kA_{2h}v^n.$$

(7.3.10)

If the operators A_i are approximated to second-order accuracy, the scheme is accurate of first-order in time and second-order in space.

Boundary Conditions for ADI Schemes

ADI schemes require values of the intermediate values on the boundary. If we consider the case of Dirichlet boundary conditions, i.e., $u(t, x, y)$ specified on the boundary, then values of $\tilde{v}^{n+1/2}$ on the boundaries are obtained by using the two steps of the scheme with v^n and v^{n+1} specified to obtain $\tilde{v}^{n+1/2}$.

For example, consider the Peaceman-Rachford method with

$$A_1 = b_1 \frac{\partial^2}{\partial x^2}, \qquad A_2 = b_2 \frac{\partial^2}{\partial y^2},$$

and $u = \beta(t, x, y)$ on the boundary of the unit square. For step (7.3.8a), $\tilde{v}^{n+1/2}$ is needed at $x = 0$ and $x = 1$. By adding the two parts of (7.3.8), we have

$$\tilde{v}^{n+1/2} = \frac{1}{2}\left(I + \frac{k}{2}A_{2h}\right)\beta^n + \frac{1}{2}\left(I - \frac{k}{2}A_{2h}\right)\beta^{n+1}, \tag{7.3.11}$$

which can be used to compute $\tilde{v}^{n+1/2}$ along the boundaries at $x = 0$ and $x = 1$. Thus $\tilde{v}^{n+1/2}$ is determined where needed.

For the Douglas-Rachford method, the second equation gives

$$\tilde{v}^{n+1/2} = (I - kA_{2h})\beta^{n+1} + kA_{2h}\beta^n.$$

Note again that $\tilde{v}^{n+1/2}$ need not be a good approximation to the solution at the intermediate time level with $t = \left(n + \frac{1}{2}\right)k$.

The boundary condition

$$\tilde{v}^{n+1/2}_{\ell,m} = \beta^{n+1/2}_{\ell,m} = \beta(t_{n+1/2}, x_\ell, y_m) \tag{7.3.12}$$

is very easy to implement but is only first-order accurate. If this condition is used with the Peaceman-Rachford method or similar second-order methods, the overall accuracy will be only first order.

Stability for ADI Methods

The Peaceman-Rachford and Douglas-Rachford methods are unconditionally stable, as is easily seen by von Neumann analysis for two dimensions. As an example we show the stability of the Douglas-Rachford method applied to the two-dimensional heat equation (7.3.2).

Replacing $v^n_{\ell,m}$ by $g^n e^{i\ell\theta}e^{im\phi}$ and $\tilde{v}^{n+1/2}_{\ell,m}$ by $\tilde{g}g^n e^{i\ell\theta}e^{im\phi}$, we obtain

$$\left(1 + 4b_1\mu_1 \sin^2 \tfrac{1}{2}\theta\right)\tilde{g} = 1 - 4b_2\mu_2 \sin^2 \tfrac{1}{2}\phi$$

$$\left(1 + 4b_2\mu_2 \sin^2 \tfrac{1}{2}\phi\right)g = \tilde{g} + 4b_2\mu_2 \sin^2 \tfrac{1}{2}\phi.$$

Thus

$$g = \frac{1 + 16b_1b_2\mu_1\mu_2 \sin^2 \tfrac{1}{2}\theta \sin^2 \tfrac{1}{2}\phi}{(1 + 4b_1\mu_1 \sin^2 \tfrac{1}{2}\theta)(1 + 4b_2\mu_2 \sin^2 \tfrac{1}{2}\phi)} \leq 1.$$

Implementing ADI Methods

To implement ADI methods on a rectangular domain, we begin with a grid consisting of points (x_ℓ, y_m), given by $x_\ell = \ell \Delta x$ and $y_m = m \Delta y$ for $\ell = 0, \ldots, L$, and $m = 0, \ldots, M$, respectively. We illustrate the implementation using the Peaceman-Rachford algorithm (7.3.8). The numerical method is most conveniently programmed using two two-dimensional arrays, one for the values of v and one for $\tilde{v}$. (It is possible to program the method using only one two-dimensional array and several one-dimensional arrays, but it requires very careful programming, and we do not discuss this implementation.) In addition to these two two-dimensional arrays, two one-dimensional arrays are needed to store the variables p and q used in the Thomas algorithm as given in Section 3.4.

As formulas (7.3.8) show, the computation of v^{n+1} from v^n involves two distinct stages: the first to compute $\tilde{v}$ from v and the second to compute v from $\tilde{v}$. We have dropped the superscripts on $\tilde{v}$ and v, since in the programming of the method there is no index corresponding to n on these arrays.

The difference equations for $\tilde{v}$ corresponding to (7.3.8a) are

$$
\begin{aligned}
&-\frac{b_1 \mu_1}{2} \tilde{v}_{\ell-1,m} + (1 + b_1 \mu_1) \tilde{v}_{\ell,m} - \frac{b_1 \mu_1}{2} \tilde{v}_{\ell+1,m} \\
&= \frac{b_2 \mu_2}{2} v_{\ell,m-1} + (1 - b_2 \mu_2) v_{\ell,m} + \frac{b_2 \mu_2}{2} v_{\ell,m+1}
\end{aligned}
\tag{7.3.13}
$$

for $\ell = 1, \ldots, L-1$ and for $m = 1, \ldots, M-1$.

This system of equations consists of $M-1$ tridiagonal systems of equations, one for each value of m. For each value of m, the Thomas algorithm can be used to solve for the values of $\tilde{v}_{\ell,m}$. The standard way to implement the method uses a loop on the m, and within each loop the Thomas algorithm is used to solve for the values of $\tilde{v}_{\ell,m}$, for $\ell = 0, \ldots, L$. The boundary values of $\tilde{v}$ are given by (7.3.11), or in this specific case,

$$
\begin{aligned}
\tilde{v}_{0,m} =\ & \frac{b_2 \mu_2}{4} \beta_{0,m-1}^n + \frac{1 - b_2 \mu_2}{2} \beta_{0,m}^n + \frac{b_2 \mu_2}{4} \beta_{0,m+1}^n \\
&-\frac{b_2 \mu_2}{4} \beta_{0,m-1}^{n+1} + \frac{1 + b_2 \mu_2}{2} \beta_{0,m}^{n+1} - \frac{b_2 \mu_2}{4} \beta_{0,m+1}^{n+1},
\end{aligned}
\tag{7.3.14}
$$

and similarly for $\tilde{v}_{L,m}$. Notice that this formula gives $\tilde{v}_{0,m}$ only for values of m from 1 to $M-1$. These boundary conditions and the equations (7.3.13) completely determine $\tilde{v}_{\ell,m}$ for $\ell = 0, \ldots, L$ and $m = 1, \ldots, M-1$. Values of $\tilde{v}_{\ell,0}$ and $\tilde{v}_{L,m}$ are not determined by these formulas, and, as we shall see, these values are not needed at all.

Having computed $\tilde{v}$, the second stage of the computation uses (7.3.8b); the difference equations are

$$
-\frac{b_2\mu_2}{2}v_{\ell,m-1} + (1 + b_2\mu_2)v_{\ell,m} - \frac{b_2\mu_2}{2}v_{\ell,m+1}
$$

$$
= \frac{b_1\mu_1}{2}\tilde{v}_{\ell-1,m} + (1 - b_1\mu_1)\tilde{v}_{\ell,m} + \frac{b_1\mu_1}{2}\tilde{v}_{\ell+1,m} \qquad (7.3.15)
$$

for $\ell = 1, \ldots, L-1$ and for $m = 1, \ldots, M-1$.

Similar to (7.3.13) this is a system of $L-1$ tridiagonal systems of equations, one tridiagonal system for each value of ℓ. The boundary conditions for v are the specification of the exact values of the solution at time level $n+1$, that is, for $t = (n+1)k$. Again, the standard implementation uses a loop on ℓ, within which the Thomas algorithm is used to solve for the values of $v_{\ell,m}$ for $m = 0, \ldots, M$.

It is important to notice that in equation (7.3.15) the required values of $\tilde{v}$ are precisely the values computed by (7.3.13). In particular, there is no need to assign values to $\tilde{v}_{\ell,0}$ or $\tilde{v}_{\ell,M}$ for any values of ℓ. It is also important to realize that the boundary values $v_{0,m}$ and $v_{L,m}$ are not needed in the solution of (7.3.15), but these values must be updated as part of the solution process.

A useful suggestion for implementing ADI methods is first to use the very simple boundary condition (7.3.12) rather than more complex formulas such as (7.3.13). After the program is found to be free of programming errors, then more complex and more accurate boundary conditions such as (7.3.13) can be implemented.

The Mitchell-Fairweather Scheme

The Mitchell-Fairweather scheme [36] is an ADI scheme for (7.3.2) that is second-order accurate in time and fourth-order accurate in space. The fourth-order accurate formula (3.2.7),

$$
\left(1 + \frac{h^2}{12}\delta^2\right)^{-1}\delta^2 u = \frac{d^2 u}{dx^2} + O\left(h^4\right), \qquad (7.3.16)
$$

is used rather than the second-order approximation. We consider (7.3.6)

$$
\left(I - \frac{k}{2}A_1\right)\left(I - \frac{k}{2}A_2\right)u^{n+1} = \left(I + \frac{k}{2}A_1\right)\left(I + \frac{k}{2}A_2\right)u^n + O\left(k^3\right),
$$

where A_1 and A_2 are the second derivative operators; then we multiply both sides by

$$
\left(1 + \frac{h^2}{12}\delta_x^2\right)\left(1 + \frac{h^2}{12}\delta_y^2\right)
$$

and replace

$$
\left(1 + \frac{h^2}{12}\delta_x^2\right)\frac{\partial^2}{\partial x^2}
$$

by $\delta_x^2 + O\left(h^4\right)$. Similar changes are made for the derivatives with respect to y. The result is

$$\left(1 + \frac{h^2}{12}\delta_x^2 - \frac{k}{2}b_1\,\delta_x^2\right)\left(1 + \frac{h^2}{12}\delta_y^2 - \frac{k}{2}b_2\,\delta_y^2\right)u^{n+1}$$

$$= \left(1 + \frac{h^2}{12}\delta_x^2 + \frac{k}{2}b_1\,\delta_x^2\right)\left(1 + \frac{h^2}{12}\delta_y^2 + \frac{k}{2}b_2\,\delta_y^2\right)u^n + O\left(k^3\right) + O\left(kh^4\right).$$

We obtain the Mitchell-Fairweather scheme, which is similar to the Peaceman-Rachford scheme:

$$\left[1 - \frac{1}{2}\left(b_1\mu_1 - \frac{1}{6}\right)h_1^2\,\delta_x^2\right]v^{n+1/2} = \left[1 + \frac{1}{2}\left(b_2\mu_2 + \frac{1}{6}\right)h_2^2\,\delta_y^2\right]v^n$$

$$\left[1 - \frac{1}{2}\left(b_2\mu_2 - \frac{1}{6}\right)h_2^2\,\delta_y^2\right]v^{n+1} = \left[1 + \frac{1}{2}\left(b_1\mu_1 + \frac{1}{6}\right)h_1^2\,\delta_x^2\right]v^{n+1/2}$$

$$(7.3.17)$$

This scheme is second-order in time and fourth-order in space and is not much more work than the Peaceman-Rachford method.

As an example, suppose the Peaceman-Rachford scheme is used with grid spacings h_1 and k_1 and the Mitchell-Fairweather scheme is used with grid spacings h_2 and k_2. The amount of work for the schemes is proportional to $k_1^{-1}h_1^{-2}$ and $k_2^{-1}h_2^{-2}$, respectively, whereas the accuracy is $O(k_1^2) + O(h_1^2)$ for the Peaceman-Rachford scheme and $O(k_2^2)+O(h_2^4)$ for the Mitchell-Fairweather scheme. It is usually not difficult to choose the grid parameters so that the Mitchell-Fairweather scheme requires less work and gives more accuracy than the Peaceman-Rachford method (see Exercises 7.3.8, 7.3.10, and 7.3.12).

Boundary conditions for the Mitchell-Fairweather scheme are obtained as for the other ADI schemes. We can eliminate the terms with $\delta_x^2 v^{n+1/2}$ from (7.3.17) by multiplying the first equation by $b_1\mu_1+\frac{1}{6}$ and the second by $b_1\mu_1-\frac{1}{6}$, and then eliminating the terms containing $\delta_x^2 v^{n+1/2}$. In this way we obtain for Dirichlet boundary conditions the following condition for $v^{n+1/2}$.

$$v^{n+1/2} = \frac{1}{2b_1\mu_1}\left\{\left(b_1\mu_1 + \frac{1}{6}\right)\left[1 + \frac{1}{2}(b_2\mu_2 + \frac{1}{6})h_2^2\delta_y^2\right]\beta^n\right.$$

$$\left.+ \left(b_1\mu_1 - \frac{1}{6}\right)\left[1 - \frac{1}{2}(b_2\mu_2 - \frac{1}{6})h_2^2\delta_y^2\right]\beta^{n+1}\right\}$$

$$(7.3.18)$$

ADI with Mixed Derivative Terms

The ADI methods that have been discussed for equation (7.3.2) can be extended to include the general equation (7.3.1), with the mixed derivative term as well.

We confine our discussion to the Peaceman-Rachford method for simplicity. One scheme that can be used is

$$\left(1 - \frac{k}{2}b_{11}\delta_x^2\right)v^{n+1/2} = \left(1 + \frac{k}{2}b_{22}\delta_y^2\right)v^n \qquad + kb_{12}\delta_{0x}\delta_{0y}v^n$$

$$\left(1 - \frac{k}{2}b_{22}\delta_y^2\right)v^{n+1} = \left(1 + \frac{k}{2}b_{11}\delta_x^2\right)v^{n+1/2} + kb_{12}\delta_{0x}\delta_{0y}v^{n+1/2},$$

(7.3.19)

which is only first-order accurate in time. Beam and Warming [4] have shown that no ADI scheme involving only time levels n and $n+1$, such as (7.3.19), can be second-order accurate unless b_{12} is zero. A simple modification to (7.3.19) that is second-order accurate in time is

$$\left(1 - \frac{k}{2}b_{11}\delta_x^2\right)v^{n+1/2} = \left(1 + \frac{k}{2}b_{22}\delta_y^2\right)v^n \qquad + kb_{12}\delta_{0x}\delta_{0y}\tilde{v}^{n+1/2}$$

$$\left(1 - \frac{k}{2}b_{22}\delta_y^2\right)v^{n+1} = \left(1 + \frac{k}{2}b_{11}\delta_x^2\right)v^{n+1/2} + kb_{12}\delta_{0x}\delta_{0y}\tilde{v}^{n+1/2}$$

(7.3.20)

where

$$\tilde{v}^{n+1/2} = \tfrac{3}{2}v^n - \tfrac{1}{2}v^{n-1}.$$

This scheme requires extra storage to compute $\tilde{v}^{n+1/2}$, but it is relatively easy to implement.

The boundary condition

$$v^{n+1/2} = \frac{1}{2}\left(1 + \frac{k}{2}b_{22}\delta_y^2\right)\beta^n + \frac{1}{2}\left(1 - \frac{k}{2}b_{22}\delta_y^2\right)\beta^{n+1},\qquad(7.3.21)$$

can be used with this scheme without loss of the second-order accuracy (see Exercise 7.3.13). Notice that this is essentially the same formula as (7.3.11).

EXERCISES 7.3

1. Show that the inhomogeneous equation

$$u_t = A_1 u + A_2 u + f$$

corresponding to equation (7.3.3) can be approximated to second-order accuracy by

$$\left(I - \frac{k}{2}A_{1h}\right)\tilde{v}^{n+1/2} = \left(I + \frac{k}{2}A_{2h}\right)v^n \qquad + \frac{k}{2}f^{n+1/2}$$

$$\left(I - \frac{k}{2}A_{2h}\right)v^{n+1} = \left(I + \frac{k}{2}A_{1h}\right)\tilde{v}^{n+1/2} + \frac{k}{2}f^{n+1/2},$$

where A_{1h} and A_{2h} are as in scheme (7.3.7). Also show that the scheme

$$\left(I - \frac{k}{2}A_{1h}\right)\tilde{v}^{n+1/2} = \left(I + \frac{k}{2}A_{2h}\right)v^n \quad + \frac{k}{2}f^n$$

$$\left(I - \frac{k}{2}A_{2h}\right)v^{n+1} = \left(I + \frac{k}{2}A_{1h}\right)\tilde{v}^{n+1/2} + \frac{k}{2}f^{n+1}$$

is second-order accurate.

2. Consider the system in one space dimension

$$\begin{pmatrix} u^1 \\ u^2 \end{pmatrix}_t = \begin{pmatrix} 1 & 0 \\ 0 & 1 \end{pmatrix}\begin{pmatrix} u^1 \\ u^2 \end{pmatrix}_{xx} + \begin{pmatrix} 0 & -4 \\ 4 & 0 \end{pmatrix}\begin{pmatrix} u^1 \\ u^2 \end{pmatrix}.$$

Discuss the efficiency of the ADI method using

$$A_1 = \begin{pmatrix} 1 & 0 \\ 0 & 1 \end{pmatrix}\frac{\partial^2}{\partial x^2} \quad \text{and} \quad A_2 = \begin{pmatrix} 0 & -4 \\ 4 & 0 \end{pmatrix}$$

compared with using a Crank-Nicolson scheme with a block tridiagonal system. Solve this system using one of these methods on the interval $-1 \le x \le 1$ for $0 \le t \le 1$ with the exact solution

$$u^1 = e^{3t}\sin x \cosh 2x$$

$$u^2 = e^{3t}\cos x \sinh 2x$$

with Dirichlet boundary conditions at $x = -1$ and $x = 1$.

3. Apply the Peaceman-Rachford method to the hyperbolic equation

$$u_t + u_x + 2u_y = 0$$

on the square $-1 \le x \le 1$, $-1 \le y \le 1$ for $0 \le t \le 1$. Specify the exact solution along the sides with $y = 0$ and $x = 0$. Apply the extrapolation conditions $v^{n+1}_{L,m} = v^n_{L-1,m}$ and $v^{n+1}_{\ell,M} = v^n_{\ell,M-1}$ along the sides $x_L = 1$ and $y_M = 1$, respectively. Use the exact solution

$$u(t, x, y) = u_0(x - t, y - 2t)$$

with

$$u_0(x, y) = \begin{cases} (1 - 2|x|)(1 - 2|y|) & \text{if } |x| \le \frac{1}{2} \text{ and } |y| \le \frac{1}{2}, \\ 0 & \text{otherwise} \end{cases}$$

for initial and boundary data.

4. Show that scheme (7.3.20) for the parabolic equation (7.3.1) with the mixed derivative terms is second-order accurate and unconditionally stable. *Hint:* It may be simpler to use the methods of Section 4.3 rather than to solve explicitly for the two roots of the amplification polynomial.

5. Show that (7.3.10) is equivalent to the formula preceding it.

6. Derive boundary condition (7.3.18) for the Mitchell-Fairweather scheme.

7. Use the Peaceman-Rachford ADI method to solve

$$u_t = 2u_{xx} + u_{yy}$$

on the unit square for $0 \le t \le 1$. The initial and boundary data should be taken from the exact solution

$$u = \exp(1.68t) \sin[1.2(x - y)] \cosh(x + 2y).$$

Use $\Delta x = \Delta y = \Delta t = \frac{1}{10}, \frac{1}{20}$, and $\frac{1}{40}$. Demonstrate the second-order accuracy.

8. Solve the same problem as in Exercise 7 but by the Mitchell-Fairweather ADI method. Use $\Delta x = \Delta y = \frac{1}{10}$ and $\Delta t = \frac{1}{30}$. Compare this case with the use of the Peaceman-Rachford method with $\Delta x = \Delta y = \Delta t = \frac{1}{20}$.

9. Use the Peaceman-Rachford ADI method to solve

$$u_t = u_{xx} + 2u_{yy}$$

on the unit square for $0 \le t \le 1$. The initial and boundary data should be taken from the exact solution

$$u = \exp(1.5t) \sin(x - 0.5y) \cosh(x + y)$$

Use $\Delta x = \Delta y = \Delta t = \frac{1}{10}, \frac{1}{20}$, and $\frac{1}{40}$. Demonstrate the second-order accuracy.

10. Solve the same problem as in Exercise 9 but by the Mitchell-Fairweather ADI method. Use $\Delta x = \Delta y = \frac{1}{10}$ and $\Delta t = \frac{1}{30}$. Compare this case with the use of the Peaceman-Rachford method with $\Delta x = \Delta y = \Delta t = \frac{1}{20}$.

11. Use the Peaceman-Rachford ADI method to solve

$$u_t = u_{xx} + 2u_{yy}$$

on the unit square for $0 \le t \le 1$. Take initial and boundary data from the exact solution

$$u = \exp(0.75t) \sin(2x - y) \cosh[1.5(x + y)].$$

Use $\Delta x = \Delta y = \Delta t = \frac{1}{10}, \frac{1}{20}$, and $\frac{1}{40}$. Demonstrate the second-order accuracy.

12. Solve the same problem as in Exercise 11, but by the Mitchell-Fairweather ADI method. Use $\Delta x = \Delta y = \frac{1}{10}$ and $\Delta t = \frac{1}{30}$. Compare this case with the use of the Peaceman-Rachford method with $\Delta x = \Delta y = \Delta t = \frac{1}{20}$.

13. Use the scheme (7.3.20) with boundary conditions (7.3.21) to compute an approximation to the parabolic equation (7.3.1), with the mixed derivative term. Let the coefficients have the values $b_{11} = 1$, $b_{12} = 0.5$, and $b_{22} = 1$ on the square $-1 \leq x \leq 1$, $-1 \leq y \leq 1$, for $0 \leq t \leq 1$. Use the exact solution

$$e^{2t} \sin(x + y) \cosh(x + y)$$

with Dirichlet boundary conditions.

14. Show that the three-dimensional ADI method for

$$u_t = A_1 u + A_2 u + A_3 u$$

given by

$$\left(I - \frac{k}{2} A_{1h} \right) \tilde{v}^{n+1/3} = \left(I + \frac{k}{2} A_{3h} \right) v^n \tag{7.3.22a}$$

$$\left(I - \frac{k}{2} A_{2h} \right) \tilde{v}^{n+2/3} = \left(I + \frac{k}{2} A_{2h} \right) \tilde{v}^{n+1/3} \tag{7.3.22b}$$

$$\left(I - \frac{k}{2} A_{3h} \right) v^{n+1} = \left(I + \frac{k}{2} A_{1h} \right) \tilde{v}^{n+2/3}. \tag{7.3.22c}$$

is equivalent to

$$\left(I - \frac{k}{2} A_{1h} \right) \left(I - \frac{k}{2} A_{2h} \right) \left(I - \frac{k}{2} A_{3h} \right) v^{n+1}$$

$$= \left(I + \frac{k}{2} A_{1h} \right) \left(I + \frac{k}{2} A_{2h} \right) \left(I + \frac{k}{2} A_{3h} \right) v^n,$$

only if the operators A_{1h} and A_{2h} commute.

Chapter 8

Second-Order Equations

In this chapter we study partial differential equations that are of second-order in the time derivatives and show that the methods introduced in previous chapters can easily be applied to the equations treated here. As will be seen, no significantly new ideas are needed here.

8.1 Second-Order Time-Dependent Equations

We begin with the second-order wave equation in one space dimension, which is

$$u_{tt} - a^2 u_{xx} = 0 \tag{8.1.1}$$

where a is a nonnegative real number. Equations such as (8.1.1), which are second-order in time, require two functions for initial data, typically these are $u(0, x)$ and $u_t(0, x)$. If

$$u(0, x) = u_0(x) \quad \text{and} \quad u_t(0, x) = u_1(x), \tag{8.1.2}$$

then the exact solution of (8.1.1) may be written as

$$u(t, x) = \frac{1}{2}\left[u_0(x - at) + u_0(x + at)\right] + \frac{1}{2a}\int_{x-at}^{x+at} u_1(y)\, dy. \tag{8.1.3}$$

This formula shows that there are two characteristic speeds, a and $-a$, associated with equation (8.1.1). In terms of the Fourier transform the solution may be written as

$$\hat{u}(t, \omega) = \hat{u}_0(\omega)\cos a\omega t + \hat{u}_1(\omega)\frac{\sin a\omega t}{a\omega}$$
$$= \hat{u}_+(\omega)e^{ia\omega t} + \hat{u}_-(\omega)e^{-ia\omega t}, \tag{8.1.4}$$

or

$$u(t, x) = \frac{1}{\sqrt{2\pi}}\int_{-\infty}^{\infty} e^{ix\omega}\left[\hat{u}_0(\omega)\cos a\omega t + \hat{u}_1(\omega)\frac{\sin a\omega t}{a\omega}\right] d\omega$$
$$= \frac{1}{\sqrt{2\pi}}\int_{-\infty}^{\infty} \hat{u}_+(\omega)e^{i\omega(x+at)} + \hat{u}_-(\omega)e^{i\omega(x-at)}\, d\omega \tag{8.1.5}$$
$$= u_+(x + at) + u_-(x - at).$$

154

These formulas for the solution show that in general the solution of the wave equation (8.1.1) consists of two waves, one moving to the left and one moving to the right.

It is appropriate at this point to discuss the origin of the names *hyperbolic* and *parabolic* as applied to the systems treated in Chapters 1 and 6. The second-order equation (8.1.1) was originally called hyperbolic because of the similarity of its symbol to the equation of a hyperbola. If we set $\omega = i\eta$, the symbol of (8.1.1) is $s^2 - a^2\eta^2$, and the equations

$$s^2 - a^2\eta^2 = \text{constant}$$

are hyperbolas in the (s, η) plane. Similarly, the symbol of the heat equation (6.1.1) is $s - b\eta^2$, and this is related to the equation of a parabola. The symbols of second-order elliptic equations are likewise related to equations of ellipses. Even though these names are based only on this formal similarity, they have persisted.

As mathematicians studied other equations and systems of equations they extended the names to cover those systems that shared certain important features with the original hyperbolic, parabolic, and elliptic equations. The essential feature of a hyperbolic system is that the solution propagates with certain finite speeds. For a parabolic equation the essential feature is that the solution becomes smoother than its initial data. The essential feature of elliptic systems, which we discuss in Chapter 12, is that the solution is more differentiable than the data.

The general second-order hyperbolic equation in one space dimension is

$$u_{tt} + 2bu_{tx} = a^2 u_{xx} + cu_x + du_t + eu + f(t, x) \tag{8.1.6}$$

where $b^2 < a^2$. The initial value problem for (8.1.6) is well-posed in the sense that for $0 \le t \le T$ there is a constant C_T such that

$$\int_{-\infty}^{\infty} |u_t(t, x)|^2 + |u_x(t, x)|^2 + |u(t, x)|^2 \, dx \tag{8.1.7}$$

$$\le C_T \left[\int_{-\infty}^{\infty} |u_t(0, x)|^2 + |u_x(0, x)|^2 + |u(0, x)|^2 \, dx + \int_0^t \int_{-\infty}^{\infty} |f(\tau, x)|^2 \, dx d\tau \right].$$

The estimate (8.1.7) can be established either by use of the Fourier transform or the energy method (see Exercises 8.1.3 and 8.1.4).

The Euler-Bernoulli Equation

The second-order equation

$$u_{tt} = -b^2 u_{xxxx} \tag{8.1.8}$$

is called the Euler-Bernoulli beam equation. It models the vertical motion of a thin, horizontal beam with small displacements from rest. Using the Fourier transform we easily obtain the solution in either of the two forms

$$u(t,x) = \frac{1}{\sqrt{2\pi}} \int_{-\infty}^{\infty} e^{i\omega x} \left[\hat{u}_0(\omega) \cos b\omega^2 t + \hat{u}_1(\omega) \frac{\sin b\omega^2 t}{b\omega^2} \right] d\omega$$

$$= \frac{1}{\sqrt{2\pi}} \int_{-\infty}^{\infty} e^{i\omega(x+b\omega t)} \hat{u}_+(\omega) + e^{i\omega(x-b\omega t)} \hat{u}_-(\omega)\, d\omega,$$

(8.1.9)

where u_0 and u_1 are the initial data as given by (8.1.2). From the second of these formulas we see that the frequency ω propagates with speeds $\pm b\omega$. Because the speed of propagation depends on the frequency, the equation is said to be *dispersive*. The idea of dispersion was applied in Section 5.2 to finite difference schemes for hyperbolic systems, but it is applicable to study any wave phenomena. From (8.1.9) we see that the phase velocity is $b\omega$ or $-b\omega$, and the group velocity is twice the phase velocity.

The Euler-Bernoulli equation is neither hyperbolic nor parabolic. As (8.1.9) shows, the solution does not become smoother as t increases, as do solutions of parabolic equations, nor does it have a finite speed of propagation, as do the solutions of hyperbolic equations.

Another equation that models the motion of a beam is the Rayleigh equation

$$u_{tt} - c^2 u_{ttxx} = -b^2 u_{xxxx}.$$

(8.1.10)

From the formula

$$\hat{u}_{tt}(t,\omega) = -\frac{b^2\omega^4}{1+c^2\omega^2} \hat{u}(t,\omega)$$

(8.1.11)

we see that for small ω the solution to (8.1.10) behaves in a similar manner as the solution of the Euler-Bernoulli equation (8.1.8), and for large ω the solution to (8.1.10) behaves like the solution of the wave equation (8.1.1) with speed b/c. In particular, both the phase velocity and group velocity are bounded.

EXERCISES 8.1

1.   Write (8.1.1) as a first-order hyperbolic system with the two variables $u^1 = u_x$ and $u^2 = u_t$. Compare the solution of this system as given by the formulas of Chapter 1 with the formulas (8.1.3) and (8.1.4).

2. Find an explicit relationship between the pair of functions u_0 and u_1 in the formula (8.1.3) and the pair of functions u_+ and u_- in formula (8.1.5). *Hint:* Use the antiderivative of u_1.

3. Prove (8.1.7) using Fourier transform methods.

4.   Prove (8.1.7) by multiplying (8.1.6) by $u(t,x)$ and integrating by parts. This method is often called the energy method.

5. Show that the initial value problem for the two-dimensional wave equation $u_{tt} = u_{xx} + u_{yy}$ is well-posed.

6. Show that the Euler-Bernoulli equation (8.1.8) satisfies

$$\int_{-\infty}^{\infty} u_t(t,x)^2 + b^2 u_{xx}(t,x)^2 dx = \int_{-\infty}^{\infty} u_t(0,x)^2 + b^2 u_{xx}(0,x)^2 \, dx$$

by the energy method and by utilizing the Fourier transform.

7. Show that the initial value problem for the Rayleigh equation (8.1.10) is well-posed.

8. The Schrödinger equation is $u_t = ibu_{xx}$. Show that the real and imaginary parts of the solution the Schrödinger equation each satisfy the Euler-Bernoulli equation.

9. Show that the solution to the initial value problem

$$u_{tt} + 2b\, u_{tx} = a^2 u_{xx} - cu \qquad (8.1.12)$$

with $0 \le b < a$, $0 < c$, and initial data (8.1.2) is given by

$$u(t,x) = \frac{1}{2}\left(1 + \frac{b}{\sqrt{a^2+b^2}}\right) u_0(x + a_+t) + \frac{1}{2}\left(1 - \frac{b}{\sqrt{a^2+b^2}}\right) u_0(x - a_-t)$$

$$-\frac{\tilde{c}}{4} \int_{x-a_-t}^{x+a_+t} \frac{J_1\left(\tilde{c}[a^2t^2 + 2bt(x-y) - (x-y)^2]^{1/2}\right)}{[a^2t^2 + 2bt(x-y) - (x-y)^2]^{1/2}} \times$$

$$[(a^2 + 2b^2)t - b(x-y)]u_0(y)\,dy$$

$$+ \frac{1}{2\sqrt{a^2+b^2}} \int_{x-a_-t}^{x+a_+t} J_0\left(\tilde{c}[a^2t^2 + 2bt(x-y) - (x-y)^2]^{1/2}\right) u_1(y)\,dy$$

where $\tilde{c}$ is $\sqrt{c/(a^2+b^2)}$ and a_+ and $-a_-$ are the roots of $\eta^2 + 2b\eta - a^2 = 0$ with $-a_- \le a_+$. The functions $J_0(\xi)$ and $J_1(\xi)$ are the Bessel functions of order 0 and 1, respectively. They satisfy the system of ordinary differential equations

$$J_0'(\xi) = -J_1(\xi)$$

$$J_1'(\xi) = J_0(\xi) - \xi^{-1}J_1(\xi)$$

with $J_0(0) = 1$ and $J_1(0) = 0$. *Hint:* Let $K(u_1)$ be the last integral in the above expression. Show that $K(u_1)$ is a solution. Then show that the general solution is

$$\frac{\partial K(u_0)}{\partial t} + 2b\frac{\partial K(u_0)}{\partial x} + K(u_1).$$

10.   Show that the solution to the initial value problem

$$u_{tt} + 2b\, u_{tx} = a^2 u_{xx} + cu \tag{8.1.13}$$

with $0 \le b < a$, $0 < c$, and initial data (8.1.2) is given by

$$u(t,x) = \frac{1}{2}\left(1 + \frac{b}{\sqrt{a^2 + b^2}}\right) u_0(x + a_+ t) + \frac{1}{2}\left(1 - \frac{b}{\sqrt{a^2 + b^2}}\right) u_0(x - a_- t)$$

$$-\frac{\tilde{c}}{4}\int_{x-a_-t}^{x+a_+t} \frac{I_1\left(\tilde{c}\big[a^2 t^2 + 2bt(x-y) - (x-y)^2\big]^{1/2}\right)}{[a^2 t^2 + 2bt(x-y) - (x-y)^2]^{1/2}} \times$$

$$[(a^2 + 2b^2)t - b(x-y)]u_0(y)\,dy$$

$$+\frac{1}{2\sqrt{a^2 + b^2}}\int_{x-a_-t}^{x+a_+t} I_0\left(\tilde{c}\big[a^2 t^2 + 2bt(x-y) - (x-y)^2\big]^{1/2}\right) u_1(y)\,dy$$

where $\tilde{c}$ is $\sqrt{c/(a^2 + b^2)}$ and a_+ and $-a_-$ are the roots of $\eta^2 + 2b\eta - a^2 = 0$ with $-a_- \le a_+$. The functions $I_0(\xi)$ and $I_1(\xi)$ are the modified Bessel functions of the first kind of order 0 and 1, respectively. They satisfy the system of ordinary differential equations

$$I_0'(\xi) = I_1(\xi) \quad \text{and} \quad I_1'(\xi) = I_0(\xi) - \xi^{-1}I_1(\xi)$$

with $I_0(0) = 1$ and $I_1(0) = 0$.

11.   Show that the general second-order hyperbolic equation (8.1.6) can be reduced to either of the equations (8.1.12) or (8.1.13) by setting

$$u(t,x) = e^{at}e^{\beta x}v(t,x)$$

when the parameters α and β are chosen suitably.

8.2 Finite Difference Schemes for Second-Order Equations

The definitions of convergence, consistency, and order of accuracy for finite difference schemes as given in Chapters 1 and 3 hold without modification for second-order equations. The stability definition, however, must be altered slightly. In place of Definition 1.5.1 we require the following definition.

Definition 8.2.1   *A finite difference scheme* $P_{k,h}v_m^n = 0$ *for an equation that is second-order in* t *is stable in a stability region* Λ *if there is an integer* J *such that for any positive time* T, *there is a constant* C_T *such that*

$$h\sum_{m=-\infty}^{\infty} |v_m^n|^2 \le (1 + n^2)\, C_T h \sum_{j=0}^{J} \sum_{m=-\infty}^{\infty} |v_m^j|^2 \tag{8.2.1}$$

for $0 \le nk \le T$ *with* $(k,h) \in \Lambda$.

The extra factor of $(1 + n^2)$ in (8.2.1) is the only change required by the second-order equation and reflects the linear growth in t allowed by these equations. In the von Neumann analysis of schemes for second-order equations, Definition 8.2.1 requires that the amplification factors g_ν (there will always be at least two) satisfy

$$|g_\nu| \leq 1 + Kk$$

and permits two such amplification factors to coalesce near the unit circle. If there are no lower-order terms then the stability condition is $|g_\nu| \leq 1$ with double roots on the unit circle permitted. The integer J in Definition 8.2.1 must always be at most 1, since data must always be given at two time levels for second-order equations.

The necessity of including the factor of $1 + n^2$ in the estimate (8.2.1) can be seen by considering the function $u(t,x) = t$, which is a solution of the equations (8.1.1), (8.1.8), (8.1.10) and all other second-order equations without lower-order terms. Most schemes for these equations will compute this solution exactly, i.e., $v_m^n = nk$. This is represented by the amplification factor $g_0(\xi)$ at ξ equal to 0, which is a double root. That is,

$$v_m^n = 0 \cdot g_0(0)^n + nkg_0(0)^{n-1}.$$

From this we observe that without the factor of $1 + n^2$ in the estimate (8.2.1), all consistent schemes for a second-order equations would be "unstable." (The fact that the function $u(t,x)$, which is everywhere equal to t, is not in $L^2(R)$ as a function of x is not important to the argument. One can approximate $u(t,x)$ by functions that are in $L^2(R)$ as functions of x, and the argument will proceed to the same conclusion.) This point about the factor of $1 + n^2$ is not made by Richtmyer and Morton [44]. They reduce all second-order equations to first-order equations and use the definition corresponding to (1.3.3). The Lax-Richtmyer equivalence theorem for second-order equations can be proved using the methods of Section 10.7.

The first scheme we consider is the standard second-order accurate scheme for (8.1.1),

$$\frac{v_m^{n+1} - 2v_m^n + v_m^{n-1}}{k^2} = a^2 \frac{v_{m+1}^n - 2v_m^n + v_{m-1}^n}{h^2}. \tag{8.2.2}$$

We now show that this scheme is stable for $a\lambda \leq 1$ (we take a to be nonnegative). As in the von Neumann analysis in Chapter 2, we have that the equation for the amplification factors is

$$g - 2 + g^{-1} = -4a^2\lambda^2 \sin^2 \tfrac{1}{2}\theta,$$

or

$$\left(g^{1/2} - g^{-1/2}\right)^2 = \left(\pm \, 2ia\lambda \sin \tfrac{1}{2}\theta\right)^2.$$

Hence

$$g^{1/2} - g^{-1/2} = \pm \, 2ia\lambda \sin \tfrac{1}{2}\theta$$

and so

$$g \pm 2ia\lambda \sin \tfrac{1}{2}\theta g^{1/2} - 1 = 0,$$

which is a quadratic equation for $g^{1/2}$. We then have the roots

$$g_{\pm}^{1/2} = \pm ia\lambda \sin \tfrac{1}{2}\theta \ \pm \ \sqrt{1 - a^2\lambda^2 \sin^2 \tfrac{1}{2}\theta}$$

or

$$g_{\pm} = \left(\sqrt{1 - a^2\lambda^2 \sin^2 \tfrac{1}{2}\theta} \ \pm \ ia\lambda \sin \tfrac{1}{2}\theta \right)^2.$$

It is easily seen that $|g|$ is bounded by 1 if and only if $a\lambda$ is at most 1. When θ is equal to 0, then g_+ and g_- are equal; this also occurs if $a\lambda$ is 1 and θ is π. Recall that the solution of the difference scheme is given by

$$\hat{v}^n = A_+(\xi)g_+^n + A_-(\xi)g_-^n$$

when $g_+ \neq g_-$ and

$$\hat{v}^n = A(\xi)g^n + B(\xi)ng^{n-1}$$

when $g_+ = g_- = g$. Because linear growth in n is permitted by Definition 8.2.1, the scheme is stable even when the roots are equal. Thus the scheme is stable if and only if $a\lambda \leq 1$.

At this point it is worthwhile to compare the analysis and conclusions given here with those of Section 4.1 for the leapfrog scheme for first-order hyperbolic equations. The analysis for the two cases is similar, but the coalesence of the two amplification factors was not permitted for the first-order equation. For the second-order scheme (8.2.2), we would usually take $a\lambda$ to be strictly less than 1 to avoid the linear growth of the wave with $\theta = \pi$. However, the presence of the high-frequency oscillation, that with $\theta = \pi$, does not affect the convergence of the scheme (8.2.2) as it would for the leapfrog scheme for the one-way wave equation because the extra initial data for (8.2.2) restricts the amplitude of high frequencies that are growing linearly.

For the Euler-Bernoulli equation (8.1.8), the simplest scheme is the second-order accurate scheme

$$\frac{v_m^{n+1} - 2v_m^n + v_m^{n-1}}{k^2} = -b^2 \frac{v_{m+2}^n - 4v_{m+1}^n + 6v_m^n - 4v_{m-1}^n + v_{m-2}^n}{h^4}$$

$$= -b^2 \delta^4 v_m^n. \tag{8.2.3}$$

The equation for the amplification factors is

$$g - 2 + g^{-1} = -16b^2\mu^2 \sin^4 \tfrac{1}{2}\theta$$

where $\mu = k/h^2$. The stability analysis is almost exactly like that of scheme (8.2.2) for the wave equation, and it is easy to see that scheme (8.2.3) is stable if and only if

$$2b\mu \sin^2 \tfrac{1}{2}\theta \leq 1,$$

which requires that

$$b\mu \leq \tfrac{1}{2}.$$

Higher-Order Accurate Schemes for Second-Order Equations

We now present two $(2,4)$ accurate schemes for the wave equation $(8.1.1)$. The first is

$$\frac{v_m^{n+1} - 2v_m^n + v_m^{n-1}}{k^2} = a^2 \left(\frac{-v_{m+2}^n + 16v_{m+1}^n - 30v_m^n + 16v_{m-1}^n - v_{m-2}^n}{12h^2} \right)$$

$$= a^2 \left(1 - \frac{h^2}{12}\delta^2 \right) v_m^n.$$

$$(8.2.4)$$

The equation for the amplification factors is

$$g - 2 + g^{-1} = a^2\lambda^2 \left(\frac{-2\cos 2\theta + 32\cos\theta - 30}{12} \right)$$

$$= -\frac{4}{3}a^2\lambda^2 \sin^2 \tfrac{1}{2}\theta \left(3 + \sin^2 \tfrac{1}{2}\theta \right),$$

or

$$g^{1/2} - g^{-1/2} = \pm\, 2i \left[\frac{a^2\lambda^2 \sin^2 \tfrac{1}{2}\theta \left(3 + \sin^2 \tfrac{1}{2}\theta \right)}{3} \right]^{1/2}$$

As in the previous analyses, the scheme is stable, i.e., $|g_\pm| \le 1$, if and only if

$$\frac{a^2\lambda^2 \sin^2 \tfrac{1}{2}\theta \left(3 + \sin^2 \tfrac{1}{2}\theta \right)}{3} \le 1.$$

Obviously the maximum of the left-hand side of this inequality occurs when $\sin^2 \tfrac{1}{2}\theta$ is 1, and so we obtain the stability condition

$$a\lambda \le \frac{\sqrt{3}}{2}$$

for the $(2,4)$ scheme $(8.2.4)$.

An implicit $(2,4)$ scheme for the wave equation $(8.1.1)$ is given by

$$\delta_t^2 v_m^n = a^2 \left(1 + \frac{h^2}{12}\delta_x^2 \right)^{-1} \delta_x^2 v_m^n, \qquad (8.2.5)$$

or

$$v_{m+1}^{n+1} + 10v_m^{n+1} + v_{m-1}^{n+1} - 2\left(v_{m+1}^n + 10v_m^n + v_{m-1}^n \right) + v_{m+1}^{n-1} + 10v_m^{n-1} + v_{m-1}^{n-1}$$

$$= 12a^2\lambda^2 \left(v_{m+1}^n - 2v_m^n + v_{m-1}^n \right).$$

Although this scheme requires the solution of a tridiagonal system of equations at each step, it has the advantage over the scheme (8.2.4) of having a narrower stencil; i.e., it does not use $v_{m\pm2}^n$ to compute v_m^{n+1}. The narrower stencil makes it easier to implement boundary conditions.

This scheme, though implicit, is not unconditionally stable. We have

$$\left(g^{1/2} - g^{-1/2}\right)^2 = -\frac{4a^2\lambda^2 \sin^2\frac{1}{2}\theta}{1 - \frac{1}{3}\sin^2\frac{1}{2}\theta},$$

and thus for stability we must enforce

$$\frac{a^2\lambda^2 \sin^2\frac{1}{2}\theta}{1 - \frac{1}{3}\sin^2\frac{1}{2}\theta} \le 1.$$

The maximum of the left-hand side occurs at $\sin\frac{1}{2}\theta$ equal to 1, and thus

$$a\lambda \le \sqrt{\tfrac{2}{3}}$$

is the stability condition. As for the previous scheme, this is not a serious restriction, since k should be small compared with h to achieve good accuracy and efficiency with a $(2,4)$ accurate scheme. (See the discussion at the end of Section 4.1 on higher-order accurate schemes.)

Computing the First Time-Step

All the schemes for equations that are second-order in time require some means of computing the solution on the first time-step after the initial time level. Perhaps the simplest procedure is to use the Taylor series expansion

$$u(k, x) = u(0, x) + ku_t(0, x) + \tfrac{1}{2}k^2 u_{tt}(0, x) + O(k^3).$$

The values of $u(0, x)$ and $u_t(0, x)$ are given data and, by using the differential equation, $u_{tt}(0, x)$ can be expressed as a derivative of u with respect to x, e.g., as $a^2 u_{xx}(0, x)$ for (8.1.1) or $-b^2 u_{xxxx}(0, x)$ for (8.1.8). Using the finite difference scheme we easily obtain an expression for v_m^1 that is of the same order of accuracy as the rest of the scheme. For example, for (8.1.1) we have

$$v_m^1 = v_m^0 + k\left(u_t\right)_m + \tfrac{1}{2}a^2 k^2 \delta^2 v_m^0. \qquad (8.2.6)$$

As with initializing multistep methods for first-order equations (see Section 4.1), the initialization method has no effect on the stability of the overall method. If we regard formula (8.2.6) as an approximation to $u_t(0, x)$, that is, in the form

$$u_t(0, x_m) = \frac{v_m^1 - v_m^0}{k} - \frac{1}{2}a^2 k\delta^2 v_m^0 + O(k^2),$$

then the approximation must be of at least the same order of accuracy as the scheme in order not to degrade the accuracy of the overall method.

Von Neumann Polynomials and Stability

We can modify the algorithms for von Neumann and Schur polynomials, as discussed in Section 4.3, to test for the stability of second-order schemes. We first extend the definition of von Neumann polynomials.

Definition 8.2.2 *The polynomial φ is a von Neumann polynomial of order q if all its roots, r_ν, satisfy $|r_\nu| \leq 1$, and the roots with $|r_\nu| = 1$ have multiplicity at most q. A von Neumann polynomial of order 0 is defined to be a Schur polynomial.*

Comparing this definition with Definition 4.3.3 we see that a simple von Neumann polynomial is a von Neumann polynomial of order 1. We then have the following generalization of Theorems 4.3.1 and 4.3.2.

Theorem 8.2.1 *φ_j is a von Neumann polynomial of order q if and only if either $|\varphi_j(0)| \leq |\varphi_j^*(0)|$ and φ_{j+1} is a von Neumann polynomial of order q or φ_{j+1} is identically zero and φ_j' is a von Neumann polynomial of degree $q - 1$.*

The proof of this theorem is similar to the proofs of Theorems 4.3.1 and 4.3.2 and is left as an exercise. We note that if φ_j is a von Neumann polynomial of order 0 and degree 1 or more, then it is impossible for φ_{j+1} to be identically zero.

Theorem 8.2.1 can be used to analyze the stability of schemes for second-order equations. If $\Phi(g, \theta)$ is the amplification polynomial of a finite difference scheme for a second-order equation for which the restricted condition $|g_\nu| \leq 1$ can be employed, then the scheme is stable if and only if $\Phi(g, \theta)$ is a von Neumann polynomial of order 2.

EXERCISES 8.2

1. Show that the implicit scheme for (8.1.1) given by

$$\delta_t^2 v_m^n = \tfrac{1}{4} a^2 \delta_x^2 \left(v_m^{n+1} + 2v_m^n + v_m^{n-1} \right)$$

is a second-order accurate scheme and is unconditionally stable.

2. Show that the scheme

$$\frac{v_m^{n+2} - 2v_m^n + v_m^{n-2}}{4k^2} - a^2 \left(1 + \frac{h^2}{12} \delta_x^2 \right)^{-1} \delta_x^2 v_m^n$$

$$- \frac{a^2}{3} \left(1 + \frac{h^2}{12} \delta_x^2 \right)^{-1} \delta_x^2 \left(v_m^{n+2} + 12v_m^{n+1} - 26v_m^n + 12v_m^{n-1} + v_m^{n-1} \right) = 0$$

is a $(4, 4)$ scheme for the wave equation (8.1.1) and use Theorem 8.2.1 to show that it is stable if and only if $a\lambda < 1$.

3. Prove Theorem 8.2.1.

4. Show that the scheme for the wave equation (8.1.1)

$$\delta_t^2 v_m^n = a^2 \delta_x^2 v_m^n + \varepsilon k^{-2} \left(\frac{h\delta_x}{2} \right)^4 v_m^{n-1}$$

is dissipative for small positive values of the parameter ε. Show that the scheme is second-order accurate when λ is constant.

5. Show that the implicit scheme

$$\delta_t^2 v_m^n + 2c\delta_{t0}\delta_{x0} v_m^n = a^2 \delta_x^2 v_m^n \tag{8.2.7}$$

for the equation

$$u_{tt} + 2cu_{tx} = a^2 u_{xx} \tag{8.2.8}$$

is second-order accurate and stable for $a\lambda \le 1$.

6. Use scheme (8.2.7) to obtain approximate solutions to equation (8.2.8) on the interval $-1 \le x \le 1$ for $0 \le t \le 1$. As initial data take

$$u_0(x) = \cos \pi x \quad \text{and} \quad u_1(x) = c \sin \pi x.$$

For boundary data use the exact solution

$$u(t,x) = \tfrac{1}{2} \left[\cos \pi(x - \eta_+ t) + \cos \pi(x - \eta_- t) \right]$$

where $\eta_\pm = c \pm \sqrt{c^2 + a^2}$. Take c equal to 0.5 and a equal to 1. Use grid spacings of $\frac{1}{10}$, $\frac{1}{20}$, and $\frac{1}{40}$ and λ equal to 1. Demonstrate the second-order accuracy of the scheme.

8.3 Boundary Conditions for Second-Order Equations

The second-order wave equation (8.1.1) on an interval, say, $0 \le x \le 1$, requires one boundary condition at each end. This is easily seen by relating (8.1.1) to a first-order system (see Exercise 8.1.1). The two most common boundary conditions are to specify the value of the solution at the boundary, the Dirichlet boundary condition, and to specify the first derivative with respect to x at the boundary, the Neumann boundary condition.

For all the schemes for the wave equation (8.1.1) other than (8.2.4), the boundary conditions where the value of u is prescribed on the boundary present no problem. If the derivative of u with respect to x is specified, then several options are available. For example, suppose the boundary condition at x equal to 0 is

$$u_x(t, 0) = 0.$$

For the finite difference scheme at m equal to 0, we can use either

$$v_0^{n+1} = \frac{4v_1^{n+1} - v_2^{n+1}}{3} \qquad (8.3.1)$$

or

$$v_0^{n+1} = 2v_0^n - v_0^{n-1} - 2a^2\lambda^2 \left(v_0^n - v_1^n\right). \qquad (8.3.2)$$

Formula (8.3.1) is from the second-order accurate one-sided approximation

$$u_x(0) = \frac{4u(h) - 3u(0) - u(2h)}{2h} + O\left(h^2\right)$$

(see Exercise 3.2.10). Formula (8.3.2) arises from employing scheme (8.2.2) at m equal to 0 and then eliminating the value of v_{-1}^n by using

$$\frac{v_1^n - v_{-1}^n}{2h} = 0$$

which is the central difference approximation to the first derivative. Other boundary conditions are also possible.

The use of first-order accurate boundary conditions, such as

$$\frac{v_1^n - v_0^n}{h} = 0, \qquad (8.3.3)$$

degrade the overall accuracy of the second-order accurate scheme.

For scheme (8.2.4) we require a numerical boundary condition at the grid point next to the boundary, since the scheme can not be applied there. Various conditions can be used. Using the second-order accurate scheme (8.2.4) at these points can degrade the accuracy. If the value on the boundary is specified, then the value next to the boundary can be determined by interpolation, for example,

$$v_1^{n+1} = \tfrac{1}{4}\left(v_0^{n+1} + 6v_2^{n+1} - 4v_3^{n+1} + v_4^{n+1}\right)$$

which is obtained from

$$\delta_+^4 v_0^{n+1} = 0.$$

The scheme (8.2.4) with derivative boundary conditions is rather unwieldy.

For the Euler-Bernoulli scheme (8.2.3) and similar schemes for the Rayleigh equation, the boundary conditions can be obtained by standard methods, but now there are two boundary conditions required by the differential equation. For example, if the beam is held fixed and clamped at x equal to 0, the boundary conditions would be

$$u(t,0) = u_x(t,0) = 0. \qquad (8.3.4)$$

If the beam is fixed in place but allowed to pivot, the boundary conditions are

$$u(t,0) = u_{xx}(t,0) = 0, \qquad (8.3.5)$$

and if the end of the beam is free to move, the conditions are

$$u_{xx}(t,0) = u_{xxx}(t,0) = 0. \tag{8.3.6}$$

The implementation of these boundary conditions with a finite difference scheme can be done in several ways. The use of second-order accurate formulas applied at x equal to 0 can be used to give boundary conditions for (8.2.3) and schemes for the Rayleigh equation. For example, for (8.3.5) v_0^{n+1} is prescribed and at $m = 1$, we can use (8.2.3) with the formula

$$v_{-1}^n - 2v_0^n + v_1^n = 0 \tag{8.3.7}$$

to eliminate v_{-1}^n. Similarly for (8.3.6) we can use (8.2.3) with the conditions (8.3.7) and

$$-v_{-2}^n + 2v_{-1}^n - 2v_1^n + v_2^n = 0, \tag{8.3.8}$$

which is the second-order accurate formula for $2h^3\delta_0\delta^2 v_0^n = 0$, to eliminate v_{-2}^n and v_{-1}^n from (8.2.3) applied at m equal to 0 and m equal to 1. In the actual computer implementation we can either have variables v_{-2}^n and v_{-1}^n and use (8.3.7) and (8.3.8) to define their values, or we can eliminate these variables from the difference formula (8.2.3), obtaining formulas to calculate v_0^{n+1} and v_1^{n+1}. The two approaches are equivalent.

EXERCISE 8.3

1. Use the scheme (8.2.2) to obtain approximate solutions to the wave equation $u_{tt} = u_{xx}$ on the interval $0 \le x \le 1$ for $0 \le t \le 1$. For initial data and Dirichlet boundary data at x equal to 1, use the exact solution

$$u(t,x) = \cos(x+t) + \cos(x-t),$$

and at x equal to 0, use the Neumann condition $u_x = 0$. Implement the boundary conditions (8.3.1) and (8.3.2) as well as the first-order accurate boundary approximation $\delta_+ u_0 = 0$.

Use grid spacings of $\frac{1}{10}$, $\frac{1}{20}$, and $\frac{1}{40}$ and λ equal to 1. Demonstrate the second-order accuracy of the solution with boundary conditions (8.3.1) and (8.3.2) and the first-order accuracy when boundary condition (8.3.3) is used.

8.4 Second-Order Equations in Two and Three Dimensions

The extension of most of the results of the previous sections to higher dimensions is straightforward. As noted in Section 7.2, the stability conditions usually become more severe. For example, the wave equation in two spatial dimensions is

$$u_{tt} = a^2\left(u_{xx} + u_{yy}\right) \tag{8.4.1}$$

and the simplest scheme for this equation is

$$\delta_t^2 v_{\ell,m}^n = a^2 \left(\delta_x^2 v_{\ell,m}^n + \delta_y^2 v_{\ell,m}^n \right). \tag{8.4.2}$$

The stability condition for this scheme when $\Delta x = \Delta y = h$ is

$$a\lambda \le \frac{1}{\sqrt{2}}. \tag{8.4.3}$$

As for the leapfrog scheme (7.2.5), this can be improved to

$$a\lambda \le 1 \tag{8.4.4}$$

for the scheme

$$\delta_t^2 v_{\ell,m}^n = \tfrac{1}{4}a^2 \big[\delta_x^2 (v_{\ell,m+1}^n + 2v_{\ell,m}^n + v_{\ell,m-1}^n) \\ + \delta_y^2 (v_{\ell+1,m}^n + 2v_{\ell,m}^n + v_{\ell-1,m}^n) \big]. \tag{8.4.5}$$

It is also possible to develop ADI schemes for (8.4.1). One possible scheme is

$$\left(1 - \tfrac{1}{4}k^2 a^2 \delta_x^2 \right) \tilde{v}_{\ell,m}^{n+1/2} = \left(1 + \tfrac{1}{4}k^2 a^2 \delta_y^2 \right) v_{\ell,m}^n$$

$$\left(1 - \tfrac{1}{4}k^2 a^2 \delta_y^2 \right) \tilde{v}_{\ell,m}^{n+1} = \left(1 + \tfrac{1}{4}k^2 a^2 \delta_x^2 \right) \tilde{v}_{\ell,m}^{n+1/2} \tag{8.4.6}$$

$$v_{\ell,m}^{n+1} = 2\tilde{v}_{\ell,m}^{n+1} - v_{\ell,m}^{n-1}$$

which is second-order accurate and unconditionally stable (see Exercise 8.4.2). This scheme is implemented in a fashion similar to the ADI schemes of Section 7.3. Other ADI schemes for the two-dimensional wave equation are discussed by Fairweather and Mitchell [15].

Dispersion for Schemes in Higher Dimensions

It is interesting to analyze the dispersion of the scheme (8.4.2) from the formula for the amplification factors. The amplification factors are

$$g_\pm = \left\{ \left[1 - a^2\lambda^2 (\sin^2 \tfrac{1}{2}\theta + \sin^2 \tfrac{1}{2}\phi) \right]^{1/2} \pm ia\lambda (\sin^2 \tfrac{1}{2}\theta + \sin^2 \tfrac{1}{2}\phi)^{1/2} \right\}^2.$$

Comparing this with

$$e^{ia(\xi_1^2 + \xi_2^2)^{1/2}k}$$

we have that the phase velocity satisfies

$$\sin \left[\tfrac{1}{2}\alpha(\xi_1, \xi_2)k \left(\xi_1^2 + \xi_2^2 \right)^{1/2} \right] = a\lambda \left(\sin^2 \tfrac{1}{2}h\xi_1 + \sin^2 \tfrac{1}{2}h\xi_2 \right)^{1/2}.$$

It is important to note that the phase error is not independent of direction. We have

$$\alpha\left(\xi_1, \xi_2\right) = a\left[1 - \frac{h^2|\xi|^2}{24}\left(\cos^4\beta + \sin^4\beta - a^2\lambda^2\right) + O\left(h|\xi|\right)^4\right] \qquad (8.4.7)$$

where $|\xi| = \left(\xi_1^2 + \xi_2^2\right)^{1/2}$ and $\tan\beta = \xi_1/\xi_2$. This formula shows that the phase error depends on the direction of propagation of the wave, where $(\cos\beta, \sin\beta)$ is the unit vector in the direction of propagation. For most computations it is difficult to notice the distortion caused by the dependence of the dispersion on the direction of propagation unless the grid is quite coarse.

EXERCISES 8.4

1. Verify stability condition (8.4.3) for scheme (8.4.2).

2. Verify that the scheme given by (8.4.6) is a second-order accurate and unconditionally stable approximation to the wave equation (8.4.1).

3. Verify stability condition (8.4.4) for scheme (8.4.5).

4. Show that the hyperbolic equation

$$u_{tt} = a_{11}u_{xx} + 2a_{12}u_{xy} + a_{22}u_{yy}$$

with $a_{12}^2 < a_{11}a_{22}$ and $a_{11}, a_{22} > 0$, can be approximated by the ADI scheme

$$\left(1 - \frac{k}{2}a_{11}\delta_x^2\right)\tilde{v}_{\ell,m}^{n+1/2} = \left(1 + \frac{k}{2}a_{22}\delta_y^2\right)v_{\ell,m}^n \quad + ka_{12}\delta_{0x}\delta_{0y}v_{\ell,m}^n$$

$$\left(1 - \frac{k}{2}a_{22}\delta_y^2\right)\tilde{v}_{\ell,m}^{n+1} = \left(1 + \frac{k}{2}a_{11}\delta_x^2\right)\tilde{v}_{\ell,m}^{n+1/2} + ka_{12}\delta_{0x}\delta_{0y}v_{\ell,m}^n$$

$$v_{\ell,m}^{n+1} = 2\tilde{v}_{\ell,m}^{n+1} - v_{\ell,m}^{n-1}.$$

Show that this scheme is unconditionally stable and is second-order accurate.

5. Verify formula (8.4.7) for the phase velocity.

Chapter 9

Analysis of Well-Posed and Stable Problems

In this chapter we examine initial value problems for partial differential equations and finite difference schemes from a more general perspective than in the previous chapters. We begin by examining the concept of a well-posed initial value problem, first for a single partial differential equation and then for a system of equations. These results are used in Chapter 10 as part of the proofs of the convergence theorems. The analysis used to study initial value problems for partial differential equations is analogous to the von Neumann analysis presented in Section 2.2. The concept of a well-posed initial value problem is important in scientific modeling and in understanding finite difference schemes being used in scientific calculations. As we will see, the analysis of this section gives another example of the power and usefulness of Fourier analysis.

A central result for the general study of stability of finite difference schemes is the Kreiss matrix theorem. This result is of importance in proving stability results for equations with variable coefficients (see Wade [56] and Kreiss [26]) and for systems whose stability cannot be verified by the methods of Section 7.1. The last section of this chapter contains a proof and discussion of the Kreiss matrix theorem.

9.1 The Theory of Well-Posed Initial Value Problems

We begin by considering conditions under which initial value problems for partial differential equations are well-posed. This study can be motivated by the question of why certain equations, such as the wave equation (8.1.1) and the heat equation (6.1.1), arise frequently in applied mathematics and others, such as

$$u_{tt} = u_x \tag{9.1.1}$$

do not arise as governing the time evolution of physical systems.

For a partial differential equation to model the time evolution of a well-behaved physical process, there are several properties it should have. An important condition is that of continuity of the solution in terms of the initial data. In particular, small errors such as those due to experimental error and interpolation of data should lead to small changes in the solution. The norms used to define "small" errors must also be reasonable. For example, a condition that the third derivative of measurement errors be small is an unreasonable demand.

For linear problems such as we are concerned with here, this continuity condition is satisfied if the solutions to the partial differential equation satisfy

$$\|u(t,\cdot)\| \leq C_t \|u(0,\cdot)\| \tag{9.1.2}$$

for some norm such as the L^2 norm, L^1 norm, or L^∞ norm and a constant C_t independent of the solution. Because of the linearity of the equations, we have by (9.1.2) that two different initial functions $u^1(0,x)$ and $u^2(0,x)$ give different solutions whose difference is bounded by their initial difference, i.e.,

$$\|u^1(t,\cdot) - u^2(t,\cdot)\| \leq C_t \|u^1(0,\cdot) - u^2(0,\cdot)\|.$$

This estimate expresses the notion that small changes in the initial data will result in small changes in the solution at later times.

Definition 9.1.1   *The initial value problem for a first-order equation is well-posed if the inequality (9.1.2) holds for all initial data $u(0,\cdot)$.*

Unless otherwise specified, we take the norm in estimate (9.1.2) to be the L^2 norm. Using the L^2 norm we can use Fourier analysis to give necessary and sufficient conditions for initial value problems to be well-posed. In the L^1 norm or L^∞ norm, it is often easy to get necessary conditions or sufficient conditions but harder to obtain conditions that are both necessary and sufficient. The main reason for this is that there is no relation like Parseval's relation for norms other than the L^2 norm. We also say that an equation is well-posed, by which we mean that the initial value problem for the equation is well-posed.

A second important property for a partial differential equation to have as a model of a physical system is that the qualitative behavior of the solution be unaffected by the addition of or changes in lower-order terms and by sufficiently small changes in the coefficients. This condition is not always met, but it does serve as a guide to the most "robust" systems and types of equations.

This last property, which we refer to as *robustness,* is important because almost all derivations of equations to model physical processes make some assumptions that certain effects are not important to understanding the physical process being studied. Statements such as "assume that the temperature of the body is constant," "we may ignore gravitational forces," and "consider a homogeneous body" can be made because it is assumed that small variations in some quantities may be ignored without affecting the conclusions of the analysis.

This robustness property is also important when we consider numerical methods for solving the equations that model a physical system. Finite difference schemes and other numerical methods may be regarded as perturbations, or approximations, of the equations similar to modification of the equations by adding lower-order terms. If the equation is not robust, then the construction of difference schemes for the equation will be more difficult.

We begin our analysis by considering a general linear partial differential equation with constant coefficients that is first order in the time differentiation.

Examples of such equations are the one-way wave equation (1.1.1), the three equations (1.4.1), and the heat equation (6.1.1). We assume that the Fourier transform is well defined for $u(t, \cdot)$ for all t and for $u(0, \cdot)$.

Any equation of first order in the time derivative can be put in the form

$$\hat{u}_t(t, \omega) = q(\omega)\hat{u}(t, \omega) \qquad (9.1.3)$$

after applying the Fourier transform in space. The initial value problem for this equation has the solution

$$\hat{u}(t, \omega) = e^{q(\omega)t}\hat{u}_0(\omega). \qquad (9.1.4)$$

Theorem 9.1.1   *The necessary and sufficient condition for equation (9.1.3) to be well-posed, that is, satisfy the basic estimate (9.1.2), is that there is a constant $\bar{q}$ such that*

$$\mathrm{Re}\, q(\omega) \leq \bar{q}. \qquad (9.1.5)$$

for all real values of ω.

Proof If the function $q(\omega)$ satisfies (9.1.5) for some constant $\bar{q}$, then from (9.1.4)

$$|\hat{u}(t, \omega)| \leq e^{\bar{q}t}|\hat{u}_0(\omega)|$$

and we obtain estimate (9.1.2) by Parseval's relation. However, if $q(\omega)$ does not satisfy (9.1.5), then by choosing $\hat{u}_0(\omega)$ appropriately we can have

$$\|u(t, \cdot)\|_2 > C\|u_0\|_2$$

for any large constant C and some function u_0. This construction is similar to that used in the proof of Theorem 2.2.1. This proves the theorem. ■

To relate estimate (9.1.5) to our discussion of continuity, if inequality (9.1.5) is violated, then some small errors of high frequency, i.e., large $|\omega|$, can cause the solution to be vastly different from the true solution without the errors. Therefore, the condition (9.1.5), which is the necessary and sufficient condition for the estimate (9.1.2) to hold for an equation of first-order in time, is an analytical consequence of the requirement of continuity.

For many single equations of first order in the time derivative, the robustness condition is also satisfied. For example, the equations

$$u_t = au_x + cu$$

$$u_t = u_{xx} + cu_x$$

$$u_t - u_{txx} = au_x + cu$$

$$u_t + u_{tx} = bu_{xx} + cu_x$$

all satisfy the condition (9.1.5) regardless the value of c, although the value of $\bar{q}$ may depend on c (but not on ω).

Example 9.1.1 An example of an equation violating the robustness condition is

$$u_t + u_{txx} = au_x + cu.$$

We have

$$q(\omega) = \frac{ia\omega}{1 - \omega^2} + \frac{c}{1 - \omega^2},$$

and if c is zero, then $q(\omega)$ is purely imaginary and thus satisfies (9.1.5), but if c is nonzero then $q(\omega)$ is unbounded. $\square$

Example 9.1.2 Another example is given by

$$u_t = u_{xxx} + cu_{xx}$$

for which $q(\omega)$ satisfies (9.1.5) for c nonnegative but not if c is negative. Thus this equation with c equal to zero does not satisfy the robustness condition, although it does for c positive. $\square$

Higher-Order Equations

We next consider equations of higher order in the time derivative. For these equations the symbol $p(s, \omega)$ is a polynomial in s. If the roots of the symbol are $q_1(\omega), \ldots, q_r(\omega)$, then any function of the form

$$e^{q_v(\omega)t} e^{i\omega x} \psi(\omega)$$

is a solution of the partial differential equation. Based on our previous arguments, we see that a necessary condition for the initial value problem to be well-posed is that each root $q_v(\omega)$ satisfies the estimate (9.1.5).

We would have to properly define a well-posed initial value problem for higher-order equations if we were to pursue this discussion. The definition would have to take account of the additional initial data required by higher-order equations. Rather than develop a general theory we consider several typical cases. First we consider the second-order equation of the form

$$u_{tt} = R(\partial_x)u \tag{9.1.6}$$

whose symbol is of the form

$$p(s, \omega) = s^2 - r(\omega). \tag{9.1.7}$$

For the condition (9.1.5) to be satisfied for both roots of (9.1.7), which are

$$q_\pm(\omega) = \pm \left(r(\omega) \right)^{1/2},$$

we see that $r(\omega)$ must be close to or on the negative real axis. Examples are given by the wave equation (8.1.1) and the Euler-Bernoulli equation (8.1.8).

Example 9.1.3 Lower-order terms can affect the well-posedness of the problem, as can be seen by the equation

$$u_{tt} = -b^2 u_{xxxx} + c u_{xxx}.$$

We have that

$$r(\omega) = -b^2 \omega^4 - i c \omega^3$$

and so

$$q_\pm = \pm \left(-b^2 \omega^4 - i c \omega^3\right)^{1/2}$$

$$= \pm i b \omega^2 \left(1 + \frac{ic}{b^2 \omega}\right)^{1/2}$$

$$= \pm i b \omega^2 \left[1 + \frac{1}{2} \frac{ic}{b^2 \omega} + O(\omega^{-2})\right]$$

$$= \pm \left[i b \omega^2 - \frac{c\omega}{2b} + O(1)\right]$$

Hence if c is nonzero, each root violates (9.1.5) for either positive or negative values of ω. Thus the Euler-Bernoulli equation (8.1.8) is not robust, although the wave equation (8.1.1) is robust (see Exercise 9.1.3). □

For completeness we also give the definition of a well-posed initial value problem for equation (9.1.6), which is second-order in the differentiation in time. Let 2ρ be the degree of the polynomial $r(\omega)$, which is the symbol of $R(\partial_x)$.

Definition 9.1.2 *The initial value problem for equation (9.1.6) is well-posed if for each $t > 0$ there is a constant C_t such that for all solutions u*

$$\|u(t, \cdot)\|_{H^\rho} + \|u_t(t, \cdot)\|_{H^0} \le C_t \left(\|u(0, \cdot)\|_{H^\rho} + \|u_t(0, \cdot)\|_{H^0}\right). \tag{9.1.8}$$

Condition (9.1.5) is necessary and sufficient for the initial value problem to be well-posed. This result is stated in the following theorem. The theorem applies to a more general class of equations (see Exercises 9.1.3 and 9.1.5) and it is stated so as to apply to this more general case.

Theorem 9.1.2 *A necessary and sufficient condition for the initial value problem for an equation of second order in the time differentiation to be well-posed is that there exists a constant $\bar{q}$ such that (9.1.5) holds for each root of the symbol.*

Proof We give the proof only for equations in the form (9.1.6). It extends without difficulty to more general equations. The necessity of condition (9.1.5) is clear from our earlier arguments.

To show the sufficiency, let $q_+(\omega)$ and $q_-(\omega)$ be the two roots of the symbol (9.1.7). If these roots are not equal, we have that the solution satisfies

$$\hat{u}(t, \omega) = A(\omega) e^{q_+(\omega)t} + B_-(\omega) e^{q_-(\omega)t}$$

for some functions $A(\omega)$ and $B(\omega)$. These functions are determined by the two relations

$$\hat{u}(0,\omega) = A(\omega) + B(\omega)$$

and

$$\hat{u}_t(0,\omega) = A(\omega)q_+(\omega) + B(\omega)q_-(\omega).$$

Therefore,

$$A(\omega) = \frac{\hat{u}_t(0,\omega) - q_-(\omega)\hat{u}(0,\omega)}{q_+(\omega) - q_-(\omega)}$$

and

$$B(\omega) = \frac{\hat{u}_t(0,\omega) - q_+(\omega)\hat{u}(0,\omega)}{q_-(\omega) - q_+(\omega)}.$$

Now $q_+(\omega)$ is equal to $q_-(\omega)$ only when $r(\omega)$ is zero, and since $r(\omega)$ is a polynomial in the one variable ω, this can occur only for $|\omega|$ less than some value c_0. Consider first the case with $|\omega|$ greater than $2c_0$. We then have

$$|\hat{u}(t,\omega)| \le (|A(\omega)| + |B(\omega)|)\,e^{\bar{q}t}$$

$$\le \left[|\hat{u}(0,\omega)|\,\frac{|q_+(\omega)| + |q_-(\omega)|}{|q_+(\omega) - q_-(\omega)|} + \frac{2|\hat{u}_t(0,\omega)|}{|q_+(\omega) - q_-(\omega)|}\right]e^{\bar{q}t}.$$

Since $|\omega|$ is greater than $2c_0$, there is a constant C such that the preceding estimate implies

$$(1 + |\omega|^p)\,|\hat{u}(t,\omega)| \le C\,[(1 + |\omega|^p)\,|\hat{u}(0,\omega)| + |\hat{u}_t(0,\omega)|]\,e^{\bar{q}t}.$$

We also have that

$$|\hat{u}_t(t,\omega)| \le [|A(\omega)q_+(\omega)| + |B(\omega)q_-(\omega)|]\,e^{\bar{q}t}$$

$$\le C\,[(1 + |\omega|^p)|\hat{u}(0,\omega)| + |\hat{u}_t(0,\omega)|]\,e^{\bar{q}t}.$$

For $|\omega|$ less than $2c_0$ we write the equation for $\hat{u}(t,\omega)$ as

$$\hat{u}(t,\omega) = C(\omega)\left[\frac{e^{q_+(\omega)t} + e^{q_-(\omega)t}}{2}\right] + D(\omega)\left[\frac{e^{q_+(\omega)t} - e^{q_-(\omega)t}}{q_+(\omega) - q_-(\omega)}\right].$$

We have that

$$C(\omega) = \hat{u}(0,\omega)$$

and

$$D(\omega) = -\hat{u}(0,\omega)\left(\frac{q_+(\omega) + q_-(\omega)}{2}\right) + \hat{u}_t(0,\omega).$$

The function

$$\frac{e^{q_+(\omega)t} - e^{q_-(\omega)t}}{q_+(\omega) - q_-(\omega)}$$

is uniformly bounded by $Cte^{\bar{q}t}$ for some constant C. Thus for $|\omega|$ less than $2c_0$,

$$(1 + |\omega|^p) \, |\hat{u}(t, \omega)| \leq C(1 + t) \left((1 + |\omega|^p) \, |\hat{u}(0, \omega)| + |\hat{u}_t(0, \omega)| \right) e^{\bar{q}t}$$

and $|\hat{u}_t(t, \omega)|$ is also bounded by the same quantity.

Combining the estimates for $|\omega|$ both greater than and less than $2c_0$, we obtain

$$(1 + |\omega|^p)^2 \, |\hat{u}(t, \omega)|^2 + |\hat{u}_t(t, \omega)|^2$$

$$\leq C_t \left((1 + |\omega|^p)^2 \, |\hat{u}(0, \omega)|^2 + |\hat{u}_t(0, \omega)|^2 \right),$$

which, by Parseval's relation, gives (9.1.8). ∎

To return to equation (9.1.1) we see that this equation is ill-posed, since the roots of its symbol are

$$q_{\pm}(\omega) = \pm \frac{1 + i}{\sqrt{2}} |\omega|^{1/2}$$

and (9.1.5) is not satisfied.

It should be pointed out that equations for which the initial value problem is ill-posed can arise in applications. They will not, however, describe the time evolution of a system.

Example 9.1.4 As an example of how equation (9.1.1) can arise in an application, suppose for the heat equation (6.1.1) that we knew both $u(t, 0)$ and $u_x(t, 0)$ for $t > 0$ and we wished to know the initial data $u(0, x)$. This problem requires the solution of an initial value problem with an equation like (9.1.1), but where x is the time-like variable and t is the spatial variable. Because the problem is ill-posed, we know before starting to calculate that we cannot hope to get "the" solution. At best, we can hope for a reasonable estimate of a solution. To make the problem into a well-posed problem we might solve

$$bu_{xx} = u_t + \varepsilon u_{tt},$$

in the notation of (6.1.1), with ε positive, rather than attempting to solve the true equation with ε zero. □

Based on the previous discussion, it is easy to see that any equation of the form

$$\left(\frac{\partial}{\partial t} \right)^{\nu} u = R(\partial_x) u \qquad (9.1.9)$$

for ν greater than 2 is ill-posed unless $R(\partial_x)$ is a constant. If $r(\omega)$, the symbol of $R(\partial_x)$, grows with ω, then at least one of the νth roots of $r(\omega)$ must violate (9.1.5). This shows that equations of order greater than two must be of very special form if they are to have well-posed initial value problems. Since higher-order equations have more possibilities for lower-order terms, the class of reasonable equations is further restricted.

Example 9.1.5 The initial value problem for the third-order equation

$$(\partial_t - a\partial_x)\left(\partial_t^2 - \partial_x^2\right) u = 0 \tag{9.1.10}$$

is well-posed. However, the equation

$$(\partial_t - a\partial_x)\left(\partial_t^2 - \partial_x^2\right) u + 2\partial_x^2 u = 0 \tag{9.1.11}$$

is well-posed only if a is not equal to ± 1. The symbol of this equation is

$$(s - ia\omega)\left(s^2 + \omega^2\right) - 2\omega^2 = 0.$$

For $|a| \neq 1$ we set $s = ia\omega + \varepsilon$ where ε is $o(\omega)$ and obtain

$$\varepsilon\left(\varepsilon^2 - 2ia\omega\varepsilon + (1 - a^2)\omega^2\right) - 2\omega^2 = 0.$$

Since ε is small compared with $|\omega|$ for large ω, we have $\varepsilon(1 - a^2) \approx 2$ or $\varepsilon = 2/(1 - a^2) + O(\omega^{-1})$.

So one root is

$$s = ia\omega + \frac{2}{1 - a^2} + O(\omega^{-1})$$

and, similarly, the other roots are

$$s = i\omega - \frac{1}{1 - a} + O(\omega^{-1})$$

$$s = -i\omega - \frac{1}{1 + a} + O(\omega^{-1}).$$

However, if a is 1 we have

$$s = i\omega \pm \sqrt{-i\omega} + O(1)$$

for two of the roots, and therefore the initial value problem for (9.1.11) is ill-posed. □

EXERCISES 9.1

1.   Show that equations (1.4.1) can all be put in the form (9.1.3). Determine conditions on the coefficients of these equations so that they are well-posed.

2.   Show that if the operator $R(\partial_x)$ in (9.1.6) is of odd order—i.e., the polynomial $r(\omega)$ has an odd number of roots—then the equation (9.1.6) is not well-posed.

3.   Show that if

$$u_{tt} = R(\partial_x)u$$

is well-posed, then so is

$$u_{tt} + 2a\,u_t = R(\partial_x)u. \tag{9.1.12}$$

4.   Show that the following two equations are well-posed.

a. $u_{tt} + 2au_{txxx} + bu_{xxxx} = 0$ for all real a and $b, a \neq 0$

b. $u_{tt} + 2au_{txx} + b^2 u_{xxxx} = 0$ if $a \leq 0$

5.   Verify that the proof of Theorem 9.1.2 applies to equations of the form of (9.1.12).

9.2 Well-Posed Systems of Equations

We next consider the well-posedness of initial value problems for systems of equations. We restrict our discussion to systems that are of first order in the time differentiation. We consider linear systems with constant coefficients and require that after application of the Fourier transform, the system can be put in the form

$$\hat{u}_t = Q(\omega)\hat{u} \tag{9.2.1}$$

where $\hat{u}$ is a vector function of dimension d and Q is a $d \times d$ matrix function of ω. We also consider systems in N space dimensions, so that ω is in R^N. The concepts of this section together with those of the previous section can be used to study well-posed initial value problems of systems of higher order and mixed order in the time derivative.

The solution to (9.2.1) is

$$\hat{u}(t, \omega) = e^{tQ(\omega)}\hat{u}_0(\omega)$$

and in place of Theorem 9.1.1 we have Theorem 9.2.1.

Theorem 9.2.1   *The necessary and sufficient condition for system (9.2.1) to be well-posed is that for each nonnegative t, there is a constant C_t such that*

$$\|e^{Q(\omega)t}\| \leq C_t \tag{9.2.2}$$

for all $\omega \in R^N$. A necessary condition for (9.2.2) to hold is that (9.1.5) hold for each eigenvalue of $Q(\omega)$.

The proof of this theorem is similar to that in the scalar case and is not given. Matrix exponentials are not as easy to analyze as scalar exponentials, and there are no simple conditions such as (9.1.5), which guarantee that (9.2.2) follows. We develop some tools and apply them in several particular cases.

To analyze the norm of the exponential of a matrix we use the following lemma.

Lemma 9.2.2   *Let U be an upper triangular square matrix of dimension d and let*

$$\bar{u} = \max_{1 \leq i \leq d} \text{Re } u_{ii}$$

and

$$u^* = \max_{j>i} |u_{ij}|.$$

Then there is a constant C_d, independent of U, such that

$$\|e^{tU}\| \le C_d e^{t\bar{u}} \left(1 + (tu^*)^{d-1}\right).$$

Proof   To facilitate the proof we introduce polynomials $m_k(\tau)$ defined by

$$m_0(\tau) \equiv 1$$

and

$$m'_k(\tau) = \sum_{\ell=0}^{k-1} m_\ell(\tau), \qquad m_k(0) = 0$$

for k greater than 0. The prime on $m_k(\tau)$ denotes differentiation with respect to τ.

Let $E(t)$ be the matrix e^{tU} and denote the elements of $E(t)$ by $e_{ij}(t)$. We will prove by induction that

$$|e_{ij}(t)| \le e^{t\bar{u}} m_{j-i}(tu^*) \tag{9.2.3}$$

for $j \ge i$. The assertion (9.2.3) holds for $j = i$, since $e_{ii}(t) = e^{tu_{ii}}$. Assuming that (9.2.3) holds for $j - i < k$, we prove that it holds for $j - i = k$. From the definition of $E(t)$ we have that

$$E'(t) = U \; E(t)$$

or

$$e'_{ij}(t) = \sum_{i \le \ell \le j} u_{i\ell} e_{\ell j}(t).$$

Therefore,

$$\frac{d}{dt} \left[e^{-tu_{ii}} e_{ij}(t) \right] = \sum_{i < \ell \le j} u_{i\ell} e_{\ell j}(t) e^{-tu_{ii}}$$

and hence

$$e^{-tu_{ii}} e_{ij}(t) = \int_0^t \sum_{i < \ell \le j} u_{i\ell} e_{\ell j}(\tau) e^{-\tau u_{ii}} \, d\tau.$$

Using (9.2.3) for $j - \ell$ less than $j - i$, we have

$$|e^{-tu_{ii}} e_{ij}(t)| \le \int_0^t u^* \sum_{i < \ell \le j} m_{j-\ell}(\tau u^*) |e^{\tau(\bar{u} - u_{ii})}| \, d\tau$$

$$\le u^* \int_0^t \sum_{i < \ell \le j} m_{j-\ell}(\tau u^*) \, d\tau$$

$$= u^* \int_0^t m'_{j-i}(\tau u^*) \, d\tau = m_{j-i}(tu^*),$$

by the defining equation for $m_k(\tau)$. This proves (9.2.3).

Depending on the matrix norm being used, there is a constant C_d' such that

$$\|E(t)\| \leq C_d' \max |e_{ij}(t)| \leq C_d' \, e^{t\bar{u}} \, (1 + m_{d-1}(tu^*))$$

since $m_k < m_{k+1}$ for positive k. Since $m_{d-1}(tu^*)$ is of degree $d-1$, the lemma follows. ∎

We use this lemma to study the matrix exponential in (9.2.2). By Schur's lemma (see Appendix A) there is a unitary matrix function $O(\omega)$ such that $O(\omega)Q(\omega)O(\omega)^{-1}$ is upper triangular. Let

$$\tilde{Q}(\omega) = O(\omega)Q(\omega)O(\omega)^{-1}.$$

Then, using the ℓ^2 norm for matrices,

$$\|e^{tQ(\omega)}\| = \|e^{t\tilde{Q}(\omega)}\| \leq C_d \, e^{t\bar{q}(\omega)} \left[1 + |tq^*(\omega)|^{d-1}\right] \tag{9.2.4}$$

where

$$\bar{q}(\omega) = \max_{1 \leq v \leq d} \mathrm{Re} \, q_v(\omega)$$

and

$$q^*(\omega) = \max_{j>i} |\tilde{Q}_{ij}(\omega)|,$$

similar to the definition of u^* in Lemma 9.2.2. Moreover, since the diagonal elements of $e^{t\tilde{Q}(\omega)}$ are $e^{tq_v(\omega)}$, where $q_v(\omega)$ is an eigenvalue of $Q(\omega)$, we see that a necessary condition for (9.2.2) to hold is that (9.1.5) hold for each eigenvalue of $Q(\omega)$. We also see that sufficient conditions for (9.2.2) to hold must usually involve some information about the off-diagonal elements of $\tilde{Q}(\omega)$.

We next give general definitions of parabolic and hyperbolic systems in N dimensions.

Definition 9.2.1 *The system*

$$u_t = \sum_{j_1,j_2=1}^{N} B_{j_1 j_2} \frac{\partial^2 u}{\partial x_{j_1} \partial x_{j_2}} + \sum_{j=1}^{N} C_j \frac{\partial u}{\partial x_j} + Du, \tag{9.2.5}$$

for which

$$Q(\omega) = -\sum_{j_1,j_2=1}^{N} B_{j_1 j_2} \omega_{j_1} \omega_{j_2} + i \sum_{j=1}^{N} C_j \omega_j + D,$$

is parabolic if the eigenvalues, $q_v(\omega)$, of $Q(\omega)$ satisfy

$$\mathrm{Re} \, q_v(\omega) \leq a - b|\omega|^2 \tag{9.2.6}$$

for some constant a and positive constant b.

For a parabolic system we have, in the notation of Lemma 9.2.2, that

$$\bar{q}(\omega) \leq a - b|\omega|^2$$

for some positive constant b. The quantity $q^*(\omega)$ is bounded by a constant multiple of $1 + |\omega|^2$, in general. Thus from (9.2.4)

$$\|e^{tQ(\omega)}\| \leq C \, e^{t(a-b\omega^2)} \left(1 + (1+|\omega|^2)^{d-1}t^{d-1}\right) \leq C_t$$

where C_t is independent of ω.

We see that condition (9.2.6), which is only on the eigenvalues of $Q(\omega)$, is sufficient to assure that the system is well-posed. No other assumptions on the matrix $Q(\omega)$ are needed.

We show later, in Theorem 9.2.4, that the lower-order terms, those involving the C_j and D, do not affect the well-posed nature of the system and so can be ignored in applying Definition 9.2.1.

We see from (9.2.4) that if $\bar{q}(\omega)$ is bounded below for large ω, then the system will not be well-posed unless $q^*(\omega)$ is zero. This is why hyperbolic systems are required to be diagonalizable.

Definition 9.2.2   *The system*

$$u_t = \sum_{j=1}^{N} A_j \frac{\partial u}{\partial x_j} + Bu \tag{9.2.7}$$

with

$$Q(\omega) = i \sum_{j=1}^{N} A_j \omega_j + B$$

is hyperbolic if the eigenvalues of $Q(\omega)$, $q_v(\omega)$, *satisfy*

$$\operatorname{Re} q_v(\omega) \leq c \tag{9.2.8}$$

for some constant c *and if* $Q(\omega)$ *is uniformly diagonalizable for large* ω, *that is, for each* ω *with* $|\omega|$ *greater than some value* K, *there is a matrix* $M(\omega)$ *such that*

$$M(\omega)Q(\omega)M^{-1}(\omega)$$

is diagonal and the norms of $M(\omega)$ *and* $M(\omega)^{-1}$ *are bounded independently of* ω.

The conditions for a hyperbolic system are precisely those needed to make the expression in (9.2.4) bounded; that is, $\bar{q}(\omega)$ is bounded by (9.2.8) and $q^*(\omega)$ can be taken to be zero, since $Q(\omega)$ is diagonalizable. Note, however, that $M(\omega)$ need not be unitary as was $O(\omega)$ in deriving (9.2.4), but $M(\omega)$ and $M(\omega)^{-1}$ need to be bounded in norm. As with parabolic systems the lower-order term, in this case Bu, does not effect the well-posed nature of the hyperbolic system (9.2.7).

Lower-Order Terms

We next show that lower-order terms do not affect the well-posedness of hyperbolic and parabolic systems. We begin with a theorem applicable to the hyperbolic systems and to the undifferentiated term in parabolic systems.

Theorem 9.2.3 *If the system*

$$\hat{u}_t = Q(\omega)\hat{u} \tag{9.2.9}$$

is well-posed and $Q_0(\omega)$ is bounded independently of ω, then the system

$$\hat{u}_t = (Q(\omega) + Q_0(\omega))\,\hat{u} \tag{9.2.10}$$

is also well-posed.

Proof Let c_0 be a constant such that

$$\|Q_0(\omega)\| \leq c_0$$

and assume that C_t as defined by (9.2.2) is a nondecreasing function of t. From (9.2.10) we have

$$\left[e^{-Q(\omega)t}\hat{u}(t,\omega)\right]_t = e^{-Q(\omega)t}Q_0(\omega)\hat{u}(t,\omega)$$

and so

$$\hat{u}(t,\omega) = e^{Q(\omega)t}\hat{u}_0(\omega) + \int_0^t e^{Q(\omega)(t-\tau)}Q_0(\omega)\hat{u}(\tau,\omega)\,d\tau.$$

Therefore, by the well-posedness of (9.2.9),

$$|\hat{u}(t,\omega)| \leq C_t|\hat{u}_0(\omega)| + c_0 C_t \int_0^t |\hat{u}(\tau,\omega)|\,d\tau, \tag{9.2.11}$$

where we have used our assumption that C_t is a nondecreasing function of t. If we define the function $U(t,\omega)$ by

$$U(t,\omega) = \int_0^t |\hat{u}(\tau,\omega)|\,d\tau,$$

then (9.2.11) can be written

$$\frac{d}{dt}U(t,\omega) \leq C_t|\hat{u}_0(\omega)| + c_0 C_t\, U(t,\omega).$$

We then obtain, using a method similar to that used for obtaining (9.2.11),

$$U(t,\omega) \leq \frac{e^{c_0 C_T t} - 1}{c_0}|\hat{u}_0(\omega)|$$

for $0 \leq t \leq T$. Substituting this inequality in (9.2.11), we have that $|\hat{u}(t, \omega)|$ is bounded by $C_T e^{c_0 C_T t} |\hat{u}_0(\omega)|$ for $0 \leq t \leq T$. Taking T equal to t, we have

$$|\hat{u}(t, \omega)| \leq C_t e^{c_0 C_t t} |\hat{u}_0(\omega)| = C_t^* |\hat{u}_0(\omega)|.$$

Since

$$\hat{u}(t, \omega) = e^{\left(Q(\omega) + Q_0(\omega)\right)t} \hat{u}_0(\omega)$$

and $\hat{u}_0(\omega)$ is an arbitrary value for each ω, we have

$$\left\| e^{(Q(\omega) + Q_0(\omega))t} \right\| \leq C_t^*$$

which shows that (9.2.10) is well-posed. ∎

Theorem 9.2.3 shows that the matrix B, the lower-order term in the hyperbolic system (9.2.7), does not affect the well-posedness of the system (9.2.7). If the matrix B is zero, then the constant c in (9.2.8) can be taken to be zero, and the constant K in Definition 9.2.2 can also be taken to be zero. These last results follow from the observation that if B is zero, then $Q(\omega)$ is a homogeneous matrix function of ω, that is, $Q(\alpha \omega) = \alpha Q(\omega)$ for any real number α.

Theorem 9.2.3 also shows that the matrix D in the parabolic system (9.2.5) does not affect the well-posedness. We next show that the first-derivative terms, the C_j in (9.2.5), also do not affect the well-posed nature of the system. We actually prove a more general theorem.

Theorem 9.2.4   *If the system*

$$\hat{u}_t = Q(\omega)\, u \tag{9.2.12}$$

satisfies

$$\left\| e^{Q(\omega)t} \right\| \leq K_t e^{-b|\omega|^\rho t}$$

for some positive constants b and ρ, with K_t independent of ω, and if $Q_0(\omega)$ satisfies

$$\|Q_0(\omega)\| \leq c_0 |\omega|^\sigma$$

with $\sigma < \rho$, then the system

$$\hat{u}_t = [Q(\omega) + Q_0(\omega)]\, \hat{u}$$

is also well-posed.

Proof We prove this theorem dealing directly with the exponential of the matrix $(Q(\omega) + Q_0(\omega))\, t$ rather than the functions $\hat{u}(t, \omega)$, as was done in the proof of Theorem 9.2.3. Let

$$E(t, \omega) = e^{(Q(\omega)+Q_0(\omega))t}.$$

Then $E(t, \omega)$ satisfies the ordinary differential equation

$$\frac{d}{dt} E(t, \omega) = Q(\omega)E(t, \omega) + Q_0(\omega)E(t, \omega)$$

with $E(0, \omega) = I$. Thus

$$\frac{d}{dt}\left[e^{-Q(\omega)t} E(t, \omega) \right] = e^{-Q(\omega)t} Q_0(\omega)E(t, \omega),$$

and so we have the representation

$$E(t, \omega) = e^{Q(\omega)t} + \int_0^t e^{Q(\omega)(t-\tau)} Q_0(\omega)E(\tau, \omega)\, d\tau.$$

Therefore, using the estimates on $e^{Q(\omega)t}$ and $Q_0(\omega)$,

$$\|E(t, \omega)\| \;\leq\; K_t\, e^{-b|\omega|^\rho t} + c_0 K_t |\omega|^\sigma \int_0^t e^{-b|\omega|^\rho (t-\tau)} \|E(\tau, \omega)\|\, d\tau. \qquad (9.2.13)$$

If we define the function $F(t)$ by

$$F(t) = \int_0^t e^{b|\omega|^\rho \tau} \|E(\tau, \omega)\|\, d\tau,$$

then (9.2.13) can be rewritten as

$$\frac{d}{dt} F(t) \;\leq\; K_t + c_0 K_t |\omega|^\sigma F(t)$$

from which we obtain

$$F(t) \;\leq\; \frac{e^{c_0 K_T |\omega|^\sigma t} - 1}{c_0 |\omega|^\sigma} \quad \text{for } 0 \leq t \leq T,$$

where we have assumed, without loss of generality, that K_t is a nondecreasing function of t. Applying this in (9.2.13) with $t = T$, we obtain

$$\|E(t, \omega)\| \;\leq\; K_t e^{-(b|\omega|^\rho - c_0 K_t |\omega|^\sigma)t} \;\leq\; K_t^*$$

since ρ is greater than σ. This proves the theorem. ∎

We next show that the function C_t in (9.1.2) can always be chosen to be an exponential function of t.

Lemma 9.2.5 *The function C_t in (9.1.2) and (9.2.2) can always be taken in the form*

$$Ke^{at}$$

for some constants K and a.

Proof   We have

$$\|e^{Q(\omega)t}\| \leq K \quad \text{for } 0 \leq t \leq 1$$

where

$$K = \max_{0 \leq t \leq 1} C_t.$$

For t larger that 1, set

$$t = n + t'$$

where $0 \leq t' < 1$. Then

$$e^{Q(\omega)t} = \left(e^{Q(\omega)}\right)^n e^{Q(\omega)t'},$$

and so

$$\|e^{Q(\omega)t}\| \leq \|e^{Q(\omega)}\|^n \|e^{Q(\omega)t'}\| \leq K^{n+1} \leq K e^{at}$$

where $K = e^a$. This proves the lemma. ∎

The value of this lemma is that it shows that expressions such as

$$C_t e^{c_0 C_t t},$$

which was obtained in the proof of Theorem 9.2.3, are unnecessarily pessimistic. The actual growth will never be worse than exponential growth in t.

Weakly Hyperbolic Systems

It is also worthwhile to consider the consequences of relaxing the definition of a well-posed initial value problem for systems. For example, the system

$$\begin{pmatrix} u^1 \\ u^2 \end{pmatrix}_t = \begin{pmatrix} 1 & 1 \\ 0 & 1 \end{pmatrix} \begin{pmatrix} u^1 \\ u^2 \end{pmatrix}_x, \tag{9.2.14}$$

is similar to a hyperbolic system, since the eigenvalues of the symbol are purely imaginary; however, the symbol

$$Q(\omega) = i\omega \begin{pmatrix} 1 & 1 \\ 0 & 1 \end{pmatrix}$$

is not diagonalizable. Such a system is sometimes called a *weakly hyperbolic system*. It is easy to see that the solution to (9.2.14) is

$$u^1(t, x) = u^1(0, x + t) + t u_x^2(0, x + t)$$

$$u^2(t, x) = u^2(0, x + t).$$

As these equations show, the solution depends on the first derivative of the initial data as well as the data itself, i.e.,

$$\|u^{(1)}(t,\cdot)\| + \|u^{(2)}(t,\cdot)\| \leq C \left[\|u^{(1)}(0,\cdot)\| + \|u^2(0,\cdot)\| + \|u_x^2(0,\cdot)\| \right]. \quad (9.2.15)$$

This is not serious in itself; the difficulty with such a system is that the addition of lower-order terms will make the system ill-posed. In particular, the system

$$u_t^{(1)} = u_x^{(1)} + u_x^{(2)}$$

$$u_t^{(2)} = \varepsilon u^{(1)} + u_x^{(2)}$$

is ill-posed for any nonzero value of ε. The eigenvalues of the system are

$$q_\pm = i\omega \pm (i\varepsilon\omega)^{1/2}$$

and it is easily seen that condition (9.2.2) is not satisfied.

As this example shows, Theorem 9.2.3 does not extend to the situation where weaker estimates such as (9.2.15) hold. This example was used by Kreiss [27] to demonstrate the effect of variable coefficients on the well-posed nature of systems. Examples such as this show that estimate (9.1.2) is that which best embodies the notion of a well-behaved process and which also leads to a reasonable mathematical theory of well-posed initial value problems.

EXERCISE 9.2

1. Show that the system

$$u_t + v_{txx} = u_x$$

$$u_{tx} + v_t = v_{xx}$$

can be put into the form (9.2.1). Determine if the system is well-posed.

9.3 Estimates for Inhomogeneous Problems

We now consider the inhomogeneous initial value problem, $Pu = f$, to estimate the solution at time t in terms of the initial data and the data $f(t, x)$. We consider a single partial differential equation, $Pu = f$, with constant coefficients, that is first-order in the derivative with respect to t. Under the Fourier transform it may be written as

$$\hat{u}_t(t, \omega) = q(\omega)\hat{u}(t, \omega) + r(\omega)\hat{f}(t, \omega) \quad (9.3.1)$$

where the factor of $r(\omega)$ arises from normalizing the equation so that the coefficient of $\hat{u}_t$ is 1 (see Exercise 9.3.1). We also require that there are constants $\bar{q}$ and C_1 such that the well-posedness estimate (9.1.5) holds, i.e.,

$$\text{Re } q(\omega) \leq \bar{q}$$

and also

$$|r(\omega)| \leq C_1 . \tag{9.3.2}$$

The solution of (9.3.1) can be written as

$$\hat{u}(t, \omega) = e^{q(\omega)t}\hat{u}_0(\omega) + r(\omega) \int_0^t e^{q(\omega)(t-s)} \hat{f}(s, \omega) \, ds. \tag{9.3.3}$$

From this we easily obtain, from (9.3.1) and (9.3.2),

$$|\hat{u}(t, \omega)|^2 \leq Ce^{2\bar{q}t} \left[|\hat{u}_0(\omega)|^2 + \int_0^t |\hat{f}(s, \omega)|^2 \, ds \right],$$

and hence

$$\|u(t, \cdot)\|^2 \leq Ce^{2\bar{q}t} \left[\|u_0\|^2 + \int_0^t \|f(s, \cdot)\|^2 \, ds \right]. \tag{9.3.4}$$

For a stable finite difference scheme an analogous estimate holds. We prove it now for one-step schemes. All the one-step schemes we have considered may be written as

$$\hat{v}^{n+1}(\xi) = g(h\xi)\hat{v}^n(\xi) + k\hat{F}^n(\xi) \tag{9.3.5}$$

where g is the amplification factor and

$$|\hat{F}^n(\xi)| \leq C \left[|\hat{f}^n(\xi)| + |\hat{f}^{n+1}(\xi)| \right]. \tag{9.3.6}$$

The solution to (9.3.5) can be written as

$$\hat{v}^n(\xi) = g(h\xi)^n \hat{v}^0(\xi) + k \sum_{\ell=0}^{n-1} g(h\xi)^{n-\ell} \hat{F}^\ell(\xi). \tag{9.3.7}$$

We then have

$$|\hat{v}^n(\xi)|^2 \leq 2 \left[|g(h\xi)|^{2n} |\hat{v}^0(\xi)|^2 + \left| k \sum_{\ell=0}^{n-1} g(h\xi)^{n-\ell} \hat{F}^\ell(\xi) \right|^2 \right]$$

$$\leq 2 \left[|g(h\xi)|^{2n} |\hat{v}^0(\xi)|^2 + k \sum_{\ell=0}^{n-1} |g(h\xi)|^{2(n-\ell)} k \sum_{\ell=0}^{n-1} |\hat{F}^\ell(\xi)|^2 \right]$$

$$\leq 2 \left[(1 + Kk)^{2n} |\hat{v}^0(\xi)|^2 + k \sum_{\ell=0}^{n-1} (1 + Kk)^{2(n-\ell)} k \sum_{\ell=0}^{n-1} |\hat{F}^\ell(\xi)|^2 \right]$$

$$\leq 2(1 + Kk)^{2n} \left[|\hat{v}^0(\xi)|^2 + (kn)k \sum_{\ell=0}^{n-1} |\hat{F}^\ell(\xi)|^2 \right]$$

$$\leq C_T \left[|\hat{v}^0(\xi)|^2 + k \sum_{\ell=0}^{n-1} |\hat{F}^\ell(\xi)|^2 \right].$$

Then by Parseval's relation and (9.3.6),

$$\|v^n\|^2 \le C_T (\|v^0\|^2 + k \sum_{\ell=0}^{n} \|f^\ell\|^2).\tag{9.3.8}$$

Estimates (9.3.4) and (9.3.8) show that for both the well-posed partial differential equation and the stable finite difference scheme, the solution depends continuously on the data. For example, consider the two initial value problems

$$Pu^{(1)} = f^{(1)} \qquad u^{(1)}(0, x) = u_0^{(1)}(x)$$

$$Pu^{(2)} = f^{(2)} \qquad u^{(2)}(0, x) = u_0^{(2)}(x).$$

The difference of the solutions can be estimated in terms of the difference in the data, i.e.,

$$\|u^{(1)}(t, \cdot) - u^{(2)}(t, \cdot)\|^2 \le C_T \left(\|u_0^{(1)} - u_0^{(2)}\|^2 + \int_0^t \|f^{(1)}(s, \cdot) - f^{(2)}(s, \cdot)\|^2 \, ds \right).$$

It is essential that a differential equation describing the evolution of a physical system satisfy such an estimate. The estimate expresses the idea that small changes in the data result in small changes in the solution at the later times. In particular, it shows that errors in the data will be magnified by only a fixed amount, determined by C_T. For finite difference schemes the estimate shows that the round-off error, which is inherent in all computation, will grow at a limited rate. It is for this reason that the effects of round-off error are not a major concern in the study of finite difference schemes for partial differential equations.

Duhamel's Principle

Solution formulas (9.3.3) and (9.3.7) express *Duhamel's principle*, which states that the solution to an inhomogeneous initial value problem can be regarded as the superposition of solutions to homogeneous initial value problems. For (9.3.3), consider the homogeneous initial value problems for (9.3.1) with solutions $u(t, \omega; s)$ that have initial data prescribed at $t = s$ given by

$$\hat{u}(s, \omega; s) = r(\omega)\hat{f}(s, \omega).$$

Then (9.3.3) can be written as

$$\hat{u}(t, \omega) = e^{q(\omega)t}\hat{u}_0(\omega) + \int_0^t \hat{u}(t, \omega; s) \, ds.$$

Similarly, for (9.3.7) we have

$$\hat{v}^n = g^n \hat{v}^0 + \sum_{\ell=0}^{n-1} \hat{v}^{n,\ell}$$

where $\hat{v}^{n,\ell}$ is the solution to the homogeneous initial value problem starting at time level ℓ with

$$\hat{v}^{\ell,\ell} = k\widehat{F}^{\ell}.$$

The well-posedness and stability estimates for the inhomogeneous initial value problems are direct consequences of the estimates for the homogeneous problems.

EXERCISE 9.3

1. Show that equations (1.1.3) and (1.4.1) may be put in the form (9.3.1).

9.4 The Kreiss Matrix Theorem

In Section 7.1 the stability condition for a one-step scheme for a system was shown to be as follows: For each $T > 0$, there is a constant C_T such that

$$\|G(\theta, k, h)^n\| \le C_T \tag{9.4.1}$$

for all n with $0 \le nk \le T$. As for the constants in the estimates for well-posed initial value problems, we can always take the constant C_T in (9.4.1) to have the form

$$C_T = Ke^{at} = Ke^{akn}$$

(see Lemma 9.2.5). Thus estimate (9.4.1) is equivalent to

$$\|\tilde{G}(\theta, k, h)^n\| \le K \tag{9.4.2}$$

for all n where $\tilde{G} = e^{-ak}G$.

The Kreiss matrix theorem gives several equivalent characterizations of families of matrices satisfying conditions such as (9.4.2). The theorem considers a family, or set, F, of $M \times M$ matrices. In the context of finite difference schemes, the matrices would depend continuously on the parameters θ, k, and h; however, the theorem can be stated as a result in matrix theory without referring to our intended applications.

Theorem 9.4.1   The Kreiss Matrix Theorem. *For a family F of $M \times M$ matrices, the following statements are equivalent.*
  A: There exists a positive constant C_a such that for all $A \in F$ and each nonnegative integer n,

$$\|A^n\| \le C_a. \tag{9.4.3}$$

  R: There exists a positive constant C_r such that for all $A \in F$ and all complex numbers z with $|z| > 1$,

$$\|(zI - A)^{-1}\| \le C_r(|z| - 1)^{-1}. \tag{9.4.4}$$

S: There exist positive constants C_s and C_b such that for each $A \in F$ there is a nonsingular hermitian matrix S such that $B = SAS^{-1}$ is upper triangular and

$$\|S\|, \|S^{-1}\| \leq C_s \tag{9.4.5a}$$

$$|B_{ii}| \leq 1 \tag{9.4.5b}$$

$$|B_{ij}| \leq C_b \min[1 - |B_{ii}|, 1 - |B_{jj}|] \tag{9.4.5c}$$

for $i < j$.

H: There exists a positive constant C_h such that for each $A \in F$ there is a hermitian matrix H such that

$$C_h^{-1} I \leq H \leq C_h I \tag{9.4.6a}$$

$$A^* H A \leq H. \tag{9.4.6b}$$

N: There exists constants C_n and c_n such that for each $A \in F$ there is a hermitian matrix N such that

$$C_n^{-1} I \leq N \leq C_n I \tag{9.4.7a}$$

$$\mathrm{Re}\,(N(I - zA)) \geq c_n(1 - |z|)I \tag{9.4.7b}$$

for all complex numbers z with $|z| \leq 1$.

Ω : There exists a positive constant C_ω such that for each $A \in F$ there is a hermitian matrix Ω such that

$$C_\omega^{-1} I \leq \Omega \leq C_\omega I \tag{9.4.8a}$$

$$\sup_{x \neq 0} \frac{|(\Omega A^n x, x)|}{(\Omega x, x)} \leq 1. \tag{9.4.8b}$$

The original Kreiss matrix theorem (Kreiss [26]) contained only the first four conditions, $A, R, S,$ and H. The condition Ω was proved equivalent to the original four conditions by Tadmor [48] and condition N was added by Strikwerda and Wade [47].

In some applications it is important to know when the matrices $H, N,$ and Ω can be constructed to be (locally) continuous functions of the elements of F. Although this result can be established for some special families, it has not been established in general.

Proof   We will prove that these conditions are all equivalent by showing that each condition implies the next one, in the given order, and finally that condition Ω implies condition A.

We first show that condition A implies condition R. We have that

$$(zI - A)^{-1} = \sum_{j=0}^{\infty} z^{-(j+1)} A^j$$

for large values of z. Thus

$$\|(zI - A)^{-1}\| \leq \sum_{j=0}^{\infty} |z|^{-(j+1)} C_a \leq C_a(|z| - 1)^{-1}$$

which is condition R. The expression $(zI - A)^{-1}$ is called the *resolvent* of A; it is an analytic matrix-valued function of z, and condition R is often called the resolvent condition.

The proof that condition R implies condition S is the most difficult portion of the proof and we postpone this until the end.

We next show that condition S implies condition H. We construct the matrix H as $S^* D^2 S$, where the matrix D is a diagonal matrix whose jth entry is ε^{M-j}, where ε is a positive parameter to be chosen later. Condition (9.4.6b) is then seen to be

$$A^* S^* D^2 S A \leq S^* D^2 S$$

or

$$B^* D^2 B \leq D^2.$$

Finally, if we set $\tilde{B} = DBD^{-1}$, this condition is

$$\tilde{B}^* \tilde{B} \leq I$$

or, equivalently,

$$|\tilde{B}x|^2 \leq |x|^2 \tag{9.4.9}$$

for any vector x in C^M. Since B is an upper triangular matrix, we have that the elements of $\tilde{B}$ are given by

$$\tilde{B}_{ij} = B_{ij} \varepsilon^{j-i}.$$

Thus, by the Cauchy-Schwarz inequality,

$$|\tilde{B}x|^2 = \sum_{i=1}^{M} |(\tilde{B}x)_i|^2 = \sum_{i=1}^{M} \left| \sum_{j=i}^{M} B_{ij} \varepsilon^{j-i} x_j \right|^2$$

$$\leq \sum_{i=1}^{M} \left(\sum_{j=i}^{M} |B_{ij}| \varepsilon^{j-i} |x_j|^2 \right) \left(\sum_{j=i}^{M} |B_{ij}| \varepsilon^{j-i} \right).$$

Now we consider each portion of this sum, beginning with the sum over j. Using estimate (9.4.5c), we obtain

$$\sum_{j=i}^{M} |B_{ij}| \varepsilon^{j-i} = |B_{ii}| + \sum_{j=i+1}^{M} |B_{ij}| \varepsilon^{j-i}$$

$$\leq |B_{ii}| + C_b (1 - |B_{ii}|) \sum_{j=i+1}^{M} \varepsilon^{j-1} \qquad (9.4.10)$$

$$\leq |B_{ii}| + C_b \frac{\varepsilon}{1 - \varepsilon} (1 - |B_{ii}|) \leq 1$$

if ε is chosen so that

$$\frac{C_b \varepsilon}{1 - \varepsilon} \leq 1. \qquad (9.4.11)$$

With this choice of ε we have

$$|\tilde{B}x|^2 \leq \sum_{i=1}^{M} \sum_{j=i}^{M} |B_{ij}| \varepsilon^{j-i} |x_j|^2 = \sum_{j=1}^{M} |x_j|^2 \sum_{i=1}^{j} |B_{ij}| \varepsilon^{j-i}.$$

We next employ an argument similar to (9.4.10). Considering the sum over j we obtain

$$\sum_{i=1}^{j} |B_{ij}| \varepsilon^{j-i} \leq |B_{jj}| + \frac{C_b \varepsilon}{1 - \varepsilon} (1 - |B_{jj}|) \leq 1.$$

Thus if ε is chosen to satisfy (9.4.11), then (9.4.9) holds, which is equivalent to condition (9.4.6b). The choice of ε is seen to depend only on C_b. Thus

$$H = S^* D^2 S \leq C_s^2 \varepsilon^{-2M}$$

and, similarly, $H \geq C_s^{-2} \varepsilon^{2M}$, which establishes condition H.

To prove condition N, we start with

$$0 \leq (I - zA)^* H (I - zA)$$

$$= H - 2 \operatorname{Re}(HzA) + |z|^2 A^* HA$$

$$= 2 \operatorname{Re}[H(I - zA)] - H + |z|^2 A^* HA$$

$$\leq 2 \operatorname{Re}[H(I - zA)] + (|z|^2 - 1)H.$$

Thus if $|z| \leq 1$ and using the bounds on H,

$$C_n^{-1}(1 - |z|)I \leq H(1 - |z|) \leq H(1 - |z|^2) \leq 2 \operatorname{Re}[H(I - zA)]$$

and condition N holds with N equal to H.

The proof that condition N implies condition Ω is similar to the proof of the Halmos inequality given by Pearcy [42]. We begin with two relationships for all complex numbers z,

$$1 - z^n = \prod_{k=1}^n (1 - \zeta_k z) \tag{9.4.12}$$

$$1 = \frac{1}{n} \sum_{j=1}^n \prod_{\substack{k=1 \\ k \neq j}}^n (1 - \zeta_k z), \tag{9.4.13}$$

where the ζ_k are the nth roots of unity.

As purely algebraic relationships these relationships hold also when z is replaced by a matrix A. For any vector x and complex number γ, with $|\gamma| = 1$, we define

$$x_j = \prod_{\substack{k=1 \\ k \neq j}}^n (1 - \zeta_k \gamma A) x.$$

By (9.4.13) we have that

$$x = \frac{1}{n} \sum_{j=1}^n x_j.$$

Condition N with $z = \gamma \zeta_j$ implies that

$$0 \leq \frac{1}{n} \sum_{j=1}^n \mathrm{Re}\ (N(I - \zeta_j \gamma A)x_j, x_j)$$

$$= \frac{1}{n} \sum_{j=1}^n \mathrm{Re}\ (N(I - \gamma^n A^n)x, x_j)$$

$$= \mathrm{Re}\ (N(I - \gamma^n A^n)x, x).$$

By choosing γ so that

$$\mathrm{Re}\ (\gamma^n N A^n x, x) = |(N A^n x, x)|$$

we obtain

$$|(N A^n x, x)| \leq (Nx, x).$$

Thus condition N is satisfied with Ω equal to N and C_ω equal to C_n.

The last implication is that condition Ω implies condition A. We use the following relations: For a symmetric matrix S we have

$$\sup_{|x|=1} |(Sx, x)| = \|S\|$$

and for any matrix B

$$B = \frac{1}{2}(B + B^*) - \frac{i}{2}(B - B^*),$$

so

$$\|B\| \le \frac{1}{2}\|(B + B^*)\| + \frac{1}{2}\|(B - B^*)\| \le 2 \sup_{|x|=1} |(Bx, x)|.$$

Since the matrix Ω is positive definite and hermitian, it has a positive definite and hermitian square root T, with both $\|T\|$ and $\|T^{-1}\|$ bounded by $C_\omega^{1/2}$. Thus we have

$$\|A^n\| = \|T^{-1}T\,A^nT^{-1}T\| \le \|T^{-1}\|\,\|T\|\,\|T\,A^nT^{-1}\|$$

$$\le 2\|T^{-1}\|\,\|T\| \sup_{|x|=1} |(T\,A^nT^{-1}x, x)|$$

$$= 2\|T^{-1}\|\,\|T\| \sup_{|x|=1} |(\Omega\,A^nT^{-1}x, T^{-1}x)|$$

$$\le 2\|T^{-1}\|\,\|T\| \sup_{|x|=1} |(\Omega\,T^{-1}x, T^{-1}x)|$$

$$= 2\|T^{-1}\|\,\|T\| \le 2C_\omega.$$

It remains to prove that condition R implies condition S. We begin this portion of the proof by assuming that the matrix A is upper triangular. This is permissible by Schur's lemma (Proposition A.5 in Appendix A). We may also assume that the diagonal elements of A are ordered so that

$$|a_{ii}| \ge |a_{jj}| \quad \text{for } i < j, \tag{9.4.14}$$

that is, the eigenvalues are in order of decreasing magnitude. The resolvent of A, which is $R_z(A) = (zI - A)^{-1}$, is also an upper triangular matrix. We also note that any element of a matrix is bounded by the norm of the matrix.

The ith diagonal element of $R_z(A)$ is $(z - a_{ii})^{-1}$, and this is bounded by $C_r(|z| - 1)^{-1}$. It is then immediate that $|a_{ii}| \le 1$. We now proceed to construct the matrices B and S recursively, one diagonal at a time, for each diagonal above the main diagonal of the matrices.

Let r_{ij} denote the elements of the matrix $R_z(A)$. Since $R_z(A)$ is the inverse of $zI - A$, we obtain for j greater than i

$$[(zI - A)R_z(A)]_{ij} = (z - a_{ii})r_{ij} - \sum_{k=i+1}^{j} a_{ik}r_{kj} = 0. \tag{9.4.15}$$

For j equal to $i + 1$ we have

$$(z - a_{ii})r_{ij} - a_{ij}r_{jj} = 0.$$

Therefore, since $r_{jj} = (z - a_{jj})^{-1}$,

$$r_{ij} = \frac{a_{ij}}{(z - a_{ii})(z - a_{jj})}$$

Since $|r_{ij}| \leq C_r(|z| - 1)^{-1}$, we have

$$|a_{ij}| \leq C_r \frac{|(z - a_{ii})(z - a_{jj})|}{|z| - 1} \tag{9.4.16}$$

for all z such that $|z| > 1$. If the eigenvalue a_{ii} has magnitude of $\frac{1}{2}$ or less, then from (9.4.16), with z equal to $\frac{5}{2}$, we obtain

$$|a_{ij}| \leq C_r \frac{(|z| + \frac{1}{2})^2}{|z| - 1} \leq 6C_r \tag{9.4.17}$$

(Recall that by (9.4.14), $|a_{jj}|$ also has magnitude less than $\frac{1}{2}$.)

If $|a_{ii}|$ is greater than $\frac{1}{2}$ in magnitude, then we set $z = t(\bar{a}_{ii})^{-1}$ in (9.4.16), where t is real and greater than 1, and then take the limit as t approaches 1. We obtain

$$|a_{ij}| \leq C_r \frac{(1 - |a_{ii}|^2)|1 - \bar{a}_{ii}a_{jj}|}{(1 - |a_{ii}|)|a_{ii}|} \leq 4C_r|1 - \bar{a}_{ii}a_{jj}|. \tag{9.4.18}$$

As in the proof given by Morton and Schecter [37] (see also Richtmyer and Morton [44]), we have

$$|1 - \bar{a}_{ii}a_{jj}| = |1 - |a_{ii}|^2 + \bar{a}_{ii}(a_{ii} - a_{jj})|$$

$$\leq (1 + |a_{ii}|)(1 - |a_{ii}|) + |a_{ii}||a_{ii} - a_{jj}|$$

$$\leq (1 + 2|a_{ii}|)\max(1 - |a_{ii}|, |a_{ii} - a_{jj}|)$$

$$\leq 3\max(1 - |a_{ii}|, |a_{ii} - a_{jj}|).$$

Combining this estimate with (9.4.17) and (9.4.18), we obtain

$$|a_{ij}| \leq 12C_r \max(1 - |a_{ii}|, |a_{ii} - a_{jj}|). \tag{9.4.19}$$

If the maximum of $1 - |a_{ii}|$ and $|a_{ii} - a_{jj}|$ is the latter quantity, we consider the matrix $S^{(i,j)}$, which is the identity matrix except that the entry in location (i, j) is $a_{ij}(a_{ii} - a_{jj})^{-1}$. The matrix

$$S^{(i,j)}A(S^{(i,j)})^{-1} = A^{(i,j)}$$

has a zero in location (i, j). Moreover the elements of $A^{(i,j)}$ differ from those of A only in the locations (i', j') with $i' \leq i$ and $j' \geq j$. Taking the product of all $S^{(i,j)}$ formed in this way, call it S, we have that the matrix

$$\tilde{A} = SAS^{-1}$$

satisfies

$$|\tilde{a}_{ij}| \leq 12 C_r (1 - |\tilde{a}_{ii}|) \tag{9.4.20}$$

which is (9.4.5c) for $j = i + 1$. We also have that the norm of S is at most

$$(1 + 12 C_r)^{M-1},$$

since each $S^{(i,j)}$ has norm bounded by $1 + 12 C_r$. The matrix $\tilde{A}$ satisfies the resolvent condition (9.4.4) but with the constant $\tilde{C}_r$ equal to $\|S\| \|S^{-1}\| C_r$.

We continue for $j = i + \ell$ with $\ell > 1$, assuming that (9.4.20) is satisfied for all $j - i$ less than ℓ. From (9.4.15) we have

$$0 = (z - a_{ii}) r_{ij} - \sum_{k=i+1}^{j-1} a_{ik} r_{kj} - a_{ij} r_{jj}.$$

So, since r_{jj} is $(z - a_{jj})^{-1}$,

$$a_{ij} = r_{ij} (z - a_{ii})(z - a_{jj}) - \sum_{k=i+1}^{j-1} a_{ik} r_{kj} (z - a_{jj})$$

and so by (9.4.20)

$$|a_{ij}| \leq C_r \frac{|(z - a_{ii})(z - a_{jj})|}{|z| - 1} + 12 C_r \frac{|z - a_{jj}|(1 - |a_{ii}|)}{|z| - 1}.$$

We may proceed as in the case with $j = i + 1$. Notice that the constant C_r may increase at each step of the proof. However, it can always be chosen to depend only on the value of C_r at the earlier step and on M. This recursive alteration of A terminates in at most $M - 1$ steps, and thus the proof is complete, with B being the result of the modifications to A and S being the product of all the $S^{(i,j)}$ matrices. This proves that condition R implies condition S.

Since we have shown that each condition implies the succeeding one, the proof of the Kreiss matrix theorem is complete. ∎

The Kreiss matrix theorem is of theoretical importance because it relates the usual concept of stability, condition A, with equivalent conditions that may be useful in different contexts. It is of limited practical use in determining stability because the verification of any of the conditions is usually quite as difficult as verifying condition A itself.

It is also notable that the only portion of the theorem that depends on the finite dimensionality of the linear operators is that involving condition S. The conditions H, N, and Ω are all equivalent for families of operators on Hilbert spaces. Condition H states that in the norm $\| \cdot \|_H$, defined by

$$\|x\|_H = (x, Hx)^{1/2},$$

the operator A is a contraction, that is,

$$\|Ax\|_H \le \|x\|_H.$$

If this condition is satisfied, we say that A is equivalent to a contraction. It is easy to see that if A is equivalent to a contraction, with H satisfying (9.4.6a) then A is power bounded in the original norm, i.e., condition A holds. However, Foquel [17] has shown that there exist power-bounded operators on an infinite dimensional Hilbert space that are not equivalent to a contraction. Thus condition S is an essential part of the finite dimensional Kreiss matrix theorem.

EXERCISES 9.4

1.   Two other conditions that are equivalent to those of the Kreiss matrix theorem are:

M_1: There is a positive constant C_1 such that for each $N \ge 0$, each real value of θ, and each A in F,

$$\left\| \frac{1}{N+1} \sum_{n=0}^{N} A^n e^{in\theta} \right\| \le C_1.$$

M_2: There is a positive constant C_2 such that for each $N \ge 0$, each real value of θ, and each A in F,

$$\left\| \frac{2}{N+1} \sum_{n=0}^{N} (1 - \frac{n}{N}) A^n e^{in\theta} \right\| \le C_2.$$

Prove directly that condition A implies condition M_1, condition M_1 implies condition M_2, and condition M_2 implies condition R. *Hint:* To prove that condition M_2 implies R, consider the sum

$$\sum_{N=1}^{\infty} r^{N-1} \sum_{n=0}^{N} (N-n) A^n e^{in\theta}.$$

2.   Show that condition M_2, of Exercise 1, is equivalent to condition R for operators on a Hilbert or Banach space. To prove that condition R implies condition M_2, consider the contour integral

$$\frac{1}{2\pi i} \oint_\Gamma \left(\frac{z^{N/2} - z^{-N/2}}{z^{1/2} - z^{-1/2}} \right)^2 (zI - A)^{-1} dz$$

where Γ is the circle $|z| = 1 + N^{-1}$. Prove that

$$\frac{1}{2\pi} \int_\Gamma \left| \frac{z^{N/2} - z^{-N/2}}{z^{1/2} - z^{-1/2}} \right|^2 d\theta \le 4eN \left[1 + O(N^{-1}) \right].$$

3. By considering the contour integral

$$\frac{1}{2\pi i} \int_\Gamma z^n (zI - A)^{-1}\, dz$$

where Γ is the circle $|z| = 1 + (n+1)^{-1}$, show that if A satisfies the resolvent condition (9.4.4), then

$$\|A^n\| \le C^*(n+1)$$

for some constant C^* depending only on C_r and not on A.

Chapter 10

Convergence Estimates
for Initial Value Problems

In this chapter we derive estimates that give the rate at which the discrete solutions of finite difference schemes converge to the solution of the differential equation. We restrict ourselves at first to one-step schemes, for simplicity; multistep schemes are considered in Section 10.6. We also consider only scalar equations; the extension of these results to systems of equations is straightforward.

Only constant coefficient equations are considered in this text. The theorems we give can be extended to cover equations with variable coefficients, but the extension requires techniques beyond the scope of this text. Estimates for variable coefficient equations are proved by Peetre and Thomée [43] and by Wade [56]. Convergence estimates similar to what we prove here, but using different norms, are given in the lecture notes of Brenner, Thomée, and Wahlbin [5].

For simplicity we consider only one-dimensional problems. The theorems for higher-dimensional cases are given in the exercises.

10.1 Convergence Estimates for Smooth Initial Functions

We begin by addressing the problem of how to compare discrete functions defined on the mesh hZ with functions defined on the real line.

Definition 10.1.1 *The truncation operator T maps functions in $L^2(R)$ to functions in $L^2(hZ)$. Given $u \in L^2(R)$, we have*

$$u(x) = \frac{1}{\sqrt{2\pi}} \int_{-\infty}^{\infty} e^{ix\xi}\, \hat{u}(\xi)\, d\xi$$

and Tu is defined as

$$Tu_m = \frac{1}{\sqrt{2\pi}} \int_{-\pi/h}^{\pi/h} e^{imh\xi}\, \hat{u}(\xi)\, d\xi$$

for each grid point $mh \in hZ$. Alternatively, the Fourier transform of Tu is given by

$$\widehat{Tu}(\xi) = \hat{u}(\xi) \quad \text{for } |\xi| \le \frac{\pi}{h}.$$

Definition 10.1.2 *The interpolation operator* S *maps functions in* $L^2(hZ)$ *to functions on* $L^2(R)$. *Given* $v \in L^2(hZ)$, *we have*

$$v_m = \frac{1}{\sqrt{2\pi}} \int_{-\pi/h}^{\pi/h} e^{imh\xi} \, \hat{v}(\xi) \, d\xi$$

and $Sv(x)$ *is defined as*

$$Sv(x) = \frac{1}{\sqrt{2\pi}} \int_{-\pi/h}^{\pi/h} e^{ix\xi} \, \hat{v}(\xi) \, d\xi$$

for each $x \in R$. *Alternatively, the Fourier transform of* Sv *is given by*

$$\widehat{Sv}(\xi) = \begin{cases} \hat{v}(\xi) & \text{if } |\xi| \leq \pi/h, \\ 0 & \text{if } |\xi| > \pi/h. \end{cases}$$

Both of the operators T and S depend on the parameter h. We do not explicitly show this in the notation in order to keep our notation simple.

We now consider the numerical solution of partial differential equations in the form of (9.1.3), that is,

$$\hat{u}_t = q(\omega)\hat{u}, \tag{10.1.1}$$

by a stable one-step scheme. If the partial differential equation has initial function $u_0(x)$, we take as initial function for the scheme

$$v_m^0 = (Tu_0)_m. \tag{10.1.2}$$

Although this is not what we do in practice, it is the initial function for the scheme that gives the simplest estimates. Later we consider the effect of using other initial functions for the scheme.

We also need to refine the concept of order of accuracy as given in Section 3.1. The next definition of the order of accuracy of a finite difference scheme also takes account of the power of the dual variable ξ in the approximation of $e^{kq(\xi)}$ by the amplification factor. This is needed to quantify the idea of how much smoothness is required of the initial function so that the order of accuracy of the solutions of the scheme is equal to the order of accuracy of the scheme. In Theorem 10.1.1 we show that this definition is consistent with Definition 3.1.2.

Definition 10.1.3 *A one-step scheme for a first-order system in the form (10.1.1) with* $k = \Lambda(h)$ *is accurate of order* $[r, \rho]$ *if there is a constant* C *such that for* $|h\xi| \leq \pi$

$$\left| \frac{e^{kq(\xi)} - g(h\xi, k, h)}{k} \right| \leq Ch^r (1 + |\xi|)^\rho. \tag{10.1.3}$$

Note that square brackets are used in Definition 10.1.3 to distinguish this order of accuracy, i.e., $[r, \rho]$, from the parentheses used in Definition 3.1.1, i.e., (p, q).

Theorem 10.1.1   *If a one-step finite difference scheme for a well-posed initial value problem is accurate of order r according to Definition 3.1.2, then there is a nonnegative integer ρ such that the scheme is accurate of order $[r, \rho]$ according to Definition 10.1.3.*

Example 10.1 We illustrate the use of Definition 10.1.1 with the Lax-Wendroff and Lax-Friedrichs schemes for the one-way wave equation (1.1.1). For each case we take λ constant, i.e., $k = \lambda h$, and since there are no lower-order terms, we may replace the factor $(1 + |\xi|)^\rho$ by $|\xi|^\rho$. We have

$$e^{kq(\xi)} = e^{-ia\lambda\theta} = 1 - ia\lambda\theta - \frac{a^2\lambda^2\theta^2}{2} + i\frac{a^3\lambda^3\theta^3}{6} + O(\theta^4),$$

and for the Lax-Wendroff scheme the amplification factor is

$$g(\theta)_{LW} = 1 - ia\lambda\sin\theta - 2a^2\lambda^2\sin^2\frac{1}{2}\theta,$$

$$= 1 - ia\lambda\theta - \frac{a^2\lambda^2\theta^2}{2} + i\frac{a\lambda\theta^3}{6} + O(\theta^4),$$

whereas for the Lax-Friedrichs scheme it is

$$g(\theta)_{LF} = \cos\theta - ia\lambda\sin\theta = 1 - ia\lambda\theta - \frac{\theta^2}{2} + O(\theta^3).$$

For the Lax-Wendroff scheme,

$$k^{-1}\left|e^{-ia\lambda\theta} - g(\theta)_{LW}\right| \le k^{-1}C_1\,|\theta|^3 = \lambda^{-1}C_1\,h^2|\xi|^3$$

showing that the scheme is accurate of order $[2, 3]$; for the Lax-Friedrichs scheme,

$$k^{-1}\left|e^{-ia\lambda\theta} - g(\theta)_{LF}\right| \le k^{-1}C_2\,|\theta|^2 = \lambda^{-1}C_2\,h|\xi|^2$$

showing that the scheme is accurate of order $[1, 2]$. $\square$

We postpone the proof of Theorem 10.1.1 until after we state and prove the main results of this section. For now we merely point out that for schemes for hyperbolic equations with λ constant, ρ is usually equal to $r + 1$, and for parabolic equations with μ constant, ρ is often $r + 2$ (see Exercises 10.1.1 and 10.1.2), however, these relationships do not hold in general.

Notice also that if a scheme is accurate of order $[r, \rho]$, then it is also accurate of order $[r - 1, \rho - 1]$ (see Exercise 10.1.5). Finally, we note that Theorem 10.1.1 requires the initial value problem for the differential equation to be well-posed but does not require the scheme to be stable. This last observation is important in proving convergence estimates for multistep schemes that are initialized with unstable schemes (see Section 10.6).

We now state the main result of this section.

Theorem 10.1.2 *If the initial value problem for a partial differential equation of the form (10.1.1), for which the initial value problem is well-posed, is approximated by a stable one-step finite difference scheme that is accurate of order $[r, \rho]$ with $r \leq \rho$ and the initial function is Tu_0, where u_0 is the initial function for the differential equation, then for each time T there exists a constant C_T such that*

$$\|u(t_n, \cdot) - Sv^n\| \leq C_T h^r \|u_0\|_{H^\rho} \tag{10.1.4}$$

for each $t_n = nk$ with $0 \leq t_n \leq T$.

Before beginning the proof of this theorem we make several observations. First notice that to get the optimal accuracy we must have sufficiently smooth functions. If the initial function is not in H^ρ (the space H^ρ is defined in Section 2.1), then the order of convergence in h will be less than r, as we show in the next section. Secondly, the choice of the initial function for the scheme, Tu_0, is not natural in actual computation, nor is the comparison of u with Sv. Later we examine the consequences of using $u_0(mh)$ instead of $Tu_0(mh)$ as the initial function and also comparing $u(t_n, x_m)$ with v_m^n.

For simplicity of exposition we make two assumptions to reduce the technical details. We assume that $\bar{q}$ in (9.1.5) is zero and that the restricted stability condition (2.2.7) is applicable, that is, we assume

$$|e^{tq(\xi)}| \leq 1 \quad \text{and} \quad |g(h\xi)| \leq 1. \tag{10.1.5}$$

The proof without these assumptions is left as an exercise (see Exercise 10.1.6).

Proof of Theorem 10.1.2 To begin, we seek an estimate of the difference between $Sv^n(x)$ and $u(t_n, x)$. We have by the discussion of Section 2.2 and the definition of the amplification factor in Section 2.2 that

$$v_m^n = \frac{1}{\sqrt{2\pi}} \int_{-\pi/h}^{\pi/h} e^{imh\xi} g(h\xi)^n \hat{u}_0(\xi) \, d\xi,$$

and so

$$Sv^n(x) = \frac{1}{\sqrt{2\pi}} \int_{-\pi/h}^{\pi/h} e^{ix\xi} g(h\xi)^n \hat{u}_0(\xi) \, d\xi.$$

Also, by equation (9.1.4),

$$u(t_n, x) = \frac{1}{\sqrt{2\pi}} \int_{-\infty}^{\infty} e^{ix\xi} e^{q(\xi)t_n} \hat{u}_0(\xi) \, d\xi.$$

The formula for Sv^n differs from that for $u(t_n, x)$ in only two respects: There is $g(h\xi)^n$ in place of $e^{q(\xi)t_n}$ and the interval of integration is $[-\pi/h, \pi/h]$ instead of $(-\infty, \infty)$. We have, therefore,

$$u(t_n, x) - Sv^n(x) = \frac{1}{\sqrt{2\pi}} \int_{-\pi/h}^{\pi/h} e^{ix\xi}(e^{q(\xi)t_n} - g(h\xi)^n)\hat{u}_0(\xi)\, d\xi$$

$$+ \frac{1}{\sqrt{2\pi}} \int_{|\xi|>\pi/h} e^{ix\xi} e^{q(\xi)t_n} \hat{u}_0(\xi)\, d\xi.$$

By Parseval's relation, it follows that

$$\int_{-\infty}^{\infty} |u(t_n, x) - Sv^n(x)|^2\, dx = \int_{-\pi/h}^{\pi/h} \left| e^{q(\xi)t_n} - g(h\xi)^n \right|^2 |\hat{u}_0(\xi)|^2\, d\xi$$

$$+ \int_{|\xi|>\pi/h} \left| e^{q(\xi)t_n} \hat{u}_0(\xi) \right|^2\, d\xi.$$

(10.1.6)

The first term on the right-hand side of (10.1.6) measures the error due to the finite difference scheme and the second term, as we will see, is related to the smoothness of the function u_0.

We estimate the first term on the right-hand side of (10.1.6) as follows. Let

$$z = e^{q(\xi)k}.$$

Then, since $t_n = nk$, we have that

$$e^{q(\xi)t_n} - g(h\xi)^n = z^n - g^n = (z - g)\sum_{j=0}^{n-1} z^{n-j-1}g^j.$$

Since $|z| \le 1$ and $|g| \le 1$ by stability, it follows that

$$|z^n - g^n| \le |z - g|\, n,$$

or

$$\left| e^{q(\xi)t_n} - g(h\xi)^n \right| \le n \left| e^{q(\xi)k} - g(h\xi) \right|.$$

(10.1.7)

Another estimate that will be useful is

$$\left| e^{q(\xi)t} - g(h\xi)^n \right| \le 2,$$

(10.1.8)

which is trivial since $|z|$ and $|g|$ are both at most 1, by (10.1.5).

We now use estimate (10.1.3) together with (10.1.7) in the first integral on the right-hand side of (10.1.6).

$$\int_{-\pi/h}^{\pi/h} \left| e^{q(\xi)t_n} - g(h\xi)^n \right|^2 |\hat{u}_0(\xi)|^2 \, d\xi$$

$$\leq n^2 \int_{-\pi/h}^{\pi/h} \left| e^{q(\xi)k} - g(h\xi) \right|^2 |\hat{u}_0(\xi)|^2 \, d\xi$$

$$\leq n^2 C^2 \int_{-\pi/h}^{\pi/h} k^2 h^{2r} (1 + |\xi|)^{2\rho} |\hat{u}_0(\xi)|^2 \, d\xi$$

$$\leq C^2 t_n^2 h^{2r} \int_{-\pi/h}^{\pi/h} (1 + |\xi|)^{2\rho} |\hat{u}_0(\xi)|^2 \, d\xi \leq C^2 t_n^2 h^{2r} \|u_0\|_{H^\rho}^2,$$

(10.1.9)

where $\|u_0\|_{H^\rho}$ is as defined in Section 2.1.

We now need only estimate the last term in (10.1.6). To do this we note that the exponential factor is bounded by (10.1.5), and in the range of the integral we have $1 \leq |\xi| h/\pi$, so

$$\int_{|\xi|>\pi/h} \left| e^{q(\xi)t_n} \hat{u}_0(\xi) \right|^2 \, d\xi \leq \int_{|\xi|>\pi/h} |\hat{u}_0(\xi)|^2 \, d\xi$$

$$\leq \left(\frac{h}{\pi}\right)^{2\rho} \int_{|\xi|>\pi/h} |\xi|^{2\rho} |\hat{u}_0(\xi)|^2 \, d\xi \leq C_2 h^{2\rho} \|u_0\|_{H^\rho}^2.$$

(10.1.10)

Combining (10.1.6), (10.1.9), and (10.1.10) we obtain the basic estimate

$$\|u(t_n, \cdot) - Sv^n\| \leq C(t)h^r \|u_0\|_{H^\rho},$$

(10.1.11)

which implies (10.1.4) and proves Theorem 10.1.2. ∎

As we remarked earlier, the choice of initial function for the scheme and the comparison of u with Sv^n in (10.1.4) are not natural in a computational setting. We now consider the consequences of using $u_0(mh)$ instead of $Tu_0(mh)$ as the initial function.

The Evaluation Operator

Given a continuous initial function $u_0(x)$ for a partial differential equation, it is natural to take the values $u_0(mh)$ as the discrete initial function for the scheme. Indeed, this is what has been done in each of the computational examples in this text and in the exercises. This is a mapping taking functions defined on the real line R to functions defined on the grid hZ; we call it the evaluation operator and use the symbol E. Thus for a function $u(x)$ the evaluation operator is defined by

$$Eu_m = u(mh).$$

Notice that the evaluation operator E cannot be defined for all functions in $L^2(R)$, since functions in $L^2(R)$ are equivalent if they differ on a set of measure zero (see Appendix B). Since the grid hZ is a set of measure zero, the evaluation of $L^2(R)$ functions is not well defined. As we will see, the evaluation operator can be defined for functions that have some degree of smoothness.

Our first goal is to find the discrete Fourier transform of Eu. We have

$$Eu_m = \frac{1}{\sqrt{2\pi}} \int_{-\infty}^{\infty} e^{imh\xi} \hat{u}(\xi) \, d\xi.$$

To get this in the form of the Fourier inversion formula for a discrete function, the integral must be over the interval $[-\pi/h, \pi/h]$; we can do this using the periodicity of $e^{imh\xi}$.

$$
\int_{-\infty}^{\infty} e^{imh\xi} \hat{u}(\xi) \, d\xi = \sum_{\ell=-\infty}^{\infty} \int_{(2\pi\ell-\pi)h^{-1}}^{(2\pi\ell+\pi)h^{-1}} e^{imh\xi} \hat{u}(\xi) \, d\xi
$$

$$
= \sum_{\ell=-\infty}^{\infty} \int_{-\pi/h}^{\pi/h} e^{imh\xi} \hat{u}(\xi + 2\pi\ell h^{-1}) \, d\xi
$$

$$
= \int_{-\pi/h}^{\pi/h} e^{imh\xi} \sum_{\ell=-\infty}^{\infty} \hat{u}(\xi + 2\pi\ell h^{-1}) \, d\xi.
$$

We conclude that

$$\widehat{Eu}(\xi) = \sum_{\ell=-\infty}^{\infty} \hat{u}(\xi + 2\pi\ell h^{-1}). \tag{10.1.12}$$

Formula (10.1.12) illustrates the idea of *aliasing* of Fourier modes. In sampling the function u at the discrete points x_m, we are unable to distinguish frequencies that differ by multiples of $2\pi/h$.

We now wish to compare Eu with Tu; both of these operations take functions on R to functions on hZ. Observe that the Fourier transform of Tu is just the term with ℓ equal to 0 in the sum (10.1.12) for the transform of Eu. We have, therefore,

$$
\left| \widehat{Eu}(\xi) - \widehat{Tu}(\xi) \right|^2 = \left| \sideset{}{'}\sum_{\ell=-\infty}^{\infty} \hat{u}(\xi + 2\pi\ell h^{-1}) \right|^2
$$

$$
\leq \left(\sideset{}{'}\sum_{\ell=-\infty}^{\infty} |\hat{u}(\xi + 2\pi\ell h^{-1})|^2 |\xi + 2\pi\ell h^{-1}|^{2\sigma} \right) \cdot \left(\sideset{}{'}\sum_{\ell=-\infty}^{\infty} |\xi + 2\pi\ell h^{-1}|^{-2\sigma} \right)
$$

where the prime on the $\sum$ means the term for ℓ equal to 0 is not taken in the sum. Since $|\xi| \leq \pi h^{-1}$, the second factor can be bounded by

$$
2 \sum_{\ell=1}^{\infty} \left[(2\ell - 1)\pi h^{-1} \right]^{-2\sigma} = 2 \left(\frac{h}{\pi} \right)^{2\sigma} \sum_{\ell=1}^{\infty} \frac{1}{(2\ell - 1)^{2\sigma}} = h^{2\sigma} C(\sigma)^2
$$

when $\sigma > \frac{1}{2}$.

We then have

$$\|Eu - Tu\|_h^2 \leq C(\sigma)^2 h^{2\sigma} \int_{-\pi/h}^{\pi/h} {\sum_\ell}' \left|\hat{u}(\xi + 2\pi\ell h^{-1})\right|^2 \left|\xi + 2\pi\ell h^{-1}\right|^{2\sigma} d\xi$$

$$= C(\sigma)^2 h^{2\sigma} \int_{|\xi| \geq \pi/h} |\hat{u}(\xi)|^2 |\xi|^{2\sigma} d\xi$$

$$\leq C(\sigma)^2 h^{2\sigma} \|D^\sigma u\|^2.$$

We collect this result in a theorem.

Theorem 10.1.3   *If $\|D^\sigma u\|$ exists for $\sigma > \frac{1}{2}$, then*

$$\|Eu - Tu\|_h \leq C(\sigma) h^\sigma \|D^\sigma u\|.$$

Theorem 10.1.3 shows that if a function has "more than half a derivative," i.e., is in H^σ for $\sigma > \frac{1}{2}$, then the evaluation operator can be defined. Later we show that it can also be defined for a special class of functions that are in H^σ for σ less than $\frac{1}{2}$ but not in $H^{1/2}$.

We now consider a stable finite difference approximation for the partial differential equation (10.1.1) with initial function v_m^0 for the scheme equal to $u_0(mh)$. In addition, consider the finite difference solution w_m^n with $w_m^0 = Tu_0(mh)$. We wish to estimate the difference between Eu_m^n, which is $u(nk, mh)$, and v_m^n. We have

$$\|Eu^n - v^n\|_h \leq \|Eu^n - Tu^n\|_h + \|Tu^n - w^n\|_h + \|w^n - v^n\|_h. \qquad (10.1.13)$$

By Theorem 10.1.3 we can estimate the first term on the right-hand side using σ equal to r. We have

$$\|Eu^n - Tu^n\|_h \leq C(r) h^r \|D^r u(t_n, \cdot)\| \leq C_T C(r) h^r \|D^r u(t_0, \cdot)\|$$

because the initial value problem is well-posed.

We can estimate the last term using Theorem 10.1.3 and the stability estimate (1.5.1). We have, for nk equal to t,

$$\|w^n - v^n\|_h \leq C_t \|w^0 - v^0\|_h = C_t \|Tu_0 - Eu_0\|_h \leq C_t C(r) h^r \|D^r u_0\|.$$

We now consider the middle term on the right-hand side of (10.1.13). First we use Parseval's relation for discrete functions:

$$\|Tu^n - w^n\|_h^2 = \int_{-\pi/h}^{\pi/h} |\hat{u}(nk, \xi) - \hat{w}^n(\xi)|^2 d\xi$$

$$= \int_{-\infty}^\infty |\hat{u}(nk, \xi) - S\hat{w}^n(\xi)|^2 d\xi - \int_{|\xi| \geq \pi/h} |\hat{u}(nk, \xi)|^2 d\xi$$

$$\leq \|u(t, \cdot) - Sw^n\|^2 \leq C(t) h^{2r} \|u_0\|_{H^r}^2.$$

by (10.1.11). In this way we pass from a norm on the grid to one on the line.

Combining this with Theorem 10.1.2, we obtain the next theorem.

Theorem 10.1.4   *If the initial value problem for a partial differential equation of the form (10.1.1), for which the initial value problem is well-posed, is approximated by a stable one-step finite difference scheme that is accurate of order $[r, \rho]$ with $\rho > \frac{1}{2}$ and $r \le \rho$ and the initial function v_m^0 is equal to $u_0(mh)$, where u_0 is in H^ρ, then for each positive time T, there is a constant C_T such that*

$$\|Eu(t, \cdot) - v^n\|_h \le C_T h^r \|u_0\|_{H^\rho}$$

for each t with $0 \le t = nk \le T$.

We now complete this section by proving Theorem 10.1.1.

Proof of Theorem 10.1.1   This proof is in two parts. In the first part we obtain an estimate of the form

$$\frac{e^{kq(\xi)} - g(h\xi, k, h)}{k} = O(h^r) \tag{10.1.14}$$

for each value of ξ, and then in the second part we prove the existence of the value of ρ.

Since the differential equation is first order in the time differentiation, its symbol $p(s, \xi)$ is linear in s and may be written as

$$p(x, \xi) = q_0(\xi)s + q_1(\xi).$$

The value of $q(\xi)$ in (10.1.1) is then

$$q(\xi) = -q_0(\xi)^{-1}q_1(\xi).$$

By Definition 3.1.2 with $\phi = e^{ix\xi}e^{q(\xi)t}$ or Corollary 3.1.2 with s equal to $q(\xi)$, we have that

$$p_{k,h}(q(\xi), \xi) - r_{k,h}(q(\xi), \xi)\ p(q(\xi), \xi) = O(h^r).$$

Since $q(\xi)$ is the unique root of $p(x, \xi)$, we obtain

$$p_{k,h}(q(\xi), \xi) = O(h^r). \tag{10.1.15}$$

Moreover, $g(h\xi)$ is the solution to

$$p_{k,h}\left(k^{-1}\ln g(h\xi), \xi\right) = k^{-1}\Phi(g, h\xi) = 0 \tag{10.1.16}$$

where $\Phi(g, h\xi)$ is the amplification polynomial defined in Section 4.2. Thus

$$p_{k,h}\left(k^{-1}\ln g(h\xi), \xi\right) - p_{k,h}(q(\xi), \xi) = O(h^r).$$

Now $g(h\xi)$ is the unique root of (10.1.16), and so by the implicit function theorem (see [7] or [3]),

$$k^{-1}\ln g(h\xi) - q(\xi) = O(h^r).$$

This last relation implies

$$g(h\xi) = e^{kq(\xi)}e^{O(kh^r)}$$

from which we obtain (10.1.14).

We next use the well-posed nature of the initial value problem and the accuracy of the scheme to prove that a value of ρ exists. We begin with the Taylor series with remainder for the exponential function for complex variables in the form

$$e^z = \sum_{j=0}^{J-1}\frac{z^j}{j!} + \frac{z^J}{(J-1)!}\int_0^1 (1-t)^{J-1}e^{tz}\,dt.$$

From this we obtain

$$e^{kq(\xi)} = \sum_{j=0}^{J-1}\frac{k^j q(\xi)^j}{j!} + \frac{k^J q(\xi)^J}{(J-1)!}\int_0^1 (1-t)^{J-1}e^{tkq(\xi)}\,dt.$$

We also have that $g(\theta)$ is a ratio of finite trigonometric sums and thus is infinitely differentiable for real values of θ. We can expand $g(\theta)$ as a Taylor series in θ as

$$g(\theta) = \sum_{i=0}^{I-1}\frac{\theta^i}{i!}g^{(i)}(0) + \frac{\theta^I}{I!}g^{(I)}(\theta')$$

or

$$g(h\xi) = \sum_{i=0}^{I-1}\frac{h^i\xi^i}{i!}g^{(i)}(0) + \frac{h^I\xi^I}{I!}g^{(I)}(\theta').$$

Substituting these expansions for $e^{kq(\xi)}$ and $g(h\xi)$ into (10.1.14), we obtain

$$\frac{e^{kq(\xi)} - g(h\xi, k, h)}{k} = \sum_{j=0}^{J-1}\frac{1}{j!}k^{j-1}q(\xi)^j - \sum_{i=0}^{I-1}\frac{k^{-1}h^i\xi^i}{i!}g^{(i)}(0)$$

$$+ \frac{k^{J-1}q(\xi)^J}{(J-1)!}\int_0^1 (1-t)^{J-1}e^{tkq(\xi)}\,dt - \frac{k^{-1}h^I\xi^I}{I!}g^{(I)}(\theta') = O(h^r).$$

$$(10.1.17)$$

Now, recalling that $k = \Lambda(h)$, we can choose J and I large enough so that the two sums combine to be $O(h^r)$. Similarly, k^{J-1}, which is $\Lambda(h)^{J-1}$, and $k^{-1}h^I$ which is $\Lambda(h)^{-1}h^I$, can be made to be $O(h^r)$. The value of $g^{(I)}(\theta')$ is then bounded by some constant, and the integral is also bounded independently of ξ because the equation is well-posed. Finally, $q(\xi)$ is a rational function of ξ, and so the growth of (10.1.17) in ξ is at most polynomial. Thus (10.1.17) is bounded by h^r times a constant multiple of $(1+|\xi|)^\rho$ for some nonnegative integer ρ. ∎

EXERCISES 10.1

1.   Show that the Lax-Wendroff-like scheme

$$\frac{v_m^{n+1} - v_m^n}{k} + a\delta_0 v_m^n - \frac{a^2 k}{2}\delta^2 v_m^n + v_m^n = 0$$

for the equation

$$u_t + a\,u_x + u = 0$$

is accurate of order $[1, 2]$ when λ is held constant.

2.a.   Show that the forward-time central-space scheme (6.3.1) for the heat equation (6.1.1) is accurate of order $[2, 4]$ when μ is a constant.
  b.   Show the backward-time central-space implicit scheme (6.3.3) is accurate of order $[1, 4]$ if λ is constant and of order $[2, 4]$ if μ is constant.

3.a.   Show that the scheme

$$(1 - \delta^2)\left(\frac{v_m^{n+1} - v_m^n}{k}\right) = a\,\delta_0\left(\frac{v_m^{n+1} + v_m^n}{2}\right)$$

for the equation

$$u_t - u_{txx} = a\,u_x \tag{10.1.18}$$

is unconditionally stable and accurate of order $[2, 3]$ if λ is constant.
  b. Show that the scheme

$$(1 - \delta^2)\left(\frac{v_m^{n+1} - v_m^n}{k}\right) = a\,\delta_0 v_m^n$$

for (10.1.18) is unconditionally stable and accurate of order $[1, 0]$ if λ is a constant.

4.   Show that if a stable one-step scheme for $u_t + a u_x = 0$ is accurate of order $[r, \rho]$, then

$$|v_m^n - u(t, mh)| \le C(t) h^r \int_{-\infty}^{\infty} |\xi|^\rho |\hat{u}_0(\xi)|\, d\xi$$

where $t_n = nk$ and when the initial function is Tu_0, i.e.,

$$v_m^0 = \frac{1}{\sqrt{2\pi}} \int_{-\pi/h}^{\pi/h} e^{imh\xi}\, \hat{u}_0(\xi)\, d\xi.$$

To obtain estimates of convergence in the L^∞ norm, use the simple inequality

$$|f(x)| \le \frac{1}{\sqrt{2\pi}} \int_{-\infty}^{\infty} |\hat{f}(\xi)|\, d\xi$$

in place of Parseval's inequality. *Hint:* The proof is similar to those in the text for the L^2 results. Note that there is no Parseval's relation for the L^∞ norm and that the interpolation operator S is not needed, since v_m^n and $u(t_n, mh)$ can be compared directly.

5. Show that if a scheme is accurate of order $[r, \rho]$, according to Definition 10.1.3, then it is accurate also of order $[r-1, \rho-1]$.

6. Prove Theorem 10.1.2 under the more general assumptions that

$$|e^{tq(\xi)}| \leq C_t \quad \text{and} \quad |g(h\xi)| \leq 1 + Kk$$

rather than the special case given by (10.1.5).

7. Prove that the estimate (10.1.4) holds for N-dimensional space.

8. Prove that for functions in $L^2(R^N)$, the evaluation operator and truncation operator satisfy

$$\|Eu - Tu\|_h \leq C(\sigma)h^\sigma \|D^\sigma u\|.$$

for σ greater than $N/2$.

9. Use the matrix identity

$$Z^n - G^n = \sum_{j=0}^{n-1} Z^{n-1-j}(Z-G)G^j$$

to prove Theorem 10.1.2 for systems of partial differential equations. (See Exercise A.9.)

10.2 Related Topics

In this section we consider two topics that are related to those covered in the previous section. First, we prove the assertions made in Section 5.3 about the group velocity of wave packets. Secondly, we present the Poisson summation formula, which is useful in many areas of applied mathematics.

Group Velocity and Wave Packets

We now consider the estimate of the finite difference solution of a wave packet, as given in Section 5.3. Recall that we chose for our initial function (5.3.1) evaluated at the grid points, i.e.,

$$v_m^0 = (Eu_0)_m = e^{i\xi_0 x_m} Ep_m.$$

In Section 5.3 we referred to the function Ep as p_h.

The claim in Section 5.3 was that the function $v^*(t,x)$ given in (5.3.4) is a good approximation to v_m^n and, for large values of ξ_0, this is a better approximation than is v^n to $u(t_n, \cdot)$. We now justify this claim. We begin with an estimate of $\|v^*(t_n, \cdot) - Sv^n\|$.

$$\|v^*(t_n, \cdot) - Sv^n\| \leq \|v^*(t_n, \cdot) - \tilde{v}(t_n, \cdot)\| + \|\tilde{v}(t_n, \cdot) - Sv^n\|$$

where $\tilde{v}$ is defined by (5.3.8). First, we estimate the difference between $\tilde{v}$ and Sv^n.

$$\|\tilde{v}(t_n, \cdot) - Sv^n\|^2 = \int_{-\pi/h}^{\pi/h} |\hat{p}(\omega) - \hat{p}_h(\omega)|^2 d\omega + \int_{h|\xi|\geq\pi} |\hat{p}(\omega)|^2 d\omega \quad (10.2.1)$$
$$= \|p - SEp\|^2 \leq (c_r h^r \|p\|_{H^r})^2$$

for any r greater than $\frac{1}{2}$ (see Exercise 10.2.6). This justifies the claim, given after the definition of $\tilde{v}$ in (5.3.8), that the replacement of v by $\tilde{v}$ is not a significant error.

We next examine the difference between $\tilde{v}$ and v^*. We have

$$\|v^*(t_n, \cdot) - \tilde{v}(t_n, \cdot)\|^2 = \int_{-\infty}^{\infty} |e^{ihr(\omega)t_n} - 1|^2 |\hat{p}(\omega)|^2 d\omega$$

from the formulas (5.3.10) and (5.3.11). Moreover, since

$$r(\omega) = \frac{1}{2} \omega^2 \left. \frac{d^2\theta\alpha(\theta)}{d\theta^2} \right|_{\theta=\theta^*}$$

for some value of θ^* and $|\theta| \leq \pi$, we have that

$$|r(\omega)| \leq c|\omega|^2$$

for some constant c. Thus

$$\|v^*(t_n, \cdot) - \tilde{v}(t_n, \cdot)\|^2 \leq c^2 t_n^2 h^2 \int_{-\infty}^{\infty} |\omega|^4 |\hat{p}(\omega)|^2 d\omega \leq c^2 t_n^2 h^2 (\|p\|_{H^2})^2.$$

Combining this estimate with (10.2.1) we obtain

$$\|v^*(t_n, \cdot) - Sv^n\| \leq C(t_n) h \|p\|_{H^2}. \quad (10.2.2)$$

This estimate shows that v^* is a good approximation to the solution of the finite difference scheme.

We now can explain how the first-order approximation in (10.2.2) can be a better approximation than the higher-order approximation (10.1.4) and the related estimates. The explanation is that the estimate (10.2.2) is essentially independent of ξ_0. In the general estimate (10.1.4), if the initial function u_0 is a wave packet such as (5.3.1), then $\|(d/dx)^p u_0\|$ contains terms proportional to $|\xi_0|^p \|p\|$. Therefore, the quantity $h^r \|u_0\|_H^r$ will not be small if $h\xi_0$ is not small, whereas $h\|p\|_{H^2}$ can be small independently of ξ_0.

The Poisson Summation Formula

A very interesting formula related to the topics of this chapter is the Poisson summation formula. This formula is useful in many areas of applied mathematics, although we will not need to make explicit use of it. The formula is obtained by considering the evaluation operator applied to a function and evaluating Fourier transform of the discrete function in two ways. We have formula (10.1.12); also, from the definition of the discrete Fourier transform (2.1.5),

$$\widehat{Eu}(\xi) = \frac{1}{\sqrt{2\pi}} \sum_{m=-\infty}^{\infty} e^{-imh\xi} u(mh)\, h$$

for the Fourier transform of Eu. Equating these two expressions, we have the Poisson summation formula

$$\frac{1}{\sqrt{2\pi}} \sum_{m=-\infty}^{\infty} e^{-imh\xi} u(mh)\, h = \sum_{\ell=-\infty}^{\infty} \hat{u}(\xi + 2\pi\ell h^{-1}). \tag{10.2.3}$$

This formula is valid whenever both infinite summations are convergent.

One use of the Poisson summation formula arises when u is a slowly decreasing, smooth function, making the series on the left-hand side converge slowly. Then the transform $\hat{u}$ may be a more rapidly decreasing function, making the series on the right-hand side converge rapidly, and vice versa. Another use of the summation formula is when one of the two series is more amenable to obtaining an explicit formula for the summation. Often quite difficult sums can be explicitly evaluated in this way.

Example 10.2.1 We illustrate the use of the Poisson summation formula with the function $u(x) = e^{-ax^2/2}$. The Fourier transform of this function is $\hat{u}(\omega) = a^{-1/2}e^{-\omega^2/2a}$, and applying the Poisson summation formula (10.2.3) with ξ equal to 0 and h equal to 1 gives

$$\frac{1}{\sqrt{2\pi}} \sum_{m=-\infty}^{\infty} e^{-am^2/2} = \frac{1}{\sqrt{a}} \sum_{\ell=-\infty}^{\infty} e^{-(2\ell\pi)^2/2a}$$

or, if we set $b = a/2\pi$,

$$\sqrt{b} \sum_{m=-\infty}^{\infty} e^{-b\pi m^2} = \sum_{\ell=-\infty}^{\infty} e^{-\pi\ell^2/b}.$$

If b is small then the sum on the left-hand side will converge slowly, but the sum on the right-hand side will converge rapidly. Thus the quantity represented by these sums can be evaluated very efficiently for all values of the parameter b. Notice that this same formula can be obtained from (10.2.3) by setting h equal to $\sqrt{2\pi}$ and ξ equal to 0. □

Example 10.2.2 We illustrate a second use of the Poisson summation formula with the function

$$u(x) = \begin{cases} 1 - |x|/a & \text{if } |x| \leq a, \\ 0 & \text{if } |x| > a. \end{cases}$$

The transform of u is

$$\hat{u}(\omega) = \frac{1}{\sqrt{2\pi}} \int_{-a}^{a} e^{-i\omega x}(1 - \frac{|x|}{a}) \, dx = \sqrt{\frac{2}{\pi}} \int_{0}^{a} \cos \omega x \ (1 - \frac{x}{a}) \, dx$$

$$= 2\sqrt{\frac{2}{\pi}} \frac{\sin^2 \frac{1}{2}a\omega}{a\omega^2}.$$

We apply the Poisson summation formula (10.2.3) with ξ equal to 0 and h equal to 1, obtaining

$$\frac{1}{\sqrt{2\pi}} \sum_{|n| \leq a} \left(1 - \frac{|n|}{a}\right) = 2\sqrt{\frac{2}{\pi}} \sum_{\ell=-\infty}^{\infty} \frac{\sin^2 a\ell\pi}{4a\ell^2\pi^2},$$

or

$$\sum_{|n| \leq a} \left(1 - \frac{|n|}{a}\right) = \frac{1}{a\pi^2} \sum_{\ell=-\infty}^{\infty} \frac{\sin^2 a\ell\pi}{\ell^2} = a + \frac{2}{a\pi^2} \sum_{\ell=1}^{\infty} \frac{\sin^2 a\ell\pi}{\ell^2}.$$

We can then obtain the explicit representation for the sum on the left:

$$\sum_{\ell=1}^{\infty} \frac{\sin^2 a\ell\pi}{\ell^2} = \frac{a\pi^2}{2} [(a - \lfloor a \rfloor)(1 - (a - \lfloor a \rfloor))]$$

where $\lfloor a \rfloor$ is the greatest integer not larger than a. Thus for $0 \leq a \leq 1$,

$$\sum_{\ell=1}^{\infty} \frac{\sin^2 a\ell\pi}{\ell^2} = \frac{a(1 - a)\pi^2}{2}. \quad \square$$

The Poisson summation formula can be used in a similar fashion to evaluate many other sums.

EXERCISES 10.2

1. Repeat the computations of Example 5.3.1 and verify the estimate (10.2.2) that $v^*(t_n, \cdot)$ is a better approximation to v^n than v^n is to $u(t_n, \cdot)$. Compute the norm of the difference between v^n and both $v^*(t_n, \cdot)$ and $u(t_n, \cdot)$.

2. Use the Poisson summation formula to verify the formula

$$\sqrt{b} \sum_{m=-\infty}^{\infty} (-1)^m e^{-b\pi m^2} = \sum_{\ell=-\infty}^{\infty} e^{-\pi(\ell+1/2)^2/b}.$$

3. Given the relation

$$\int_{-\infty}^{\infty} \frac{\cos \omega x}{\cosh x} \, dx = \frac{\pi}{\cosh(\frac{\pi}{2}\omega)},$$

use the Poisson summation formula to develop an efficient algorithm for computing the value of the function

$$C(a) = \sum_{n=0}^{\infty} \frac{1}{\cosh(an)}$$

for $0 < a < \infty$. Demonstrate your algorithm with a computer program. *Hint:*

$$\int_{-\infty}^{\infty} \frac{e^{i\omega x}}{\cosh x} \, dx = \int_{-\infty}^{\infty} \frac{\cos \omega x}{\cosh x} \, dx.$$

4. Use the Poisson summation formula to evaluate:

$$\sum_{n=0}^{\infty} \frac{1}{n^2 + 1} \quad \text{and} \quad \sum_{n=0}^{\infty} \frac{(-1)^n}{n^2 + 1}$$

Hint: Consider the Fourier transform of $e^{-|x|}$.

5. Use the function

$$u(x) = \begin{cases} 1 & \text{if } |x| < 1, \\ \frac{1}{2} & \text{if } |x| = 1, \\ 0 & \text{if } |x| > 1 \end{cases}$$

and the Poisson summation formula to prove the relation

$$\sum_{\ell=-\infty}^{\infty} \frac{\sin 2\pi\ell a}{2\pi\ell} = \begin{cases} \lfloor a \rfloor + \frac{1}{2} & \text{if } a \text{ is not an integer,} \\ a & \text{if } a \text{ is an integer.} \end{cases}$$

In the sum the term for $\ell = 0$ is evaluated to be a.

6. Verify the estimate

$$\|p - SEp\| \le c_r h^r \|p\|_{H^r}$$

that was used in equation (10.2.1).

10.3 Convergence Estimates for Nonsmooth Initial Functions

The convergence estimates of the previous section are valid only if the initial function is sufficiently smooth. Since many applications involve initial functions that are not as smooth as required for the general estimates of Theorem 10.1.2, it is important to obtain estimates for when the initial functions are not smooth. The estimates of this section give the convergence rate for the solutions of finite difference schemes with order of accuracy $[r, \rho]$ when the initial function, u_0, has less than ρ derivatives in $L^2(R)$, that is, when $\|u_0\|_{H^\rho}$ is infinite. The estimates given here are for general one-step schemes and first-order equations of the form (10.1.1) satisfying the restricted stability and well-posedness conditions (10.1.5). In the next section we show that for parabolic equations and dissipative schemes we can improve on the results of this section.

We now modify the proof of Theorem 10.1.2 under the assumption that $\|u_0\|_{H^\rho}$ is infinite and $\|u_0\|_{H^\sigma}$ is finite for some σ less than ρ. Notice that the critical estimate in that proof is given by the estimate (10.1.9). We begin by splitting the first integral in (10.1.9) into an integral with $|\xi|$ less than η and one with $|\xi|$ greater than η, where η is chosen as $\pi h^{-\alpha}$ with α positive and less than 1.

We then have

$$\|u(t_n, \cdot) - Sv^n\|^2 = \int_{-\pi/h}^{\pi/h} \left| e^{q(\xi)nk} - g(h\xi)^n \right|^2 |\hat{u}_0(\xi)|^2 \, d\xi$$

$$+ \int_{|\xi|>\pi/h} \left| e^{q(\xi)nk} \hat{u}_0(\xi) \right|^2 \, d\xi$$

$$= \int_{-\eta}^{\eta} \left| e^{q(\xi)nk} - g(h\xi)^n \right|^2 |\hat{u}_0(\xi)|^2 \, d\xi$$

$$+ \int_{\eta \le |\xi| \le \pi/h} \left| e^{q(\xi)nk} - g(h\xi)^n \right|^2 |\hat{u}_0(\xi)|^2 \, d\xi$$

$$+ \int_{|\xi|>\pi/h} \left| e^{q(\xi)nk} \hat{u}_0(\xi) \right|^2 \, d\xi.$$

In this last expression we use (10.1.7) and (10.1.3) on the first term, (10.1.8) on the second, and (10.1.5) on the third to obtain

$$\|u(t_n, \cdot) - Sv^n\|^2 \le n^2 C^2 \int_{-\eta}^{\eta} k^2 h^{2r} (1 + |\xi|)^{2\rho} |\hat{u}_0(\xi)|^2 \, d\xi + 4 \int_{|\xi| \ge \eta} |\hat{u}_0(\xi)|^2 \, d\xi$$

$$\le n^2 C^2 k^2 h^{2r} \int_{-\eta}^{\eta} (1 + \eta)^{2(\rho-\sigma)} (1 + |\xi|)^{2\sigma} |\hat{u}_0(\xi)|^2 \, d\xi$$

$$+ 4\eta^{-2\sigma} \int_{|\xi| \ge \eta} |\xi|^{2\sigma} |\hat{u}_0(\xi)|^2 \, d\xi$$

$$= t^2 C^2 h^{2r-2(\rho-\sigma)\alpha} (h^\alpha + \pi)^{2(\rho-\sigma)} \int_{-\eta}^{\eta} (1 + |\xi|)^{2\sigma} |\hat{u}_0(\xi)|^2 \, d\xi$$

$$+ 4\pi^{-2\sigma} h^{2\sigma\alpha} \int_{|\xi| \geq \eta} |\xi|^{2\sigma} |\hat{u}_0(\xi)|^2 \, d\xi.$$

If we choose α equal to r/ρ, then both terms have h to the power $2\sigma r/\rho$; this estimate gives the following theorem.

Theorem 10.3.1 *If a stable one-step finite difference scheme is accurate of order $[r, \rho]$, with $r \leq \rho$, the initial function to the partial differential equation is u_0 with $\|D^\sigma u_0\|$ finite and σ less than ρ, and the initial function v_m^0 is Tu_0, then the solution v^n to the finite difference scheme satisfies*

$$\|u(t_n, \cdot) - Sv^n\| \leq C_2 h^\beta \|u_0\|_{H^\sigma} \tag{10.3.1}$$

where $\beta = \sigma r/\rho$. If σ is greater than $\frac{1}{2}$ and the initial function is either Eu_0 or Tu_0, then in addition

$$\|Eu^n - v^n\|_h \leq C_1 h^\beta \|u_0\|_{H^\sigma}. \tag{10.3.2}$$

Convergence Estimates for Piecewise Smooth Initial Functions

The convergence estimates of Theorem 10.3.1 often cannot be conveniently applied to many functions that are useful in actual computations. For example, the function

$$u(x) = \begin{cases} 1 & \text{if } |x| < 1, \\ \frac{1}{2} & \text{if } |x| = 1, \\ 0 & \text{if } |x| > 1 \end{cases} \tag{10.3.3}$$

is in H^σ for each σ less that $\frac{1}{2}$, but not in $H^{1/2}$ (see Example 10.3.1). Similarly the functions

$$u(x) = \begin{cases} 1 - |x| & \text{if } |x| \leq 1, \\ 0 & \text{if } |x| \geq 1 \end{cases} \tag{10.3.4}$$

and

$$u(x) = \begin{cases} \cos^2 \frac{\pi}{2} x & \text{if } |x| \leq 1, \\ 0 & \text{if } |x| \geq 1 \end{cases} \tag{10.3.5}$$

are in H^σ for σ less than $\frac{3}{2}$ and $\frac{5}{2}$, respectively, but not in $H^{3/2}$ or $H^{5/2}$, respectively (see Exercise 10.3.1). Because the function (10.3.4) is almost but not quite in $H^{3/2}$, it is difficult to see what value of β should be used in the estimate (10.3.1). We now show that we can take σ equal to the limiting value if the estimate is modified appropriately.

Each of the functions (10.3.3), (10.3.4), and (10.3.5) satisfy the relation

$$\|u\|_\sigma \leq \frac{C(u)}{\sqrt{\sigma_0 - \sigma}} \tag{10.3.6}$$

where σ_0 is $\frac{1}{2}$, $\frac{3}{2}$, and $\frac{5}{2}$ for the three functions (10.3.3), (10.3.4), and (10.3.5), respectively, and $C(u)$ depends on u but not on σ. We demonstrate this only for the function given by (10.3.3). The demonstration for the other two functions is left as an exercise (Exercise 10.3.1).

Example 10.3.1 For the function (10.3.3) we have

$$\hat{u}(\omega) = \sqrt{\frac{2}{\pi}} \frac{\sin \omega}{\omega},$$

so, for σ with $0 \leq \sigma < \frac{1}{2}$,

$$\|u\|_{H^\sigma}^2 = \int_{-\infty}^{\infty} (1 + \omega^2)^\sigma \frac{2}{\pi} \frac{\sin^2 \omega}{\omega^2} \, d\omega \leq C \int_0^\infty (1 + \omega^2)^{\sigma-1} \, d\omega$$

$$= \frac{C}{2} \int_0^\infty \frac{1}{(1+\xi)^{1-\sigma}} \frac{d\xi}{\xi^{1/2}} \leq \frac{C}{2} \left(\int_0^1 \frac{d\xi}{\xi^{1/2}} + \int_1^\infty \frac{d\xi}{(1+\xi)^{3/2-\sigma}} \right)$$

$$= \frac{C}{2} \left(2 + \frac{1}{\frac{1}{2} - \sigma} 2^{-(1/2-\sigma)} \right) \leq C^* \frac{1}{\frac{1}{2} - \sigma}.$$

Thus (10.3.6) is demonstrated for this function, and we also see that function (10.3.3) is in H^σ for each σ less than $\frac{1}{2}$. $\square$

When the initial function satisfies (10.3.6) we apply Theorem 10.3.1 with σ equal to $\sigma_0 - |\ln h|^{-1}$. First notice that $h^{-(r/\rho)|\ln h|^{-1}} = e^{-(r/\rho) \ln h |\ln h|^{-1}} = e^{r/\rho}$, and so for $\beta = \sigma r/\rho$ and $\beta_0 = \sigma_0 r/\rho$,

$$h^\beta = h^{\beta_0} h^{-r/\rho |\ln h|^{-1}} = e^{r/\rho} h^{\beta_0}$$

In this way we obtain, from (10.3.1),

$$\|u(t_n, \cdot) - Sv^n\| \leq C_2 e^{r/\rho} h^{\beta_0} |\ln h|^{1/2} C(u_0).$$

We state this result formally as a corollary to Theorem 10.3.1.

Corollary 10.3.2   *If the initial function u_0 satisfies (10.3.6), then estimate (10.3.1) in Theorem 10.3.1 may be replaced by*

$$\|u(t_n, \cdot) - Sv^n\| \leq C_2' h^{\beta_0} |\ln h|^{1/2} C(u_0) \tag{10.3.7}$$

where $\beta_0 = \sigma_0 r/\rho$.

In computations to check the order of accuracy of solutions, the factor of $|\ln h|^{1/2}$ in the estimate (10.3.7) is difficult to verify. For the order of accuracy we usually obtain only the exponent of β_0, and the factor involving $\ln h$ is not noticed (see Exercise 10.3.4).

Evaluation of Piecewise Smooth Functions

In many practical computations the initial function is piecewise differentiable with several jump discontinuities. As an example, the function (10.3.3) is not in $H^{1/2}$, and the evaluation operator is not defined for all functions in $H^{1/2}$. However, as we will show, the evaluation operator can be extended to function (10.3.3) and to many other functions of common occurrence. In this section we show how the results of Theorem 10.1.5 can be extended to cover these functions.

We begin by considering the function

$$
\gamma(x) = \begin{cases} 0 & \text{if } x = 0, \\[2mm] \frac{1}{2}e^{-x} & \text{if } x > 0, \\[2mm] -\frac{1}{2}e^{-|x|} & \text{if } x < 0. \end{cases}
$$

We will show that even though it is not in $H^{1/2}$, the evaluation operator can still be applied to it. The Fourier transform of γ is

$$
\hat{\gamma}(\omega) = \frac{1}{\sqrt{2\pi}} \frac{-i\omega}{1+\omega^2}
$$

and by Definition 10.1.1 and (10.1.12),

$$
\widehat{E\gamma}(\xi) - \widehat{T\gamma}(\xi) = \sideset{}{'}\sum_{\ell=-\infty}^{\infty} \hat{\gamma}(\xi + 2\pi\ell h^{-1})
$$

$$
= \frac{-i}{\sqrt{2\pi}} \sum_{\ell=1}^{\infty} \frac{\xi + 2\pi\ell h^{-1}}{1 + (\xi + 2\pi\ell h^{-1})^2} + \frac{\xi - 2\pi\ell h^{-1}}{1 + (\xi - 2\pi\ell h^{-1})^2}
$$

$$
= \frac{-i}{\sqrt{2\pi}} \sum_{\ell=1}^{\infty} \frac{2\xi \left[1 + \xi^2 - (2\pi\ell h^{-1})^2\right]}{[1 + (\xi + 2\pi\ell h^{-1})^2][1 + (\xi - 2\pi\ell h^{-1})^2]},
$$

where the prime on the first sum means the term for ℓ equal to 0 is not taken in the sum. Therefore, for ξ satisfying $|\xi| \le \pi h^{-1}$,

$$
|\widehat{E\gamma}(\xi) - \widehat{T\gamma}(\xi)| \le \sqrt{\frac{2}{\pi}} |\xi| \frac{h^2}{\pi^2} \sum_{\ell=1}^{\infty} \frac{(1 + 5\ell^2)}{(2\ell - 1)^4} \le Ch^2|\xi|,
$$

and hence

$$\|E\gamma - T\gamma\|_h^2 \leq C^2 h^4 \int_{-\pi/h}^{\pi/h} |\xi|^2 \, d\xi = C^2 h^4 \frac{2}{3} \left(\frac{\pi}{h}\right)^3 = C_0^2 h.$$

So for the function γ we have

$$\|E\gamma - T\gamma\|_h \leq C_0 h^{1/2}. \tag{10.3.8}$$

Notice that γ is not in $H^{1/2}$, so this estimate for γ is stronger than the general result of Theorem 10.1.3. Also notice that this estimate is valid for translates of the function γ.

Now we extend this result to any function $u(x)$ that is a piecewise differentiable function except for a finite number of jump discontinuities. That is, there are a finite number of points $x_1 < x_2 < \ldots < x_L$, such that in each interval (x_i, x_{i+1}) the function $u(x)$ is differentiable. Let $[u](x_i)$ be the jump in u at x_i, i.e.,

$$[u](x_i) = \lim_{\varepsilon \to 0+} [u(x_i + \varepsilon) - u(x_i - \varepsilon)].$$

(The notation $\varepsilon \to 0+$ means that ε is restricted to positive values as it tends to 0.) We take for $u(x_i)$ the average of the values on either side, i.e.,

$$u(x_i) = \tfrac{1}{2} \lim_{\varepsilon \to 0} [u(x_i + \varepsilon) + u(x_i - \varepsilon)].$$

Finally, we assume that

$$\int_{|x|>K} |u(x)|^2 + |Du(x)|^2 \, dx \tag{10.3.9}$$

is finite where K is larger than $|x_1|$ and $|x_L|$.

We now consider the function

$$u_1(x) = \sum_{i=1}^{L} [u](x_i)\gamma(x - x_i)$$

and the function $u_2(x) = u(x) - u_1(x)$. Notice that u_1 has precisely the same jump discontinuities as does u; therefore, u_2 is continuous and in H^1 (see Exercise 10.3.2). (Recall that u_0 is piecewise *differentiable*.)

$$\|Eu_1 - Tu_1\|_h \leq \sum_{i=1}^{L} |[u](x_i)| \, \|E\gamma(\cdot - x_i) - T\gamma(\cdot - x_i)\|_h$$

$$\leq \sum_{i=1}^{L} |[u](x_i)| h^{1/2} C_0.$$

Using this result for u_1 and Theorem 10.1.3 on u_2, we obtain

$$\|Eu - Tu\|_h \leq \|Eu_2 - Tu_2\|_h + \|Eu_1 - Tu_1\|_h$$

$$\leq C(1)h\|Du_2\| + \sum_{i=1}^{L} |[u](x_i)|h^{1/2}C_0 \leq C^*(u)\,h^{1/2}.$$

We state this result as a corollary to Theorem 10.3.1.

Corollary 10.3.3 *If the initial function u_0 of Theorem 10.3.1 is a piecewise differentiable function except for a finite number of jump discontinuities and if (10.3.9) is finite for u_0, then the estimate (10.3.2) can be replaced by*

$$\|Eu^n - v^n\|_h \leq |\ln h|^{1/2}h^{\beta}C(u_0)$$

where $\beta = \frac{1}{2}r/\rho$ and $C(u_0)$ depends only on u_0.

Exercise 10.3.4 provides demonstrations of the estimates of Theorem 10.3.1 and Corollary 10.3.3.

EXERCISES 10.3

1.a. Verify that the relation (10.3.6) holds for the function (10.3.4) with σ_0 equal to $\frac{3}{2}$.
   b. Verify that the relation (10.3.6) holds for the function (10.3.5) with σ_0 equal to $\frac{5}{2}$.

2. Show that the function u_2 used in the proof of Corollary 10.3.3 is in H^1.

3. Show that if $r > \rho$, then the value of β in estimate (10.3.1) must be $\sigma + r - \rho$.

4.a. Solve the initial value problems for the one-way wave equation $u_t + u_x = 0$ on the interval $[-1, 1]$ with periodic boundary conditions up to $t = 0.96$ Use the Lax-Wendroff scheme with $\lambda = 0.8$ and grid spacing $h = \frac{1}{10}, \frac{1}{20}, \frac{1}{40}$, and $\frac{1}{80}$. Use the following initial functions.

a.
$$u_0(x) = \begin{cases} 1 & \text{if } |x| < \frac{1}{2}, \\ \frac{1}{2} & \text{if } |x| = \frac{1}{2}, \\ 0 & \text{otherwise} \end{cases}$$

b.
$$u_0(x) = \cos(\pi x)$$

c.
$$u_0(x) = \begin{cases} \cos^2(\pi x) & \text{if } |x| \leq \frac{1}{2}, \\ 0 & \text{otherwise} \end{cases}$$

Determine the rates of convergence of the numerical solution to the exact solution as a function of h. Compare the actual rates of convergence with those obtained in this section. Discuss the results. Note that the convergence rate obtained for (a) can be quite sensitive to the method of programming.
   b. Repeat the computations of part (a) using the Lax-Friedrichs scheme.

10.4 Convergence Estimates for Parabolic Differential Equations

The estimates of Theorems 10.1.1 and 10.3.1 are fairly sharp for hyperbolic equations but unnecessarily pessimistic for many schemes for parabolic equations. Because of the smoothing inherent in parabolic equations, it is reasonable to believe that nonsmooth initial functions should not seriously degrade the rate of convergence of the finite difference solution to the solution of the differential equations. Indeed, for dissipative schemes the convergence rates are much better than those given by Theorem 10.3.1 and Corollaries 10.3.2 and 10.3.3.

Theorem 10.4.1   *If a one-step scheme that approximates an initial value problem for a parabolic equation is accurate of order $[r, \rho]$, for $\rho \geq r + 2$ and dissipative of order 2 with μ a constant and with $\mu = kh^{-2}$, then for each time T, there is a constant C_T such that for any t with $nk = t \leq T$,*

$$\|u(t, \cdot) - Sv^n\| \leq C_T(1 + t^{-(\rho-1)/2})h^r\|u_0\| \tag{10.4.1}$$

and

$$\|Eu^n - v^n\|_h \leq C_T(1 + t^{-(\rho-1)/2})h^r\|u_0\|. \tag{10.4.2}$$

Notice that these estimates require only that u_0 be in $L^2(R)$, which, for our purposes, places no requirement at all on the smoothness of u_0.

Proof   To obtain the sharper estimates (10.4.1) and (10.4.2), we begin with sharper estimates than we used in the proof of Theorem 10.3.1. In place of (10.1.5) we use

$$|e^{tq(\xi)}| \leq e^{Kt}e^{-c\xi^2 t} \tag{10.4.3}$$

which holds for parabolic equations (see Definition 9.2.1) and, since μ is constant and the scheme is dissipative,

$$|g(h\xi)| \leq \left(1 - c_0 \sin^2 \tfrac{1}{2}h\xi\right)(1 + kK) \leq e^{Kk}e^{-c\xi^2 k}. \tag{10.4.4}$$

The values of c and K can be taken to be the same in both (10.4.3) and (10.4.4). In (10.4.4) the value of $|h\xi|$ is at most π.

Using these estimates rather than (10.1.5), we obtain in place of (10.1.7)

$$|e^{q(\xi)t} - g(h\xi)^n| \leq n|e^{q(\xi)k} - g(h\xi)| \max\left(|e^{q(\xi)k}|, |g(h\xi)|\right)^{n-1}$$

$$\leq n|e^{q(\xi)k} - g(h\xi)| e^{Kt}e^{-c\xi^2(t-k)}$$

$$\leq ne^{c\pi^2\mu}|e^{q(\xi)k} - g(h\xi)| e^{Kt}e^{-c\xi^2 t},$$

where we have used that $e^{c\xi^2 k} \leq e^{c\pi^2\mu}$ for $|h\xi|$ at most π. Then in place of (10.1.9) we have

$$\int_{-\pi/h}^{\pi/h} |e^{q(\xi)t} - g(h\xi)^n|^2 |\hat{u}_0(\xi)|^2 \, d\xi \leq C n^2 k^2 h^{2r} \int_{-\pi/h}^{\pi/h} (1 + |\xi|)^{2\rho} e^{-c\xi^2 t} |\hat{u}_0(\xi)|^2 \, d\xi.$$

The expression $(1+|\xi|)^{2\rho}e^{-c\xi^2 t}$ is bounded by a constant, depending on ρ and c, times $(1+t^{-1/2})^{2\rho}$ or, equivalently, $(1+t^{-\rho/2})^2$ (see Exercise 10.4.1). Thus the preceding integral is bounded by

$$C't\left(1+t^{-\frac{\rho}{2}}\right)^2 h^{2r}\int_{-\pi/h}^{\pi/h}|\hat{u}_0(\xi)|^2\,d\xi \le C''\left(1+t^{-\frac{\rho-1}{2}}\right)^2 h^{2r}\int_{-\pi/h}^{\pi/h}|\hat{u}_0(\xi)|^2\,d\xi.$$

In place of (10.1.10) we have the estimate

$$\int_{|\xi|\ge\pi/h}|e^{q(\xi)t}\hat{u}_0(\xi)|^2\,d\xi \le \left(\frac{h}{\pi}\right)^{2r}e^{2Kt}\int_{|\xi|\ge\pi/h}|\xi|^{2r}e^{-c\xi^2 t}|\hat{u}_0(\xi)|^2\,d\xi$$

$$\le \left(\frac{h}{\pi}\right)^{2r}C\,e^{2Kt}t^{-r}\int_{|\xi|\ge\pi/h}|\hat{u}_0(\xi)|^2\,d\xi$$

for some constant C. Combining these estimates and using the relation $\rho \ge r+2$, we have (10.4.1). The estimate (10.4.2) follows easily using the methods of Section 10.1. ∎

EXERCISES 10.4

1.   Show that the expression $(1+|\xi|)^{2\rho}e^{-c\xi^2 t}$ is bounded by a constant, depending on ρ and c, times $(1+t^{-1/2})^{2\rho}$ and that this is equivalent to $(1+t^{-\rho/2})^2$.

2.   Solve the initial value problems for the heat equation $u_t = u_{xx}$ on the interval $[-1,1]$ with periodic boundary conditions up to $t=1$. Use the explicit forward in time, centered in space scheme with $\mu = 0.4$ and grid spacing $h = \frac{1}{10}, \frac{1}{20}, \frac{1}{40}$, and $\frac{1}{80}$, with the following initial functions.

a.

$$u_0(x) = \begin{cases} 1 & \text{if } |x| < \frac{1}{2}, \\ \frac{1}{2} & \text{if } |x| = \frac{1}{2}, \\ 0 & \text{otherwise} \end{cases}$$

b.

$$u_0(x) = \cos(\pi x)$$

The exact solution to (*a*) is

$$u(t,x) = \frac{1}{2} + \frac{2}{\pi}\sum_{k=0}^{\infty}e^{-t(2k+1)^2\pi^2}\frac{(-1)^k}{2k+1}\cos[(2k+1)\pi x]$$

For $t=1$ only a few terms are needed to give seven-place accuracy. Show that the solution is computed to second-order accuracy in the L^2 norm.

3. Solve the initial boundary value problem for $u_t = u_{xx}$ on $-1 \leq x \leq 1$ for $0 \leq t \leq \frac{1}{2}$ with initial function given by the function a of Exercise 2 and using Dirichlet boundary conditions. The exact solution, from which the boundary values can be obtained, is the same as in Exercise 2. Use the Crank-Nicolson scheme with $h = \frac{1}{10}$, $\frac{1}{20}$, and $\frac{1}{40}$. Compare the convergence behavior in the L^2 norm and the L^∞ norm for the case in which $\lambda = 1$ with the case in which $\mu = 10$.

10.5 The Lax-Richtmyer Equivalence Theorem

In this section we prove the Lax-Richtmyer theorem, Theorem 1.5.1, for one-step schemes; the extension to multistep schemes is discussed in Section 10.6. The definition of convergence given in Section 1.4 is not complete, since the nature of the convergence of the functions is not specified. We now make the idea of a convergent scheme precise using the interpolation operator S as defined in Definition 10.1.2.

Definition 10.5.1 *A finite difference scheme approximating the homogeneous initial value problem for a partial differential equation is a convergent scheme if Sv^n converges to $u(t_n, \cdot)$ in $L^2(R)$, where $t_n = nk$, for every solution u to the differential equation and every set of solutions to the difference scheme v, depending on h and k, for which Sv^0 converges to $u(0, \cdot)$ in $L^2(R)$ as h and k tend to 0.*

The study of inhomogeneous initial value problems is easily done using the results for homogeneous problems and Duhamel's principle as described in Section 9.3. We now restate Theorem 1.5.1 for one-step schemes.

Theorem 10.5.1 The Lax-Richtmyer Equivalence Theorem. *A consistent one-step scheme for a well-posed initial value problem for a partial differential equation is convergent if and only if it is stable.*

The proof of this theorem is somewhat similar to the proof of Theorem 10.1.2; however, here we have much less information about the scheme than we did in Section 10.1. For example, we do not even assume that the order of accuracy is $O(h^\alpha)$ for any positive α. However, since we are making so few assumptions about the scheme, we are also able to obtain the equivalence of convergence and stability.

Proof We first prove that stability of the scheme implies the convergence of the scheme. Later we show that an unstable scheme is nonconvergent, which completes the proof of the theorem.

We prove that stability implies convergence without making the special assumptions (10.1.5); rather we assume only that there is a constant C_T such that

$$|e^{q(\xi)t}| \leq C_T \quad \text{and} \quad |g(h\xi)^n| \leq C_T \tag{10.5.1}$$

for $0 \leq t \leq T$ and $0 \leq nk \leq T$.

For the first part of the proof we assume that the initial function for the scheme is Tu_0. Then we have

$$\|u_0 - Sv^0\|^2 = \int_{|\xi|>\pi/h} |\hat{u}_0(\xi)|^2 \, d\xi,$$

which converges to zero as h tends to zero (see Appendix B). We use consistency to obtain the estimate

$$\frac{e^{kq(\xi)} - g(h\xi)}{k} = o(1) \quad \text{in } h \text{ and } k. \tag{10.5.2}$$

The meaning of the notation $o(1)$ is that for each ξ the left-hand side of (10.5.2) tends to zero as h and k tend to zero. The estimate (10.5.2) is obtained as was (10.1.3), with the replacement of $O(h^r)$ by $o(1)$.

We now consider the L^2 norm of $u(t_n, \cdot) - Sv^n$. As in (10.1.6) we have the relation

$$\int_{-\infty}^{\infty} |u(t_n, x) - Sv^n(x)|^2 \, dx \tag{10.5.3}$$

$$= \int_{-\pi/h}^{\pi/h} \left| e^{q(\xi)t_n} - g(h\xi)^n \right|^2 |\hat{u}_0(\xi)|^2 \, d\xi + \int_{|\xi|>\pi/h} \left| e^{q(\xi)t_n} \hat{u}_0(\xi) \right|^2 \, d\xi.$$

We consider the right-hand side of (10.5.3) as one integral over R, with the specification of the integrand given piecewise. That is, the integrand is the function

$$\phi_h(\xi) = \begin{cases} \left| e^{q(\xi)t_n} - g(h\xi)^n \right|^2 |\hat{u}_0(\xi)|^2 & \text{if } |\xi| \leq \dfrac{\pi}{h}, \\[2mm] \left| e^{q(\xi)t_n} \hat{u}_0(\xi) \right|^2 & \text{if } |\xi| > \dfrac{\pi}{h}. \end{cases}$$

Furthermore, for each ξ, when h is small enough, i.e., small enough that $|\xi| < \pi h^{-1}$, the integrand is given as in the first piece. The expression $e^{q(\xi)t_n} - g(h\xi)^n$ satisfies

$$\left| e^{q(\xi)t_n} - g(h\xi)^n \right| \leq n \left| e^{q(\xi)k} - g(h\xi) \right| C_T,$$

which is essentially the same as (10.1.7) except it uses the more general estimates (10.5.1) rather than (10.1.5). By (10.5.2) we have the estimate

$$\left| e^{q(\xi)t_n} - g(h\xi)^n \right| \leq nkC_T \, o(1) \leq o(1).$$

We conclude that the integrand on the right-hand side of (10.5.3) converges to zero for each value of ξ as h and k tend to zero. We thus have the set of functions ϕ_h that are in $L^1(R)$ and tend to zero at each point as h and k tend to zero.

Before we can conclude that the norms of these functions tend to zero, we need one more piece of information. This is given by observing that

$$\left| e^{q(\xi)t_n} - g(h\xi)^n \right|^2 |\hat{u}_0(\xi)|^2 \leq (2C_T)^2 |\hat{u}_0(\xi)|^2.$$

This shows that the functions ϕ_h are bounded uniformly by a function in $L^1(R)$, namely, $4C_T^2|\hat{u}_0(\xi)|^2$. By the Lebesgue dominated convergence theorem (see Appendix B), we conclude that

$$\int_{-\infty}^{\infty} \phi_h(\xi) \, d\xi = \int_{-\infty}^{\infty} |\hat{u}(t_n,\xi) - \widehat{Sv^n}(\xi)|^2 \, d\xi$$

converges to zero as h and k tend to zero, and thus the scheme is convergent.

We now briefly consider the case where v^0 is not equal to Tu_0. First, define the grid function w^n, which is the solution to the difference scheme with initial function Tu^0. We then have

$$\|u(t_n,\cdot) - Sv^n\| \leq \|u(t_n,\cdot) - Sw^n\| + \|Sw^n - Sv^n\|.$$

The norm of $u(t_n,\cdot) - Sw^n$ converges to zero by our previous result. We have, by the definition of S and by stability,

$$\|Sw^n - Sv^n\| = \|S(w^n - v^n)\| = \|w^n - v^n\|_h$$

$$\leq C_T\|w^0 - v^0\|_h = C_T\|Tu^0 - v^0\|_h$$

$$\leq C_T\|u^0 - Sv^0\|,$$

which converges to zero by assumption. This concludes the first part of the proof, showing that a stable scheme is convergent.

We now prove that a consistent one-step scheme is nonconvergent if it is unstable.

The proof consists of constructing a function $u_0(x)$ such that the scheme with initial function Tu_0 does not converge to the solution of the partial differential equation. The function $u_0(x)$ is constructed as the sum of functions $w_M(x)$ determined as follows.

If the scheme is unstable, then by Theorem 2.2.1 the estimate

$$|g(h\xi, k, h)| \leq 1 + Ck \tag{10.5.4}$$

does not hold for any constant C and sufficiently small h and k. Thus for any positive integer M, there are values of ξ_M, k_M, and h_M such that

$$|g(h_M\xi_M, k_M, h_M)| \geq 1 + Mk_M \tag{10.5.5}$$

and $|h_M\xi_M| \leq \pi$. Since $g(h\xi, k, h)$ is a continuous function, there is a positive number η_M such that

$$|g(h_M\xi, k_M, h_M)| \geq 1 + \tfrac{1}{2}Mk_M \tag{10.5.6}$$

for $|\xi - \xi_M| \leq \eta_M$, and moreover we may choose η_M to satisfy

$$\eta_M \leq M^{-2}$$

and choose h_M and k_M less than h_{M-1} and k_{M-1}, respectively. We now need a crucial result, which relies on the consistency of the scheme.

Lemma 10.5.2 *If the finite difference scheme is consistent, then the intervals $I_M = [\xi_M - \eta_M, \xi_M + \eta_M]$ can be chosen to be disjoint.*

Proof We prove this lemma by induction on M. For $M = 1$, there is only one interval and the assertion is trivial.

Suppose that for some M the interval I_M cannot be chosen as disjoint from I_N with N less than M. Let

$$J = \bigcup_{N < M} I_N$$

and by our supposition, for any h and k less than h_{M-1} and k_{M-1}, respectively, the estimate

$$|g(h\xi, k, h)| \leq 1 + Mk \tag{10.5.7}$$

holds for $\xi \notin J$. From consistency of the scheme to the equation, it follows from (10.5.2) that

$$\left| \frac{g(h\xi, k, h) - e^{q(\xi)k}}{k} \right| \leq C(\xi) \tag{10.5.8}$$

for each ξ as h and k tend to zero. Since J is a compact set, being the union of a finite number of closed intervals,

$$\sup_{\xi \in J} C(\xi) = C^*$$

exists and is finite. From (10.5.1) we also have that

$$|e^{q(\xi)k}| = |e^{q(\xi)t_n}|^{1/n} \leq C_T^{1/n} \leq 1 + Kk$$

for some value of K. These estimates imply, by (10.5.7) for $\xi \notin J$ and (10.5.8) for $\xi \in J$, that

$$|g(h\xi, k, h)| \leq 1 + \max(M, C^* + K)k$$

for $h < h_{M-1}$ and $k < k_{M-1}$, which contradicts our assumption that the scheme is unstable. Therefore, our supposition must be false, and there is a $\xi_M \notin J$ such that (10.5.5) holds for some h_M and k_M small enough. Since J is a closed set and g is continuous, there is an interval $[\xi_M - \eta_M, \xi_M + \eta_M]$ disjoint from J such that (10.5.6) holds. This proves the lemma. ∎

We now continue our construction of the functions $w_M(x)$. Define the positive numbers α_M by $\alpha_M^2 \eta_M = M^{-2}$ and then define the function w_M by

$$\hat{w}_M(\xi) = \begin{cases} \alpha_M & \text{if } |\xi - \xi_M| \leq \eta_M, \\ 0 & \text{otherwise.} \end{cases}$$

We define our initial function as the sum of the functions w_M. Let $u_0(x) = \sum_{M=1}^{\infty} w_M(x)$; we will show that u_0 is in $L^2(R)$. Because the intervals I_M are disjoint, we have that

$$\int_{-\infty}^{\infty} |u_0(x)|^2 \, dx = \int_{-\infty}^{\infty} |\hat{u}_0(\xi)|^2 \, d\xi = \sum_{M=1}^{\infty} \int_{-\infty}^{\infty} |\hat{w}_M(\xi)|^2 \, d\xi$$

$$= 2 \sum_{M=1}^{\infty} \alpha_M^2 \eta_M = 2 \sum_{M=1}^{\infty} M^{-2} = \frac{\pi^2}{3}$$

which shows that u_0 is in $L^2(R)$.

We now show that the solution of the scheme applied to Tu_0 does not converge. Let v_m^n be the solution to the scheme with this initial function. Given a time T, choose a time level n and a value of M such that

$$\frac{T}{2} \leq nk_M \leq T, \quad \text{and} \quad \frac{C_T - 1}{M} \leq \frac{T}{8}, \tag{10.5.9}$$

where C_T is the constant bounding $e^{q(\xi)t}$ in (10.5.1). We then have

$$\|Sv^n - u(t_n, \cdot)\|^2 \geq \|v^n - Tu(t_n, \cdot)\|_h^2 = \int_{-\pi/h}^{\pi/h} |g(h\xi)^n - e^{q(\xi)nk}|^2 |\hat{u}_0(\xi)|^2 \, d\xi \,.$$

For $h = h_M$ and ξ in I_M, we have the estimate

$$|g(h\xi)^n - e^{q(\xi)kn}| \geq |g(h\xi)|^n - C_T \geq (1 + \tfrac{1}{2}Mk_M)^n - C_T.$$

Thus

$$\|Sv^n - u(t_n, \cdot)\|^2 \geq \int_{|\xi - \xi_M| \leq \eta_M} |g(h\xi)^n - e^{q(\xi)nk}|^2 |\hat{u}_0(\xi)|^2 \, d\xi$$

$$\geq \left[(1 + \frac{1}{2}Mk_M)^n - C_T\right]^2 \alpha_M^2 \, 2\eta_M$$

$$= 2\left[\frac{(1 + \frac{1}{2}Mk_M)^n - C_T}{M}\right]^2.$$

We estimate this last expression using the inequality $(1 + x)^n \geq 1 + nx$ for positive x. We then have, by (10.5.9),

$$\|Sv^n - u(t_n, \cdot)\|^2 \geq 2\left(\frac{1}{2}nk_M - \frac{C_T - 1}{M}\right)^2 \geq \frac{T^2}{32} \not\to 0.$$

Thus Sv^n does not converge to $u(t_n, \cdot)$, hence the scheme is nonconvergent. This completes the proof of the Lax-Richtmyer equivalence theorem. ∎

Notice that the proof we have given shows only that Sv^n does not converge to $u(t_n, \cdot)$; in fact the norm of v^n must become unbounded as n increases.

EXERCISES 10.5

1. State and prove the Lax-Richtmyer theorem for the inhomogeneous initial value problem. *Hint:* Use Duhamel's principle; see Section 9.3.

2. Using the computation of Exercise 10.4.3, show that in the L^∞ norm the solution computed with $\lambda = 1$ does not converge to the exact solution. This is a demonstration that the Lax-Richtmyer theorem does not hold in the L^∞ norm when the initial function for the scheme is Eu_0.

10.6 Analysis of Multistep Schemes

In this section we extend the results of the previous sections to multistep schemes. The primary estimate for Section 10.1 is (10.1.3) and for Section 10.5 it is the similar estimate (10.5.2). We will show that the convergence estimates for multistep schemes follow from these results for one-step schemes. For a multistep scheme there is not a unique amplification factor, and thus estimates (10.1.3) and (10.5.2) cannot be used without some clarification. We restrict the discussion to schemes for single equations; the results for systems may be proved in a similar fashion.

The first stage in the reduction of a multistep scheme to a one-step scheme is to distinguish a special amplification factor.

Theorem 10.6.1 *If a multistep scheme is accurate of order r as an approximation to a partial differential equation in the form (10.1.1), then there is a unique amplification factor $g_0(h\xi)$ defined for $|h\xi| \le \theta_0$ for some positive value θ_0 such that*

$$g_0(h\xi) = 1 + kq(\xi) + o(k) \tag{10.6.1}$$

as h and k tend to zero. Moreover, there exists a nonnegative integer ρ such that

$$\left| \frac{e^{kq(\xi)} - g_0(h\xi, k, h)}{k} \right| \le Ch^r(1 + |\xi|)^\rho.$$

If g_0 satisfies this last estimate, the scheme is said to be accurate of order $[r, \rho]$.

Example 10.6.1 As illustrations of this theorem we consider the leapfrog scheme for the one-way wave equation. By the formula for the amplification factor for the leapfrog scheme (see (4.1.2))

$$g_0(h\xi) = g_+(h\xi) = -ia\lambda \sin h\xi + \sqrt{1 - a^2\lambda^2 \sin^2 h\xi}$$
$$= 1 + k(-ia\xi) + O(k^2) + O(h^2). \tag{10.6.2}$$

Also, for the Du Fort–Frankel scheme (6.3.7) for the heat equation (6.1.1), we have

$$g_0(h\xi) = g_+(h\xi) = \frac{2b\mu \cos h\xi + \sqrt{1 - 4b^2\mu^2 \sin^2 h\xi}}{1 + 2b\mu}$$
$$= 1 + k(-b\xi^2) + O(k^2) \tag{10.6.3}$$

when μ is a constant. In (10.6.2) we can take θ_0, the limit of the range where g_0 is defined, equal to π, since $|a\lambda| < 1$; a similar statement can be made for (10.6.3) if $b\mu < 1$. However, if $b\mu \ge 1$, θ_0 should be chosen so that $\sin(\theta_0) < (b\mu)^{-1}$. This is necessary to define g_0 uniquely. $\square$

Proof This proof is similar to the first part of the proof of Theorem 10.1.1. If we set $g(h\xi) = 1 + kq(\xi) + o(k)$, then

$$k^{-1} \ln g(h\xi) = q(\xi) + o(1).$$

Since there is at most one root of $\Phi(z, h\xi)$ such that z is 1 when $h\xi$ is zero, the implicit function theorem guarantees the existence of a root, $g_0(h\xi)$, to $\Phi(g, h\xi) = 0$ such that $k^{-1} \ln g_0(h\xi) = q(\xi) + o(1)$. This is equivalent to (10.6.1). The existence of ρ is essentially the same as in the proof of Theorem 10.1.1. ∎

The amplification factor $g_0(h\xi)$ may not represent a one-step scheme, e.g., (10.6.2) or (10.6.3), but nonetheless it can be used to generate the sequence of functions

$$\hat{w}^n(\xi) = g_0(h\xi)^n \, \hat{v}^0(\xi). \tag{10.6.4}$$

For $|h\xi|$ greater than θ_0 we can set $g_0(h\xi)$ equal to zero. We will call the method in (10.6.4) for generating the functions $\hat{w}^n(\xi)$ a *pseudoscheme*. An important observation is that the results of the previous sections apply to one-step pseudoschemes as well as for actual schemes. For multistep schemes, the methods of Section 10.1, such as Definition 10.1.3, apply for $g_0(h\xi)$.

Now consider a multistep scheme for an initial value problem. Let $J+1$ be the number of initial time levels that must be specified to determine the solution. That is, assume that $v^0, v^1, \ldots, v^J$ must be specified before v^n for $n > J$ can be computed by the scheme.

Let w be the function generated by (10.6.4). By the results of Section 10.1 applied to the pseudoscheme (10.6.4), we have that

$$\|u(t_n, \cdot) - Sw^n\| = O(h^r).$$

Now consider the norm of the difference between $u(t_n, \cdot)$ and Sv^n.

$$\|u(t_n, \cdot) - Sv^n\| \le \|u(t_n, \cdot) - Sw^n\| + \|Sw^n - Sv^n\|$$

$$= \|u(t_n, \cdot) - Sw^n\| + \|w^n - v^n\|_h.$$

We have by the stability definition, Definition 1.5.1, that

$$\|w^n - v^n\|_h \le C_T \sum_{j=0}^{J} \|w^j - v^j\|_h = C_T \sum_{j=1}^{J} \|g_0^j \hat{v}^0 - \hat{v}^j\|_h.$$

We thus see that to obtain the optimal accuracy of r, we must have that v^j approximates w^j to within $O(h^r)$. But

$$\hat{w}^j(\xi) = g_0(h\xi)^j \, \hat{v}^0 = e^{kjq(\xi)} \hat{v}^0(\xi) + O(kh^r)$$

$$= e^{q(\xi)t_j} \, \hat{u}_0(\xi) + O(kh^r).$$

Thus

$$\hat{v}^j(\xi) - \hat{w}^j(\xi) = \hat{v}^j(\xi) - e^{q(\xi)t_j}\,\hat{u}_0(\xi) + O(kh^r).$$

To obtain the optimal order of accuracy for the scheme, the initial functions for the multistep scheme must satisfy

$$v^j = u(t_j, \cdot) + O(h^r). \tag{10.6.5}$$

If the initial time levels are initialized using a one-step scheme with accuracy r' and amplification factor $\tilde{g}(h\xi)$, we have $\hat{v}^j(\xi) = \tilde{g}(h\xi)^j\,\hat{v}^0$, and requirement (10.6.5) becomes

$$\tilde{g}(h\xi)^j\,\hat{v}^0(\xi) - e^{q(\xi)t_j}\,\hat{u}_0(\xi) = O(h^r).$$

Since

$$\tilde{g}(h\xi) = e^{q(\xi)k} + O(kh^{r'})$$

we see that $kh^{r'}$ should be $O(h^r)$. Thus the initializing scheme may have order of accuracy less than r and not degrade the overall accuracy. All that is required is that $kh^{r'}$ be $O(h^r)$. Notice also that the initializing scheme need not be stable.

In particular, the leapfrog scheme may be initialized with the forward-time central-space scheme, which is first-order accurate, and still be second-order accurate overall. Similarly, the Du Fort–Frankel scheme with μ constant may be initialized using v_m^1 equal to v_m^0, a scheme accurate of order 0, and the overall scheme will be second-order accurate.

EXERCISES 10.6

1. Show that the leapfrog scheme (1.3.4) is accurate of order $[2, 3]$.

2. Show that the Du Fort–Frankel scheme (6.3.7) is accurate of order $[2, 4]$.

3. Show that for the implicit multistep scheme (4.2.3)

$$g_0(\theta) = \frac{1}{2 - \sqrt{1 - 2ia\lambda\sin\theta}}$$

and show that this scheme is accurate of order $[2, 3]$.

4. Solve the heat equation with the Du Fort–Frankel scheme using the data of Exercise 6.3.10.
  a. Show that the initialization $v_m^1 = v_m^0$ gives second-order accurate solutions if μ is constant.
  b. Show that if $k = h^{3/2}$ then the initialization in (a) is accurate of order less than 2.

5. Repeat Exercise 10.3.4 using the leapfrog scheme, using the forward-time central-space scheme to compute the first time step.

10.7 Convergence Estimates for Second-Order Differential Equations

The proofs for the convergence estimates for schemes approximating second-order equations are similar to those of first-order equations. We give only a brief discussion with emphasis on the points of difference between the two types of equations.

The class of equations we consider is that for which the equations can be put in the form

$$\hat{u}_{tt} + 2a(\xi)\hat{u}_t = b(\xi)\hat{u}. \tag{10.7.1}$$

We assume also that the initial value problem for (10.7.1) is well-posed. That is, we assume that the two zeros of

$$q^2 + 2a(\xi)q - b(\xi) = 0$$

satisfy the estimate

$$\operatorname{Re} q_\pm(\xi) \le \bar{q}, \tag{10.7.2}$$

as discussed in Section 9.1. We have

$$q_\pm(\xi) = -a(\xi) \pm \sqrt{a(\xi)^2 + b(\xi)}. \tag{10.7.3}$$

A further technical assumption that we need is that there is a constant c_0 such that

$$|q_\pm(\xi)| \le c_0|q_+(\xi) - q_-(\xi)|, \tag{10.7.4}$$

for all real values of ξ. Inequality (10.7.4) is satisfied for most second-order equations arising in applications (see Exercise 10.7.1).

We initially restrict ourselves to two-step schemes, which have two amplification factors, denoted by $g_+(h\xi)$ and $g_-(h\xi)$. These correspond to the two roots $q_+(\xi)$ and $q_-(\xi)$ of the symbol.

Corresponding to Definition 10.1.3 and Theorem 10.1.1, we have the next definition and theorem.

Definition 10.7.1   *A two-step scheme for a second-order equation of the form (10.7.1) with $k = \Lambda(h)$ is accurate of order $[r, \rho]$ if there is a constant C such that for $|h\xi| \le \pi$*

$$\left| \frac{e^{kq_\pm(\xi)} - g_\pm(h\xi, k, h)}{k} \right| \le Ch^r(1 + |\xi|)^\rho. \tag{10.7.5}$$

Theorem 10.7.1   *If a two-step finite difference scheme for a second-order equation with a well-posed initial value problem is accurate of order r according to Definition 3.1.2, then there is a nonnegative integer ρ such that the scheme is accurate of order $[r, \rho]$ according to Definition 10.7.1. Moreover, if χ is such that $q_\pm(\xi)$ is $O(|\xi|^\chi)$ for large values of $|\xi|$, then*

$$\left| \frac{e^{kq_\pm(\xi)} - g_\pm(h\xi, k, h)}{kq_\pm(\xi)} \right| \le ch^r(1 + |\xi|)^{\rho-\chi}. \tag{10.7.6}$$

We do not prove Theorem 10.7.1, since the proof parallels that of Theorem 10.1.1. The main distinction between the proofs is that for second-order equations, there are the two roots $q_\pm(\xi)$ instead of only the one root as for first-order equations.

The solution to the initial value problem (10.7.1) with initial functions

$$\hat{u}(0,\xi) = u_0(\xi) \quad \text{and} \quad \hat{u}_t(0,\xi) = u_1(\xi) \tag{10.7.7}$$

may be written as

$$\hat{u}(t,\xi) = e^{q_+(\xi)t}\,\frac{-q_-(\xi)\hat{u}_0(\xi) + \hat{u}_1(\xi)}{q_+(\xi) - q_-(\xi)} + e^{q_-(\xi)t}\,\frac{q_+(\xi)\hat{u}_0(\xi) - \hat{u}_1(\xi)}{q_+(\xi) - q_-(\xi)}. \tag{10.7.8}$$

For the two-step finite difference scheme, we consider a special solution of the scheme, which we denote by w. We choose $\hat{w}^0(\xi)$ equal to $\widehat{Tu_0}(\xi)$ and $\hat{w}^1(\xi)$ so that the solution is

$$\hat{w}^n(\xi) = g_+(\xi)^n\,\frac{-q_-(\xi)\hat{u}_0(\xi) + \hat{u}_1(\xi)}{q_+(\xi) - q_-(\xi)} + g_-(\xi)^n\,\frac{q_+(\xi)\hat{u}_0(\xi) - \hat{u}_1(\xi)}{q_+(\xi) - q_-(\xi)} \tag{10.7.9}$$

for $h|\xi| \le \pi$. This special choice of initial function, as in Section 10.1, is convenient in order to obtain the simplest convergence estimate.

Theorem 10.7.2   *If the initial value problem for a second-order partial differential equation of the form (10.7.1), for which the initial value problem is well-posed, is approximated by a stable two-step finite difference scheme with the solution (10.7.9), then for each time T there is a constant C_T such that*

$$\|u(t_n,\cdot) - Sw^n\| \le C_T h^r (\|u_0\|_{H^\rho} + \|u_1\|_{H^{\rho-x}}) \tag{10.7.10}$$

for $t_n = nk$ with $0 \le t_n \le T$.

Proof   This proof is similar in spirit to that of Theorem 10.1.2. We have, for $h|\xi| \le \pi$,

$$\hat{u}(t_n\xi) - \hat{w}^n(\xi) = (e^{q_+(\xi)t_n} - g_+(\xi)^n)A_+(\xi) + (e^{q_-(\xi)t_n} - g_-(\xi)^n)A_-(\xi),$$

where $A_\pm(\xi)$ are the coefficients in (10.7.8) and (10.7.9). As with (10.1.7) we have

$$|e^{q_\pm(\xi)t} - g_\pm(h\xi)^n| \le n\,C_T\,|e^{q_\pm(\xi)k} - g_\pm(h\xi)|.$$

We then have by (10.7.5)

$$|e^{q_+(\xi)k} - g_+(h\xi)||A_+(\xi)| \le \frac{|q_-(\xi)|}{|q_+(\xi) - q(\xi)|}|e^{q_+(\xi)k} - g_+(h\xi)||\hat{u}_0(\xi)|$$

$$+ \frac{|q_+(\xi)|}{|q_+(\xi) - q_-(\xi)|}\frac{|e^{q_+(\xi)k} - g_+(h\xi)|}{|q_+(\xi)|}|\hat{u}_1(\xi)|.$$

By (10.7.6), this estimate becomes

$$|e^{q_+(\xi)k} - g_+(h\xi)||A_+(\xi)| \leq Ckh^r \left[(1 + |\xi|)^\rho |\hat{u}_0(\xi)| + (1 + |\xi|)^{\rho - \chi} |\hat{u}_1(\xi)| \right].$$

A similar estimate holds for $A_-(\xi)$. For $|\xi| > h^{-1}\pi$, we have

$$\hat{u}(t_n, \xi) = \frac{q_+(\xi)e^{q_-(\xi)t} - q_-(\xi)e^{q_+(\xi)t}}{q_+(\xi) - q_-(\xi)} \hat{u}_0(\xi) + \frac{e^{q_+(\xi)t} - e^{q_-(\xi)t}}{q_+(\xi) - q_-(\xi)} \hat{u}_1(\xi).$$

from which we obtain the estimate

$$|\hat{u}(t_n, \xi)| \leq Ch^r(|\xi|^r |\hat{u}_0(\xi)| + |\xi|^{r-\chi} |\hat{u}_1(\xi)|)$$

for r less than ρ. These estimates for $h|\xi| \leq \pi$ and $h|\xi| > \pi$ give estimate (10.7.10). ∎

Before considering solutions to the finite difference scheme other than those of the form (10.7.9), we note that

$$\hat{u}(k, \xi) - \widehat{Sw^1}(\xi) = O(kh^r)$$

where w^1 is given by (10.7.9).

Now let v be any solution to a two-step finite difference scheme approximating the second-order equation (10.7.1). We let w be the particular solution given by (10.7.9), and then we have

$$\|u(t_n, \cdot) - Sv^n\| \leq \|u(t_n, \cdot) - Sw^n\| + \|Sw^n - Sv^n\|.$$

The first term on the right-hand side is estimated using Theorem 10.7.2, and the second term is estimated using the stability estimate (8.2.1). We have

$$\|Sw^n - Sv^n\| = \|w^n - v^n\|_h \leq (1 + n)C_t \sum_{j=0}^{1} \|w^j - v^j\|_h$$

We see that if $\|w^j - v^j\|_h$ is of the order of kh^r, then we have the estimate $\|u(t_n,) - Sv^n\| \leq O(h^r)$.

These observations give us the next theorem.

Theorem 10.7.3   *If the initial value problem for a well-posed second-order partial differential equation of the form (10.7.1) is approximated by a stable finite difference scheme that is accurate of order $[r, \rho]$ and the initial functions are accurate of order r, then the solution v satisfies*

$$\|u(t_n, \cdot) - Sv^n\| \leq C_T h^r(\|u_0\|_{H^\rho} + \|u_1\|_{H^{\rho - \chi}}).$$

EXERCISES 10.7

1. Show that the estimate (10.7.4) holds for the three second-order equations (8.1.1), (8.1.8), and (8.1.10).

2. Solve the wave equation $u_{tt} = u_{xx}$ for $x \in [0, 1]$, using the initial functions

$$u(0, x) = \sin x \quad \text{and} \quad u_t(0, x) = \cos x.$$

Obtain the boundary values from the exact solution $u(t, x) = \sin(x+t)$. Demonstrate by computation, using scheme (8.2.2) that the initialization

$$v_m^1 = u(0, x_m) + ku_t(0, x_m)$$

results in a first-order accurate solution but the initialization (8.2.6) gives a second-order accurate solution.

3. Prove the Lax-Richtmyer theorem for second-order equations under the restrictions $|e^{tq_{\pm}(\xi)}| \leq 1$ and $|g_{\pm}(\theta)| \leq 1$.

4. Prove the analogue of Theorem 10.3.1 for second-order equations and verify the conclusion with computations using piecewise smooth functions.

5. Extend Theorem 10.7.2 to cover multistep schemes for second-order equations.

Chapter 11

Well-Posed and Stable
Initial-Boundary Value Problems

In this chapter we present the theory pertaining to the well-posedness of boundary conditions for partial differential equations and stability of boundary conditions for finite difference schemes. We begin the chapter by reducing the general initial-boundary value problem to a special form in which the only nonzero data are those associated with the boundary conditions. Then after introducing the Laplace transform, we give a rather general discussion of the basic formulation of the analysis of boundary conditions. We introduce the basic ideas of the analysis of boundary conditions for finite difference schemes in Section 11.2 by considering the leapfrog scheme with four boundary conditions, and then present the more general theory in Section 11.3. Section 11.4 deals with the theory of initial-boundary value problems for hyperbolic and parabolic partial differential equations. The chapter concludes by presenting the matrix method for analyzing the stability of finite difference initial-boundary value problems.

11.1 Preliminaries

Consider an initial-boundary value problem for either a partial differential equation or a finite difference scheme

$$Pu = f \tag{11.1.1}$$

on a domain Ω in R^n with initial function

$$u(0, x) = u_0(x) \tag{11.1.2}$$

and boundary conditions

$$Bu = \beta \quad \text{on} \quad \partial\Omega. \tag{11.1.3}$$

We first assume that there is an extension of equation (11.1.1) and the initial data (11.1.2) to all of R^n and that the resulting initial value problem is well-posed in the case of the differential equation or stable in the case of the difference scheme.

Let w be the solution to equation (11.1.1) on R^n satisfying the initial condition (11.1.2), suitably extended to all of R^n. Writing the solution u to (11.1.1) as $w + u'$, we obtain an initial-boundary value problem for u' on the

234

domain Ω similar to the original problem for u except that the data f of (11.1.1) and the initial data u_0 for (11.1.2) are equal to zero. The only nonzero data are the boundary data in (11.1.3).

We now make a further modification, which simplifies the analysis. This is to extend the time interval from $(0, \infty)$ to $(-\infty, \infty)$. This extension allows for a convenient use of the Laplace transform in the analysis of the boundary condition.

The next simplification depends on the idea that well-posedness of boundary conditions of partial differential equations is essentially a local property. That is, we need consider only the differential equation and boundary condition at each boundary point, and if it is well-posed at each of these points, then the global problem is well-posed. The proof of this result is beyond this text, but this principle is extremely useful. For a general domain Ω with smooth boundary, the analysis of the initial-boundary value problem at a boundary point x_0 at time t_0 is reduced to considering the differential equation with the values of the coefficients fixed at (t_0, x_0) and also the boundary conditions with their coefficients evaluated at (t_0, x_0). The domain Ω can be replaced by the half-space formed by the tangent plane to the boundary of Ω at x_0 and the interior normal at x_0. In this way the general analysis of initial-boundary value problems can be reduced to the analysis of constant coefficient equations on half-spaces. If each of these *frozen coefficient problems* is well-posed, then the original problem is well-posed.

Similar results hold for finite difference schemes, although the theory is not as complete as it is for partial differential equations. We consider only one-dimensional problems for difference schemes, and in this case the stability of an initial-boundary value problem can be analyzed by considering the pure initial value problem and the two initial-boundary value problems arising from the two endpoints. As with the well-posedness of partial differential equations, the stability of the initial-boundary value problem can be determined by examining only the frozen coefficient problems.

The Laplace Transform

The Laplace transform is employed with an independent variable such as time, for which the directionality is important. For a function $u(t)$ defined for $t \in R$, the Laplace transform of u is a function $\tilde{u}$ of a complex variable $s = \eta + i\tau$ defined as follows.

Definition 11.1.1 *The Laplace transform $\tilde{u}(s)$ is equal to the Fourier transform of $e^{-\eta t} u(t)$ with dual variable τ, that is,*

$$\tilde{u}(s) = \frac{1}{\sqrt{2\pi}} \int_{-\infty}^{\infty} e^{-(\eta + i\tau)t} u(t) \, dt \qquad (11.1.4)$$

where $s = \eta + i\tau$. (Note that most definitions of the Laplace transform omit the factor of $(2\pi)^{-1/2}$; we include it for symmetry with the Fourier transform.)

Based on the Fourier transform we have the Laplace inversion formula,

$$u(t) = \frac{1}{\sqrt{2\pi}} \int_{-\infty}^{\infty} e^{(\eta+i\tau)t} \tilde{u}(\eta + i\tau) \, d\tau$$

$$= \frac{1}{\sqrt{2\pi} \, i} \int_{\eta-i\infty}^{\eta+i\infty} e^{st} \tilde{u}(s) \, ds. \tag{11.1.5}$$

An important result for the Laplace transform is that $\tilde{u}(s)$ is an analytic function of the complex variable s. The discrete Laplace transform is defined similarly.

Definition 11.1.2   *The Laplace transform of a discrete function v_m^n on a grid with spacing k is defined by*

$$\tilde{v}(s) = \frac{1}{\sqrt{2\pi}} k \sum_{n=-\infty}^{\infty} e^{-(\eta+i\tau)nk} v^n.$$

Usually we set $z = e^{(\eta+i\tau)k}$ and, with an abuse of notation, set

$$\tilde{v}(z) = \frac{1}{\sqrt{2\pi}} k \sum_{n=-\infty}^{\infty} z^{-n} v^n.$$

We have the inversion formula

$$v^n = \frac{1}{\sqrt{2\pi}} \int_{-\pi/k}^{\pi/k} e^{snk} \tilde{v}(s) \, d\tau$$

$$= \frac{1}{\sqrt{2\pi} \, i} \oint_{|z|=e^{\eta k}} z^{(n-1)} \tilde{v}(z) \, dz. \tag{11.1.6}$$

There should be no confusion about the use of either s or z as the Laplace transform dual variable.

From Parseval's relations for the Fourier transform, we have equality of the norm of the function and its transform,

$$\|u\|_\eta^2 = \int_{-\infty}^{\infty} e^{-2\eta t} |u(t)|^2 \, dt = \int_{-\infty}^{\infty} |\tilde{u}(\eta + i\tau)|^2 \, d\tau \tag{11.1.7}$$

and

$$\|v\|_{\eta,k}^2 = k \sum_{n=-\infty}^{\infty} e^{-2\eta kn} |v^n|^2 = \int_{-\pi/k}^{\pi/k} |\tilde{v}(\eta + i\tau)|^2 \, d\tau \tag{11.1.8a}$$

or, equivalently,

$$\|v\|_{\eta,k}^2 = k \sum_{n=-\infty}^{\infty} |z|^{-2n} |v^n|^2 = k^{-1} \oint_{|z|=e^{\eta k}} |\tilde{v}(z)|^2 \, d\theta \tag{11.1.8b}$$

where $z = e^{\eta k} e^{i\theta}$, i.e., $\theta = \tau k$. The subscript of η on the norm identifies η as a parameter. By choosing η to be positive we are specifying that we are considering the initial-boundary problem for t in the positive direction.

When we consider both time and the space dimensions, we have the norms

$$\|u\|_\eta^2 = \int_{-\infty}^\infty \int_0^\infty \int_{-\infty}^\infty e^{-2\eta t} |u(t, x, y)|^2 \, dt \, dx \, dy$$

$$= \int_{-\infty}^\infty \int_0^\infty \int_{-\infty}^\infty |\hat{u}(\eta + i\tau, x, \omega)|^2 \, d\tau \, dx \, d\omega$$

where $\hat{u}$ is the transform in both t and y. We also use the norm symbol with single bars for the norm over the boundary; for example,

$$|\beta|_\eta^2 = \int_{-\infty}^\infty \int_{-\infty}^\infty e^{-2\eta t} |\beta(t, y)|^2 \, dt \, dy = \int_{-\infty}^\infty \int_{-\infty}^\infty |\hat{\beta}(\eta + i\tau, \omega)|^2 \, d\tau \, d\omega.$$

The estimates for well-posed initial-boundary value problems are of the form

$$\|u\|_\eta^2 + |u|_\eta^2 \le C(\eta) \left(|\beta|_\eta^2 + \|f\|_\eta^2 + \|u_0\|^2 \right) \tag{11.1.9}$$

showing that the norms of the solution in the interior and on the boundary are bounded by the norms of the data β on the boundary as in (11.1.3), the data f as in (11.1.1), and the initial data u_0 as in (11.1.2). By the process given earlier, the general problem can be reduced to the case in which the only nonzero data are the boundary data β. The estimate relating the norms of the solution to the boundary data can be used to give the general estimate, but these arguments are beyond this text.

A General Analysis of Boundary Conditions

Before delving into the particular details of the analysis of boundary conditions, it will be helpful to make some general comments. The purpose of these comments is to illuminate the basic ideas of these theories.

Each boundary value problem, when transformed under the Fourier and Laplace transforms, gives rise to a set of linear equations, one equation for each boundary condition. The unknowns to be determined by these equations characterize the solution in the interior of the domain. The boundary value problem is well-posed or stable if and only if this linear system can be solved and if the solution can be bounded appropriately by the boundary data.

To emphasize the basic ideas and to illustrate the approach, we consider first a simple problem in linear algebra. Given a system of linear equations

$$Ax = b,$$

it is an elementary result that there is a unique solution to this system if and only if there are no nontrivial solutions to the system

$$Az = 0.$$

If the only solution to this homogeneous equation is the trivial solution, then there is a constant, namely, $\|A^{-1}\|$, such that

$$\|x\| \le \|A^{-1}\|\,\|b\|.$$

In the theory for boundary conditions we wish to know if there is a constant such that the solution is bounded in terms of the boundary data. To do this, we need examine only homogeneous equations, as with the simple case just discussed. Many of the theorems in the theory of boundary conditions state that if there are no nontrivial solutions to a certain class of problems, then there is a constant by which the solution to the boundary value problem is bounded by the boundary data.

We now consider a set of linear equations

$$A(\rho)x(\rho) = b(\rho) \tag{11.1.10}$$

where the matrix $A(\rho)$ and data $b(\rho)$ depends continuously on a parameter ρ, which is an element of an open set, say $\rho \in (0,1)$. There is a solution to equation (11.1.10) for each value of ρ if and only if there are no nontrivial solutions to the homogeneous problems. However if we desire the bound on $x(\rho)$ to be independent of ρ, we must also consider the homogeneous problem for ρ equal to 0 and to 1. Assuming that $A(\rho)$ is defined for ρ in $[0,1]$, if there are no nontrivial solutions to

$$A(\rho)\,z = 0$$

for ρ in the closed set $[0,1]$, then there is a constant C, independent of ρ, such that

$$\|x(\rho)\| \le C\|b\|$$

for $\rho \in (0,1)$. For boundary value problems the parameters, such as (s,ω) or z, are in open sets, e.g., $\mathrm{Re}\,s > 0$ or $|z| > 1$, and it is to be determined whether the solution can be bounded by the boundary data uniformly, that is, independently of the parameters. It is rarely found in practical applications that a boundary condition is ill-posed or unstable for values of the parameters in the interior of the parameter set, the nontrivial solutions to the homogeneous equations usually occur at the boundary of the parameter set. This may present some difficulties, as we will see, but a consideration of the basic ideas will give guidance toward handling the difficulties.

In the next two sections we examine the stability of boundary conditions for finite difference schemes, and in Section 11.4 we examine the well-posedness of boundary conditions for partial differential equations.

EXERCISES 11.1

1. Verify Parseval's relations (11.1.7) and (11.1.8) for the Laplace transform by using the Parseval's relations for the Fourier transform.

2. Compute the Laplace transform for the function

$$u(t) = \begin{cases} e^{\alpha t} & \text{if } t \geq 0, \\ 0 & \text{if } t < 0. \end{cases}$$

Verify the Laplace inversion formula (11.1.5) for this function.

11.2 Analysis of Boundary Conditions for the Leapfrog Scheme

We begin our analysis of boundary conditions for finite difference schemes by considering the leapfrog scheme for $u_t - au_x = 0$, with a positive, written as

$$v_m^{n+1} = v_m^{n-1} + a\lambda \left(v_{m+1}^n - v_{m-1}^n \right) \tag{11.2.1}$$

on the region R_+, which is the semi-infinite interval $[0, \infty)$, for $-\infty < t < \infty$. The differential equation requires no boundary condition, but the scheme requires a numerical boundary condition at $x = 0$. We will examine in detail four boundary conditions for this scheme. This analysis will serve to motivate the more general discussion of the next section.

The first two boundary conditions are extrapolations to determine v_0^n from values of $v_m^{n'}$ for m positive, and the second two are one-sided difference approximations to the differential equation. These boundary conditions are

$$v_0^{n+1} = v_1^{n+1} + \beta^{n+1} \tag{11.2.2a}$$

$$v_0^{n+1} = v_1^n + \beta^{n+1} \tag{11.2.2b}$$

$$v_0^{n+1} = v_0^{n-1} + 2a\lambda \left(v_1^n - v_0^n \right) + \beta^{n+1} \tag{11.2.2c}$$

$$v_0^{n+1} = v_0^n + a\lambda \left(v_1^n - v_0^n \right) + \beta^{n+1} \tag{11.2.2d}$$

where, again, the function β^{n+1} is the result of subtracting solutions so that the initial function is zero.

We begin by transforming scheme (11.2.1) via the Laplace transform in the time variable to form the *resolvent equation*

$$\left(z - \frac{1}{z} \right) \tilde{v}_m = a\lambda \left(\tilde{v}_{m+1} - \tilde{v}_{m-1} \right). \tag{11.2.3}$$

We wish to obtain solutions to the resolvent equation that are in $L^2(hZ_+)$ as functions of x. The general solution to (11.2.3) is obtained as follows. Replacing $\tilde{v}_m$ by κ^m for $m \geq 0$, we obtain the equation

$$z - \frac{1}{z} = a\lambda \left(\kappa - \frac{1}{\kappa} \right) \tag{11.2.4}$$

for κ as a function of z. Equation (11.2.4) has in general two roots $\kappa_-(z)$ and $\kappa_+(z)$, which are continuous functions of z. The general solution of (11.2.3) is then given by

$$\tilde{v}_m = A\kappa_-(z)^m + B\kappa_+(z)^m$$

when κ_- and κ_+ are distinct.

The first significant result is that for $|z| > 1$, one of the roots, which we denote by $\kappa_-(z)$, satisfies $|\kappa_-(z)| < 1$, and the other root, denoted by $\kappa_+(z)$, satisfies $|\kappa_+(z)| > 1$. In particular, this means that the two roots do not cross the unit circle for z larger than 1 in magnitude. This result is a direct consequence of the stability of the scheme. The general result is stated in Theorem 11.3.1. We could verify this result by directly solving equation (11.2.4), essentially a quadratic in κ, for the two roots κ_- and κ_+. We will, however, regard equation (11.2.4) as implicitly defining the two functions and avoid explicitly determining $\kappa_-(z)$ and $\kappa_+(z)$. As we will see, there are only a few facts we need regarding these functions, and the information we need can be determined by avoiding the algebra involved in explicitly computing $\kappa_-(z)$ and $\kappa_+(z)$. We use this same approach on more difficult problems in the next section.

Because we are interested only in those solutions of the resolvent equation that are in $L^2(hZ_+)$ when $|z| > 1$, the general form of $\tilde{v}_m$ is

$$\tilde{v}_m = A(z)\kappa_-(z)^m \qquad (11.2.5)$$

where $|\kappa_-(z)| < 1$ for $|z| > 1$.

The coefficient $A(z)$ is to be determined by the transform of the boundary function, $\tilde{\beta}(z)$. Substituting form (11.2.5) into the boundary conditions, we obtain

$$A(z)\left[1 - \kappa_-(z)\right] = \tilde{\beta}(z) \qquad (11.2.6a)$$

$$A(z)\left[z - \kappa_-(z)\right] = z\tilde{\beta}(z) \qquad (11.2.6b)$$

$$A(z)\left\{z - z^{-1} - 2a\lambda[\kappa_-(z) - 1]\right\} = z\tilde{\beta}(z) \qquad (11.2.6c)$$

$$A(z)\left\{z - 1 - a\lambda[\kappa_-(z) - 1]\right\} = z\tilde{\beta}(z) \qquad (11.2.6d)$$

for each of the boundary conditions (11.2.2a), (11.2.2b), (11.2.2c), and (11.2.2d), respectively.

The norm of the solution $\tilde{v}_m$ in $L^2(hZ_+)$ is given by

$$\|\tilde{v}(z)\|^2 = h\sum_{m=0}^{\infty} |\tilde{v}_m(z)|^2 = h|A(z)|^2 \sum_{m=0}^{\infty} |\kappa_-(z)|^{2m}$$

$$= |A(z)|^2 \frac{h}{1 - |\kappa_-(z)|^2}.$$

In terms of the function v_m^n the norm is

$$\|v\|_{\eta,h}^2 = \int_{-\pi/k}^{\pi/k} |A(e^{sk})|^2 \frac{h}{1 - |\kappa_-(e^{sk})|^2}\, d\tau$$

where $s = \eta + i\tau$. For simplicity, we use only the subscript h rather than both h and k to denote the norm involving both x and t.

To obtain an estimate of the form

$$\|v\|^2_{\eta,h} \le C|\beta|^2_{\eta,h} \tag{11.2.7}$$

we must substitute the expression giving $A(z)$ as a function of $\tilde\beta$. For the first two boundary conditions, i.e., (11.2.2a) and (11.2.2b), we have, from (11.2.2a) and (11.2.2b),

$$\|v\|^2_{\eta,h} = \int_{-\pi/k}^{\pi/k} \frac{|\tilde\beta(e^{sk})|^2}{|1 - \kappa_-(e^{sk})|^2} \frac{h}{1 - |\kappa_-(e^{sk})|^2} \, d\tau \tag{11.2.8a}$$

and

$$\|v\|^2_{\eta,h} = \int_{-\pi/k}^{\pi/k} \frac{|z|^2|\tilde\beta(e^{sk})|^2}{|e^{sk} - \kappa_-(e^{sk})|^2} \frac{h}{1 - |\kappa_-(e^{sk})|^2} \, d\tau, \tag{11.2.8b}$$

respectively.

These equations show that we must obtain some lower bound on $|1 - \kappa_-|$ for (11.2.8a) and on $|e^{sk} - \kappa_-|$ for (11.2.8b). Because we choose η positive, we have that $|z| > 1$ and, by Theorem 11.3.1, $|\kappa_-(z)| < 1$; therefore, neither of the expressions $|1 - \kappa_-(z)|$ or $|z - \kappa_-|$ is zero, but, as k tends to zero, z—which is e^{sk}—approaches arbitrarily close to the unit circle. Moreover, because $\kappa_-(z)$ is a continuous, even analytic, function of z, we can examine the behavior of $\kappa_-(z)$ for k equal to 0, that is, for $|z| = 1$. The behavior for k positive but near to 0 can then be determined by methods such as Taylor series.

This analysis reduces to checking for nontrivial solutions of form (11.2.5), which solve the homogeneous boundary condition. Thus we must check whether there is a $\kappa_-(z)$ such that

$$A(z)\,[1 - \kappa_-(z)] = 0 \tag{11.2.9a}$$

or

$$A(z)\,[z - \kappa_-(z)] = 0 \tag{11.2.9b}$$

for the two boundary conditions (11.2.2a) and (11.2.2b), respectively.

To analyze boundary conditions (11.2.2a)–(11.2.2d), we first set $\kappa = 1$ in (11.2.4) and we find that if $\kappa = 1$, then either $z = 1$ or $z = -1$. Conversely, if $z = 1$ or $z = -1$, then $\kappa = 1$ is a root. This shows us that for z equal to 1, either $\kappa_-(1) = 1$ and $\kappa_+(1) = -1$, or, alternatively, $\kappa_-(1) = -1$ and $\kappa_+(1) = 1$. To determine if the first of these cases holds, i.e., if $\kappa_-(1) = 1$, we consider $z = 1 + \varepsilon$ and let $\kappa = 1 + \delta$ for small values of ε and δ. If for $\varepsilon > 0$ we find that $\delta < 0$, then $\kappa_-(1)$ is 1, but if instead for $\varepsilon > 0$ we find that $\delta > 0$, then it is $\kappa_+(1)$ that is 1 and so $\kappa_-(1)$ is -1.

Substituting $z = 1 + \varepsilon$ and $\kappa = 1 + \delta$ in (11.2.4), we obtain

$$z - \frac{1}{z} = 2\varepsilon + O\left(\varepsilon^2\right) = a\lambda\left(\kappa - \frac{1}{\kappa}\right) = a\lambda\left(2\delta + O(\delta^2)\right).$$

Since $a\lambda$ is positive, we see that $\varepsilon > 0$ implies $\delta > 0$; thus it is $\kappa_+(1)$ that is 1, and by default $\kappa_-(1)$ is -1.

Similarly, for $z = -(1 + \varepsilon)$ and $\kappa = 1 + \delta$, we find

$$-2\varepsilon + O\left(\varepsilon^2\right) = a\lambda\left(2\delta + O(\delta^2)\right)$$

and $\varepsilon > 0$ implies $\delta < 0$. Thus $\kappa_-(-1) = 1$. Notice that for z near -1, $1 - \kappa_-(z) = -\delta = O(\varepsilon) = O(|z| - 1)$.

Thus for boundary condition (11.2.2a) we have

$$|1 - \kappa_-(z)| \geq ck \tag{11.2.10a}$$

and this is the best possible estimate for the denominator of (11.2.8a), being achieved at $\tau = \pm\pi/k$, i.e., for z near -1.

For boundary condition (11.2.2b) we consider the quantity $z - \kappa_-(z)$. To see if this quantity can be zero or close to zero, we substitute $\kappa = z$ in (11.2.4), obtaining

$$z - \frac{1}{z} = a\lambda\left(z - \frac{1}{z}\right).$$

Since $a\lambda$ is less than 1, this equation is satisfied only if $z - 1/z$ is zero, i.e., only if $z = 1$ or $z = -1$. As we showed in the preceding analysis, $\kappa_-(1) = -1$ and $\kappa_-(-1) = 1$. Therefore, it cannot be true that $|z - \kappa_-(z)|$ is zero for $|z| \geq 1$. Hence there is a constant c, independent of k, such that

$$|z - \kappa_-(z)| \geq c. \tag{11.2.10b}$$

From these estimates we see that the dependence of the solution on the data is given by

$$\|v\|_{\eta,h}^2 \leq \frac{1}{c^2 k^2} \int_{-\pi/k}^{\pi/k} \frac{|\beta|^2 h}{1 - |\kappa_-|^2}\, d\tau \qquad \text{for (11.2.2a)} \tag{11.2.11a}$$

and

$$\|v\|_{\eta,h}^2 \leq c^{-2} \int_{-\pi/k}^{\pi/k} \frac{|\beta|^2 h}{1 - |\kappa_-|^2}\, d\tau \qquad \text{for (11.2.2b)}. \tag{11.2.11b}$$

It remains to estimate the term $h(1 - |\kappa_-(z)|^2)^{-1}$ in the two expressions (11.2.8a) and (11.2.8b). For general schemes, as we will show in Lemma 11.2.2, we have that

$$1 - |\kappa_-(z)| \geq c_0 \eta k \tag{11.2.12}$$

for some constant c_0. We now show this for the particular case of the leapfrog scheme. We set $z = e^{sk} = e^{i\tau}\left(1 + \eta k + O(\eta k)^2\right)$ and consider two cases. Either $|\kappa_-(z)| = 1$ for $k\eta$ equal to 0 or $|\kappa_-(z)| < 1$ for $k\eta$ equal to 0. In the first case set $\kappa_-(z) = e^{i\varphi}(1 - \delta)$, and then, from equation (11.2.4),

$$2i \sin\tau + 2\eta k \cos\tau + O(\eta k)^2 = a\lambda\left[2i\sin\varphi + 2\delta\cos\varphi + O(\delta^2)\right].$$

We obtain that $\sin\tau = a\lambda\sin\varphi$, and so $|\sin\tau| \le a\lambda$, from which we conclude that

$$|\cos\tau| \ge \sqrt{1 - (a\lambda)^2}.$$

Thus we obtain for δ,

$$\delta = \frac{\cos\tau}{\cos\varphi}\eta k + O(\eta k)^2 \ge \sqrt{1 - (a\lambda)^2}\,\eta k + O(\eta k)^2.$$

For $|\sin\tau|$ greater than $a\lambda$, the value of $|\kappa_-(z)|$ is strictly less than 1. Therefore, for η positive and k in some range $0 < k \le k_0(\eta)$, it follows that (11.2.12) holds; thus, since λ is constant,

$$\frac{h}{1 - |\kappa_-(z)|^2} \le \frac{h}{1 - |\kappa_-(z)|} \le \frac{c}{\eta}.$$

From (11.2.14a) we obtain the estimate

$$\|v\|_{\eta,h}^2 \le \frac{k^{-2}}{\eta}c^*|\beta|_{\eta,h}^2 \tag{11.2.13a}$$

for boundary condition (11.2.2a), where c^* is some constant, and from (11.2.14b)

$$\|v\|_{\eta,h}^2 \le \frac{c^*}{\eta}|\beta|_{\eta,h}^2 \tag{11.2.13b}$$

for boundary condition (11.2.2b), for some other value of c^*.

Estimate (11.2.13b) is of the form of (11.2.7) and shows that boundary condition (11.2.2b) is stable. However, because the estimate (11.2.10a) and, therefore, the estimate (11.2.13a) are the best possible estimates, boundary condition (11.2.2a) is unstable. By considering when the estimate (11.2.10a) is achieved, we can choose v and β so that

$$\|v\|_{\eta,h}^2 \ge ck^{-2}|\beta|_{\eta,h}^2.$$

For particular small data, i.e., $|\beta|_{\eta,h}$, we can have $\|v\|_{\eta,h}$ arbitrarily large, and thus boundary condition (11.2.2a) is unstable.

We complete this section by analyzing boundary conditions (11.2.2c) and (11.2.2d). We have that $\kappa_-(z)$ is given by equation (11.2.4) for $|z| \ge 1$ and, as before, $|\kappa_-(z)| < 1$ for z outside the unit circle. Boundary condition (11.2.2c), by (11.2.8), gives the equation

$$z - z^{-1} = 2a\lambda(\kappa_- - 1) \tag{11.2.9c}$$

as the equation to be solved if there is to be a nontrivial solution to the homogeneous boundary value problem. (The numbering of this last equation is chosen to show the relationship to (11.2.9a) and (11.2.9b).) From (11.2.4) and (11.2.9c) we obtain

$$z - \frac{1}{z} = 2a\lambda(\kappa_- - 1) = a\lambda\left(\kappa_- - \frac{1}{\kappa_-}\right).$$

Since $a\lambda$ is not zero, we have that $\kappa_- = 1$ is the only solution to this equation. We have already determined from equation (11.2.4) that κ_- is equal to 1 only when z is -1. We see that this also satisfies equation (11.2.10a), and thus the boundary condition (11.2.2c) is unstable.

Boundary condition (11.2.2d) gives the equation

$$z - 1 = a\lambda(\kappa_- - 1) \tag{11.2.9d}$$

to be solved for a solution to the homogeneous initial-boundary value problem. Dividing equation (11.2.4) by (11.2.9d), we obtain for z and κ_- not equal to 1,

$$\frac{z+1}{z} = \frac{z - 1/z}{z - 1} = \frac{a\lambda(\kappa_- - 1/\kappa_-)}{a\lambda(\kappa_- - 1)} = \frac{\kappa_- + 1}{\kappa_-}$$

which implies that z equals κ_-. However, our analysis for boundary conditions (11.2.2a) and (11.2.2b) showed that $\kappa_-(1)$ is not equal to 1, nor is $\kappa_-(z)$ equal to z for any z. Thus there is no solution to (11.2.9d), and therefore boundary condition (11.2.2d) is stable.

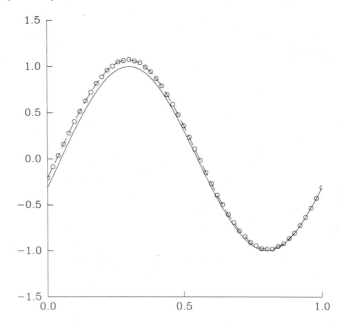

Figure 11.1

Example 11.2.1 The conclusions of this section are illustrated in plots of the solution of the one-way wave equation computed with the leapfrog scheme and boundary condition

$$v_0^{n+1} = 2v_1^{n+1} - v_2^{n+1},$$

which is similar to (11.2.2a) and is unstable; see Exercise 11.2.3. Figures 11.1, 11.2, and 11.3 show the results of using the leapfrog scheme (11.2.1) with a

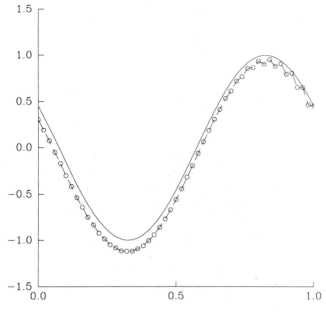

Figure 11.2

equal to 1 on the interval $[0, 1]$, with the solution specified at the right-hand endpoint. The value of h is 0.02 and λ is 0.95. The exact solution of the differential equation is $u(t, x) = \sin 2\pi(x + t)$ and is plotted with a solid line in the figure. The solution of the finite difference scheme is plotted with the circles at the grid points. The exact solution was also used to initialize the first time-step. Figure 11.1 shows the solution for boundary condition (11.2.2a) at time 0.95. At this time, there is a noticeable inaccuracy in the neighborhood of the numerical boundary condition. Figure 11.2 shows the result of the computation at time 1.425. In addition to the inaccuracy at the left boundary, there are oscillations in the solution at the right boundary. The propagation of the effects of the unstable boundary condition on the left to the right boundary is due to the presence of the parasitic mode. In Figure 11.3, which shows the solution at time 1.90, it is seen that the solution using the unstable boundary condition has become very oscillatory. Within a few more time steps the solution becomes much worse.

By comparison, the use of the more accurate boundary condition (11.2.14b) (see Exercise 11.2.3), which is similar to (11.2.2b), will produce very accurate solutions. $\square$

EXERCISES 11.2

1. Show that the leapfrog scheme (11.2.1) with the boundary condition

$$v_0^{n+1}(1 + a\lambda) - a\lambda v_1^{n+1} - v_0^n = \beta^{n+1}$$

is stable.

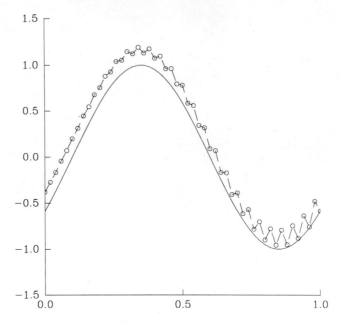

Figure 11.3

2. Show that the leapfrog scheme (11.2.1) with the boundary condition

$$\frac{1}{2}(v_1^{n+1} + v_0^{n+1} - v_1^n - v_0^n) = \frac{a\lambda}{2}(v_1^{n+1} - v_0^{n+1} + v_1^n - v_0^n) + \beta^{n+1}$$

is stable.

3. Based on the results for (11.2.2a) and (11.2.2b), conclude that for the leapfrog scheme the boundary condition

$$v_0^{n+1} = 2v_1^{n+1} - v_2^{n+1} + \beta^{n+1} \qquad\qquad (11.2.14a)$$

is unstable and that the boundary condition

$$v_0^{n+1} = 2v_1^n - v_2^{n-1} + \beta^{n+1} \qquad\qquad (11.2.14b)$$

is stable.

4. Repeat the computations given in Example 11.2.1 and verify the results. Also use the boundary condition (11.2.14b) and comment on the improvement this boundary condition gives.

11.3 The General Analysis of Boundary Conditions

In this section we present the general method for checking the stability of boundary conditions for finite difference schemes. These results were developed in the papers of Gustaffson, Kreiss, and Sundström [23] and Osher [39], [40], and we will refer to it as the GKSO theory. In these papers the method is developed for hyperbolic equations and systems, but the method is applicable, with some minor changes, to more general time-dependent equations. For simplicity we restrict our discussion to hyperbolic equations for now.

We consider a scheme defined for all time and for x on the half-space R_+, with the boundary at 0. Let the scheme be

$$P_{k,h} v_m^n = R_{k,h} f_m^n. \tag{11.3.1}$$

We assume the scheme is stable for the initial value problem and consistent with a hyperbolic equation or system of partial differential equations. We also assume that there are no lower-order terms for the scheme, so that the restrictive von Neumann stability condition holds for this scheme. The boundary conditions will be written

$$B_{k,h} v_0^n = \beta(t_n). \tag{11.3.2}$$

We assume that system (11.3.1) contains d equations and that each v_m^n is a vector of dimension d. As discussed at the beginning of Section 11.1, we need consider only the homogeneous version of (11.3.1). The definition of a stable finite difference scheme for a hyperbolic initial-boundary value problem is one in which the following estimate holds:

$$\eta \|v\|_{\eta,h}^2 + |v|_{\eta,h}^2 \le C(\eta^{-1}\|f\|_{\eta,h}^2 + |\beta|_{\eta,h}^2)$$

where the norms with double bars refer to functions defined for x in R_+ and t in R, and the single-bar norms refer to functions of t defined only on the boundary.

The general method begins by transforming in t with the Laplace transform to give the resolvent equation, which we will write as

$$\tilde{P}_{k,h}(z)\tilde{v}_m(z) = 0. \tag{11.3.3}$$

The general solution of the resolvent equation (11.3.3) is obtained by considering particular solutions of the form

$$\tilde{v}_m(z) = A(z)\kappa^m$$

where $A(z)$ is a vector of dimension d. Substituting this form of solution in (11.3.3), we obtain

$$\tilde{P}_{k,h}(z)A(z)\kappa^m = k^{-1}\tilde{p}(z,\kappa)A(z)\kappa^m.$$

The matrix function $\tilde{p}(z,\kappa)$ is related to the symbol of $P_{k,h}$ as defined in Section 3.1, and the amplification polynomial defined in Section 4.2 by the relations

$$\tilde{p}(e^{sk}, e^{ih\xi}) = kp_{k,h}(s,\xi)$$

and

$$\tilde{p}(g, e^{i\theta}) = \Phi(g, \theta).$$

We see that there will be solutions of the particular form only if

$$\det\left(\tilde{p}(z,\kappa)\right) = 0 \qquad (11.3.4)$$

where we regard this as an equation for κ as a function of z. The vector $A(z)$ is a null vector of $\tilde{p}(z,\kappa)$. Our first important result is the following theorem.

Theorem 11.3.1 *If scheme (11.3.1) is stable, then there are integers K_- and K_+ such that the roots, $\kappa(z)$, of equation (11.3.4) separate into two groups, one with K_- roots and one with K_+ roots. The group of roots denoted by $\kappa_{-,\nu}(z)$ satisfy*

$$|\kappa_{-,\nu}(z)| < 1 \quad \text{for } |z| > 1, \text{ and } \nu = 1, \ldots, K_-$$

and the group of roots denoted by $\kappa_{+,\nu}(z)$ satisfy

$$|\kappa_{+,\nu}(z)| > 1 \quad \text{for } |z| > 1, \text{ and } \nu = 1, \ldots, K_+.$$

Proof The proof depends on the relations between $\tilde{p}$ and the amplification polynomial. If some κ assumed the magnitude of 1 when the magnitude of z was larger than 1, then we may write $\kappa = e^{i\theta}$ for some real value of θ, and we have

$$\Phi(z, \theta) = \tilde{p}(z, \kappa) = 0.$$

But if the scheme is stable, then z, regarded as a function of θ, must satisfy the von Neumann condition, that is, $|z| \le 1$. This contradiction shows that for $|z|$ larger than 1, the value of $|\kappa|$ cannot be 1. Thus the roots split into two groups, those less than 1 in magnitude and those greater than 1 in magnitude. This proves the theorem. ∎

As an extension of Theorem 11.3.1 we prove the following lemma, which is important in proving (11.2.14) for general schemes for hyperbolic equations.

Lemma 11.3.2 *If $\kappa(z)$ is a root of the equation (11.3.4) with $|\kappa(z)| = 1$ for $|z| = 1$, then there is a constant C such that*

$$\left||\kappa| - 1\right| > C(|z| - 1).$$

Proof The proof depends on the observation that the roots of the amplification polynomial $\Phi(g, \theta)$, which are on the unit circle, are simple and that κ is an analytic function of z. Moreover, since $|\kappa|$ is not 1 for $|z|$ larger than 1, it follows from the Taylor series expansion of κ as a function of z, that the estimate of the lemma must hold for some constant. ∎

By Theorem 11.3.1 K_- is independent of z and we may write the general solution in $L^2(R_+)$ of the resolvent equation as

$$\tilde{v}_m(z) = \sum_{\nu=1}^{K_-} \alpha_\nu(z) A_\nu(z) \kappa_{-,\nu}^m \qquad (11.3.5)$$

in the case that all the $\kappa_{-,\nu}$ are distinct. The vectors $A_\nu(z)$ are particular null vectors of $\tilde{p}(z, \kappa_{-,\nu})$ and the α_ν are arbitrary scalar coefficients. If the $\kappa_{-,\nu}$ are not distinct, then the preceding representation will have to be altered to account for the multiplicity of the root. Since this occurs infrequently, we omit the details of the construction here (see Example 11.3.2). Note that the functions $\kappa_{-,\nu}(z)$ are distinguished by the property that they are less than 1 in magnitude for z outside the unit circle, but they are also defined by continuity for z on the unit circle. When z is on the unit circle, we must take some care to distinguish between the functions $\kappa_{-,\nu}$ and those functions $\kappa_{+,\nu}$ that may also have magnitude 1.

Definition 11.3.1 *An admissible solution to the resolvent equation is a solution that is in $L^2(hZ_+)$ in the case that $|z|$ is larger than 1, and, when $|z|$ is equal to 1, an admissible solution is the limit of admissible solutions with z greater than 1 in magnitude. That is, $v(z)$ is an admissible solution if $|z|$ is larger than 1 and $v(z)$ is in $L^2(hZ_+)$, or if $|z|$ is equal to 1, then*

$$v(z) = \lim_{\varepsilon \to 0+} v(z(1 + \varepsilon))$$

where $v(z(1 + \varepsilon))$ is in $L^2(hZ_+)$ for each positive value of ε.

Admissible solutions will have the form (11.3.5) when the roots $\kappa_{-,\nu}$ are distinct. It is easily seen that the set of admissible solutions is a vector space of dimension K_-.

The number of boundary conditions necessary for stability must be precisely K_-. If we substitute expression (11.3.5) into the transformed boundary conditions, obtained from (11.3.2) by applying the Laplace transform,

$$\tilde{B}\tilde{v}_0(z) = \tilde{\beta}(z),$$

we obtain K_- equations for the K_- coefficients α_ν. This equation is of the form (11.1.10). As discussed in Section 11.1, the coefficients $\alpha_\nu(z)$ can be determined by these equations, and the solution can be bounded independently of z only if there are no nontrivial solutions to the homogeneous equation for z satisfying $|z| \geq 1$.

Thus the check for stability of the boundary conditions reduces to checking that there are no admissible solutions to the resolvent equation that also satisfy the homogeneous boundary conditions,

$$\tilde{B}\tilde{v}_0(z) = 0. \tag{11.3.6}$$

The basic result is given by the following theorem.

Theorem 11.3.3   *The initial-boundary value problem for the stable scheme (11.3.1), for a hyperbolic equation with boundary conditions (11.3.2), is stable if and only if there are no nontrivial admissible solutions of the resolvent equation that satisfy the homogeneous boundary conditions (11.3.6).*

The proof of this theorem is not given here. In the generality given by Gustaffson, Kreiss, and Sundström [23] it applies to schemes for hyperbolic equations with variable coefficients and uses techniques beyond those of this text.

We also state the corresponding theorem for schemes for parabolic equations. We restrict ourselves to the case when the finite difference scheme requires no numerical boundary conditions, that is, when the finite difference scheme requires as many boundary conditions as does the differential equation.

Theorem 11.3.4   *If the initial-boundary value problem for the stable scheme (11.3.1) with boundary conditions (11.3.2) approximates a well-posed initial-boundary value problem for a parabolic differential equation and the number of boundary conditions required by the scheme is equal to the number required by the differential equation, then the initial-boundary value problem is is stable if and only if there are no admissible solutions of the resolvent equation that satisfy the homogeneous boundary conditions (11.3.6) for $|z| \geq 1$ except for $z = 1$.*

The main difference between these theorems is that in Theorem 11.3.4, there is no need to check for admissible solutions in the case when z is 1. The reason for this is that the assumption that the differential problem is well-posed removes the need to check at z equal to 1. There may be solutions to the resolvent equation with z equal to 1 and κ_- on the unit circle, but these do not cause instability because of the well-posedness of the initial-boundary value problem for the partial differential equation.

We now illustrate Theorem 11.3.3 and Theorem 11.3.4 by applying it to several schemes and boundary conditions.

Example 11.3.1   Our first example is for the Crank-Nicolson scheme (3.1.3) for the one-way wave equation and the quasi-characteristic extrapolation boundary condition (3.3.1c), or, equivalently, the scheme for $u_t = au_x$, with a positive, given by

$$-\frac{a\lambda}{4}v_{m+1}^{n+1} + v_m^{n+1} + \frac{a\lambda}{4}v_{m-1}^{n+1} = \frac{a\lambda}{4}v_{m+1}^n + v_m^n - \frac{a\lambda}{4}v_{m-1}^n \tag{11.3.7}$$

with boundary condition (11.2.2b).

Corresponding to equation (11.3.2) we obtain

$$\frac{z-1}{z+1} = \frac{a\lambda}{4}\left(\kappa - \frac{1}{\kappa}\right). \tag{11.3.8}$$

This equation is equivalent to a quadratic equation in κ and we see that if $\kappa(z)$ is a root, then so is $-1/\kappa(z)$. Thus there is one root inside the unit circle and one outside, and by Theorem 11.3.1 they remain separated for z outside the unit circle. Thus the functions $\kappa_-(z)$ and $\kappa_+(z)$ are well defined. An alternate way of deducing that K_- and K_+ are both 1, one that can apply in more general cases (e.g., Example 11.3.2 and Exercise 11.3.5), is to examine the roots for z near -1 where the left-hand side becomes infinite. If we set $z = -(1+\varepsilon)$, then from (11.3.8) we have that one root satisfies

$$\frac{2}{\varepsilon} \approx \frac{a\lambda}{4}\kappa$$

and is therefore outside the unit circle, and the other satisfies

$$\frac{2}{\varepsilon} \approx -\frac{a\lambda}{4}\frac{1}{\kappa}$$

and is therefore inside the unit circle. Thus K_- and K_+ are both 1.

The boundary condition equation (11.3.5) resulting from the substitution $\tilde{v}_m = \kappa_-^m$ results in the equation

$$z - \kappa_-(z) = 0.$$

Since z is restricted to $|z| \geq 1$ and κ_- is restricted by $|\kappa_-(z)| \leq 1$, the only way that equation (11.3.8) can be satisfied is if $z = \kappa_-(z) = e^{i\theta}$ for some real value of θ. Substituting this relation in equation (11.3.8), we obtain

$$\frac{e^{i\theta} - 1}{e^{i\theta} + 1} = \frac{a\lambda}{4}(e^{i\theta} - e^{-i\theta})$$

or

$$\tan\tfrac{1}{2}\theta = \tfrac{1}{2}a\lambda \sin\theta = a\lambda \sin\tfrac{1}{2}\theta \cos\tfrac{1}{2}\theta.$$

This equation is satisfied either if $\sin\tfrac{1}{2}\theta$ is zero or if $\cos^2\tfrac{1}{2}\theta = (a\lambda)^{-1}$.

We first check the possibility that $\sin\tfrac{1}{2}\theta$ is zero. This is equivalent to showing that $\kappa_-(1)$ is 1. Notice that for z equal to 1, there is a root κ of (11.3.8) equal to 1, but it is must be determined whether this root is $\kappa_-(1)$ or $\kappa_+(1)$. As done earlier in analyzing boundary conditions (11.2.2a) and (11.2.2b) for the leapfrog scheme (see estimates (11.2.10a) and (11.2.10b)) we set $z = 1 + \varepsilon$ and $\kappa = 1 + \delta$. We easily obtain from (11.3.8),

$$\frac{\varepsilon}{2} + O(\varepsilon^2) = \frac{a\lambda}{2}[\delta + O(\delta^2)]$$

and thus we see that it is $\kappa_+(1)$ that is 1, and not $\kappa_-(1)$. Thus there is no difficulty with the case when z is 1.

We next consider the situation with

$$\cos^2 \tfrac{1}{2}\theta = (a\lambda)^{-1}. \tag{11.3.9}$$

We see immediately that if $a\lambda$ is less than 1, then the boundary condition is stable, since this equation cannot be satisfied for real values of θ. For $a\lambda$ equal to 1, (11.3.9) holds only for θ equal to 0, and as we have already shown, this is not an admissible solution. If $a\lambda$ is greater than 1 then we set

$$z = e^{i\theta}\frac{1+\varepsilon}{1-\varepsilon} \quad \text{and} \quad \kappa = e^{i\theta}(1+\delta),$$

where we have chosen the form of z to facilitate the algebraic manipulations. Substituting these expressions into (11.3.8), we obtain

$$i\tan\frac{1}{2}\theta \, \frac{1 - i\varepsilon\cot\frac{1}{2}\theta}{1 + i\varepsilon\tan\frac{1}{2}\theta} + O(\varepsilon^2) = \frac{a\lambda}{2}[i\sin\theta + \delta\cos\theta - \delta^2 e^{i\theta} + O(\delta^3)],$$

and hence to within $O(\varepsilon^2)$ and $O(\delta^2)$,

$$\varepsilon(1 + \tan^2\tfrac{1}{2}\theta) = \delta\tfrac{1}{2}a\lambda\cos\theta.$$

Thus, if $\cos\theta$ is positive, then it is $\kappa_+(z)$ that is equal to z, and if $\cos\theta$ is negative, then $\kappa_-(z)$ is equal to z and the scheme with boundary condition is unstable. The condition that $\cos\theta$ is negative is equivalent to the condition that $\cos^2\frac{1}{2}\theta$ is less than $\frac{1}{2}$, and so by (11.3.9) we see that the scheme is unstable for $a\lambda$ larger than 2. When $a\lambda$ is equal to 2, then both $\kappa_-(z)$ and $\kappa_+(z)$ are equal to z, and thus this case is also unstable.

We conclude that the Crank-Nicolson scheme (11.3.7) with boundary condition (11.2.2b) is stable for $a\lambda$ less than 2 and unstable if this quantity is greater than or equal to 2. $\square$

Example 11.3.2 Our next example is for the $(2,4)$ leapfrog scheme

$$\frac{v_m^{n+1} - v_m^{n-1}}{2k} = \left(1 - \frac{h^2}{6}\delta^2\right)\delta_0 u_m^n \tag{11.3.10}$$

for $u_t = u_x$ on $x \geq 0$. This is the same scheme as (4.1.9). Because this scheme involves v_{m-1}^n and v_{m-2}^n to compute v_m^{n+1}, it requires two boundary conditions. This can also be seen from the equation for the roots of $\tilde{p}(z, \kappa)$, which is equivalent to

$$z - z^{-1} = \frac{\lambda}{6}\left(\kappa - \frac{1}{\kappa}\right)\left[8 - \left(\kappa + \frac{1}{\kappa}\right)\right]. \tag{11.3.11}$$

For z very large we see that there are two roots satisfying

$$z \approx \frac{\lambda}{6}(-\kappa^2)$$

so that K_+ is 2. There are two roots satisfying

$$z \approx \frac{\lambda}{6}(\kappa^{-2})$$

so that K_- is 2, and this must be the number of boundary conditions. For our boundary conditions at m equal to 0 and 1, we take the quasi-characteristic extrapolations

$$v_0^{n+1} = 2v_1^n - v_2^{n-1} \tag{11.3.12a}$$

and

$$v_1^{n+1} = 2v_2^n - v_3^{n-1}. \tag{11.3.12b}$$

Recall that the stability condition for scheme (11.3.10) is

$$\lambda < \bar{\lambda} = \left(1 + \frac{1}{\sqrt{6}}\right)^{-1}\left(\sqrt{6} - \frac{3}{2}\right)^{-1/2} \tag{11.3.13}$$

as shown in Example 4.1.2. (See (4.1.11).)

The general admissible solution to the resolvent equation for the scheme (11.3.10) is

$$\tilde{v}_m = \alpha_1(z)\kappa_{-,1}(z)^m + \alpha_2(z)\kappa_{-,2}(z)^m \tag{11.3.14}$$

when the two roots are not equal and is of the form

$$\tilde{v}_m = \alpha(z)\kappa_{-,1}(z)^m + \alpha'(z)m\kappa_{-,1}(z)^{m-1} \tag{11.3.15}$$

when $\kappa_{-,1}$ equals $\kappa_{-,2}$.

Applying the boundary conditions (11.3.12) to the solution (11.3.14), we obtain the equations

$$[z - \kappa_{-,1}(z)]^2\,\alpha_1 + [z - \kappa_{-,2}(z)]^2\,\alpha_2 = 0$$

and

$$(z - \kappa_{-,1}(z))^2\,\kappa_{-,1}\alpha_1 + (z - \kappa_{-,2}(z))^2\,\kappa_{-,2}\alpha_2 = 0.$$

There will be a nontrivial solution to this system of equations for α_1 and α_2 only if the determinant of the system is zero. The determinant is

$$\det \begin{vmatrix} (z - \kappa_{-,1})^2 & (z - \kappa_{-,2})^2 \\ (z - \kappa_{-,1})^2\kappa_{-,1} & (z - \kappa_{-,2})^2\kappa_{-,2} \end{vmatrix} = (z - \kappa_{-,1})^2(z - \kappa_{-,2})^2(\kappa_{-,2} - \kappa_{-,1}).$$

Since we have assumed that the values of the κ_- are distinct we see that the only way that the determinant can vanish is when at least one of the two functions

$\kappa_{-,1}$ or $\kappa_{-,2}$ is equal to z. We may assume that $\kappa_{-,1}$, which we will now denote as $\kappa_-(z)$, is equal to z and, as we have discussed before, this can only happen when both z and κ_- are on the unit circle, that is, when $z = \kappa_-(z) = e^{i\theta}$ for some real value of θ. Substituting this relation in (11.3.11), we see that several cases are possible. Either $z = \kappa_- = 1$, $z = \kappa_- = -1$, or

$$1 = \frac{\lambda}{6}\left[8 - \left(\kappa_- + \frac{1}{\kappa_-}\right)\right] = \frac{\lambda}{3}(4 - \cos\theta),$$

which is equivalent to λ and θ being related by

$$\cos\theta = 4 - \frac{3}{\lambda}. \tag{11.3.16}$$

It is not hard to show that the first two cases are not possible, that is, $\kappa_-(1) \neq 1$ and $\kappa_-(-1) \neq -1$. This is left as an exercise (see Exercise 11.3.6). In the third case, the scheme is unstable if the value of θ is determined by (11.3.16). Since the scheme itself is stable for $0 \le \lambda < \bar{\lambda}$, (see (11.3.13)), instability can only occur for $\frac{3}{5} \le \lambda < \bar{\lambda}$. Notice that in this case, $\cos\theta$ is negative. For λ in this range we check on whether it is a κ_- root, or a κ_+ root which is equal to z. As before, we set

$$z = e^{i\theta}(1 + \varepsilon) \quad \text{and} \quad \kappa = e^{i\theta}(1 + \delta)$$

and we obtain the equation for δ from (11.3.11) as

$$\delta = \varepsilon \frac{3}{\lambda} \frac{1 + 4\cos\theta - 2\cos^2\theta}{\cos\theta} + O(\varepsilon^2).$$

Since $\cos\theta$ is negative, we have that the root κ will be inside the unit circle when z is outside, i.e., $\delta < 0$ when $\varepsilon > 0$, only when

$$1 + 4\cos\theta - 2\cos^2\theta > 0.$$

This happens when $|\cos\theta|$ is greater than $|\cos\theta_0|$, determined by

$$\cos\theta_0 = 1 - \sqrt{\frac{3}{2}} = 4 - \frac{3}{\lambda_0}.$$

For λ greater than λ_0, the value of $\cos\theta$ as given by (11.3.16) is greater in magnitude than $\cos\theta_0$, and the scheme with the boundary conditions (11.3.12) is unstable. As in the previous cases, when λ is equal to λ_0 then two roots, one a κ_- root and one a κ_+ root, are equal and equal to z. It remains to check that there are no additional admissible solutions of the form (11.3.15) that satisfy the homogeneous boundary conditions. This is left as an exercise (see Exercise 11.3.7). Thus the scheme is unstable for λ equal to λ_0. We conclude that scheme (11.3.10) with boundary conditions (11.3.12) is stable only for

$$\lambda < \lambda_0 = \left(1 + \frac{1}{\sqrt{6}}\right)^{-1} < \bar{\lambda}.$$

Since $\lambda_0 \approx 0.7101$ and $\bar{\lambda} \approx 0.7287$, the boundary conditions exclude a rather small range of values for λ. $\square$

Example 11.3.3 We consider the heat equation (6.1.1) with the Neumann boundary condition $u_x = 0$ at $x = 0$. The scheme is the Crank-Nicolson scheme

$$v_m^{n+1} - v_m^n = \frac{b\mu}{2}\delta^2(v_m^{n+1} + v_m^n)$$

and the boundary condition to implement the Neumann condition is

$$\frac{3v_0^{n+1} - 4v_1^{n+1} + v_2^{n+1}}{2h} = 0.$$

The equation relating z and κ is

$$\frac{z-1}{z+1} = b\mu(\kappa - 2 + \frac{1}{\kappa})$$

and the boundary condition yields the relation

$$0 = 3 - 4\kappa_- + \kappa_-^2 = (1 - \kappa_-)(3 - \kappa_-).$$

From the boundary condition, we see that the only possible solution is with κ_- equal to 1, and the relation between z and κ implies that κ is 1 only when z is 1. Since the differential equation with the boundary condition is well-posed by Theorem 11.3.4, there is nothing further to check. The finite difference equation and boundary condition are stable. $\square$

EXERCISES 11.3

1. Show that the scheme

$$\frac{3v_m^{n+1} - 4v_m^n + v_m^{n-1}}{2k} = \frac{v_{m+1}^{n+1} - v_{m-1}^{n+1}}{2h}$$

for the equation $u_t = u_x$ on $x \geq 0$ with the boundary condition

$$\frac{v_0^{n+1} - v_0^n}{k} = \frac{v_1^n - v_0^n}{h}$$

is stable only if $\lambda < \frac{5}{3}$. (See also (4.2.3) and Exercise 4.3.3.) *Hint:* The critical values are

$$\kappa_- = -\frac{\sqrt{1 + 4(\lambda - 1)^2} - 1}{2\lambda} \quad \text{and} \quad z = -\frac{2\lambda - 3 + \sqrt{1 + 4(\lambda - 1)^2}}{2}.$$

(See also Exercise 11.3.12.)

2. Show that the scheme

$$\frac{3v_m^{n+1} - 4v_m^n + v_m^{n-1}}{2k} = \frac{v_{m+1}^{n+1} - v_{m-1}^{n+1}}{2h}$$

for the equation $u_t = u_x$ on $x \geq 0$ with the boundary condition

$$\frac{v_0^{n+1} - v_0^n}{k} = \frac{v_1^{n+1} - v_0^{n+1}}{h}$$

is unconditionally stable.

3. Show for the Lax-Wendroff and Crank-Nicolson schemes for the one-way wave equation $u_t + u_x = 0$ on $x \geq 0$, for which the data should be specified at $x = 0$, that extrapolation of the solution given by either (11.2.2a) or (11.2.2b) is unstable.

4. Show that the Crank-Nicolson scheme discussed in Example 11.3.1 with boundary condition (11.2.2a) is stable.

5. Show that the $(2, 4)$ Crank-Nicolson scheme

$$\frac{v_m^{n+1} - v_m^n}{k} = (1 + \frac{h^2}{6}\delta^2)^{-1}\delta_0(\frac{v_m^{n+1} + v_m^n}{2})$$

for the equation $u_t = u_x$ on $x \geq 0$ with the boundary condition

$$v_0^{n+1} = v_1^n$$

is stable only for $\lambda < 2$.

6. Show that for the $(2, 4)$ leapfrog scheme in Example 11.3.2 that $\kappa_-(1)$ is not equal to 1 and $\kappa_-(-1)$ is not equal to -1.

7. Show that for the $(2, 4)$ leapfrog scheme in Example 11.3.2 that there are no admissible solutions of the form (11.3.15) that satisfy the homogeneous boundary conditions.

8. Show that the Du Fort–Frankel scheme (6.3.7) for the heat equation (6.1.1) with the boundary condition

$$\frac{3v_0^{n+1} - 4v_1^{n+1} + v_2^{n+1}}{2h} = 0,$$

is a stable approximation to the heat equation with the Neumann boundary condition.

9. Show that when the Crank-Nicolson scheme for the heat equation (6.1.1) with the Neumann boundary condition is approximated by the boundary condition

$$\delta_+ \left(\frac{v_0^{n+1} + v_0^n}{2}\right) = 0$$

the initial-boundary value problem is unstable.

10. Show that the $(4, 4)$ scheme for $u_t - u_x = 0$

$$\frac{v_m^{n+2} - v_m^{n-2}}{4k} - \left(1 + \frac{h^2}{6}\delta^2\right)^{-1}\delta_0\left(\frac{2v_m^{n+1} - v_m^n + 2v_m^{n-1}}{3}\right) = 0,$$

which was discussed in Example 4.3.3, is unstable with the boundary condition

$$v_0^{n+1} = 3v_1^{n+1} - 3v_2^{n+1} + v_3^{n+1}.$$

Hint: Show that $\kappa_-(-1) = 1$.

11. Show that the $(4,4)$ scheme of Exercise 10 is stable with the boundary condition

$$v_0^{n+1} = 3v_1^n - 3v_2^{n-1} + v_3^{n-2}.$$

12. Demonstrate with a computer program the instability of the boundary condition given in Exercise 1 using the data $u(t,x) = |\sin(x+t)|$ on the interval $[0,1]$ for t between 0 and 17, using λ equal to 1.7, and the stability of the boundary condition when λ is 1.6 and t between 0 and 16. Use grid spacings of $\frac{1}{10}$, $\frac{1}{20}$, and $\frac{1}{40}$. The boundary condition at x equal to 1 should be that the exact solution is specified.

13. Demonstrate the instability discussed in Example 11.3.2 with numerical computations.

11.4 Initial-Boundary Value Problems for Partial Differential Equations

In this section we present the method of determining if boundary conditions for initial-boundary value problems are well-posed. We give illustrations of the method using several examples, but we do not give complete proofs of the results.

We present the theory using as an example the parabolic equation

$$u_t = b(u_{xx} + u_{yy}) + f(t,x,y) \tag{11.4.1}$$

on the region $\{(t,x,y) : t,y \in R, \ x \in R_+\}$. At the boundary we consider the boundary condition

$$u_x + \alpha u_y = \beta(t,y). \tag{11.4.2}$$

We assume that the constants b and α are complex numbers and hence that u is a complex-valued function. By considering the real and imaginary parts of u, we can replace (11.4.1) and (11.4.2) by an equivalent system of two equations involving two real-valued functions. For (11.4.1) to be parabolic we must require that the real part of b be positive.

We begin our analysis by taking the Fourier transform in the variable y and the Laplace transform in t. We obtain the equation

$$\hat{u}_{xx} = (b^{-1}s + \omega^2)\hat{u} - b^{-1}\hat{f} \tag{11.4.3}$$

for the transform $\hat{u}(s,x,\omega)$ of u. The general solution of (11.4.3) that is in $L^2(R_+)$ as a function of x is

$$\hat{u} = \hat{u}_0(s,w)e^{-\kappa x} + \frac{1}{2\kappa b}\int_x^\infty e^{(x-z)\kappa}\hat{f}(x,z,w)\,dz$$

$$+ \frac{1}{2\kappa b}\int_0^x e^{-(x-z)\kappa}\hat{f}(s,z,w)\,dz \tag{11.4.4}$$

where

$$\kappa = (b^{-1}s + \omega^2)^{1/2} \quad \text{and} \quad \text{Re } \kappa > 0.$$

Recall that the real part of s, which we denote by η, is positive.

The function $\hat{u}_0(s, \omega)$ is determined by boundary condition (11.4.2), which after transforming is

$$\hat{u}_x + \alpha i \omega \hat{u} = \hat{\beta}(s, \omega).$$

Substituting (11.4.4) in this boundary condition, we have

$$(-\kappa + i\alpha\omega)\left[\hat{u}_0 - \frac{1}{2\kappa}\int_0^\infty e^{-z\kappa}\hat{f}(s, z, \omega)\, dz\right] = \hat{\beta}(s, \omega).$$

This is a linear equation for the unknown $\hat{u}_0$ much like (11.1.10), where here the parameter ρ varies over the set $\{(s, \omega) : \text{Re } s > 0, \ \omega \in R\}$. We see that we can solve for $\hat{u}_0$ only if the quantity $-\kappa + i\alpha\omega$ is not zero. Moreover, we can get a uniform estimate for $\hat{u}_0$ in terms of $\hat{\beta}$ only if $-\kappa + i\alpha\omega$ is bounded away from zero.

Let us now determine when $\kappa + i\alpha\omega$ is zero. We have

$$\kappa = \sqrt{b^{-1}s + \omega^2} = i\alpha\omega,$$

and since ω can be either positive or negative, we lose no information if we square both sides of this relation, obtaining

$$s = -b(\alpha^2 + 1)\omega^2.$$

This equation can be satisfied for (s, ω) with Re $s \geq 0$ and ω real only if

$$\text{Re } b(\alpha^2 + 1) \leq 0.$$

Therefore, the solution cannot be uniformly bounded by the data in this case. We conclude that the condition that boundary condition (11.4.2) is well-posed for equation (11.4.1) is that

$$\text{Re } b(\alpha^2 + 1) > 0. \tag{11.4.5}$$

There are several things we should point out about this example that apply to more general problems. First, notice that the function $f(t, x, y)$ does not play a role in deciding whether or not an estimate exists, and if condition (11.4.5) is satisfied, then an estimate relating u to β and f can be obtained.

In general, for a partial differential equation of the form

$$u_t = P(\partial_x, \partial_y)u + f(t, x, y) \tag{11.4.6}$$

for $x \in R_+$ and $y \in R^d$ with boundary conditions

$$Bu = \beta(t, y) \tag{11.4.7}$$

on the boundary given by x equal to zero, the procedure to determine the well-posedness of the boundary conditions is as follows.

First, consider the resolvent equation

$$[s - P(\partial_x, i\omega)]\, \hat{u} = 0 \tag{11.4.8}$$

which is an ordinary differential equation for $\hat{u}$ as a function of x. The parameter s is restricted so that Re $s > 0$ and $\omega \in R^d$. The boundary condition for $\hat{u}$ is

$$B\hat{u} = 0. \tag{11.4.9}$$

Both the resolvent equation (11.4.8) and the boundary condition (11.4.9) are obtained by applying the Laplace transform in t and the Fourier transform in y to the homogeneous equation corresponding to (11.4.6) and the homogeneous boundary conditions (11.4.7).

Definition 11.4.1 *An admissible solution to the resolvent equation (11.4.8) is a solution that is in $L^2(R_+)$ as a function in x in the case that Re s is positive, and, when Re $s = 0$, an admissible solution is the limit of admissible solutions with Re s positive. That is, $\hat{u}(s, x, \omega)$ is an admissible solution if Re s is positive and $\hat{u}(s, x, \omega)$ is in $L^2(R_+)$, or if Re s is equal to 0, then*

$$\hat{u}(s, x, \omega) = \lim_{\varepsilon \to 0+} \hat{u}(s + \varepsilon, x, \omega)$$

where $\hat{u}(s + \varepsilon, x, \omega)$ is an admissible solution for each positive value of ε.

Theorem 11.4.1 *The initial-boundary value problem for differential equation (11.4.6) with boundary condition (11.4.7) is well-posed if and only if there are no nontrivial admissible solutions to the resolvent equation (11.4.8) that satisfy the homogeneous boundary condition (11.4.9).*

Theorem 11.4.1 deals with the strongest notion of a well-posed initial-boundary value problem. The estimates that characterize the well-posedness of Theorem 4.7.1 involve estimates of the solution in the interior of the domain and also L^2 estimates of the solution on the boundary in terms of L^2 estimates of the boundary data. For the proof of Theorem 11.4.1, see [28] or [8].

If we modify the requirement to allow other norms of the solution and data on the boundary, then some initial-boundary value problems that are ill-posed under Theorem 11.4.1 are well-posed in a weaker sense. This weaker form of the well-posed estimate occurs frequently for hyperbolic systems. Based on the work of Kreiss [28] and [29] we have the following theorem.

Theorem 11.4.2 *If a nontrivial admissible solution $\hat{u}(s_0, x, \omega_0)$ to the hyperbolic system (11.4.8) with Re $s_0 = 0$ and $|s_0|^2 + \omega_0^2 \neq 0$ satisfies the homogeneous boundary condition (11.4.9) but there is a constant c such that*

$$\|B\hat{u}(s_0 + \varepsilon, 0, \omega_0)\| \geq c\sqrt{\varepsilon}\|\hat{u}(s_0, 0, \omega)\|$$

for ε sufficiently small and positive and there are no nontrivial admissible solutions with Re $s > 0$ satisfying the homogeneous boundary conditions, then the initial-boundary value problem is weakly well-posed.

The following example illustrates the use of the two theorems.

Example 11.4.1 We consider the hyperbolic system

$$\begin{pmatrix} u^1 \\ u^2 \end{pmatrix}_t = \begin{pmatrix} -1 & 0 \\ 0 & 1 \end{pmatrix} \begin{pmatrix} u^1 \\ u^2 \end{pmatrix}_x + \begin{pmatrix} 0 & 1 \\ 1 & 0 \end{pmatrix} \begin{pmatrix} u^1 \\ u^2 \end{pmatrix}_y, \tag{11.4.10}$$

on the domain $R_+ \times R$, with boundary condition

$$u^1 + au^2 = \beta(t, y) \tag{11.4.11}$$

on $x = 0$.

The resolvent equation is equivalent to

$$\begin{pmatrix} \hat{u}^1 \\ \hat{u}^2 \end{pmatrix}_x = \begin{pmatrix} -s & i\omega \\ -i\omega & s \end{pmatrix} \begin{pmatrix} \hat{u}^1 \\ \hat{u}^2 \end{pmatrix} \tag{11.4.12}$$

and the general admissible solution is

$$\begin{pmatrix} \hat{u}^1 \\ \hat{u}^2 \end{pmatrix} = \alpha \begin{pmatrix} -i\omega \\ \kappa - s \end{pmatrix} e^{-\kappa x} \tag{11.4.13}$$

where $\kappa = \sqrt{s^2 + \omega^2}$, with the convention that Re $\kappa \geq 0$.

Substituting the admissible solution (11.4.13) into the homogeneous boundary condition, we have

$$[-i\omega + a(\kappa - s)]\alpha = 0,$$

which has a nontrivial solution for α only if

$$i\omega = a(\kappa - s) = a(\sqrt{s^2 + \omega^2} - s). \tag{11.4.14}$$

If there is a solution to (11.4.14) with $\omega \in R$ and Re $s \geq 0$, then the initial-boundary value problem consisting of the equation (11.4.10) and boundary condition (11.4.11) is ill-posed; otherwise it is well-posed.

To examine (11.4.14), set s equal to $z|\omega|$ and obtain, after dividing by $|\omega|$,

$$\pm i = a(\sqrt{z^2 + 1} - z)$$

or, after multiplying by $\sqrt{z^2 + 1} + z$,

$$\sqrt{z^2 + 1} + z = \pm ia. \tag{11.4.15}$$

The mapping taking z to $w = \sqrt{z^2 + 1} + z$ maps the plane given by Re $z \geq 0$ onto the domain $D = \{w : $ Re $w \geq 0$ and $|w| \geq 1\}$. Therefore, there is a solution to (11.4.15) with Re z nonnegative if and only if $|a| \geq 1$. Conversely, there is no solution to (11.4.15) with Re z nonnegative if $|a|$ is less than 1.

We conclude that the initial-boundary value problem for (11.4.10) with boundary condition (11.4.11) is well-posed in the strong sense only if $|a|$ is less than 1.

If a is 1 or -1, then the initial-boundary value problem is well-posed in the weaker sense, as we now show. For a equal to 1, we have an admissible solution satisfying the homogeneous boundary condition when (s_0, ω_0) is equal to $(i, -1)$ by (11.4.14). All other solutions are proportional to this solution. In this case, we have from (11.4.13)

$$\hat{u}(s_0 + \varepsilon, x, \omega_0) = \alpha \left(\frac{i}{\kappa - i - \varepsilon} \right) e^{-\kappa x}$$

where $\kappa = \left((i + \varepsilon)^2 + 1 \right)^{1/2} = \sqrt{2i\varepsilon} + O(\varepsilon)$. Notice that $\|u(s_0, 0, \omega_0)\| = \sqrt{2}|\alpha|$. Substituting this function in the boundary condition with a equal to 1, we have by (11.4.11)

$$|\hat{u}^1 + \hat{u}^2| = |\alpha||i + \kappa - i - \varepsilon|$$
$$= |\alpha||\kappa - \varepsilon| = |\alpha| \left[\sqrt{2\varepsilon} + O(\varepsilon) \right].$$

By Theorem 11.4.2 boundary condition (11.4.11) with $a = 1$ is well-posed in the weaker sense; a similar analysis holds for a equal to -1. □

Example 11.4.2 For our second example we use the system

$$u_t + au_x + bu_y + h_x = 0$$
$$v_t + av_x + bv_y + h_y = 0 \qquad (11.4.16)$$
$$h_t + ah_x + bh_y + u_x + v_y = 0,$$

which is obtained by linearizing the shallow water equations around a constant flow, see [38].

We consider this system on the domain $\{(x, y) : x \geq 0, y \in R\}$ and consider the case when the coefficient a satisfies $0 < a < 1$. The resolvent equation for this system can be written as

$$a\hat{u}_x + \hat{h}_x + s'\hat{u} = 0$$
$$a\hat{v}_x + s'\hat{v} + i\omega\hat{h} = 0 \qquad (11.4.17)$$
$$a\hat{h}_x + \hat{u}_x + i\omega\hat{v} + s'\hat{h} = 0$$

where $s' = s + ib\omega$. We first determine κ so that there are solutions to (11.4.17) of the form

$$\begin{pmatrix} \hat{u} \\ \hat{v} \\ \hat{h} \end{pmatrix} = \begin{pmatrix} \hat{u}_0(s, \omega) \\ \hat{v}_0(s, \omega) \\ \hat{h}_0(s, \omega) \end{pmatrix} e^{-\kappa x}$$

with the real part of κ being positive. The equation for κ is

$$0 = \det \begin{pmatrix} s' - a\kappa & 0 & -\kappa \\ 0 & s' - a\kappa & i\omega \\ -\kappa & i\omega & s' - a\kappa \end{pmatrix}$$

$$= (s' - a\kappa)\big((s' - a\kappa)^2 + \omega^2 - \kappa^2\big)$$

Thus the values of κ with real part positive are

1. $\kappa_0 = a^{-1}s'$,
2. $\kappa_1 = \big(-as' + \sqrt{s'^2 + (1 - a^2)\omega^2}\big)(1 - a^2).$ (11.4.18)

These two roots are distinct as long as ω is not equal to s/a.

The general form of an admissible solution when κ_0 and κ_1 are not equal is

$$\begin{pmatrix} \hat{u} \\ \hat{v} \\ \hat{h} \end{pmatrix} = A_0 \begin{pmatrix} i\omega \\ \kappa_0 \\ 0 \end{pmatrix} e^{-\kappa_0 x} + A_1 \begin{pmatrix} \kappa_1 \\ -i\omega \\ s^1 - a\kappa_1 \end{pmatrix} e^{-\kappa_1 x}.$$ (11.4.19)

Since there are two values of κ that have positive real parts, there must be two boundary conditions. For this example we consider the case where both u and v are specified. The homogeneous boundary condition corresponding to this is $\hat{u} = 0$ and $\hat{v} = 0$ at x equal to 0.

From (11.4.19) we obtain that the homogeneous boundary condition are satisfied only if the equations

$$A_0 i\omega + A_1 \kappa_1 = 0$$

$$A_0 \kappa_0 - A_1 i\omega = 0$$

are satisfied. There is a nontrivial solution for A_0 and A_1 only if

$$\kappa_1 \kappa_0 = \omega^2,$$

which is equivalent to

$$s'\big(-as' + \sqrt{s'^2 + (1 - a^2)\omega^2}\big) = a(1 - a^2)\omega^2.$$

Rearranging this last equation we have

$$s'\sqrt{s'^2 + (1 - a^2)\omega^2} = a\big[s'^2 + (1 - a^2)\omega^2\big].$$ (11.4.20)

This relation is satisfied either if $s'^2 + (1 - a^2)\omega^2$ is zero or if

$$s'^2 = a^2\big[s'^2 + (1 - a^2)\omega^2\big].$$ (11.4.21)

The expression $s'^2 + (1 - a^2)\omega^2$ is zero when s' is $\pm i(1 - a^2)^{1/2}\omega$. We will consider this possibility first.

Since for this case we have an admissible solution that satisfies the homogeneous boundary condition, the initial-boundary value problem is not well-posed in the stronger sense of Theorem 11.4.1. We now show that it is well-posed in the weaker sense of Theorem 11.4.2. We take $s_0' = i(1-a^2)^{1/2}$ and $\omega_0 = 1$; the other possibilities are equivalent.

We have for this choice of (s_0, ω_0) that the admissible solution satisfying the homogeneous boundary condition is

$$a \begin{pmatrix} i\omega_0 \\ \kappa_0 \\ 0 \end{pmatrix} e^{-\kappa_0 x} + (1-a^2)^{1/2} \begin{pmatrix} \kappa_1 \\ -i\omega_0 \\ s_0' - a\kappa_1 \end{pmatrix} e^{-\kappa_1 x}.$$

Note that $\kappa_0 = ia^{-1}(1-a^2)^{1/2}$ and $\kappa_1 = -ia(1-a^2)^{-1/2}$.
Replacing s_0' by $s_0' + \varepsilon$, we have

$$\kappa_0 = ia^{-1}(1-a^2)^{1/2} + a^{-1}\varepsilon$$

and

$$\kappa_1 = -ia(1-a^2)^{-1/2} + \sqrt{2i\varepsilon}(1-a^2)^{-3/4} + O(\varepsilon).$$

The boundary condition for the admissible solution at (s, ω) equal to $(s_0' + \varepsilon, \omega_0)$ is

$$a \begin{pmatrix} \hat{u}(s_0' + \varepsilon, 0, \omega_0) \\ \hat{v}(s_0' + \varepsilon, 0, \omega_0) \end{pmatrix} = \begin{pmatrix} ai\omega_0 + (1-a^2)^{1/2}\kappa_1 \\ a\kappa_0 - (1-a^2)^{1/2}i\omega_0 \end{pmatrix}$$

$$= \begin{pmatrix} \sqrt{2i\varepsilon}(1-a^2)^{1/4} + O(\varepsilon) \\ \varepsilon \end{pmatrix}$$

$$= \sqrt{\varepsilon} \begin{pmatrix} \sqrt{2i}(1-a^2)^{1/4} + O(\sqrt{\varepsilon}) \\ \sqrt{\varepsilon} \end{pmatrix}.$$

The norm of the vector $(\hat{u}, \hat{v}, h)^T$ therefore satisfies the condition of Theorem 11.4.2, and so this boundary condition is well-posed in the weak sense, except that we must still check the admissible solutions for (11.4.15).

Rearranging (11.4.15), we see that it is satisfied only when s' is equal to $|a\omega|$. (Recall that Re s is nonnegative.) For these values of s' and ω, the values of κ_0 and κ_1 are equal, as noted before. Thus the admissible solutions are not of the form (11.4.13) but rather

$$\begin{pmatrix} \hat{u} \\ \hat{v} \\ \hat{h} \end{pmatrix} = B_0 \begin{pmatrix} 0 \\ -1 \\ i\sigma a \end{pmatrix} e^{-\kappa x} + (B_1 + xB_0) \begin{pmatrix} i\omega \\ \kappa \\ 0 \end{pmatrix} e^{-\kappa x}$$

where $\sigma = \text{sign}(\omega)$ and $\kappa = |\omega|$. It is easy to check that the only admissible solution with $\hat{u}$ and $\hat{v}$ equal to zero is the trivial solution, i.e., with B_0 and B_1 equal to zero.

We conclude that the boundary condition specifying both u and v for the system (11.4.10) is well-posed in the weak sense. $\square$

EXERCISES 11.4

1. Show that the initial-boundary value problem for the system

$$u_t = u_{xx} + u_{yy} + v_{xy}$$
$$v_t = v_{xx} + v_{yy}$$

for $x > 0, y \in R$ with boundary conditions

$$u_x + c_1 v_y = \beta_1$$
$$v_x + c_2 u_y = \beta_2$$

at $x = 0$ is well-posed if and only if

$$c_2(c_1 - \tfrac{1}{2}) < 1.$$

2.a. Show that the boundary condition for system (11.4.16) where $u + a^{-1}h$ and v are specified at $x = 0$ is well-posed when $0 < a < 1$.
  b. Show that specifying u and h is an ill-posed boundary condition.

3. For the system (11.4.16) when $-1 < a < 0$, show that one boundary condition is needed and that specifying h is well-posed and specifying v is ill-posed.

4. Verify for a parabolic system of the form (6.2.1) that the boundary condition of the form (6.2.4) is well-posed if and only if the matrix T given in (6.2.5) is nonsingular.

5. Consider the parabolic system

$$u_t = u_{xx} + v_{xx}$$
$$v_t = v_{xx}$$

on $x \geq 0, -\infty < t < \infty$, with the boundary conditions

$$u_x + a\,v_x = \beta_1(t)$$
$$bu + v = \beta_0(t).$$

Using both the method discussed in Exercise 11.4.4 and the method discussed in this section show that this initial-boundary value problem is ill-posed if and only if $b\left(a - \tfrac{1}{2}\right) = 1$. Demonstrate this behavior with a computer program.

6. Show for the hyperbolic system (1.2.2) with $0 < a < b$ that the boundary conditions

$$c_{01}u + c_{02}v = \beta_0(t) \quad \text{at } x = 0$$
$$c_{11}u + c_{12}v = \beta_1(t) \quad \text{at } x = 1$$

are well-posed if and only if they are equivalent to (1.2.4).

11.5 The Matrix Method for Analyzing Stability

Another method that is frequently used to analyze stability of finite difference schemes is the matrix method. The method considers the total initial-boundary value problem together, not separating the initial value problem from the boundary conditions as we have done in Sections 11.2 and 11.3. Because of this it is more difficult to make conclusions about the results of the matrix method. We introduce the method with an example.

Example 11.5.1 We illustrate the matrix method and its deficiencies by applying it to the forward-time backward-space scheme (1.3.2) for the one-way wave equation (1.1.1) on the unit interval. We assume the characteristic speed a is positive and hence that v_0^n is specified. Considering the unknowns v_m^n for m from 1 to M as the components of a vector V^n, we can write the scheme as

$$V^{n+1} = CV^n + b^n \tag{11.5.1}$$

where the matrix C has the form

$$\begin{pmatrix} 1-a\lambda & 0 & & & & & 0 \\ a\lambda & 1-a\lambda & 0 & & & & \\ & a\lambda & 1-a\lambda & 0 & & & \\ & & \ddots & \ddots & \ddots & & \\ & & & a\lambda & 1-a\lambda & 0 \\ 0 & & & & a\lambda & 1-a\lambda \end{pmatrix} \tag{11.5.2}$$

and $b^n = (a\lambda v_0^n, 0, \ldots, 0)'$. The solution of this equation can be written as

$$V^n = C^n V^0 + \sum_{j=0}^{n} C^{n-j} b^j.$$

The superscript on V and b is the index for the time level, whereas the superscript on C indicates the multiplicative power. If λ is a constant and the matrix norms $\|C^j\|$ are bounded for $0 \le nk \le T$, we obtain

$$h\|V^n\| \le C_T(h\|V^0\| + k\sum_{j=0}^{n} \|V_0^j\|) \tag{11.5.3}$$

where $\|V\| = \left(\sum_{m=1}^{M} |v_m|^2\right)^{1/2}$ and V_0^j is the boundary data at $m = 0$. This is precisely the estimate we need to demonstrate the stability of the initial-boundary value problem, analogous to (1.5.1) with the addition of the boundary data. Moreover, it is not difficult to see that the boundedness of $\|C^n\|$ for $0 \le nk \le T$ is necessary and sufficient to obtain the preceding estimate. We will show that the powers of the matrix C are bounded for $0 \le a\lambda \le 1$, which agrees with our earlier results that the scheme, together with this boundary condition, are stable. To do this we first obtain relations between several matrix norms. The reader may wish to consult Appendix A for the definitions of the norms.

Lemma 11.5.1   *For a $M \times M$ matrix A,*

$$\frac{1}{\sqrt{M}} \|A\|_1 \leq \|A\|_2 \leq (\|A\|_1 \|A\|_\infty)^{1/2}.$$

Proof   We prove the right inequality first. It is easy to show that

$$\rho(B) \leq \|B\|$$

for any norm; therefore,

$$\|A\|_2^2 = \rho(A^*A) \leq \|A^*A\|_1$$
$$\leq \|A^*\|_1 \|A\|_1$$
$$= \|A\|_\infty \|A\|_1.$$

For the left inequality we use the fact that $\|v\|_1 \leq \sqrt{M}\|v\|_2$ by the Cauchy-Schwarz inequality; also, if $\|v\|_2 \leq 1$, then $\|v\|_2 \leq \|v\|_1$. Hence, by the definition of the norms,

$$\|A\|_2 = \sup_{\|v\|_2 \leq 1} \|Av\|_2 \geq \sup_{\|v\|_1 \leq 1} \|Av\|_2$$

$$\geq \frac{1}{\sqrt{M}} \sup_{\|v\|_1 = 1} \|Av\|_1 = \frac{1}{\sqrt{M}} \|A\|_1. \quad \blacksquare$$

We now consider the matrices C^n. The element of C^n on the jth lower diagonal is

$$\binom{n}{j} (1 - a\lambda)^{n-j} (a\lambda)^j$$

where we take $\binom{n}{j}$ equal to zero if j is greater than n. Thus, by Proposition A.6,

$$\|C^n\|_1 = \sum_{j=1}^{M} \binom{n}{j} |1 - a\lambda|^{n-j} |a\lambda|^j$$

$$\leq (|1 - a\lambda| + |a\lambda|)^n$$

where we have equality only if n is less than or equal to M. Lemma 11.5.1 gives us

$$\frac{1}{\sqrt{M}} (|1 - a\lambda| + |a\lambda|)^n \leq \|C^n\|_2$$

for $n \leq M$ and, since we also have $\|C^n\|_\infty = \|C^n\|_1$,

$$\|C^n\|_2 \leq (|1 - a\lambda| + |a\lambda|)^n$$

for all n. If $|a\lambda|$ is a constant, these two inequalities show that a necessary and sufficient condition for the stability of the finite difference initial value problem is that $0 \leq a\lambda \leq 1$, which agrees with the GKSO method given in Section 11.3. $\square$

Although the matrix method incorporates both the initial conditions and boundary conditions into its analysis, this advantage is offset by the difficulty of analyzing, in general, matrices such as C and proving the estimates on its powers. This arises because the order of the matrix increases as h decreases and yet the estimates must be independent of h.

A common misuse of the matrix method is to determine the conditions on C such that C^n tends to zero or is bounded as n increases without bound and regard this the finite difference stability condition. It is a well-known theorem of matrix analysis that powers of C ultimately tend to zero if and only if the eigenvalues of C have modulus less than 1 (see Exercise A.12 in Appendix A). Also, C^n is bounded if the eigenvalues of C are at most 1 in magnitude and those eigenvalues of magnitude 1 are semisimple, that is, they correspond to trivial Jordan blocks. For the particular example we have been considering, this gives

$$0 \leq a\lambda < 2$$

as the necessary and sufficient condition that $\|C^n\|$ is bounded independent of n. The explanation of the discrepancy between this result and the CFL condition is that for $a\lambda$ larger than 1 but less than 2, the norms of C^n will increase initially and then ultimately decay; however, there is no bound on C^n that is independent of M.

Another difficulty with the matrix method is that if we determine by this method that a scheme with boundary conditions is unstable, there is no way of determining whether the instability is due to the scheme itself or to the boundary conditions. Von Neumann analysis determines the stability of the scheme alone and is easier to perform than the matrix method. Although the GKSO analysis of Section 11.3 for the boundary conditions can be somewhat difficult, it is usually easier than the matrix method. Thus the separation of the stability analysis into the consideration of the two parts by themselves is, in general, easier and more informative than is the matrix method.

The analysis for Example 11.5.1 works because matrix C satisfies $\|C\|_1 = 1$ for $0 \leq a\lambda \leq 1$, which is related to all the coefficients of the scheme being positive. By Theorem 3.1.3 the matrix method will have $\|C\|_1$ greater than 1 for any scheme for hyperbolic equations that is more than first-order accurate; see Exercise 11.5.2. This means that the matrix method is more difficult to apply for higher-order schemes.

EXERCISES 11.5

1.   Using the method of Section 11.3.1, show that the the forward-time backward-space scheme for the one-way wave equation (1.1.1) on the unit interval is stable with the solution specified at the left endpoint and the scheme being applied up to the right endpoint.

2.   Use Theorem 3.1.3 to show that for any scheme for hyperbolic equations that is more than first-order accurate, other than the trivial cases given in the theorem, matrix C, as in (11.5.1) satisfies $\|C\|_1 > 1$.

3.   Determine conditions under which a matrix of the form

$$C = \begin{pmatrix} 0 & \beta & & & & & & 0 \\ \alpha & 0 & \beta & & & & & \\ & \alpha & 0 & \beta & & & & \\ & & \ddots & \ddots & \ddots & & & \\ & & & \alpha & 0 & \beta & & \\ & & & & \alpha & 0 & \beta & \\ 0 & & & & & \alpha - \beta & 2\beta \end{pmatrix}$$

satisfies $\|C\|_1 \leq 1$. Apply this result to the stability of the Lax-Friedrichs scheme (1.3.5) for the one-way wave equation on the unit interval with the solution specified at the left endpoint and the quasi-characteristic extrapolation (3.3.1c) at the right endpoint.

4.   Show by using the matrix method that the forward-time central-space scheme for the heat equation (6.1.1) with the Neumann condition approximated by (6.3.11) is stable for $b\mu \leq \frac{1}{2}$. Also show that this scheme with the Dirichlet boundary condition, where the solution is specified at the endpoints, is stable for $b\mu \leq \frac{1}{2}$.

Chapter 12

Elliptic Partial Differential Equations and Difference Schemes

12.1 Overview of Elliptic Partial Differential Equations

The archetypal elliptic equation in two spatial dimensions is Poisson's equation

$$u_{xx} + u_{yy} = f(x, y) \tag{12.1.1}$$

in a domain Ω. The Laplacian operator is the operator on the left-hand side of (12.1.1), and we will denote it by ∇^2, that is,

$$\nabla^2 = \frac{\partial^2}{\partial x^2} + \frac{\partial^2}{\partial y^2}. \tag{12.1.2}$$

The homogeneous equation corresponding to (12.1.1) is called Laplace's equation, i.e.,

$$\nabla^2 u = 0. \tag{12.1.3}$$

The solutions of Laplace's equation are called harmonic functions and are intimately connected with the area of mathematics called complex analysis (see Ahlfors [2]).

To determine completely the solution of (12.1.1) it is necessary to specify a boundary condition on the solution. Two common boundary conditions for (12.1.1) are the Dirichlet condition, in which the values of the solution are specified on the boundary, i.e.,

$$u = b_1 \quad \text{on } \partial\Omega \tag{12.1.4}$$

and the Neumann condition, in which the values of the normal derivative are specified on the boundary, i.e.,

$$\frac{\partial u}{\partial n} = b_2 \quad \text{on} \quad \partial\Omega, \tag{12.1.5}$$

where $\partial\Omega$ refers to the boundary of Ω. Only one boundary condition can be specified at each point of the boundary, perhaps with (12.1.4) specified on one portion of the boundary and (12.1.5) specified on the remaining portion.

To gain a physically intuitive understanding of (12.1.1), we may regard it as describing the steady-state temperature distribution of an object occupying the domain Ω. The solution $u(x, y)$ would represent the steady temperature of the domain Ω with heat sources and sinks given by $f(x, y)$. The Dirichlet boundary condition (12.1.4) would represent specified temperatures on the boundary and the Neumann boundary condition (12.1.5) would represent a specified heat flux. In particular (12.1.5) with b_2 equal to zero would represent a perfectly insulated boundary.

An important observation concerning (12.1.1) with the Neumann condition (12.1.5) specified on the boundary is that for a solution to exist, the data must satisfy the constraint

$$\iint_\Omega f = \int_{\partial\Omega} b_2. \tag{12.1.6}$$

This relationship is called an *integrability condition* and is easily proved by the divergence theorem as follows. We have, from equation (12.1.1), the divergence theorem, and (12.1.5) that

$$\iint_\Omega f = \iint_\Omega \nabla^2 u = \int_{\partial\Omega} \vec{n} \cdot \vec{\nabla} u = \int_{\partial\Omega} \frac{\partial u}{\partial n} = \int_{\partial\Omega} b_2.$$

The vector $\vec{n}$ is the outer unit normal vector to the boundary $\partial\Omega$. The integrability condition (12.1.6) has the physical interpretation that the heat sources in the region must balance with the heat flux on the boundary for a steady temperature to exist. Also, the solution to (12.1.1) with (12.1.5) is determined only up to an arbitrary constant. This has the physical interpretation that the average temperature of a body cannot be determined from the heat fluxes on the boundary and heat sources and sinks alone.

Definition 12.1.1   *The general (quasilinear) second-order elliptic equation in two dimensions is an equation that may be written as*

$$a(x, y)u_{xx} + 2b(x, y)u_{xy} + c(x, y)u_{yy} + d(x, y, u, u_x, u_y) = f(x, y) \tag{12.1.7}$$

where $a, c > 0$ and $b^2 < ac$.

We shall be primarily concerned with second-order elliptic equations, but there are elliptic equations of any even order. The biharmonic equation in two space dimensions is

$$\nabla^4 u = \nabla^2(\nabla^2 u) = u_{xxxx} + 2u_{xxyy} + u_{yyyy} = f. \tag{12.1.8}$$

There are also elliptic systems such as the Cauchy-Riemann equations

$$\begin{aligned} u_x - v_y &= 0 \\ u_y + v_x &= 0 \end{aligned} \tag{12.1.9}$$

and the steady Stokes equations

$$\nabla^2 u - p_x = f_1$$

$$\nabla^2 v - p_y = f_2 \qquad (12.1.10)$$

$$u_x + v_y = 0.$$

The steady Stokes equations describe the steady motion of an incompressible highly viscous fluid. The velocity field is given by the velocity components (u, v) and the function p gives the pressure field. The biharmonic equation (12.1.8) is used to describe the vertical displacement of a flexible, thin, nearly horizontal plate, subjected to small vertical displacements and stresses on the boundary.

The essential property of these equations and systems is that the solutions are more differentiable than the data. For example, the solution, u, of (12.1.1) has two more derivatives than does f. Similarly, the solution, u, to the biharmonic equation (12.1.8) has four more derivatives than does the function f. In particular, the solutions to Laplace's equation (12.1.2) and the Cauchy-Riemann equations (12.1.9) are infinitely differentiable. This property, that the solution is more differentiable than the data and that this gain in differentiability of the solution is equal to the order of the differential operator, characterizes an equation or system of equations as elliptic. (For systems such as (12.1.10) some care has to be taken in appropriately defining the order; see Douglis and Nirenberg [12].) The ellipticity of an equation is often expressed in terms of regularity estimates, as we will demonstrate in the next section.

As will be shown in the discussion of regularity estimates, the ellipticity of a single equation depends on the nonvanishing of the symbol of the differential operator. More precisely, if P is a differential operator of order $2m$, then the operator is elliptic if there is a constant c_0 such that the symbol of P, denoted by $p(x, \xi)$, satisfies

$$|p(x, \xi)| \geq c_0 |\xi|^{2m} \qquad (12.1.11)$$

for values of $|\xi|$ sufficiently large. The symbol of a differential operator is defined as in Definition 3.1.4, but for elliptic equations the factor of e^{st} is not required, since elliptic equations do not depend on time.

We point out that equations such as

$$u_{xx} - u_{yy} = 0$$

do not have the property that its solutions are more differentiable than the data. This equation is the wave equation, discussed in Chapter 8, and it has discontinuous functions in its class of solutions. It does not satisfy the ellipticity requirement (12.1.11).

EXERCISE 12.1

1.   Show that the elliptic equation with constant coefficients $au_{xx} + 2bu_{xy} + cu_{yy} + d_1 u_x + d_2 u_y + eu = f$ can be transformed to an equation of the form

$$v_{\xi\xi} + v_{\eta\eta} + \gamma v = g(\xi, \eta)$$

where γ is 1 or -1, using a linear change of coordinates, i.e., $(\xi, \eta) = (x, y)M$ for some matrix M, and where

$$v(\xi, \eta) = Au(x, y)e^{\alpha\xi + \beta\eta}$$

for some constants A, α, and β.

12.2 Regularity Estimates for Elliptic Equations

In this section we prove estimates that show how the smoothness of the solutions of elliptic equations depends on the data. We prove these estimates only for equations with constant coefficients; similar estimates hold for equations with variable coefficients but the techniques used to prove these estimates are beyond this text. We begin with the constant coefficient equation

$$au_{xx} + 2bu_{xy} + cu_{yy} + d_1 u_x + d_2 u_y + eu = f \qquad (12.2.1)$$

for $(x, y) \in R^2$, which we will study via Fourier transforms. We have the Fourier transform

$$\hat{u}(\xi_1, \xi_2) = \frac{1}{2\pi} \iint_{R^2} e^{-i(x\xi_1 + y\xi_2)} u(x, y) \, dx \, dy \qquad (12.2.2)$$

and the Fourier inversion formula

$$u(x, y) = \frac{1}{2\pi} \iint_{R^2} e^{i(x\xi_1 + y\xi_2)} \hat{u}(\xi_1, \xi_2) \, d\xi_1 \, d\xi_2 \qquad (12.2.3)$$

as given in Section 2.1. There is also Parseval's relation,

$$\iint_{R^2} |u(x, y)|^2 \, dx \, dy = \iint_{R^2} |\hat{u}(\xi_1, \xi_2)|^2 \, d\xi_1 \, d\xi_2. \qquad (12.2.4)$$

Also note that for nonnegative integers r and s,

$$\iint_{R^2} |\frac{\partial^{r+s}}{\partial x^r \partial y^s} u(x, y)|^2 \, dx \, dy = \iint_{R^2} |\xi_1^r \xi_2^s \hat{u}(\xi_1, \xi_2)|^2 \, d\xi_1 \, d\xi_2$$
$$\leq \iint_{R^2} (\xi_1^2 + \xi_2^2)^{r+s} |\hat{u}(\xi_1, \xi_2)|^2 \, d\xi_1 \, d\xi_2. \qquad (12.2.5)$$

Applying the transform to (12.2.1), we obtain

$$(a\xi_1^2 + 2b\xi_1\xi_2 + c\xi_2^2 - id_1\xi_1 - id_2\xi_2 - e)\hat{u} = -\hat{f}.$$

By the requirements that $b^2 < ac$ and a and c be positive, according to Definition 12.1.1, we have

$$a\xi_1^2 + 2b\xi_1\xi_2 + c\xi_2^2 \geq c_0(\xi_1^2 + \xi_2^2) \qquad (12.2.6)$$

for some constant c_0, and hence when $\xi_1^2 + \xi_2^2 \geq C_0^2$ for some value C_0,

$$|a\xi_1^2 + 2b\xi_1\xi_2 + c\xi_2^2 - id_1\xi_1 - id_2\xi_2 - e| \geq c_1(\xi_1^2 + \xi_2^2) \qquad (12.2.7)$$

for some positive constant c_1. Therefore, there is a constant C_1 such that

$$|\hat{u}(\xi_1, \xi_2)| \leq C_1 \frac{|\hat{f}(\xi_1, \xi_2)|}{(\xi_1^2 + \xi_2^2)}$$

for $\xi_1^2 + \xi_2^2 \geq C_0^2$. Then by Parseval's relation and (12.2.5)

$$\iint_{R^2} |\partial_x^{s_1} \partial_y^{s_2} u(x,y)|^2 \, dx \, dy = \iint_{R^2} |\xi_1^{s_1} \xi_2^{s_2} \hat{u}(\xi_1, \xi_2)|^2 \, d\xi_1 \, d\xi_2$$

$$\leq \iint_{|\xi| \leq C_0} |\xi_1^{s_1} \xi_2^{s_2} \hat{u}(\xi_1, \xi_2)|^2 \, d\xi_1 \, d\xi_2$$

$$+ C_1^2 \iint_{|\xi| \geq C_0} (\xi_1^2 + \xi_2^2)^{s_1 + s_2 - 2} |\hat{f}(\xi_1, \xi_2)|^2 \, d\xi_1 \, d\xi_2$$

$$\leq C_0^{2(s_1 + s_2)} \iint_{R^2} |\hat{u}(\xi_1, \xi_2)|^2 \, d\xi_1 \, d\xi_2$$

$$+ C_1^2 \iint_{R^2} (\xi_1^2 + \xi_2^2)^{s_1 + s_2 - 2} |\hat{f}(\xi_1, \xi_2)|^2 \, d\xi_1 \, d\xi_2.$$

If we use the norms defined by

$$\|u\|_s^2 = \sum_{s_1 + s_2 \leq s} \|\partial_x^{s_1} \partial_y^{s_2} u\|^2$$

(see Section 2.1), then the preceding estimate leads to

$$\|u\|_{s+2}^2 \leq C_s(\|f\|_s^2 + \|u\|_0^2). \qquad (12.2.8)$$

Estimate (12.2.8) is called a *regularity estimate*. It states that if a solution to (12.2.1) exists in L^2, i.e., if $\|u\|_0$ is finite, and the function f has all derivatives of order through s in $L^2(R^2)$, then the function u has $s + 2$ derivatives in $L^2(R^2)$.

Notice that the relation (12.2.6) is essential to proving the regularity estimate (12.2.8). A curve on which $a\xi_1^2 + 2b\xi_1\xi_2 + c\xi_2^2$ is constant is an ellipse. This is the historical reason for the name *elliptic*, although now the name is applied to more general equations. (See the discussion of the origin of the names hyperbolic and parabolic in Section 8.1.)

The property that characterizes an elliptic equation is that the solution of the equation is more differentiable than the data and that the increase in differentiability of the solution is equal to the order of the equation. For a second-order equation the property of ellipticity is expressed by the regularity estimate (12.2.8). The biharmonic equation and other fourth-order elliptic equations satisfy analogous estimates, showing that the solution has derivatives of order four more than the data (see Exercise 12.2.2). Elliptic systems, such as the Stokes equations, satisfy regularity estimates, but the concept of order must be generalized; see Douglis and Nirenberg [12].

If equation (12.2.1) holds on a bounded domain Ω in R^2, we can easily obtain an *interior* regularity estimate on a subdomain Ω_1 whose boundary is contained in the interior of Ω. The interior regularity estimate is

$$\|u\|_{s+2,\Omega_1}^2 \leq C_s(\Omega, \Omega_1) \left(\|f\|_{s,\Omega}^2 + \|u\|_{0,\Omega}^2 \right). \tag{12.2.9}$$

This has the same interpretation as (12.2.8), but it gives estimates only in the interior of the domain. Norms such as $\|f\|_{s,\Omega}$ are defined as in Section 2.1 for integer values of s, but the integration is only over the domain Ω.

The estimates (12.2.8) and (12.2.9) also hold if the coefficients of (12.2.1) are functions of (x, y), as long as a constant c_0 can be found so that (12.2.6) holds for all (x, y). More sophisticated techniques than those used here must be employed to obtain the estimates when the coefficients are variable. The theory of pseudodifferential operators has been developed to extend the techniques used here to the situation when the coefficients are not constant; see, for example, Taylor [49].

EXERCISES 12.2

1. Prove relation (12.2.6) for equation (12.2.1) from Definition 11.1.1.

2. For a fourth-order elliptic equation of the form

$$au_{xxxx} + 2bu_{xxyy} + cu_{yyyy} = f$$

with a and c positive and with $b > -\sqrt{ac}$, prove the regularity estimate

$$\|u\|_{s+4} \leq C_s \left(\|f\|_s + \|u\|_0 \right).$$

3. Prove (12.2.9) by considering the function ϕu, where $\phi(x, y)$ is a smooth cutoff function such that ϕ is 1 on Ω_1 and 0 on the boundary of Ω. The function of ϕu can be extended to all R^2 by setting it to zero off of Ω and ϕu satisfies a differential equation similar to (12.2.1) but where the right-hand side depends on u and its first derivatives.

12.3 Maximum Principles

A very useful set of tools in the study of second-order elliptic equations are those called maximum principles. The usefulness of maximum principles is restricted to second-order equations because the second derivatives of a function give information on the function at extrema. Since second-order elliptic equations occur frequently in applications, it is important to study maximum principles. The next two theorems are expressions of maximum principles.

Theorem 12.3.1 *Let L be a second-order elliptic operator defined by $L\phi = a\phi_{xx} + 2b\phi_{xy} + c\phi_{yy}$, that is, the coefficients a and c are positive and b satisfies $b^2 < ac$. If a function u satisfies $Lu \geq 0$ in a bounded domain Ω, then u has its maximum value on the boundary of Ω.*

This theorem can be regarded as an extension to two dimensions of the following result: If a function of one variable has a positive second derivative on a closed interval, then that function must achieve its maximum value at the ends of the interval.

Theorem 12.3.2 *If the elliptic equation*

$$au_{xx} + 2bu_{xy} + cu_{yy} + d_1 u_x + d_2 u_y + eu = 0$$

holds in a domain Ω, with a and c positive and e nonpositive, then the solution $u(x, y)$ cannot have a positive local maximum or a negative local minimum in the interior of Ω.

We prove both of these theorems under the assumption that u is in C^3. We prove Theorem 12.3.1 only in the case that Lu is positive, and we prove Theorem 12.3.2 only in the case that e is negative. The proofs for the general case, when Lu is nonnegative and e is nonpositive, require a more careful analysis.

Proof of Theorem 12.3.1 If u is any C^3 function with a local maximum at (x_0, y_0), then the gradient of u is zero at (x_0, y_0), i.e.,

$$u_x(x_0, y_0) = u_y(x_0, y_0) = 0$$

and so by the Taylor series expansion about (x_0, y_0),

$$u(x_0 + \Delta x, y_0 + \Delta y) = u(x_0, y_0) + \tfrac{1}{2}\left(\Delta x^2 u_{xx}^0 + 2\Delta x \Delta y\, u_{xy}^0 + \Delta y^2 u_{yy}^0\right)$$
$$+ O\left(\max(\Delta x, \Delta y)\right)^3.$$

We have used the superscript of 0 to indicate that the functions are evaluated at (x_0, y_0). Since $u(x_0 + \Delta x, y_0 + \Delta y) \leq u(x_0, y_0)$ for all sufficiently small values of Δx and Δy, it follows that

$$\Delta x^2 u_{xx}^0 + 2\Delta x \Delta y\, u_{xy}^0 + \Delta y^2 u_{yy}^0 \leq 0.$$

Since this expression is homogeneous of degree two in Δx and Δy, we have

$$\alpha^2 u_{xx}^0 + 2\alpha\beta u_{xy}^0 + \beta^2 u_{yy}^0 \le 0 \qquad (12.3.1)$$

for *all* real values of α and β.

We now prove Theorem 12.3.1 for the case that $Lu > 0$. Applying (12.3.1) twice, first with $\alpha = \sqrt{a^0}$ and $\beta = b^0/\sqrt{a^0}$ and then with $\alpha = 0$ and $\beta^2 = c^0 - \left(b^0\right)^2/a^0$, we have

$$
\begin{aligned}
Lu &= a^0 u_{xx}^0 + 2b^0 u_{xy}^0 + c^0 u_{yy}^0 \\
&= (\sqrt{a^0})^2 u_{xx}^0 + 2\sqrt{a^0}\left(\frac{b^0}{\sqrt{a^0}}\right)u_{xy}^0 + \left(\frac{b^0}{\sqrt{a^0}}\right)^2 u_{yy}^0 + \left(c^0 - \frac{(b^0)^2}{a^0}\right)u_{yy}^0 \\
&\le 0
\end{aligned}
$$

Since this inequality contradicts the assumption that $Lu > 0$, Theorem 12.3.1 is proved. ∎

Proof of Theorem 12.3.2   We prove the theorem only in the case that $e(x, y)$ is strictly negative. The case where $e(x, y)$ can be zero at a maximum requires a more careful analysis, and we will omit it.

We first conclude from Theorem 12.3.1 that if u has a maximum at (x_0, y_0) then Lu cannot be positive there. Thus we have

$$-Lu(x_0, y_0) = e(x_0, y_0)u(x_0, y_0) \ge 0.$$

Since $e(x_0, y_0)$ is negative, it follows that $u(x_0, y_0)$ is not positive at an interior local maximum. Similarly, by considering $-u(x, y)$, we can show that u is not negative at a local minimum. ∎

The maximum principle applied to Laplace's equation (12.1.3) on a domain has the physical interpretation that for a steady temperature distribution, both the hottest and coldest temperatures occur at the boundary of the region.

The usefulness of the maximum principle can be seen in its use to prove the uniqueness of the solution to many elliptic equations.

Example 12.3.1   As an example consider the equation

$$u_{xx} + u_{yy} - u = f \qquad (12.3.2)$$

in a domain Ω with Dirichlet boundary conditions. Assume that there are two solutions u and v to (12.3.2) and assume that u is greater than v somewhere in Ω. Set $w = u - v$; then w satisfies (12.3.2) except with f equal to zero, and w is zero on the boundary. Since w is positive somewhere in Ω and is zero on $\partial\Omega$, w must have a positive interior local maximum. But this contradicts Theorem 12.3.2, and thus equation (12.3.2) has at most one solution. In fact, (12.3.2) does have a solution if Ω has a smooth boundary, but we will not prove this. □

Example 12.3.2 As an example of an equation with a nonunique solution, consider

$$u_{xx} + u_{yy} + 2\pi^2 u = 0 \qquad (12.3.3)$$

on the unit square with u equal to zero on the boundary. It is easily checked that

$$u = A \sin \pi x \sin \pi y$$

is a solution for any value of A. Also, equation (12.3.3) with u equal to 1 everywhere on the boundary has no solution. $\square$

EXERCISES 12.3

1. Show by example that if $\nabla^4 u = 0$ in a domain Ω, then u can have an interior maximum or minimum. *Hint:* Consider quadratic functions of (x, y).

2. Show that if u satisfies the elliptic equation

$$a u_{xx} + 2b u_{xy} + c u_{yy} = 0$$

on a domain, where the coefficients $a, b,$ and c are constant, then the quantity $u_x^2 + u_y^2$ takes its maximum on the boundary of the domain.

3. Prove that if u satisfies the elliptic equation of Exercise 2 on a domain and P is a positive definite matrix, then the function

$$f(x, y) = \tfrac{1}{2} \nabla u(x, y)^T \, P \nabla u(x, y)$$

takes its maximum on the boundary of the domain. (∇u is the gradient vector of u with components $\partial u / \partial x$ and $\partial u / \partial y$.)

4. Show that the equation

$$u_{xx} + u_{yy} - e^u = f$$

on a domain Ω with u equal to zero on the boundary has a unique solution, if a solution exists. *Hint:* For two functions u and v, $(e^u - e^v)/(u - v)$ is positive.

12.4 Boundary Conditions for Elliptic Equations

We restrict our discussion of boundary conditions to second-order equations and to the Dirichlet condition (12.1.4), the Neumann condition (12.1.5), and the more general Robin condition

$$\frac{\partial u}{\partial n} + \alpha u = b. \qquad (12.4.1)$$

The existence and uniqueness of the solutions of equation (12.1.7) given boundary conditions of the form (12.1.4), (12.1.5), and (12.4.1) depend on "global" constraints, such as the integrability condition (12.1.6). For certain equations, especially (12.1.1), on domains with smooth boundaries, the existence and uniqueness questions have been answered. With the Dirichlet boundary condition (12.1.4), Poisson's equation (12.1.1) has a unique solution, and with the Neumann condition (12.1.5) there is a unique solution, up to the additive constant, if and only if the integrability condition (12.1.6) is satisfied.

General statements can be made about the local behavior of solutions to (12.1.7) given the different types of boundary conditions. If a Dirichlet boundary condition is enforced along a smooth portion of the boundary, then the normal derivative at the boundary will be as well behaved as the derivative of the boundary data function in the direction of the boundary. If the boundary data function is discontinuous, then the normal derivative will be unbounded at the discontinuities. As an example, for Laplace's equation in the upper half-plane, i.e., $y > 0$, with

$$u(x, 0) = \begin{cases} 0 & \text{if } x > 0, \\ 1 & \text{if } x < 0, \end{cases}$$

a solution is

$$u(x, y) = \frac{1}{\pi} \tan^{-1} \frac{y}{x}.$$

The normal derivative of the solution is

$$u_y(x, 0) = \frac{1}{\pi x}$$

which is unbounded at the point of discontinuity in the boundary data function.

If either the Neumann or Robin conditions are enforced along a smooth boundary, then the solution will be differentiable and the first derivatives will be as well behaved as the boundary data function. As an example, again on the upper half-plane, for the boundary data

$$\frac{\partial u}{\partial y}(x, 0) = \begin{cases} 0 & \text{if } x > 0, \\ |x|^{1/2} & \text{if } x < 0, \end{cases}$$

Laplace's equation has the solution

$$u(x, y) = -\tfrac{2}{3} r^{3/2} \cos \tfrac{3}{2}\theta$$

using the polar coordinates of (x, y). The derivatives are given by

$$\left(\frac{\partial u}{\partial x}, \frac{\partial u}{\partial y} \right) = \left(-r^{1/2} \cos \tfrac{1}{2}\theta, \; r^{1/2} \sin \tfrac{1}{2}\theta \right)$$

and we see that the tangential derivative, i.e., $\partial u/\partial x$, has the same qualitative behavior as the normal derivative.

A serious difficulty can occur at points on the boundary where the boundary conditions change from Dirichlet to Neumann or Robin type. For example, Laplace's equation in the upper half-plane with the boundary conditions

$$u(x, 0) = 0, \quad \text{for } x > 0 \quad \text{and} \quad u_y(x, 0) = 0, \quad \text{for } x < 0$$

has as a solution

$$u(x, y) = r^{1/2} \sin \tfrac{1}{2}\theta. \tag{12.4.2}$$

Note that u and its first derivatives are in $L^2(\Omega)$ for any bounded domain Ω in the upper half-plane whose boundary includes a portion of the real axis around zero. This function u, however, does not have second derivatives in $L^2(\Omega)$ because of their growth near the origin. The first derivatives are also unbounded, but are in $L^2(\Omega)$.

Similar difficulties arise at *reentrant* corners. Consider a domain containing the points (r, θ), in polar coordinates, with $0 < r \le r_0$ and $0 < \theta < \tfrac{3}{2}\pi$. Laplace's equation with the solution equal to zero on the two rays given by $\theta = 0$ and $\theta = \tfrac{3}{2}\pi$ has the solution

$$u(x, y) = r^{2/3} \sin \tfrac{2}{3}\theta. \tag{12.4.3}$$

Again, this function is in $L^2(\Omega)$, as are its first derivatives, but its second derivatives are not.

In summary, any of the boundary conditions, Dirichlet, Neumann, or Robin, will have well behaved solutions to elliptic equations near smooth portions of the boundary. At boundary points where either the boundary conditions change type or where the boundary is not smooth, difficulties in the form of singularities in the solution's derivatives can occur. An appreciation for these difficulties is important to understanding the numerical methods for elliptic equations.

EXERCISE 12.4

1. Find a function of the form $r^\alpha \sin \alpha\theta$, with α taking the least possible positive value, that is a solution to Laplace's equation in the region $0 < r < 1$ and $0 < \theta < \tfrac{3}{2}\pi$ and that satisfies the given boundary conditions.

a. $u = 0$ on $\theta = 0$, $0 < r < 1$

$u = 1$ on $\theta = \tfrac{3}{2}\pi$, $0 < r < 1$.

b. $u = 0$ on $\theta = 0$, $0 < r < 1$

$\dfrac{\partial u}{\partial n} = 0$ on $\theta = \tfrac{3}{2}\pi$, $0 < r < 1$.

Compare the behavior of these functions with (12.4.2) and (12.4.3).

12.5 Difference Schemes for Poisson's Equation

We begin our discussion of difference schemes for elliptic equations by considering Poisson's equation (12.1.1) in the unit square with equal grid spacing in the x and y directions. The standard central difference approximations for the second derivatives leads to the difference formula

$$\delta_x^2 v_{\ell,m} + \delta_y^2 v_{\ell,m} = f$$

or, equivalently,

$$\frac{1}{h^2}\left(v_{\ell+1,m} + v_{\ell-1,m} + v_{\ell,m+1} + v_{\ell,m-1} - 4v_{\ell,m}\right) = f_{\ell,m}. \qquad (12.5.1)$$

The difference operator on the left-hand side of (12.5.1) is called the five-point (discrete) Laplacian. We begin our study of finite difference schemes for elliptic equations by obtaining error estimates for the solution to (12.5.1). In the next two chapters we consider methods to solve equations of the form (12.5.1).

The Discrete Maximum Principle

We can prove a maximum principle for the discrete five-point Laplacian that is analogous to that for the differential equation. Let $\nabla_h^2 = \delta_x^2 + \delta_y^2$ be the discrete five-point Laplacian.

Theorem 12.5.1   Discrete Maximum Principle.   *If $\nabla_h^2 v \geq 0$ on a region, then the maximum value of v on this region is attained on the boundary. Similarly, if $\nabla_h^2 v \leq 0$ then the minimum value of v is attained on the boundary.*

Proof   We prove the principle only in the case that $\Delta x = \Delta y$. The condition $\nabla_h^2 v \geq 0$ is equivalent to

$$v_{\ell,m} \leq \tfrac{1}{4}(v_{\ell+1,m} + v_{\ell-1,m} + v_{\ell,m+1} + v_{\ell,m-1}),$$

i.e., $v_{\ell,m}$ in the interior of the region is less than or equal to an average of its neighbors. This easily leads to the conclusion that an interior point can be a (local) maximum only if its four neighbors also have this same maximum value and that the inequality is actually an equality. This argument then implies that at all grid points, including the boundary points, v must have the same value. This proves the principle when $\nabla_h^2 v \geq 0$.

When $\nabla_h^2 v \leq 0$, by considering $\nabla_h^2 (-v) \geq 0$, this case reduces to the previous case. This completes the proof of the discrete maximum principle. ∎

The maximum norm on a region Ω is defined by

$$\|v\|_\infty = \|v\|_{\infty,\Omega} = \max|v_{\ell,m}|$$

where the maximum is taken over all points in the region.

The chief tool in our error estimates is the following theorem.

Theorem 12.5.2   *If $v_{\ell,m}$ is a discrete function defined on a grid on the unit square with $v_{\ell,m} = 0$ on the boundary, then*

$$\|v\|_\infty \leq \frac{1}{8}\|\nabla_h^2 v\|_\infty. \qquad (12.5.2)$$

Proof Define the function $f_{\ell,m}$ in the interior of the unit square by

$$\nabla_h^2 v_{\ell,m} = f_{\ell,m}.$$

Then obviously

$$-\|f\|_\infty \le \nabla_h^2 v \le \|f\|_\infty, \tag{12.5.3}$$

where $\|f\|_\infty$ is the maximum of f over the unit square.

To prove the theorem we consider the function

$$w_{\ell,m} = \tfrac{1}{4}\left[(x_\ell - \tfrac{1}{2})^2 + (y_m - \tfrac{1}{2})^2\right]$$

and note that

$$\nabla_h^2 w = 1.$$

Thus from (12.5.3) we have

$$\nabla_h^2(v - \|f\|_\infty w) \le 0 \tag{12.5.4}$$

and

$$\nabla_h^2(v + \|f\|_\infty w) \ge 0. \tag{12.5.5}$$

By the discrete maximum principle and (12.5.4), the function $v - \|f\|_\infty w$ has its minimum on the boundary of the square, that is,

$$-\|f\|_\infty \|w\|_{\infty,\partial} \le v_{\ell,m} - \|f\|_\infty w_{\ell,m} \le v_{\ell,m}$$

where $\|w\|_{\infty,\partial}$ is the maximum value of $|w_{\ell,m}|$ for grid points on the boundary of the square.

Similarly, from (12.5.5) and the maximum principle,

$$v_{\ell,m} \le v_{\ell,m} + \|f\|_\infty w_{\ell,m} \le \|f\|_\infty \|w\|_{\infty,\partial}.$$

The value of $\|w\|_{\infty,\partial}$ is $\tfrac{1}{8}$, and so the preceding two inequalities give

$$\|v\|_\infty \le \frac{1}{8}\|f\|_\infty = \frac{1}{8}\|\nabla_h^2 v\|_\infty$$

which proves the theorem. ∎

Theorem 12.5.2 leads to the error estimate in the maximum norm for the solution of (12.1.1) as approximated by (12.5.1).

Theorem 12.5.3 *Let* $u(x, y)$ *be the solution to* $\nabla^2 u = f$ *on the unit square with Dirichlet boundary conditions and let* $v_{\ell,m}$ *be the solution to* $\nabla_h^2 v = f$ *with* $v_{\ell,m} = u(x_\ell, y_m)$ *on the boundary. Then*

$$\|u - v\|_\infty \le ch^2 \|\partial^4 u\|_\infty$$

where $\|\partial^4 u\|_\infty$ *is the maximum magnitude of all the fourth derivatives of* u *over the interior of the square.*

Proof   By using the Taylor series for the central difference approximation to the second derivative (see Section 3.2), we have that

$$\nabla_h^2 u = f + O(h^2)$$

where the $O(h^2)$ terms are bounded by

$$Ch^2 \|\partial^4 u\|_\infty$$

for some constant C. Thus

$$\|\nabla_h^2(u - v)\|_\infty \leq Ch^2 \|\partial^4 u\|_\infty$$

and $u - v$ is zero on the boundary. Together with Theorem 12.5.2, this estimate proves the theorem. ∎

Another useful approximation to Poisson's equation (12.1.1) is with the fourth-order accurate nine-point Laplacian. To derive this scheme we approximate (12.1.1) by

$$\left(1 + \frac{\Delta x^2}{12}\delta_x^2\right)^{-1}\delta_x^2 u + \left(1 + \frac{\Delta y^2}{12}\delta_y^2\right)^{-1}\delta_y^2 u = f + O(\Delta^4),$$

which gives

$$\left(1 + \frac{\Delta y^2}{12}\delta_y^2\right)\delta_x^2 u + \left(1 + \frac{\Delta x^2}{12}\delta_x^2\right)\delta_y^2 u$$

$$= \left(1 + \frac{\Delta x^2}{12}\delta_x^2\right)\left(1 + \frac{\Delta y^2}{12}\delta_y^2\right)f + O(\Delta^4)$$

$$= \left[1 + \frac{1}{12}(\Delta x^2\delta_x^2 + \Delta y^2\delta_y^2)\right]f + O(\Delta^4).$$

Rearranging this expression we have the fourth-order accurate scheme

$$\nabla_h^2 v + \tfrac{1}{12}\left(\Delta x^2 + \Delta y^2\right)\delta_x^2\delta_y^2 v = f + \tfrac{1}{12}\left(\Delta x^2\delta_x^2 + \Delta y^2\delta_y^2\right)f.$$

In the case with $\Delta x = \Delta y = h$ this scheme can be written

$$\frac{1}{6}\left(v_{\ell+1,m+1} + v_{\ell+1,m-1} + v_{\ell-1,m+1} + v_{\ell-1,m-1}\right)$$

$$+ \frac{2}{3}\left(v_{\ell+1,m} + v_{\ell-1,m} + v_{\ell,m+1} + v_{\ell,m-1}\right) - \frac{10}{3}v_{\ell,m} \qquad (12.5.6)$$

$$= \frac{h^2}{12}\left(f_{\ell+1,m} + f_{\ell-1,m} + f_{\ell,m+1} + f_{\ell,m-1} + 8f_{\ell,m}\right).$$

Comparison of Second-Order and Fourth-Order Schemes

h	Second-Order		Fourth-Order	
	Error	Order	Error	Order
0.100	2.79-5		9.40-9	
0.050	7.01-6	1.99	5.85-10	4.01
0.025	1.75-6	2.00	3.66-11	4.00

Table 12.5.1

Table 12.5.1 shows the results of computations employing both the second-order accurate five-point Laplacian (12.5.1) and the fourth-order accurate nine-point Laplacian (12.5.6) applied to Poisson's equation on the unit square. (The results were computed using a preconditioned conjugate gradient method, which is discussed in Section 14.5.) The exact solution is given by $u = \cos x \sin y$ and $f = -2 \cos x \sin y$. The second and fourth columns give the errors for the two methods, measured in the L^2 norm due to the difference between the finite difference solution and the solution of the differential equation. The third and fifth columns display the order of accuracy for each method, as computed from the approximation that

$$e(h) = ch^r$$

where $e(h)$ is the error. Thus

$$r = \frac{\log(e(h_1)/e(h_2))}{\log(h_1/h_2)}$$

for two successive errors due to grid spacings h_1 and h_2. The five-point Laplacian (12.5.1) is obviously second-order accurate, and the nine-point formula (12.5.6) is obviously fourth-order accurate. Notice that the error for the fourth-order scheme with h equal to $\frac{1}{10}$ is much smaller than that of the second-order method with h equal to $\frac{1}{40}$. The gain in accuracy of the nine-point formula is significant compared to the slight increase in work that it requires.

Schemes for the general second-order elliptic equation (12.4.1) need not satisfy a maximum principle. For example, if the mixed derivative term in (12.4.1) is approximated by

$$\delta_{0x}\delta_{0y}v,$$

then the resulting scheme does not satisfy an obvious maximum principle. If the coefficient $b(x,y)$ is positive, then the second-order accurate approximation

$$b\frac{\partial}{\partial x}\frac{\partial}{\partial y} \approx \tfrac{1}{2}b\left(\delta_{x+}\delta_{y+} + \delta_{x-}\delta_{y-}\right)$$

will satisfy a maximum principle if b is not too large compared with the coefficients a and c. Schemes that do not satisfy a maximum principle may have solutions and satisfy error estimates such as in Theorem 12.5.3; however, the proofs are not as simple as those just given. We do not need a maximum principle to hold to use the scheme.

Regularity Estimates for Schemes

We can prove discrete regularity estimates for schemes for elliptic equations as is done for the differential equation. For example, the scheme

$$a\delta_x^2 v + 2b\delta_{0x}\delta_{0y}v + c\delta_y^2 v + d_1\delta_{0x}v + d_2\delta_{0y}v + ev = f$$

has the symbol

$$p(\xi_1,\xi_2) = -4\frac{a\sin^2\frac{1}{2}h\xi_1 + 2b\sin\frac{1}{2}h\xi_1\sin\frac{1}{2}h\xi_2\cos\frac{1}{2}h\xi_1\cos\frac{1}{2}h\xi_2 + c\sin^2\frac{1}{2}h\xi_2}{h^2}$$
$$+ id_1\frac{\sin h\xi_1}{h} + id_2\frac{\sin h\xi_2}{h} + e.$$

The analogue of the estimate (12.2.7) for the symbol is, with $\theta = h\xi_1$ and $\phi = h\xi_2$,

$$\left|4\frac{a\sin^2\frac{1}{2}\theta + 2b\sin\frac{1}{2}\theta\sin\frac{1}{2}\phi\cos\frac{1}{2}\theta\cos\frac{1}{2}\phi + c\sin^2\frac{1}{2}\phi}{h^2} - id_1\frac{\sin\theta}{h} - id_2\frac{\sin\phi}{h} - e\right|$$
$$\geq c_0 4h^{-2}(\sin^2\frac{1}{2}\theta + \sin^2\frac{1}{2}\phi),$$

which holds for some positive constant c_0, when h is small enough and when $\xi_1^2 + \xi_2^2 \geq C_0^2$ for some value C_0.

The interior regularity estimate that follows from this estimate is

$$\|u\|_{h,s+2,\Omega_1}^2 \leq C_s\left(\|f\|_{h,s,\Omega} + \|u\|_{h,0,\Omega}^2\right). \tag{12.5.7}$$

The discrete interior regularity estimate can be used to prove the following result.

Theorem 12.5.4   *If the elliptic equation $Lu = f$ is approximated by the scheme $L_h v = R_h f$ on a domain Ω such that*

$$\|L_h u - R_h L u\|_{h,s-2,\Omega} \leq c_0 h^r \|u\|_s \tag{12.5.8}$$

and

$$\|u - v\|_{h,0,\Omega} \leq c_1 h^r \|u\|_s \tag{12.5.9}$$

and Ω_1 is contained in Ω, then

$$\|\delta_+^s u - \delta_+^s v\|_{h,0,\Omega_1} \leq c_2 h^r \|u\|_s \tag{12.5.10}$$

where c_2 depends on the distance between Ω_1 and $\partial\Omega$.

Proof The discrete function $u - v$ satisfies the scheme

$$L_h(u - v) = L_h u - R_h f = L_h u - R_h L u$$

and, by (12.5.7),

$$\|u - v\|^2_{h,s,\Omega} \leq C_{s-2} \left(\|L_h u - R_h L u\|^2_{h,s-2,\Omega_1} + \|u - v\|^2_{h,0,\Omega_1} \right)$$
$$\leq C_{s-2} h^{2r} \|u\|^2_s$$

from which the theorem follows. ■

This theorem shows that if the function f is smooth enough, then the divided differences of v approximate the divided differences of u to the same order that v itself approximates u.

Theorem 12.5.4 can be used to obtain approximations to derivatives of solutions of elliptic equations that are of the same order of accuracy as the solution itself. In particular, if the solutions of a fourth-order accurate scheme satisfy estimates (12.5.8) and (12.5.9) with r equal to 4, then

$$\left\| \left(1 - \frac{h^2}{12} \delta_x^2 \right) \delta_x^2 v - \partial_x^2 u \right\|_{h,0,\Omega_1} = O(h^4)$$

and

$$\left\| \delta_x^2 v - \left(1 + \frac{h^2}{12} \delta_x^2 \right) \partial_x^2 u \right\|_{h,0,\Omega_1} = O(h^4)$$

(see formulas (3.2.7) and (3.2.8)). Note, however, that

$$\|\delta_x^2 v - \partial_x^2 u\|_{h,0,\Omega_1} = O(h^2)$$

since δ_x^2 is only a second-order accurate approximation to ∂_x^2. These results apply to equations with variable coefficients; see Frank [18] or Bube and Strikwerda [6].

By comparison such results do not hold for solutions of hyperbolic problems. If v_m^n is a solution to a second-order accurate scheme for a hyperbolic equation, such as the one-way wave equation (1.1.1), then, in general, $\delta_0 v_m^n$ is only a first-order accurate approximation to the first derivative of u.

EXERCISES 12.5

1. Prove the discrete maximum principle on the unit square for the case with Δx not equal to Δy.

2. Show that on a domain that is contained in a square of side d the analog of the estimate (12.5.2) is

$$\|v\|_\infty \leq \frac{d^2}{8} \|\nabla_h^2 v\|_\infty.$$

3. Prove the equivalent of Theorems (12.5.1), (12.5.2), and (12.5.3) for scheme (12.5.6).

4. Consider the domain given by $-1 < x < 1$, $-1 < y < 1$, except for $0 < x < 1$, $-1 < y < 0$, i.e., the points in quadrants 1, 2, and 3 with $|x|$ and $|y|$ less than 1. For this domain prove the estimate

$$\|v\|_\infty \le \tfrac{5}{2}\|\nabla^2 v\|_\infty$$

corresponding to Theorem 12.5.2. *Hint:* Consider $w = (x + \tfrac{1}{2})^2 + (y - \tfrac{1}{2})^2$.

5. Using the results of Exercise 4 prove the analog of Theorem 12.5.3 for that domain. Why is this theorem nearly useless for computation? *Hint:* See Section 12.4.

6. Show that the "diagonal" five-point Laplacian scheme given by

$$\frac{1}{2h^2}\left(v_{\ell-1,m-1} + v_{\ell+1,m-1} + v_{\ell-1,m+1} + v_{\ell+1,m+1} - 4v_{\ell,m}\right) = f_{\ell,m}$$

does not satisfy a regularity estimate by showing that the symbol of the scheme $p(\xi_1, \xi_2)$ vanishes for ξ_1 and ξ_2 equal to π/h. (The vanishing of the symbol is a reflection of the fact that this scheme decomposes into two separate schemes, one for grid points with $\ell + m$ being even and the other for $\ell + m$ being odd.)

12.6 Polar Coordinates

Many applications involving elliptic equations are for domains on which it is natural to use polar coordinates, and so we now examine the effects of using polar coordinates. Consider Poisson's equation on the unit disk

$$\frac{1}{r}\frac{\partial}{\partial r}\left(r\frac{\partial u}{\partial r}\right) + \frac{1}{r^2}\frac{\partial^2 u}{\partial \theta^2} = f(r, \theta) \tag{12.6.1}$$

with $0 \le r \le 1$ and $0 \le \theta \le 2\pi$. We approximate the equation by

$$\frac{1}{r_i}\left(r_{i+1/2}\frac{u_{i+1j} - u_{ij}}{\Delta r} - r_{i-1/2}\frac{u_{ij} - u_{i-1j}}{\Delta r}\right)\frac{1}{\Delta r}$$

$$+ \frac{1}{r_i^2}\frac{u_{ij+1} - 2u_{ij} + u_{ij-1}}{\Delta\theta^2} = f_{ij} \tag{12.6.2}$$

where u_{ij} and f_{ij} are the grid functions at $(r_i, \theta_j) = (i\Delta r, j\Delta\theta)$. The grid functions are periodic in j with period $J = 2\pi/\Delta\theta$, and u_{0j} is independent of the value of j.

The main new feature of polar coordinates is the condition that must be imposed at the origin. It is important to realize that any difficulties that arise at the origin are only a result of the choice of coordinate system and are not reflected in the continuous function $u(r, \theta)$.

To derive our condition at the origin we integrate equation (12.6.1) over a disk D of radius ε, obtaining

$$\iint_D fr \, dr \, d\theta = \iint_D \frac{1}{r} \left[\frac{\partial}{\partial r} \left(r \frac{\partial u}{\partial r} \right) \right] + \frac{1}{r^2} \frac{\partial^2 u}{\partial \theta^2} r \, dr \, d\theta$$

$$= \int_0^{2\pi} \frac{\partial u}{\partial r} \varepsilon \, d\theta.$$

$(12.6.3)$

Now choose ε equal to $\Delta r/2$ and approximate (12.6.3) by

$$f(0) \left(\frac{\Delta r}{2} \right)^2 \pi = \sum_{j=1}^{J} \frac{u_{1j} - u_0}{\Delta r} \frac{\Delta r}{2} \Delta\theta.$$

Since u_{0j} is independent of j—call this value u_0,—we have

$$u_0 = \frac{1}{J} \sum_{j=1}^{J} u_{1j} - f(0) \left(\frac{\Delta r}{2} \right)^2. \qquad (12.6.4)$$

Recall that $\Delta\theta = 2\pi/J$. Using this formula preserves the second-order accuracy of scheme (12.6.2).

For parabolic and hyperbolic equations on a disk, a procedure analogous to the one that gave rise to (12.6.4) can be used to give accurate difference formulas at the origin.

EXERCISES 12.6

1. Show that the discrete maximum principle holds for finite difference scheme (12.6.2) on a disk with formula (12.6.4) used at the origin.

2. If we denote the the finite difference operator on the left-hand side of (12.6.2) by $\tilde{\nabla}_h^2$, show that the estimate

$$\|v\|_\infty \leq \tfrac{1}{4} \|\tilde{\nabla}_h^2 v\|_\infty$$

holds for disk of radius 1, where the formula (12.6.4) is used at the origin.

12.7 Coordinate Changes and Finite Differences

Frequently we must solve a system of partial differential equations on a domain that is not a rectangle, disk, or other nice shape. It is then desirable to change coordinates so that a convenient coordinate system can be used. To illustrate the techniques and the difficulties, we will work through a relatively simple example. It is not hard to come up with much more difficult examples.

We consider Poisson's equation on the trapezoidal domain given by $0 \leq x \leq 1$ and $0 \leq y \leq (1+x)/2$. We take the new coordinate system

$$\xi = x, \qquad \eta = \frac{2y}{1+x}$$

so that (ξ, η) in the unit square maps one-to-one with (x, y) in the trapezoid. To change coordinates we use the differentiation formulas

$$\frac{\partial}{\partial x} = \frac{\partial}{\partial \xi} - \frac{2y}{(1+x)^2} \frac{\partial}{\partial \eta} = \frac{\partial}{\partial \xi} - \frac{\eta}{1+\xi} \frac{\partial}{\partial \eta}$$

$$\frac{\partial}{\partial y} = \frac{2}{1+x} \frac{\partial}{\partial \eta} = \frac{2}{1+\xi} \frac{\partial}{\partial \eta}.$$

Using these relations, Poisson's equation (12.1.1) becomes

$$u_{\xi\xi} - \frac{\eta}{1+\xi} u_{\xi\eta} - \left(\frac{\eta}{1+\xi} u_\eta\right)_\xi + \frac{\eta}{(1+\xi)^2} (\eta\, u_\eta)_\eta + \frac{4}{(1+\xi)^2} u_{\eta\eta} = f(\xi, \eta).$$

$$(12.7.1)$$

If we were to discretize (12.7.1) in this form using second-order accurate central differences, the matrix arising from the matrix representation would not be symmetric. Since the iterative solution methods we will study in the next two chapters will work if the matrix is symmetric, we will show how to modify the equation (12.7.1) to obtain a symmetric, positive definite matrix. To do this we must get the equation in divergence form, that is, in the form

$$\sum_{i,j} \frac{\partial}{\partial x_i} \left(a_{ij} \frac{\partial u}{\partial x_j}\right) = \tilde{f}$$

where $(x_1, x_2) = (\xi, \eta)$ and (a_{ij}) is a symmetric matrix at each point (x_1, x_2). If we multiply (12.7.1) by $(1+\xi)$, we can collect terms such that (12.7.1) is equivalent to

$$[(1+\xi)u_\xi]_\xi - (\eta u_\xi)_\eta - (\eta u_\eta)_\xi + \left(\frac{4+\eta^2}{1+\xi} u_\eta\right)_\eta = (1+\xi) f$$

This equation may be discretized on a uniform grid in ξ and η as

$$\frac{(1+\xi_{i+1/2})(u_{i+1j} - u_{ij}) - (1+\xi_{i-1/2})(u_{ij} - u_{i-1j})}{\Delta\xi^2}$$

$$- \frac{\eta_{j+1}(u_{i+1j+1} - u_{i-1j+1}) - \eta_{j-1}(u_{i+1j-1} - u_{i-1j-1})}{4\Delta\xi\Delta\eta}$$

$$- \frac{\eta_j(u_{i+1j+1} - u_{i+1j-1}) - \eta_j(u_{i-1j+1} - u_{i-1j-1})}{4\Delta\xi\Delta\eta} \qquad (12.7.2)$$

$$+ \frac{(4 + \eta_{j+1/2}^2)(u_{ij+1} - u_{ij}) - (4 + \eta_{j-1/2}^2)(u_{ij} - u_{ij-1})}{(1+\xi_i)\Delta\eta^2}$$

$$= (1+\xi_i) f_{ij}.$$

The matrix corresponding to this discretization is symmetric.

To show that the matrix is symmetric, we notice that the coefficient of u_{i+1j+1} in the equation at (i, j) is $-(\eta_{j+1} + \eta_j)/4\Delta\xi\Delta\eta$, and this is also the coefficient of u_{ij} in the equation at $(i+1, j+1)$. The same is true for all the other nonzero coefficients. Thus the matrix is symmetric.

To show that the matrix of the equations in (12.7.2) is negative definite, we consider the operator on the left-hand side of (12.7.2) applied to a grid function ϕ_{ij} that is zero on the boundaries of the unit (ξ, η) square. Multiplying the operator applied to ϕ at (i, j) by ϕ_{ij} and summing over all (i, j) gives a long expression that we will consider in three parts. Denote these sums by $\sum_{\xi\xi}$, $\sum_{\eta\eta}$, and $\sum_{\xi\eta}$. The terms from the second difference in ξ are

$$\sum_{\xi\xi} = \Delta\xi^{-2} \sum \phi_{ij} \left[(1 + \xi_{i+1/2})(\phi_{i+1j} - \phi_{i-1j}) - (1 + \xi_{i-1/2})(\phi_{ij} - \phi_{i-1j})\right]$$

$$= -\Delta\xi^{-2} \sum \left(1 + \xi_{i+1/2}\right)\left(\phi_{i+1j} - \phi_{ij}\right)^2$$

by summation by parts. Similarly, the terms from the second differences in η are

$$\sum_{\eta\eta} = -\Delta\eta^{-2} \sum \frac{4 + \eta_{j+1/2}^2}{1 + \xi_i} \left(\phi_{ij+1} - \phi_{ij}\right)^2.$$

The sums are over all interior (i, j) values. The sums from the mixed differences are also treated by summation by parts and become

$$\sum_{\xi\eta} = (2\Delta\xi\Delta\eta)^{-1} \sum \eta_j \left(\phi_{i+1j} - \phi_{i-1j}\right)\left(\phi_{ij+1} - \phi_{ij-1}\right).$$

To show that the matrix is negative definite, we must show that

$$-\left(\sum_{\xi\xi} + \sum_{\xi\eta} + \sum_{\eta\eta}\right) \geq -C\left(\sum_{\xi\xi} + \sum_{\eta\eta}\right) \geq 0 \qquad (12.7.3)$$

for some positive number c. This is easily done, as follows

$$-\eta_j \left(\phi_{i+1j} - \phi_{i-1j}\right)\left(\phi_{ij+1} - \phi_{ij-1}\right)/2\Delta\xi\Delta\eta$$

$$\leq a\left(1 + \xi_i\right)\left(\frac{\phi_{i+1j} - \phi_{i-1j}}{2\Delta\xi}\right)^2 + \frac{1}{a}\frac{\eta_j^2}{1 + \xi_i}\left(\frac{\phi_{ij+1} - \phi_{ij-1}}{2\Delta\eta}\right)^2$$

$$\leq \frac{a}{2}\left(1 + \xi_i\right)\left[\left(\frac{\phi_{i+1j} - \phi_{ij}}{\Delta\xi}\right)^2 + \left(\frac{\phi_{ij} - \phi_{i-1j}}{\Delta\xi}\right)^2\right]$$

$$+ \frac{1}{2a}\frac{\eta_j^2}{1 + \xi_i}\left[\left(\frac{\phi_{ij+1} - \phi_{ij}}{\Delta\eta}\right)^2 + \left(\frac{\phi_{ij} - \phi_{ij-1}}{\Delta\eta}\right)^2\right].$$

Therefore,

$$-\left(\sum_{\xi\xi}+\sum_{\xi\eta}+\sum_{\eta\eta}\right) \leq (1-a)\Delta\xi^{-2}\sum \left(1+\xi_{i+1/2}\right)(\phi_{i+1j}-\phi_{ij})^2$$

$$+ \Delta\eta^{-2}\sum \frac{4-\eta_{j+1/2}^2/a + \eta_{j+1/2}^2}{1+\xi_i}(\phi_{ij+1}-\phi_{ij})^2.$$

If we choose $a = \frac{1}{2}$, say, then both sums are nonnegative. Thus the system of difference equations (12.7.2) has a matrix that is symmetric and negative definite.

This system of equations can be solved by the methods discussed in Chapters 13 and 14.

EXERCISES 12.7

1. Consider Poisson's equation (12.1.1) on the domain given by $0 \leq x \leq 1$ and $0 \leq y \leq H(x)$. Change coordinates to (ξ, η) given by $\xi = x$ and $\eta = y/H(x)$. Write the scheme in a form that gives a positive definite and symmetric matrix.

2. Consider Poisson's equation in polar coordinates (12.6.1) on the domain given by $0 \leq r \leq s(\theta)$ and $0 \leq \theta \leq 2\pi$. Change coordinates to (ρ, ϕ) given by $\rho = r/s(\theta)$ and $\phi = \theta$. Write the scheme in a form that gives a positive definite and symmetric matrix.

3. Show that by multiplying an elliptic equation of the form

$$a_{11}(x,y)u_{xx} + 2a_{12}(x,y)u_{xy} + a_{22}(x,y)u_{yy} = f(x,y)$$

by a function ϕ, the resulting equation can be put in divergence form

$$\sum_{i,j} \frac{\partial}{\partial x_i}\left(\tilde{a}_{ij}\frac{\partial u}{\partial x_j}\right) = \tilde{f}$$

if and only if the coefficients satisfy

$$\frac{\partial}{\partial x}\left[\frac{a_{11}\left(\dfrac{\partial a_{12}}{\partial x}+\dfrac{\partial a_{22}}{\partial y}\right)-a_{12}\left(\dfrac{\partial a_{11}}{\partial x}+\dfrac{\partial a_{12}}{\partial y}\right)}{a_{11}a_{22}-a_{12}^2}\right]$$

$$+\frac{\partial}{\partial y}\left[\frac{a_{12}\left(\dfrac{\partial a_{11}}{\partial x}+\dfrac{\partial a_{12}}{\partial y}\right)-a_{22}\left(\dfrac{\partial a_{12}}{\partial x}+\dfrac{\partial a_{22}}{\partial y}\right)}{a_{11}a_{22}-a_{12}^2}\right] = 0.$$

Hint: Obtain equations that ϕ and its first derivatives must satisfy; then use the identity

$$\frac{\partial}{\partial x}\left(\frac{1}{\phi}\frac{\partial\phi}{\partial y}\right) = \frac{\partial}{\partial y}\left(\frac{1}{\phi}\frac{\partial\phi}{\partial x}\right).$$

Conclude that the equation $e^{xy}u_{xx} + u_{yy} = f(x,y)$ cannot be put in divergence form.

Chapter 13

Linear Iterative Methods

In this chapter we consider the class of iterative methods known as linear methods, concentrating primarily on the class of methods related to successive-over-relaxation methods. These methods are relatively easy to implement and require little extra computer storage and, for these reasons, are very widely used in the numerical solution of elliptic equations.

13.1 Solving Finite Difference Schemes for Laplace's Equation in a Rectangle

We begin by considering methods for solving Laplace's equation (12.1.3) in a rectangular domain. The basic method can be extended to solve general elliptic equations such as (12.1.7) on general regions; see Section 12.7.

Consider Laplace's equation (12.1.3) on the unit square with equal grid spacing in the x and y directions. Using the standard second-order accurate five-point Laplacian gives the finite difference formula

$$v_{\ell+1,m} + v_{\ell-1,m} + v_{\ell,m+1} + v_{\ell,m-1} - 4v_{\ell,m} = 0 \qquad (13.1.1)$$

for all interior points (x_ℓ, y_m). We first consider the use of the Dirichlet boundary condition (12.1.4) and assume that the $v_{\ell,m}$ in (13.1.1) are given when (x_ℓ, y_m) is a boundary point.

Equations (13.1.1) comprise a system of linear equations for the interior values of $v_{\ell,m}$ with the boundary $v_{\ell,m}$ values given. These equations can be written in the standard matrix notation

$$Ax = b \qquad (13.1.2)$$

where the vector x consists of the interior values $v_{\ell,m}$ and b is composed from the values of $v_{\ell,m}$ on the boundary, i.e., the known values.

We could solve (13.1.2) by standard methods for systems of linear equations, such as Gaussian elimination. However, the matrix A in (13.1.2) is a very sparse matrix and is often quite large. For example, if the grid spacing in the unit square is N^{-1}, then A is an $(N-1)^2 \times (N-1)^2$ matrix, and each row contains at most five nonzero elements. If N is taken to be about 40, then only about 0.3% of the elements are nonzero. Gaussian elimination is not efficient for such sparse matrices, and so direct methods such as Gaussian elimination are not often used to solve (13.1.1). Instead, iterative methods are usually employed. Because matrix A has a well-defined structure, due to the finite difference scheme, using a good iterative method is usually more efficient than the use of general sparse matrix methods for Gaussian elimination.

The first iterative method we will consider is the Jacobi algorithm. It is given by the formula

$$v_{\ell,m}^{k+1} = \tfrac{1}{4}\left(v_{\ell+1,m}^{k} + v_{\ell-1,m}^{k} + v_{\ell,m+1}^{k} + v_{\ell,m-1}^{k}\right) \tag{13.1.3}$$

for all interior points. This formula describes how we proceed from an initial approximation $v_{\ell,m}^{0}$ to successive approximations $v_{\ell,m}^{k}$. Given the values of $v_{\ell,m}^{k}$ for all grid points, equation (13.1.3) shows how to compute $v_{\ell,m}^{k+1}$ at each interior grid point. Having computed v^{k+1} for all the grid points, the iterative process can be continued to compute v^{k+2}, and so on. Of course, throughout the computation the values of $v_{\ell,m}^{k}$ on the boundary all remain at their prescribed values.

The Jacobi algorithm (13.1.3) converges as k increases, and we stop the iterations when some criterion is satisfied. For example, one criterion would be to stop when the maximum value of $|v_{\ell,m}^{k+1} - v_{\ell,m}^{k}|$ taken over all values of (ℓ, m) is less than some prescribed tolerance.

The Jacobi algorithm has been described as the slowest of all converging methods; it certainly is not hard to improve on it. A method that converges twice as fast as (13.1.3) is the Gauss-Seidel algorithm, given by

$$v_{\ell,m}^{k+1} = \tfrac{1}{4}\left(v_{\ell+1,m}^{k} + v_{\ell-1,m}^{k+1} + v_{\ell,m+1}^{k} + v_{\ell,m-1}^{k+1}\right). \tag{13.1.4}$$

In the next section we prove that this method is twice as fast as the Jacobi method (13.1.3). In (13.1.4) we see that if we proceed through the grid of points in the natural order, then we do not need to keep two copies of the solution, one for the "old" values at iteration k and another for "new" values at iteration $k + 1$. In (13.1.4) we can use *immediate replacement*, that is, when $v_{\ell,m}^{k+1}$ is computed it can be stored in the location where $v_{\ell,m}^{k}$ was stored. Thus (13.1.4) uses less storage than (13.1.3) and is twice as fast.

The natural order of progressing through the grid points is also called the *lexicographic order*. It is the order we obtain in programming using two nested loops, the inner loop being on ℓ and the outer loop being on m.

A method that improves on (13.1.4) is successive-over-relaxation (S.O.R.), given by

$$v_{\ell,m}^{k+1} = v_{\ell,m}^{k} + \omega\left[\tfrac{1}{4}(v_{\ell+1,m}^{k} + v_{\ell-1,m}^{k+1} + v_{\ell,m+1}^{k} + v_{\ell,m-1}^{k+1}) - v_{\ell,m}^{k}\right]. \tag{13.1.5}$$

If the parameter ω is chosen properly, then (13.1.5) can be very much faster than (13.1.4). Notice that when ω is equal to 1, then S.O.R. reduces to the Gauss-Seidel algorithm. S.O.R. also uses immediate replacement.

In the next sections we analyze each of the preceding methods to determine their relative rates of convergence. We also present other versions of S.O.R.

Analysis of General Linear Iterative Methods

There is an extensive literature on iterative methods for solving linear systems of equations, and we give only an introduction to these methods. More exhaustive discussions are contained in the books by Young [61], Varga [53], Wachpress [55], and Hageman and Young [24]. The Jacobi, Gauss-Seidel, and S.O.R. methods are particular cases of the general class of methods called *linear iterative methods*. The general linear iterative method for solving a linear system

$$Ax = b \qquad (13.1.6)$$

involves decomposing the matrix A by writing it as

$$A = B - C \qquad (13.1.7)$$

and then iteratively solving the system of equations

$$Bx^{k+1} = Cx^k + b. \qquad (13.1.8)$$

Of course, we wish to choose B so that (13.1.8) can be easily solved. As we will show, the Jacobi, Gauss-Seidel, and S.O.R. methods that we have presented are different ways of splitting the linear system for the five-point Laplacian. Since the exact solution satisfies (13.1.6), we obtain from (13.1.8), the equation for the error,

$$Be^{k+1} = Ce^k$$

or, equivalently,

$$e^{k+1} = B^{-1}Ce^k. \qquad (13.1.9)$$

The matrix $B^{-1}C$ is called the iteration matrix for the algorithm.

A necessary and sufficient condition for the error given by (13.1.9) to converge to zero is that all the eigenvalues of $B^{-1}C$ are less than 1 in magnitude. For a matrix M, its spectral radius $\rho(M)$ is defined by

$$\rho(M) = \max_i |\lambda_i|$$

where the λ_i are the eigenvalues of M; see Appendix A. Thus (13.1.8) is a convergent method if and only if

$$\rho\left(B^{-1}C\right) < 1.$$

The quantity $\rho\left(B^{-1}C\right)$ is a measure of the error reduction per step of the iteration, furthermore, the speed of convergence of the method is dependent on the size of $\rho(B^{-1}C)$. If

$$A = B_1 - C_1$$
$$= B_2 - C_2$$

are two different splittings of A and

$$\rho\left(B_2^{-1}C_2\right) < \rho\left(B_1^{-1}C_1\right),$$

then the second method converges faster than does the first.

EXERCISES 13.1

1.   For a linear system of the form $(A_1 + A_2)x = b$, consider the iterative method

$$(I + \mu A_1)\tilde{x} \quad = (I - \mu A_2)x^k + \mu b$$
$$(I + \mu A_2)x^{k+1} = (I - \mu A_1)\tilde{x} \; + \mu b$$
$$(13.1.10)$$

where μ is a parameter. Show that this iterative method can be put in the form (13.1.8) and determine the iteration matrix for the method. (This method is based on the ADI method discussed in Section 7.3.)

2. Show for the system

$$x_j - x_{j+1} = b_j \qquad \text{for } j = 1, \ldots, K-1$$
$$x_K = b_K,$$

that the iterative method

$$x_j^{k+1} = x_{j+1}^k + b_j \qquad \text{for } j = 1, \ldots, K-1$$
$$x_K^{k+1} = b_K$$

converges in K steps. Show also that $\rho(B^{-1}C)$ is zero.

3. Prove that a linear iterative method converges in a finite number of steps if and only if $\rho(B^{-1}C) = 0$.

13.2 Analysis of the Jacobi and Gauss-Seidel Methods

To analyze the Jacobi and Gauss-Seidel methods, we rewrite (13.1.1) as

$$v_{\ell,m} - \tfrac{1}{4}v_{\ell-1,m} - \tfrac{1}{4}v_{\ell,m-1} - \tfrac{1}{4}v_{\ell+1,m} - \tfrac{1}{4}v_{\ell,m+1} = 0 \qquad (13.2.1)$$

for all interior points. If this were written in the form (13.1.2), then all values of $v_{\ell\pm1,m}$ and $v_{\ell,m\pm1}$ that correspond to boundary points would have to be placed on the right-hand side of the equation. For example, if $(\ell, m-1)$ is a boundary grid point, then instead of (13.2.1) we have

$$v_{\ell,m} - \tfrac{1}{4}v_{\ell-1,m} - \tfrac{1}{4}v_{\ell+1,m} - \tfrac{1}{4}v_{\ell,m+1} = \tfrac{1}{4}v_{\ell,m-1}.$$

Using the natural ordering of the grid points, we can write (13.2.1) as

$$Ax = b$$

with

$$A = I - L - U$$

where L is a lower triangular matrix and U is an upper triangular matrix. If the grid spacing is given by $h = 1/N$, then the matrices have order K equal to $(N-1)^2$. For the Jacobi method we see that

$$B = I \quad \text{and} \quad C = L + U, \tag{13.2.2}$$

whereas for the Gauss-Seidel method,

$$B = I - L \quad \text{and} \quad C = U. \tag{13.2.3}$$

The matrix decomposition (13.2.2) for the Jacobi method is a restatement of (13.1.3), which shows that the updated variables, those multiplied by B, are only the diagonal elements. The variables evaluated at step k in formula (13.1.3) are those corresponding to the off-diagonal elements of the matrix. Similarly, the decomposition (13.2.3) for the Gauss-Seidel method is a restatement of (13.1.4) in which the variables evaluated at step $k+1$ are those corresponding to the elements of the matrix on the diagonal and below. Notice that the matrix B, being a lower triangular matrix, is easy to invert.

It is important to realize that in the actual implementation of these methods in a computer program, we do not store the matrices A, B, and C. They are all quite sparse and it is very inefficient to store them as matrices. The matrices are useful in the analysis, but the implementation can be done without explicit reference to them. That is, a computer implementation should not have a $(N-1)^2 \times (N-1)^2$ array for storage of these matrices. Instead the implementation should use a form such as (13.1.4), in which only the current values of $v_{\ell,m}^k$ are stored. There is no reason to store other arrays.

Analysis of the Jacobi Method

To determine the spectral radius of the iteration matrix for each of these methods applied to the five-point Laplacian, we first find the eigenvalues and eigenvectors of the iteration matrix for the Jacobi method (13.1.3). That is, we must find a vector $\bar{v}$ and value μ such that

$$\mu \bar{v} = (L + U)\bar{v}.$$

If we represent $\bar{v}$ as a grid function with indices from 0 to N in each direction, with the indices 0 and N corresponding to the boundaries, we have

$$\mu v_{\ell,m} = \tfrac{1}{4}\left(v_{\ell-1,m} + v_{\ell,m-1} + v_{\ell+1,m} + v_{\ell,m+1}\right) \tag{13.2.4}$$

for all interior points and $v_{\ell,m}$ equal to zero on the boundaries.

It is important to make a distinction between the eigenvector $\bar{v}$, which has unknowns corresponding to the $(N-1)^2$ interior grid points, and the grid function v, which has $(N+1)^2$ values corresponding to both the interior and boundary points. Because we specify that the boundary values of v are zero, we can write the simple formula (13.2.4). The equations for $\bar{v}$ are different than

(13.2.4) if (ℓ, m) is next to a boundary, in which case at least one of the terms on the right-hand side of (13.2.4) would not be present. The use of the grid function v in place of the eigenvector $\bar{v}$ allows for a simpler way to write the equations.

Since $L + U$ is an $(N - 1)^2 \times (N - 1)^2$ matrix, there should be $(N - 1)^2$ eigenvalues and eigenvectors. It is easy to check that the eigenvectors are given by

$$v_{\ell,m}^{a,b} = \sin\left(\frac{a\ell\pi}{N}\right) \sin\left(\frac{bm\pi}{N}\right) \tag{13.2.5}$$

for $1 \le a, b \le N - 1$, and the corresponding eigenvalues are

$$\mu^{a,b} = \frac{1}{2}\left[\cos\left(\frac{a\pi}{N}\right) + \cos\left(\frac{b\pi}{N}\right)\right]. \tag{13.2.6}$$

See Exercise 13.2.1. From this formula we see that

$$\rho\left(B^{-1}C\right) = \rho\left(L + U\right) = \cos\frac{\pi}{N} = \mu^{1,1}.$$

The relationship $\mu^{N-a,N-b} = -\mu^{a,b}$ shows that the nonzero eigenvalues occur in pairs and also shows that if μ is an eigenvalue, then $-\mu$ is also an eigenvalue. Since $\rho(L + U)$ is less than 1, the Jacobi method will converge; however, since $\rho(L + U)$ is very close to 1, i.e.,

$$\cos\frac{\pi}{N} \approx 1 - \frac{\pi^2}{2N^2},$$

we see that the convergence will be slow.

Notice also that the eigenvalues $\mu^{a,N-a}$ for a between 1 and $N - 1$ are all equal to 0 and these are the only eigenvalues equal to 0. Thus there are $N - 1$ eigenvalues of $L + U$ that are zero, and consequently there are $(N - 1)(N - 2)$ nonzero eigenvalues.

Analysis of the Gauss-Seidel Method

We now consider the Gauss-Seidel method. An eigenvector $\bar{v}$ of the iteration matrix $(I - L)^{-1}U$ with eigenvalue λ satisfies

$$\lambda(I - L)\bar{v} = U\bar{v},$$

or, for the grid function $v_{\ell,m}$, we have

$$\lambda v_{\ell,m} = \tfrac{1}{4}\left(\lambda v_{\ell-1,m} + \lambda v_{\ell,m-1} + v_{\ell+1,m} + v_{\ell,m+1}\right) \tag{13.2.7}$$

for all interior points and $v_{\ell,m}$ equal to zero on the boundaries. Notice that the coefficient λ in (13.2.7) multiples only the variables with superscript of $k + 1$ in the formula (13.1.4). In the form (13.2.7) the formula is rather intractable;

however, there is a substitution that reduces the analysis of this case to that of the Jacobi method. If we set

$$v_{\ell,m} = \lambda^{(\ell+m)/2} u_{\ell,m} \qquad (13.2.8)$$

for each nonzero eigenvalue λ, we obtain, after dividing by $\lambda^{(\ell+m+1)/2}$,

$$\lambda^{1/2} u_{\ell,m} = \tfrac{1}{4} \left(u_{\ell-1,m} + u_{\ell,m-1} + u_{\ell+1,m} + u_{\ell,m+1} \right). \qquad (13.2.9)$$

By comparing (13.2.9) with (13.2.4), we see that the nonzero eigenvalues λ of the Gauss-Seidel method are related to the eigenvalues μ of the Jacobi method by

$$\lambda^{a,b} = \left(\mu^{a,b} \right)^2 = \frac{1}{4} \left(\cos \frac{a\pi}{N} + \cos \frac{b\pi}{N} \right)^2. \qquad (13.2.10)$$

In particular,

$$\rho\left[(I-L)^{-1}U \right] = \rho(L+U)^2$$

which shows that the Gauss-Seidel method converges twice as fast as the Jacobi method for the five-point Laplacian.

The eigenvalues of the Gauss-Seidel iteration matrix from equation (13.2.10) give only $(N-1)(N-2)/2$ eigenvalues corresponding to the $(N-1)(N-2)$ nonzero eigenvalues of the Jacobi iteration matrix. An examination of the corresponding eigenvectors for the Gauss-Seidel method shows that they are given by

$$v_{\ell,m}^{a,b} = (\mu^{a,b})^{\ell+m} \sin\left(\frac{a\ell\pi}{N} \right) \sin\left(\frac{bm\pi}{N} \right)$$

with $v_{\ell,m}^{N-a,N-b} = v_{\ell,m}^{a,b}$. All other eigenvalues are zero, and they are not semisimple. (See Appendix A for the definition of a semisimple eigenvalue.)

An alternative way to describe the preceding analysis is to consider the equation

$$\det\left[\lambda I - (I-L)^{-1}U \right] = 0$$

for the eigenvalues of the Gauss-Seidel iteration matrix. We have the relationship

$$0 = \det\left[\lambda I - (I-L)^{-1}U \right] = \det(\lambda I - \lambda L - U)\det(I-L)^{-1}.$$

The value of $\det(I-L)^{-1}$ is 1, since L is strictly lower triangular. We next transform the matrix $\lambda I - \lambda L - U$ by a similarity transformation using the diagonal matrix S, where the (ℓ,m)th entry on the diagonal is $\lambda^{(\ell+m)/2}$. (Recall that the rows and columns of L, U, and S, are indexed by the ordered pairs of integers corresponding to the grid indices.) We then have

$$S^{-1}(\lambda I - \lambda L - U)S = \lambda I - \lambda^{1/2}(L+U)$$

corresponding to (13.2.9). Thus

$$
\begin{aligned}
\det(\lambda I - \lambda L - U) &= \det\left[\lambda I - \lambda^{1/2}(L + U)\right] \\
&= \lambda^{(N-1)^2/2} \det\left[\lambda^{1/2} I - (L + U)\right] \\
&= \lambda^{(N-1)^2/2} \prod_{1 \le a,b \le N-1} (\lambda^{1/2} - \mu^{a,b}) \\
&= \lambda^{N(N-1)/2} \prod_{2 \le a+b \le N-1} \left[\lambda - (\mu^{a,b})^2\right]
\end{aligned}
$$

where in the last product we used the facts that $\mu^{a,N-a}$ is zero for each a and $\mu^{N-a,N-b} = -\mu^{a,b}$. This last formula confirms our previous conclusion that there are $N(N-1)/2$ zero eigenvalues and shows that (13.2.10) gives the $(N-1)(N-2)/2$ nonzero eigenvalues.

An examination of why the substitution (13.2.8) works shows that the updating of values in the Gauss-Seidel method can be organized either in the standard lexicographic order or in the order of increasing values of $\ell + m$. When one updates a value at a grid point with indices (ℓ, m), the computation involves only points of lower value for the sum of the indices, the points with "new" values, and points of larger value for the sum of the indices, the points with "old" values.

The Jacobi method can also be regarded as solving the heat equation

$$u_t = u_{xx} + u_{yy}$$

until a steady-state solution is reached using forward-time central-space differencing and $\Delta t = \frac{1}{4} h^2$. In general it seems that finding steady-state solutions by solving the corresponding time-dependent equations is less efficient than using special methods for the steady-state equations. The Gauss-Seidel method can be regarded as a finite difference approximation for the time-dependent evolution for the equation

$$u_t = u_{xx} + u_{yy} - \varepsilon\left(u_{xt} + u_{yt}\right)$$

where $\Delta t = \frac{1}{2} h^2$ and $\varepsilon = \frac{1}{4} h$. The equation should be discretized about (t, x, y) equal to $\left((n + \frac{1}{2})\Delta t, \ell h, mh\right)$ to obtain (13.1.4).

Methods for Diagonally Dominant Matrices

We now state and prove a theorem about the Gauss-Seidel and Jacobi methods for the class of diagonally dominant matrices. Many schemes for second-order elliptic equations, including the five-point Laplacian, give rise to diagonally dominant matrices.

Definition 13.2.1   *A matrix is diagonally dominant if*

$$\sum_{j \ne i} |a_{ij}| \le |a_{ii}| \tag{13.2.11}$$

for each value of i. A row is strictly diagonally dominant if the inequality in (13.2.11) is a strict inequality and a matrix is strictly diagonally dominant if each row is strictly diagonally dominant.

By a permutation of a matrix A, we mean a simultaneous permutation of the rows and columns of the matrix, that is, a_{ij} is replaced by $a_{\sigma(i),\sigma(j)}$ for some permutation σ.

Definition 13.2.2 *A matrix is reducible if there is a permutation σ under which A has the structure*

$$\begin{pmatrix} A_1 & O \\ A_{12} & A_2 \end{pmatrix}. \tag{13.2.12}$$

A matrix is irreducible if it is not reducible.

For an arbitrary matrix A the Jacobi iterative method for equation (13.1.1) is

$$\begin{aligned} x^{k+1} &= D^{-1}((D-A)x^k + b) \\ &= (I - D^{-1}A)x^k + D^{-1}b \end{aligned} \tag{13.2.13}$$

where D is the diagonal matrix with the same diagonal elements as A. If A is written as

$$A = D - L - U$$

where L and U are strictly lower and upper triangular matrices, respectively, then the Gauss-Seidel method for (13.1.2) is

$$(D - L)x^{k+1} = Ux^k + b. \tag{13.2.14}$$

Notice that the diagonal dominance of a matrix is preserved if the rows and columns of the matrix are permuted simultaneously. The Gauss-Seidel method is dependent on the permutations of the matrix, whereas the Jacobi method is not, and a matrix is reducible if in using the Jacobi method it is possible to have certain components of x^k be zero for all values of k while x^0 is not identically zero (see Exercises 13.2.5 and 13.2.6).

Theorem 13.2.1 *If A is an irreducible matrix that is diagonally dominant with at least one row being strictly diagonally dominant, then the Jacobi and Gauss-Seidel methods are convergent.*

Proof We prove the theorem only for the Gauss-Seidel method; the proof for the Jacobi method is easier. Our proof is based on that of James [25]. We begin by assuming that there is an eigenvalue of the iteration matrix, λ, that satisfies $|\lambda| \geq 1$. Let x be an eigenvector of the iteration matrix with eigenvalue λ, and we normalize x so that $\|x\|_\infty$ is 1.

Let x_i be a component of x with $|x_i|$ equal to 1; then we have the series of inequalities

$$
\begin{aligned}
|\lambda||a_{ii}||x_i| &= \left| \lambda \sum_{j=1}^{i-1} a_{ij} x_j + \sum_{j=i+1}^{n} a_{ij} x_i \right| \\
&\leq |\lambda| \sum_{j=1}^{i-1} |a_{ij}||x_j| + \sum_{j=i+1}^{n} |a_{ij}||x_j| \\
&\leq |\lambda| \sum_{j \neq i} |a_{ij}||x_j| \\
&\leq |\lambda| \sum_{j \neq i} |a_{ij}||x_i| \leq |\lambda||a_{ii}||x_i|.
\end{aligned}
\tag{13.2.15}
$$

Since the first and last expressions are the same, each inequality in the preceding sequence must be an equality. This implies that for each j, either $|x_j|$ is 1 or a_{ij} is zero. This conclusion follows for each i with $|x_i|$ equal to 1.

   If we permute the indices of A so that the components with $|x_j|$ equal to 1 are placed first and the others, for which $|a_{ij}|$ is zero, are last, then the structure of A is of form (13.2.12). Since A is irreducible, we conclude that $|x_j|$ is 1 for each value of j.

   By choosing a row that is strictly diagonally dominant, the last inequality of (13.2.15) is then a strict inequality, which leads to a contradiction. This implies that the assumption that λ satisfies $|\lambda| \geq 1$ is false. Therefore, $|\lambda|$ is less than 1 for the iteration matrix, and the Gauss-Seidel method is convergent. ∎

EXERCISES 13.2

1.   Verify that the eigenvalues and eigenvectors for the Jacobi iteration matrix are given by (13.2.6) and (13.2.5), respectively.

2.   Extend Theorem (13.2.1) to the case where A is reducible, but for each permutation of A to form (13.2.12), matrix A_1 must have at least one strictly diagonally dominant row.

3.   Determine the eigenvalues of the Jacobi iteration matrix when applied to the "diagonal" five-point Laplacian scheme given by

$$
\frac{1}{2h^2} \left(v_{\ell-1,m-1} + v_{\ell+1,m-1} + v_{\ell-1,m+1} + v_{\ell+1,m+1} - 4v_{\ell,m} \right) = f_{\ell,m} \tag{13.2.16}
$$

on a uniform grid with $\Delta x = \Delta y = h$. *Hint:* The eigenvectors for this Jacobi method are the same as for the Jacobi method for the usual five-point Laplacian. The eigenvalues, however, are different.

4.   Verify that zero is not a semisimple eigenvalue of the iteration matrix for the Gauss-Seidel method for the five-point Laplacian on the unit square.

5.   Show that the Jacobi method (13.2.13) is not affected by a simultaneous reordering of the rows and columns of a matrix, whereas the Gauss-Seidel method (13.2.14) is affected.   Note that such a permutation is equivalent to applying a similarity transformation using a permutation matrix P to the matrix A resulting in the matrix PAP^{-1}.

6.   Show that a matrix is reducible if in using the Jacobi method, it is possible to have certain components of x^k be zero for all values of k while x^0 is not identically zero (see Exercise 5).

7.   Show that the matrix for the five-point Laplacian on the unit square is irreducible.

13.3 Convergence Analysis of Point S.O.R.

We now analyze the convergence of S.O.R. for the approximation of Laplace's equation as given by (13.1.5). The splitting is given by

$$B = \frac{1}{\omega}I - L, \quad C = \frac{1-\omega}{\omega}I + U.$$

By the same reasoning used with the other methods, from (13.1.5) we obtain that the eigenvalues λ are given as the solutions to

$$\omega^{-1}(\lambda + \omega - 1)v_{\ell,m} = \tfrac{1}{4}(\lambda v_{\ell-1,m} + \lambda v_{\ell,m-1} + v_{\ell+1,m} + v_{\ell,m+1}) \quad (13.3.1)$$

for interior grid points, with $v_{\ell,m} = 0$ on the boundary. We use the substitution (13.2.8) for the nonzero eigenvalues, which we used on (13.2.7), obtaining

$$\frac{\lambda + \omega - 1}{\omega\lambda^{1/2}}u_{\ell,m} = \frac{1}{4}(u_{\ell-1,m} + u_{\ell,m-1} + u_{\ell+1,m} + u_{\ell,m+1}).$$

From this relation we see that the nonzero eigenvalues for S.O.R. are related to those of the Jacobi method by

$$\frac{\lambda + \omega - 1}{\omega\lambda^{1/2}} = \mu$$

for each eigenvalue μ of the Jacobi iteration matrix. We rewrite this relationship as

$$\lambda - \lambda^{1/2}\omega\mu + \omega - 1 = 0, \quad (13.3.2)$$

which is a quadratic equation in $\lambda^{1/2}$.

First note that the iteration matrix for S.O.R. is nonsingular for ω not equal to 1. We have

$$\det B^{-1}C = \det(\omega^{-1}I - L)^{-1}\det\left[\omega^{-1}(1-\omega)I + U\right]$$
$$= \omega^K\left[\omega^{-1}(1-\omega)\right]^K = (1-\omega)^K$$

where K is $(N-1)^2$, the order of the matrix. Thus zero is not an eigenvalue of the iteration matrix for S.O.R. when ω is not equal to 1.

Equation (13.3.2) relates each eigenvalue of the Jacobi iteration matrix to two eigenvalues of the S.O.R. iteration matrix. Since $\mu^{a,b} = -\mu^{N-a,N-b}$ and there is an ambiguity in the sign of $\lambda^{1/2}$, there is actually a one-to-one correspondence between the pair of nonzero eigenvalues $\{\mu^{a,b}, \mu^{N-a,N-b}\}$ of the Jacobi iteration matrix and the pair of solutions of equation (13.3.2) with μ equal to $\mu^{a,b}$. For $\mu^{a,b}$ equal to zero, there corresponds the one eigenvalue λ equal to $1-\omega$. Thus equation (13.3.2) determines the $(N-1)^2$ eigenvalues of the S.O.R. iteration matrix from the $(N-1)^2$ eigenvalues of the Jacobi iteration matrix.

Since we wish to have both roots of (13.3.2) less than 1 in magnitude and the product of the roots is $\omega - 1$, we see that a necessary condition for the convergence of S.O.R. is

$$|\omega - 1| < 1,$$

or, equivalently,

$$0 < \omega < 2. \tag{13.3.3}$$

This same conclusion is reached for the $N-1$ eigenvalues corresponding to $\mu^{a,b} = 0$. Solving (13.3.2) we obtain

$$\lambda^{1/2} = \tfrac{1}{2}\left[\omega\mu + \sqrt{\omega^2\mu^2 - 4(\omega-1)}\right]. \tag{13.3.4}$$

We choose the nonnegative square root when the square root is real in this formula so that when ω equals 1, then $\lambda = \mu^2$ for positive μ and λ is zero for negative μ. This correspondence is somewhat arbitrary, but since S.O.R. reduces to the Gauss-Seidel method for ω equal to 1, it is useful to relate the eigenvalues in this way.

We now assume, without loss of generality, that μ is positive, and we wish to find the value of ω that minimizes the magnitude of $\lambda^{1/2}$ when $\lambda^{1/2}$ is real, i.e., when

$$\omega^2\mu^2 - 4\omega + 4 = \left(\omega\mu - \frac{2}{\mu}\right)^2 - 4\left(\frac{1}{\mu^2} - 1\right) \geq 0.$$

To determine how $\lambda^{1/2}$ varies as a function of ω, we take the derivative:

$$\frac{\partial}{\partial\omega}\lambda^{1/2} = \frac{1}{2}\mu + \frac{1}{2}\left(\omega\mu^2 - 2\right)\left(\omega^2\mu^2 - 4\omega + 4\right)^{-1/2}$$

$$= \frac{\mu}{2}\left[1 - \frac{2/\mu - \omega\mu}{\sqrt{(2/\mu - \omega\mu)^2 - 4(\mu^{-2} - 1)}}\right]$$

$$< 0.$$

Since this derivative is negative, we see that to decrease the size of $\lambda^{1/2}$ we must increase ω. The maximum value of ω for which $\lambda^{1/2}$ is real is the root of

$$\omega^2\mu^2 - 4\omega + 4 = 0 \tag{13.3.5}$$

that satisfies (13.3.3).

When μ is negative and $\lambda^{1/2}$ is real, then $\lambda^{1/2}$ is less than the value of $\lambda^{1/2}$ corresponding to $|\mu|$ and thus does not affect the spectral radius of the iteration matrix. Since we are ultimately concerned with determining the spectral radius of the iteration matrix, we need not consider this case in detail.

Now consider the case when $\lambda^{1/2}$ is complex. Notice that since the polynomial in (13.3.2) has real coefficients, the two values of λ corresponding to μ and $-\mu$ are complex conjugates of each other. The magnitude of λ can be computed from (13.3.4) as follows:

$$|\lambda| = |\lambda^{1/2}|^2 = \tfrac{1}{4} \left[\omega^2 \mu^2 + 4(\omega - 1) - \omega^2 \mu^2 \right]$$
$$= \omega - 1.$$

From this relationship we see that to decrease $|\lambda|$ we must decrease ω. The minimum value of ω for which $\lambda^{1/2}$ is complex is again the root of (13.3.5) satisfying (13.3.3).

We now consider the eigenvalues $\lambda(\mu^{a,b})$ for the S.O.R. iteration matrix for all eigenvalues $\mu^{a,b}$ of $L + U$. The spectral radius for the S.O.R. iteration matrix is the maximum magnitude of all the $\lambda(\mu^{a,b})$. We wish to choose ω in order to minimize the spectral radius.

First, consider ω very close to 2, so close that

$$\omega^2 (\mu^{a,b})^2 - 4\omega + 4$$

is negative for all eigenvalues $\mu^{a,b}$. By our previous discussion, all the λ corresponding to nonzero values of $\mu^{a,b}$ are complex with magnitude equal to $\omega - 1$. The λ corresponding to $\mu^{a,b}$ that are equal to zero have the value $1 - \omega$, which means all eigenvalues have the same magnitude. The spectral radius is therefore $\omega - 1$. As we decrease ω, we will reach some value ω^* at which some $\lambda(\mu^{a,b})$ will become real. It is easy to see that this must happen for $\mu^{a,b}$ equal to $\bar{\mu}$, the largest eigenvalue of $L + U$ in magnitude. For ω less that ω^*, the spectral radius will now increase because $\partial \lambda^{1/2} / \partial \omega$ is negative for λ corresponding to $\bar{\mu}$. Thus the optimal choice for ω is ω^*, where ω^* satisfies

$$\omega^{*2} \bar{\mu}^2 - 4\omega^* + 4 = 0$$

and (13.3.3), which gives the optimal value as

$$\omega^* = \frac{2}{1 + \sqrt{1 - \bar{\mu}^2}}. \tag{13.3.6}$$

Since for Laplace's equation $\bar{\mu} = \cos \pi/N$, the value of ω^* for Laplace's equation is

$$\omega^* = \frac{2}{1 + \sin \pi/N}$$

and the spectral radius is

$$\rho^* = \omega^* - 1 = \frac{1 - \sin \pi/N}{1 + \sin \pi/N} \approx 1 - \frac{2\pi}{N}. \tag{13.3.7}$$

It is also useful to consider the behavior of the eigenvalues of the iteration matrix for S.O.R. as functions of ω as ω increases from 1. For ω equal to 1, there are $N(N-1)/2$ eigenvalues that are 0, and the rest are located between 0 and 1, given by (13.2.10). As ω is taken to be larger than 1, these eigenvalues between 0 and 1 all decrease in magnitude. Of the eigenvalues that are 0 for ω equal to 1, $N-1$ of them become negative for ω larger than 1 and have the value $1 - \omega$, and the rest become positive and increase as ω increases. When an eigenvalue from the group that is decreasing with ω coalesces with an eigenvalue from the group that is increasing with ω, they become a pair of complex conjugates of magnitude $\omega - 1$. The optimal value of ω is that value where only two eigenvalues in the interval $(0,1)$ are real and are equal to each other. This value is given by (13.3.6).

We now examine how the number of iterations for an iterative method to achieve a certain error tolerance is related to the spectral radius. Suppose an iterative method has spectral radius ρ and we wish to know how many iterations, I, it will take to reduce the norm of the error to a certain multiple, ε, of the initial error. From (13.1.9) we see that we must have

$$\rho^I \approx \varepsilon$$

or

$$I \approx \frac{-\log \varepsilon}{-\log \rho}.$$

If ρ is close to 1, then

$$I \approx \frac{\log \varepsilon^{-1}}{1 - \rho}.$$

So for the Gauss-Seidel method,

$$I \approx \frac{N^2}{\pi^2} \log \varepsilon^{-1}$$

and for S.O.R. with $\omega = \omega^*$,

$$I \approx \frac{N}{2\pi} \log \varepsilon^{-1}.$$

These formulas show that for the Gauss-Seidel method and Jacobi method, the number of iterations is proportional to N^2, whereas for S.O.R. it is proportional to N. This is why S.O.R. is a dramatic improvement in efficiency over the Gauss-Seidel method for even small values of N.

In relating the eigenvalues of the Gauss-Seidel and S.O.R. methods to the eigenvalues of the Jacobi method, we made use of the fact that if α is an eigenvalue of $\lambda L + U$, then $\alpha\lambda^{-1/2}$ is an eigenvalue of $L+U$. (See the discussion relating to (13.2.7) and (13.3.1).) If $L+U$ has this special property, it is said to be *consistently ordered*.

Definition 13.3.1 *A matrix of the form $I - L - U$ is consistently ordered if whenever α is an eigenvalue of $\lambda L + U$ then $\alpha\lambda^{-1/2}$ is an eigenvalue of $L+U$.*

An examination of our analysis shows that we have proved that if $I - L - U$ is consistently ordered, then the Gauss-Seidel method will converge if and only if the Jacobi method converges, and the Gauss-Seidel method will converge twice as fast. We also have shown that S.O.R. will converge under these conditions and the optimal value of ω is given by (13.3.6). The reader should check that in deriving (13.3.6) we used nothing special about the matrix $I - L - U$ other than that it was consistently ordered and that its eigenvalues are real (see Exercise 13.3.2). Thus we have proved the following theorem.

Theorem 13.3.1 *If the matrix A, which is equal to $I - L - U$, is consistently ordered and has real eigenvalues, then the S.O.R. method, given by*

$$\left(\omega^{-1}I - L\right)x^{k+1} = \left(\omega^{-1}(1-\omega)I + U\right)x^k + b,$$

converges to the solution of $Ax = b$ for all ω in the interval $(0,2)$ if and only if the Jacobi method converges. Moreover, the optimal value of ω is given by formula (13.3.6), where $\bar{\mu}$ is the eigenvalue of $L + U$ with largest magnitude.

In case matrix $I - L - U$ is consistently ordered but with complex eigenvalues, we can determine those values of ω for which the S.O.R method converges, but it is more difficult to determine the optimal value of ω.

Theorem 13.3.2 *If the matrix A, given by $I - L - U$, is consistently ordered, then the S.O.R. method converges for those values of ω in the interval $(0,2)$ that satisfy*

$$(\text{Re } \mu_i)^2 + \left(\frac{\omega}{2-\omega}\right)^2 (\text{Im } \mu_i)^2 < 1 \tag{13.3.8}$$

for each eigenvalue μ_i of $L + U$. In particular, if $|\text{Re } \mu_i| < 1$ for each μ_i, then there is an interval $(0,\bar{\omega})$ of values of ω for which S.O.R. converges.

Proof Let $\tau_i = \lambda_i^{1/2}$; then equation (13.3.2) can be written

$$\zeta_i = \frac{1}{2}\left(\tau_i - \frac{1-\omega}{\tau_i}\right) = \frac{\omega\mu_i}{2}.$$

We consider the mapping of the complex plane that takes the complex variable τ to $\zeta = \frac{1}{2}[\tau - (1-\omega)/\tau]$. This mapping takes circles in the complex τ plan to ellipses in the complex ζ plane. The circle $|\tau| = |1-\omega|^{1/2}$ is mapped to the degenerate ellipse given by

$$\text{Re } \zeta = 0, \qquad |\text{Im } \zeta| \leq \sqrt{1-\omega}$$

when $0 < \omega < 1$ and

$$\text{Im } \zeta = 0, \qquad |\text{Re } \zeta| < \sqrt{\omega - 1}$$

when $1 < \omega < 2$. In either case the annulus $|\omega|^{1/2} \leq |\tau| < 1$ is mapped onto the ellipse

$$\left(\frac{\text{Re } \zeta}{\omega/2}\right)^2 + \left(\frac{\text{Im } \zeta}{1 - \omega/2}\right) < 1. \tag{13.3.9}$$

For each value of ζ we obtain two roots; if τ_1 is one root, then $\tau_2 = (\omega - 1)/\tau_1$ is the other root. It is therefore necessary that $|\omega - 1| = |\tau_1 \tau_2|$ must be less than 1. We also see that one root, say τ_1, must satisfy $|\omega - 1|^{1/2} \leq |\tau_1| < 1$. If we set $\zeta = \omega \mu_i / 2$ in (13.3.9) we obtain (13.3.8) which proves the first assertion of the theorem. We also see that if $|\text{Re } \mu_i|$ is less than 1 for all μ_i, then there are values of ω near 0 that satisfy (13.3.8). This proves the theorem. ∎

Estimating the Optimal Value of ω

S.O.R. often converges when $I - L - U$ is not consistently ordered—for example, when used on more general elliptic equations with variable coefficients. Even though formula (13.3.6) is not valid, we often find that the optimal ω is close to 2. In fact, the relation

$$\omega^* = \frac{2}{1 + Ch} \tag{13.3.10}$$

is often nearly true, where h is some measure of the grid spacing and C is some constant. This formula is computationally very useful and can be employed as follows. First, for a coarse grid we could find ω^*, the optimal ω, by experimentation, i.e., by making many calculations with different values of ω. Given this ω^* and h, we can determine C and then use (13.3.10) to estimate ω^* for other values of h. This formula can considerably reduce computational effort.

Garabedian [19] showed that the optimal value of ω for Poisson's equation on a domain other than the square can be approximated by

$$\omega^* \approx \frac{2}{1 + k_1 h / \sqrt{2}}$$

where h is the mesh width and k_1 is the first eigenvalue of the Laplacian, that is, the least positive value k_1 such that

$$\nabla^2 u + k_1^2 u = 0$$

has a nontrivial solution with u equal to zero on the boundary. He also pointed out that the value of k_1 can be estimated from below by the Faber-Krahn inequality

$$k_1 \geq k_1^* \left(\frac{\pi}{A}\right)^{1/2}$$

where A is the area of the domain and k_1^* is the first eigenvalue for a circle of radius 1. The constant k_1^* is the first zero of the Bessel function J_0 and is approximately 2.4. Because the Faber-Krahn inequality is sharp for circular domains and is less sharp for elongated and nonconvex regions, we can estimate k_1 as a multiple of $k_1^*(\pi/A)^{1/2}$, the multiplying factor being determined by experiment. In ways similar to this, we can usually estimate the optimal value of ω quite well in situations for which it cannot be explicitly determined.

In estimating the optimal value of ω, it is important to realize that it is better to overestimate ω^* than it is to underestimate. This is because for ω larger than ω^*, the spectral radius varies linearly with ω, but the derivative with respect to ω of $\lambda(\bar{\mu})$, as given in (13.3.4), is infinite for the optimal value of ω.

Variations of S.O.R.

There are several variations of S.O.R. The one we have considered is often called point S.O.R. with *natural ordering*. One variation is to use a different ordering of the points. If we update all the points with $\ell + m$ equal to an even number, followed by an update of all those with $\ell + m$ equal to an odd number, we have point S.O.R. with *checkerboard ordering*.

We can also do one iteration of point S.O.R. with natural ordering followed by one iteration of point S.O.R. with reverse natural ordering. This is called *symmetric* S.O.R., or S.S.O.R.

Line S.O.R., or L.S.O.R., updates one line of grid points at a time. The formula is

$$\tilde{v}_{\ell-1,m} - 4\tilde{v}_{\ell,m} + \tilde{v}_{\ell+1,m} = -\omega \left(v_{\ell-1,m}^k + v_{\ell+1,m}^k + v_{\ell,m-1}^{k+1} + v_{\ell,m+1}^k - 4v_{\ell,m}^k \right)$$
$$v_{\ell,m}^{k+1} = v_{\ell,m}^k + \tilde{v}_{\ell,m} \qquad (13.3.11)$$

when taking the lines in the usual order. L.S.O.R. requires that a tridiagonal system be solved for each grid line. This extra work is offset by a smaller spectral radius of the iterative method. Generally it is considered to be faster than point S.O.R. by a factor of $\sqrt{2}$.

In general, line, or block, S.O.R. is derived by writing system (13.1.6) as

$$- \sum_{m<j} L_{jm} x_m + D_j x_j - \sum_{m>j} U_{jm} x_m = b_j$$

where each x_j is a vector consisting of a subset of all the components of x. The coefficients L_{jm}, U_{jm}, and D_j are matrices of the appropriate sizes. In the usual case x_j is the set of unknowns associated with the jth grid line. The line Jacobi method is given by

$$x_j^{k+1} = D_j^{-1} \left(b_j + \sum_{m<j} L_{jm} x_m^k + \sum_{m>j} U_{jm} x_m^k \right)$$

and the line S.O.R. is given by

$$x_j^{k+1} = x_j^k + \omega D_j^{-1}\left(b_j + \sum_{m<j} L_{jm}x_m^{k+1} + \sum_{m>j} U_{jm}x_m^k - D_j x_j^k\right)$$

from which we obtain (13.3.11) for the special case of the five-point Laplacian.

It is easy to implement a symmetric line S.O.R. method, in which the lines are swept in the opposite order during each successive iterations. As with point S.O.R., symmetric line S.O.R. has a better convergence rate with almost no extra work.

One case where line S.O.R. is useful is in the solution of elliptic equations on domains with polar coordinate systems (r, θ) (see Section 12.6 and Exercise 12.7.2). Each "line" consists of the grid points with fixed value of r. At the center we use formula (12.6.4). The periodic tridiagonal system for each line can be solved by the methods of Section 3.4 (see also Exercise 3.4.3). We first update all the points other than the origin; then (12.6.4) can be used to compute the new value at the origin. In the S.O.R. iterations it appears to be best to proceed from the boundary of the disk in toward the center. The equation to update the center value using (12.6.4) is

$$u_0^{k+1} = u_0^k + \omega\left[\frac{1}{J}\sum_{j=1}^{J} u_{1j}^{k+1} - u_0^k - f(0)\left(\frac{\Delta r}{2}\right)^2\right].$$

Implementing S.O.R. Methods

The implementation of S.O.R. methods is quite straightforward, but there are some small details that should be mentioned. The S.O.R methods are usually terminated when the change in the solution is sufficiently small. One usually sets a tolerance and proceeds until the changes are smaller than that tolerance. Rather than using formula (13.1.5) it is better to use the two-step procedure

$$\begin{aligned}
\tilde{v}_{\ell,m}^k &= \tfrac{1}{4}(v_{\ell+1,m}^k + v_{\ell-1,m}^{k+1} + v_{\ell,m+1}^k + v_{\ell,m-1}^{k+1}) - v_{\ell,m}^k \\
v_{\ell,m}^{k+1} &= v_{\ell,m}^k + \omega\,\tilde{v}_{\ell,m}^k.
\end{aligned} \tag{13.3.12}$$

Of course, since S.O.R. uses immediate replacement, in the computer implementation there is no need to index the solution by the index k. Also, the temporary variable $\tilde{v}_{\ell,m}$ is not stored as an array; it need only be a scalar. Both steps of (13.3.12) are computed at each grid point before proceeding to the next point. The two-step procedure (13.3.12) is less sensitive to loss of significance than is the procedure of first using (13.1.5) and then determining the change by computing the difference between the successive values of $v_{\ell,m}$. The line S.O.R. (13.3.11) is given as a two-step procedure for the same reason. For more details on the implementation, the reader is referred to Hageman and Young [24].

The changes in the solution can be measured by the L^2 norm of $\tilde{v}^k$, either with or without the factor of w. The L^2 norm preferred by the author is

$$\|\tilde{v}^k\| = \left(\sum_{\ell,m} |\tilde{v}^k_{\ell,m}|^2 \, h^2 \right)^{1/2}. \tag{13.3.13}$$

The factor of h in the measurement of the norm causes the stopping tolerance to be relatively independent of the grid size. The results given in the examples in this book use the norm (13.3.13).

In checking for the optimal value of w for a S.O.R. method, we often find that the optimal value of w to achieve convergence for a given tolerance in the norm (13.3.13) is close to, but not the same as, that given by formula (13.3.6). One reason for this discrepancy is that the convergence criteria are different; that is, the use of (13.3.13) is not a measurement of the spectral radius that was used in deriving (13.3.6). This discrepancy is of little concern, since formulas such as (13.3.6) and (13.3.10) can be used to give nearly optimal values for w.

EXERCISES 13.3

1. Determine the formula for the optimal value of w as a function of the grid spacing for line S.O.R. on the unit square in the case of equal spacing in both directions. *Hint:* You will have to use the fact that the natural ordering of the lines is a consistent ordering and also that the eigenvectors for the line Jacobi method are the same as for the point Jacobi method. The eigenvalues, however, are different.

2. Prove Theorem 13.3.1.

3. Suppose matrix A, given by $I - L - U$, is consistently ordered and $L + U$ is skew with eigenvalues μ_j. (A skew matrix is one for which $S^T = -S$.) Show that S.O.R. is convergent if and only if w is in the interval $\left(0, \, 2(1+\bar{\beta})^{-1}\right)$, where $\bar{\beta} = \max|\mu_j|$ and the optimal value of w is given by

$$w^* = \frac{2}{1 + (1 + \bar{\beta}^2)^{1/2}}.$$

Notice that w^* is less than 1.

4. Using the point S.O.R. method, solve Poisson's equation

$$u_{xx} + u_{yy} = -2 \cos x \sin y$$

on the unit square. The boundary conditions and exact solution are given by the formula $u = \cos x \sin y$. Use the standard five-point difference scheme with $h = \Delta x = \Delta y = 0.1$, 0.05, and 0.025. The initial iterate should be zero in the interior of the square. Comment on the accuracy of the scheme and the efficiency of the method. Use $w = 2/(1 + \pi h)$. Stop the iterations when the changes in the solution as measured in the L^2 norm (13.3.13) are less than 10^{-7}. *Note:* For some computers the value of 10^{-7} will be too small unless double-precision variables are used.

5.   Solve the same problem as in Exercise 4 but use the fourth-order accurate finite difference scheme (12.5.6). Comment on the efficiency and accuracy of the two methods. Even though the matrix for this scheme is not consistently ordered, the S.O.R. method will converge, as is shown in the next section. A good estimate for the optimal value of ω is $2/(1 + \pi h)$.

6.   Solve the same equation as in Exercise 4 but on the trapezoidal domain discussed in Section 12.7.

7.   Show that the fourth-order accurate finite difference scheme (12.5.6) is not consistently ordered with the natural ordering of points. Also show that it is consistently ordered for line S.O.R.

8.   Determine the optimal value of ω for S.O.R. applied to the "diagonal" five-point Laplacian (13.2.16).

9.   Show that the optimal value of ω for point S.O.R. with the checkerboard ordering applied to the five-point Laplacian on the unit square is given by formula (13.3.6). *Hint:* Show that the checkerboard ordering is a consistent ordering.

13.4 Linear Iterative Methods for Symmetric, Positive Definite Matrices

We can also analyze linear iterative methods when matrix A is symmetric and positive definite. The methods of this section can be applied to many schemes that are not consistently ordered and thus cannot be analyzed by the methods of the previous section. For example, the fourth-order accurate scheme (12.5.6) is not consistently ordered for point S.O.R., but the matrix is symmetric and positive definite (see Exercise 13.4.3). On the one hand, the method of analysis of this section requires less detailed understanding of the matrix than is required to establish the consistent ordering of A; on the other hand, it is not apparent how to determine the optimal value of ω.

It should be pointed out that one need not write out the scheme in matrix form to determine if the matrix is symmetric. The matrix A representing the scheme is symmetric when the coefficient multiplying $v_{\ell',m'}$ in the scheme applied at grid point (ℓ, m) is the same as the coefficient multiplying $v_{\ell,m}$ in the scheme applied at grid point (ℓ', m') for each of the unknown grid function values.

The main result for symmetric, positive definite matrices is the following theorem.

Theorem 13.4.1   *If A is symmetric and positive definite, then the iterative method (13.1.8) based on the splitting (13.1.7) is convergent if*

$$\text{Re } B > \tfrac{1}{2} A \tag{13.4.1}$$

or, equivalently, that $B^T + C$ is symmetric and positive definite, i.e.,

$$B^T + C > 0 \tag{13.4.2}$$

Proof We first establish that the two conditions in the conclusion are equivalent. The matrix Re B is $\frac{1}{2}(B + B^T)$, and thus (13.4.1) is equivalent to

$$B^T + B - A > 0. \tag{13.4.3}$$

The defining relation of the splitting (13.1.7) shows that this is equivalent to (13.4.2) and also shows that $B^T + C$ is symmetric.

We now begin the proof. We measure the error in the norm induced by A, i.e., $\|x\|_A = (x, Ax)^{1/2}$. In this norm we have the relation

$$\|e^{k+1}\|_A = \|B^{-1}Ce^k\|_A \le \|B^{-1}C\|_A\|e^k\|_A$$

(see Appendix A). If the norm of $B^{-1}C$ is less than 1, then the error will decrease at each iteration and the method will converge. We have the norm of $B^{-1}C$ given by

$$\|B^{-1}C\|_A^2 = \sup_{x \ne 0} \frac{(B^{-1}Cx, AB^{-1}Cx)}{(x, Ax)} = \sup_{x \ne 0} \frac{(x, C^T B^{-T} AB^{-1}Cx)}{(x, Ax)}.$$

Thus the condition $\|B^{-1}C\|_A < 1$ is equivalent to $C^T B^{-T} AB^{-1}C < A$, and we consider now the matrix $C^T B^{-T} AB^{-1}C$. We have, using relation (13.1.7) to eliminate C,

$$C^T B^{-T} AB^{-1}C = \left(I - AB^{-T}\right) A \left(I - B^{-1}A\right)$$
$$= A - \left(AB^{-T}A + AB^{-1}A - AB^{-T}AB^{-1}A\right).$$

Thus we see that $C^T B^{-T} AB^{-1}C < A$ if and only if

$$AB^{-T}A + AB^{-1}A - AB^{-T}AB^{-1}A > 0. \tag{13.4.4}$$

But this last expression can be factored as

$$AB^{-T} \left(B + B^T - A\right) B^{-1}A$$

or

$$\left(B^{-1}A\right)^T \left(B + B^T - A\right) B^{-1}A.$$

Thus (13.4.4) is true if and only if (13.4.3) is true. This proves the theorem. ∎

Example 13.4.1 As our first application of Theorem 13.4.1 we consider S.O.R. for a matrix A of the form

$$A = I - L - L^T. \tag{13.4.5}$$

Note that L need not be the lower triangular part of A, although in most applications it is. We have the splitting

$$B = \frac{1}{\omega}I - L, \qquad C = \frac{1 - \omega}{\omega}I + L^T$$

and the condition (13.4.2) is

$$B^T + C = \frac{2 - \omega}{\omega} I > 0.$$

We conclude that S.O.R. for the matrix (13.4.5) will converge for ω in the interval $(0, 2)$ if the matrix A is positive definite.

This result applies to the fourth-order accurate nine-point scheme (12.5.6), which is not consistently ordered; see Exercise 13.4.3. □

Example 13.4.2 For our second application we consider S.S.O.R. for matrix (13.4.5). For this method the splitting is

$$B = \frac{\omega}{2 - \omega} \left(\frac{1}{\omega} I - L \right) \left(\frac{1}{\omega} I - L^T \right)$$

$$C = \frac{\omega}{2 - \omega} \left(\frac{1 - \omega}{\omega} I + L \right) \left(\frac{1 - \omega}{\omega} I + L^T \right) \tag{13.4.6}$$

(see Exercise 13.4.1). In this case both B and C are symmetric and

$$B + C = \omega(2 - \omega)^{-1} \left[\omega^{-2}(2 - 2\omega + \omega^2)I - L - L^T + 2LL^T \right]$$

$$= \omega(2 - \omega)^{-1} \left[\frac{(2 - \omega)^2}{2\omega^2} I + \left(\frac{1}{\sqrt{2}} I - \sqrt{2}L \right) \left(\frac{1}{\sqrt{2}} I - \sqrt{2}L^T \right) \right]$$

$$= \frac{2 - \omega}{2\omega} + \frac{\omega}{2 - \omega} \left(\frac{1}{\sqrt{2}} - \sqrt{2}L \right) \left(\frac{1}{\sqrt{2}} - \sqrt{2}L \right)^T$$

which is positive definite if and only if $0 < \omega < 2$. □

As we see from these two examples, this analysis shows rather easily that the iterative methods will converge for ω between 0 and 2, but it does not give an indication of the optimal value of ω. The method used to prove Theorem 13.4.1 can be refined to give estimates of the optimal ω, but we will not pursue this topic. Formula (13.3.10) and the discussion of that formula should suffice for most applications.

EXERCISES 13.4

1. Verify that the matrices in (13.4.6) define the splitting for S.S.O.R.

2. Consider the iterative method (13.1.10) based on the ADI method and assume that the matrices A_1 and A_2 are symmetric. Use Theorem 13.4.1 to determine the values of μ for which the iterative method will converge.

3. Show that the matrix arising from the fourth-order accurate scheme (12.5.6) is positive definite when written in the form

$$\frac{10}{3} v_{\ell,m} - \frac{2}{3} \left(v_{\ell+1,m} + v_{\ell-1,m} + v_{\ell,m+1} + v_{\ell,m-1} \right)$$

$$- \frac{1}{6} \left(v_{\ell+1,m+1} + v_{\ell+1,m-1} + v_{\ell-1,m+1} + v_{\ell-1,m-1} \right)$$

$$= -\frac{h^2}{12} \left(f_{\ell+1,m} + f_{\ell-1,m} + f_{\ell,m+1} + f_{\ell,m-1} + 8f_{\ell,m} \right).$$

13.5 The Neumann Boundary Value Problem

In this section we examine second-order elliptic equations with the Neumann boundary condition (12.1.5). More specifically, we confine ourselves to equations of the form

$$a(x,y)u_{xx} + 2b(x,y)u_{xy} + c(x,y)u_{yy} + d_1(x,y)u_x + d_2(x,y)u_y = f(x,y) \quad (13.5.1)$$

on a domain Ω with the boundary condition

$$\frac{\partial u}{\partial n} = b(x,y) \quad \text{on } \partial\Omega, \quad (13.5.2)$$

which is the same as (12.1.5). Notice that equation (13.5.1) depends on u only through its derivatives. As opposed to the Dirichlet boundary value problem for equation (13.5.1), the solution to (13.5.1) and (13.5.2) is not unique. Indeed, if u is any solution to (13.5.1) and (13.5.2), then for any constant c the function u_c given by $u_c(x,y) = u(x,y) + c$ is also a solution. The solution of this boundary value problem is unique to within the additive constant; that is, any two solutions differ by a constant (see Exercise 13.5.2). (The nonuniqueness of the solution of elliptic equations can occur for any type of boundary condition; see Example 12.3.2.)

In addition to the solution not being unique, a solution may not exist unless the data, f and b in (13.5.1), satisfy a linear constraint. For many applications, especially symmetric problems, we can easily determine the constraint to be satisfied, but for some problems it may be quite difficult to determine this constraint. For Poisson's equation (12.1.1) with the Neumann boundary condition (12.1.5), the constraint on the data is equation (12.1.6).

As an example of an equation for which it is difficult to determine the constraint, we have

$$u_{xx} + e^{xy}u_{yy} = f \quad (13.5.3)$$

with the Neumann boundary condition (see Exercise 12.7.3). The solutions of this boundary value problem are unique to within an additive constant, and numerical evidence confirms that there is a constraint on the data.

The nonuniqueness of the solution of the differential equation boundary value problem and possible nonexistence of a solution causes some difficulties in the numerical solution. A careful examination of the difficulties leads to effective strategies to surmount these difficulties.

We now consider using a finite difference scheme to obtain an approximate solution of the Neumann problem. As an example, we consider solving the Neumann problem for the Laplacian on the unit square. Either the five-point Laplacian (12.5.1) or the nine-point Laplacian (12.5.6) might be used to approximate the differential equation. For the boundary condition, suitable approximations are

$$\frac{\partial u}{\partial x}(0, y_m) \approx \frac{-3v_{0m} + 4v_{1m} - v_{2m}}{2\Delta x} = b(0, y_m) \quad (13.5.4)$$

or

$$\frac{\partial u}{\partial x}(0, y_m) \approx \frac{v_{1m} - v_{0m}}{\Delta x} = b(0, y_m).$$ (13.5.5)

The approximation (13.5.4) is second-order accurate, whereas (13.5.5) is first-order accurate. For each of these methods we obtain one equation for each unknown $v_{\ell,m}$, $0 \leq \ell, m \leq N$. The linear system can be written as

$$Ax = b$$ (13.5.6)

as for the Dirichlet boundary conditions, except in this case the vector of unknowns, x, also contains the components of $v_{\ell,m}$ on the boundary. Thus, K, the order of the system (13.5.6), is $(N+1)^2$.

The nonuniqueness of the solution of the Neumann problem for (13.5.1) implies that the matrix A in (13.5.6) is singular or nearly singular. Because the solution of (13.5.1) with the Neumann boundary conditions is unique only up to a constant, most difference schemes for (13.5.1) and the boundary conditions will also be unique only to within an additive constant. That is, if x is a solution to (13.5.6), then

$$A(x + \alpha x_0) = b$$

is also true where x_0 is the vector all of whose components are 1 and α is any real number. Comparing this equation with (13.5.6), we see that x_0 is a null vector of A, i.e.,

$$Ax_0 = 0.$$ (13.5.7)

We will assume that the null space of the matrix A is one-dimensional. (The null space of a matrix is the linear subspace of vectors z such that Az is the zero vector.) The matrix A is said to have a (column) rank deficiency of one. This is a reasonable assumption, since the null space of the differential operator is also one-dimensional.

A fundamental result of linear algebra is that the row rank of a matrix is equal to its column rank. Thus there is a nonzero vector y_0 such that $y_0^T A$ is the zero vector. The vector y_0 represents the constraint that the data in (13.5.6) must satisfy in order for a solution to exist. We have

$$0 = (y_0^T A)x = y_0^T (Ax) = y_0^T b$$ (13.5.8)

if a solution x exists for (13.5.6). If A is symmetric, then y_0 may be taken to be x_0.

There are two problems concerning constraint (13.5.8). The first is that we may not know the constraint vector y_0, and the second is that the constraint (13.5.8) may not be satisfied exactly for the known or given data, either because of errors in the physical data or through truncation errors. One solution to these difficulties is to use only simple boundary condition discretizations that maintain the symmetry of A, when that is possible. Unfortunately, this usually results in only first-order accurate boundary conditions (see Exercise 13.5.1).

If we delete one equation from the linear system (13.5.6) and arbitrarily fix one component of x, then the resulting system will usually be nonsingular. However, the accuracy of the solution will depend on which equation is deleted.

An approach that does not single out any particular equation or variable is to use the concept of a factor space. We consider two vectors v_1 and v_2 to be equivalent if their difference, $v_1 - v_2$, is a multiple of the null vector x_0. We consider equation (13.5.6) for solutions in the resulting factor space, which we denote by $R^K/\langle x_0 \rangle$. If we consider the data in the factor space $R^K/\langle y_0 \rangle$, then the system is nonsingular. If we do not know y_0, we can consider the data in $R^K/\langle x_0 \rangle$, and the system will be nonsingular as long as $y_0^T x_0$ is nonzero (see Exercise 13.5.3). We will assume that $y_0^T x_0$ is nonzero for each system we discuss.

This abstract reasoning is useful only if it leads to a useful and convenient algorithm. In this case it does, as we now illustrate. The norm of a vector x in $R^K/\langle x_0 \rangle$, where x_0 is the vector with all components equal to 1, is given by

$$\|x\| = \left(\sum_{\nu=1}^{K} (x_\nu - \bar{x})^2 \right)^{1/2}$$

where $\bar{x}$ is the average of the components x_ν. The equation being solved is no longer (13.5.6), but rather

$$Ax = b - \gamma x_0 \tag{13.5.9}$$

where γ is the average of $b - Ax$, i.e., the average residual. When a solution to (13.5.9) is obtained, the value of γ is an indication of how closely the data vector b satisfies the constraint. A nonzero value of γ can be due either to errors in the data or to the truncation errors implicit in the use of finite difference schemes.

We now give formulas for using this method on an elliptic equation. First, we write the finite difference equation at each grid point (ℓ, m) in the form

$$v_{\ell,m} - \sum L_{(\ell,m)(\ell',m')} v_{\ell',m'} - \sum U_{(\ell,m)(\ell',m')} v_{\ell',m'} = b_{\ell,m}$$

where L and U refer to the lower and upper triangular parts of the matrix. One sweep of S.O.R. applied to this system may be described as follows. At each grid point (ℓ, m), the value of $r_{\ell,m}^k$, the update is computed:

$$r_{\ell,m}^k = \sum L_{(\ell,m)(\ell',m')} v_{\ell',m'}^{k+1} + \sum U_{(\ell,m)(\ell',m')} v_{\ell',m'}^k - v_{\ell,m}^k + b_{\ell,m}.$$

The value of $v_{\ell,m}^{k+1}$ is obtained as

$$v_{\ell,m}^{k+1} = v_{\ell,m}^k + \omega r_{\ell,m}^k.$$

The iteration continues until the updates are essentially constant, independent of (ℓ, m)—that is, until $\|r - \bar{r}\|$, the norm of the update in the factor space, is sufficiently small. To make the method efficient requires a convenient means of computing the average of the update and computing $\|r - \bar{r}\|$.

We now show how to compute both the average of the update and the norm of the update in the factor space. The algorithm for computing the averages and norms is due to West [58], who introduced it as an efficient means of computing averages and variances of statistical quantities. First, the variables $\bar{r}_0^{k+1}$ and $\bar{v}_0^{k+1}$, which will accumulate the average values of the update and v, respectively, are set to zero along with the variables R_0^k and V_0^k, which will accumulate the norms of these quantities. It is also convenient to use the variable J to count the total number of points that have been updated.

At each grid point the accumulators of the norms are computed as

$$R_{J+1}^{k+1} = R_J^{k+1} + (r_{\ell,m}^{k+1} - \bar{r}_J^{k+1})^2 \frac{J}{J+1}$$

$$V_{J+1}^{k+1} = V_J^{k+1} + (v_{\ell,m}^{k+1} - \bar{v}_J^{k+1})^2 \frac{J}{J+1}$$

(13.5.10)

and then the averages are computed:

$$\bar{r}_{J+1}^{k+1} = \bar{r}_J^{k+1} + \frac{r_{\ell,m}^{k+1} - \bar{r}_J^{k+1}}{J+1}$$

$$\bar{v}_{J+1}^{k+1} = \bar{v}_J^{k+1} + \frac{v_{\ell,m}^{k+1} - \bar{v}_J^{k+1}}{J+1}.$$

(13.5.11)

The value of J is then incremented by 1, and the computation proceeds to the next grid point.

At the completion of one S.O.R. sweep, the value of J will be equal to the total number of grid points at which values have been updated, which is K. The value of $\bar{r}_K^{k+1}$ will be equal to the average update and $\bar{v}_K^{k+1}$ will be the average value of v^{k+1}. The norms

$$\|v^{k+1} - \bar{v}^{k+1}\| = \left(\sum_{\ell,m}(v_{\ell,m}^{k+1} - \bar{v}^{k+1})^2 \Delta x \Delta y\right)^{1/2}$$

and

$$\|r^{k+1} - \bar{r}^{k+1}\| = \left(\sum_{\ell,m}(r_{\ell,m}^{k+1} - \bar{r}^{k+1})^2 \Delta x \Delta y\right)^{1/2}$$

will be equal to $(V_J^{k+1}\Delta x \Delta y)^{1/2}$ and $(R_J^{k+1}\Delta x \Delta y)^{1/2}$, respectively. The S.O.R. iterations can be stopped when $\|r^{k+1} - \bar{r}^{k+1}\|$ is sufficiently small.

Example 13.5.1 We show results of using the factor space method and the method in which a specified variable is fixed in Table 13.5.1. The equation being solved is Poisson's equation

$$u_{xx} + u_{yy} = -5\sin(x + 2y)$$

Comparison of Using Factor Space or Fixing the Center Value

h	Factor Method		Fixed Center Value		
	Iterations	Error*	Iterations	Error*	Error**
0.100	55	3.40-3	95	4.47-3	2.38-2
0.050	93	9.38-4	241	1.13-3	7.70-3
0.025	200	2.47-5	958	2.87-4	2.37-3

* In the factor space L^2 norm.
** In the usual L^2 norm.

Table 13.5.1

on the unit square with the normal derivative data being consistent with the solution

$$u(x, y) = \sin(x + 2y) + C. \qquad (13.5.12)$$

The five-point Laplacian was used, and the boundary conditions were approximated by the second-order approximation (13.5.4).

The finite difference grid used equal grid spacing in each direction. The three different grid spacings are displayed in the first column of the table. The next columns show the number of iterations required to obtain a converged solution and the error in the solutions.

For each method the initial iterate was the grid function which was identically zero. Each method was terminated when the appropriate norm of the change in the solution was less than 10^{-7}. This convergence criterion was sufficient to produce results for which the error was primarily due to the truncation error. For the factor space method, the iteration parameter ω was chosen as $2/(1+\pi h/\sqrt{2})$, since π is the smallest eigenvalue for the Laplacian on the square with Neumann boundary conditions.

For the fixed-value method, the value of ω was $2/(1 + h)$ for h equal to $\frac{1}{10}$, it was $2/(1 + 1.1h)$ for h equal to $\frac{1}{20}$, and it was $2/(1 + 2h)$ for h equal to $\frac{1}{40}$. These values give convergence but are not optimal. For this method, the exact value of the solution was fixed at the center point of the square; the constant in (13.5.12) was chosen so that $u(\frac{1}{2}, \frac{1}{2})$ was zero.

The solutions show the second-order accuracy of the finite difference methods when measured in the factor space norm. Notice that the error in the factor space norm is significantly smaller than in the usual L^2 norm. □

Example 13.5.2 Table 13.5.2 shows the results of using the factor space method on equation

$$e^{xy}u_{xx} + u_{yy} = f \qquad (13.5.13)$$

on the unit square with Neumann boundary data. The values of f and the boundary data are determined by the exact solution

$$u(x, y) = e^{-xy}.$$

The last column gives the average update for the last iteration. It can be seen that the average update is quite small compared with the error. The results

The Factor Space Method for a Nonsymmetric Equation

h	Iteration	Error	$\bar{r}$
0.100	60	2.05-4	1.13-5
0.050	103	5.07-5	1.56-6
0.025	233	1.26-5	1.98-7

Table 13.5.2

clearly show that the solution is second-order accurate. This example is interesting because there is a constraint on the boundary data and the data f in equation (13.5.13), which must be satisfied for a solution to exist. This is the integrability condition discussed in Section 12.1, but in this case the constraint is unknown. Nonetheless, the solution can be computed.

If a nonzero constant, say 1, is added to the value of f in (13.5.13), then the integrability condition is not satisfied. This method will compute a solution in the factor space, but the value of the average update, corresponding to γ in (13.5.9), will not be small, since the constraint is not close to being satisfied. □

EXERCISES 13.5

1. Show that the five-point Laplacian and first-order accurate boundary condition (13.5.5) on the unit square gives a symmetric matrix if the equations are scaled properly.

2. Using the maximum principle, show that equation (13.5.1) with boundary condition (13.5.2) has a unique solution to within an additive constant.

3. Consider a $K \times K$ matrix A that is singular with rank deficiency 1 and with a left null vector y_0 and right null vector x_0. Show that when considered as a linear mapping from the factor space $R^K/\langle x_0 \rangle$ to the factor space $R^K/\langle x_0 \rangle$, A is nonsingular if and only if the inner product of x_0 and y_0 is nonzero.

4. Solve Poisson's equation

$$u_{xx} + u_{yy} = -2\pi^2 \cos \pi x \cos \pi y$$

on the unit square with the Neumann boundary condition

$$\frac{\partial u}{\partial n} = 0.$$

The exact solution is $u(x,y) = \cos \pi x \cos \pi y$. Use both the first-order accurate approximation (13.5.5) and the second-order accurate approximation (13.5.4) to approximate the boundary conditions. Use equal grid spacing for both directions, and use grid spacings of $\frac{1}{10}$, $\frac{1}{20}$, and $\frac{1}{40}$. Use $\omega = 2/(1 + \pi h/\sqrt{2})$.

5. Consider the Jacobi iteration given by for the five-point Laplacian on the unit square given by

$$v_{\ell,m}^{k+1} = \tfrac{1}{4}\left(v_{\ell+1,m}^k + v_{\ell-1,m}^k + v_{\ell,m+1}^k + v_{\ell,m-1}^k\right)$$

for $\ell = 0,\ldots,N$ and $m = 0,\ldots,N$. with grid spacing h equal to N^{-1} and with the boundary conditions

$$\begin{array}{ll} v_{-1,m} = v_{1,m} & \text{for } m = 0,\ldots,N \\ v_{\ell,-1} = v_{\ell,1} & \text{for } \ell = 0,\ldots,N \\ v_{N+1,m} = v_{N-1,m} & \text{for } m = 0,\ldots,N \end{array}$$

and

$$v_{\ell,N+1} = v_{\ell,N-1} \qquad \text{for } \ell = 0,\ldots,N.$$

Show that the eigenvalues are given by

$$\mu^{a,b} = \frac{1}{2}\left[\cos\left(\frac{a\pi}{N}\right) + \cos\left(\frac{b\pi}{N}\right)\right]$$

for $0 \le a,b \le N$ and the corresponding eigenvectors are

$$v_{\ell,m}^{a,b} = \cos\left(\frac{a\ell\pi}{N}\right)\cos\left(\frac{bm\pi}{N}\right).$$

Show that the Jacobi method will not converge in the factor space $R^K/\langle x_0\rangle$ in which x_0 is the vector with all components equal to 1. Show also that the Gauss-Seidel method will converge and that the optimal value of ω for the point S.O.R in the factor space is

$$\omega^* = \frac{2}{1 + \sin(\pi/2N)\sqrt{1 + \cos^2(\pi/2N)}}$$

$$\approx \frac{2}{1 + \pi h/\sqrt{2}}.$$

This result does not contradict Theorem 13.3.1, since the Jacobi method in the factor space is not the true Jacobi method.

6. Verify that the following algorithm can be used to compute norms and vector products in the factor space $R^K/\langle x_0\rangle$, where x_0 is the vector with all components equal to 1: Given vectors x and y in R^K, we wish to compute their norms and inner product in the factor space $R^K/\langle x_0\rangle$. Let σ_K and τ_K denote the factor space norms of x and y, respectively, and their inner product will be denoted by π_K. The quantities $\bar{x}_K$ and $\bar{y}_K$ are the averages of x and

y, respectively. The algorithm is: Set $A_0 = 0$, $\sigma_0 = 0$, $\tau_0 = 0$, $\pi_0 = 0$, $\bar{x}_0 = 0$, $\bar{y}_0 = 0$. Then for k from 0 to $K - 1$, compute the quantities

$$A_{k+1} = A_k + 1$$

$$\sigma_{k+1} = \sigma_k + (x_{k+1} - \bar{x}_k)^2 \frac{A_k}{A_{k+1}}$$

$$\tau_{k+1} = \tau_k + (y_{k+1} - \bar{y}_k)^2 \frac{A_k}{A_{k+1}}$$

$$\pi_{k+1} = \pi + (x_{k+1} - \bar{x}_k)(y_{k+1} - \bar{y}_k) \frac{A_k}{A_{k+1}}$$

$$\bar{x}_{k+1} = \bar{x}_k + \frac{x_{k+1} - \bar{x}_k}{A_{k+1}}$$

$$\bar{y}_{k+1} = \bar{y}_k + \frac{y_{k+1} - \bar{y}_k}{A_{k+1}}.$$

Then

$$\sigma_K = \sum_{j=1}^{K} (x_j - \bar{x})^2$$

$$\tau_K = \sum_{j=1}^{K} (y_j - \bar{y})^2$$

$$\pi_K = \sum_{j=1}^{K} (x_j - \bar{x})(y_j - \bar{y})$$

$$\bar{x}_K = \frac{\sum_{j=1}^{K} x_j}{\sum_{j=1}^{K} \alpha_j} = \bar{x}$$

$$\bar{y}_K = \frac{\sum_{j=1}^{K} y_j}{\sum_{j=1}^{K} \alpha_j} = \bar{y}$$

$$A_K = K$$

7.   The algorithm of Exercise 6 can be modified to include weighted norms on R^K; that is, the norm on R^K, is given by $\|x\|^2 = \sum \alpha_j x_j^2$. Given vectors x and y in R^K, we wish to compute their norms and inner product in the factor space $R^K/\langle x_0 \rangle$, where x_0 is as in Exercise 6. Let σ_K and τ_K denote the factor space norms of x and y, respectively, and their inner product will be denoted by π_K. The norm weights are given by the coefficients (α_j). The quantities $\bar{x}_K$ and $\bar{y}_K$ give the projection onto the subspace for (x_j) and (y_j), respectively.

The algorithm is: Set $A_0 = 0$, $\sigma_0 = 0$, $\tau_0 = 0$, $\pi_0 = 0$, $\bar{x}_0 = 0$, $\bar{y}_0 = 0$.
Then for k from 0 to $K - 1$, compute the quantities

$$A_{k+1} = A_k + \alpha_{k+1}$$

$$\sigma_{k+1} = \sigma_k + \alpha_{k+1}(x_{k+1} - \bar{x}_k)^2 \frac{A_k}{A_{k+1}}$$

$$\tau_{k+1} = \tau_k + \alpha_{k+1}(y_{k+1} - \bar{y}_k)^2 \frac{A_k}{A_{k+1}}$$

$$\pi_{k+1} = \pi + \alpha_{k+1}(x_{k+1} - \bar{x}_k)(y_{k+1} - \bar{y}_k) \frac{A_k}{A_{k+1}}$$

$$\bar{x}_{k+1} = \bar{x}_k + \alpha_{k+1} \frac{x_{k+1} - \bar{x}_k}{A_{k+1}}$$

$$\bar{y}_{k+1} = \bar{y}_k + \alpha_{k+1} \frac{y_{k+1} - \bar{y}_k)}{A_{k+1}}.$$

Verify that at the completion these quantities satisfy the relations

$$\sigma_K = \sum_{j=1}^{K} \alpha_j (x_j - \bar{x})^2$$

$$\tau_K = \sum_{j=1}^{K} \alpha_j (y_j - \bar{y})^2$$

$$\pi_K = \sum_{j=1}^{K} \alpha_j (x_j - \bar{x})(y_j - \bar{y})$$

$$\bar{x}_K = \frac{\sum_{j=1}^{K} \alpha_j x_j}{\sum_{j=1}^{K} \alpha_j} = \bar{x}$$

$$\bar{y}_K = \frac{\sum_{j=1}^{K} \alpha_j y_j}{\sum_{j=1}^{K} \alpha_j} = \bar{y}$$

$$A_K = \sum_{j=1}^{K} \alpha_j.$$

8. The preceding algorithm can be further modified to compute the quantities in the factor space induced by the vector x_0 with components (η_j). The quantities to be computed are:

$$\sigma_K = \sum_{j=1}^{K} \alpha_j (x_j - \bar{x}\eta_j)^2$$

$$\tau_K = \sum_{j=1}^{K} \alpha_j (y_j - \bar{y}\eta_j)^2$$

$$\pi_K = \sum_{j=1}^{K} \alpha_j (x_j - \bar{x}\eta_j)(y_j - \bar{y}\eta_j)$$

$$\bar{x}_K = \frac{\sum_{j=1}^{K} \alpha_j x_j \eta_j}{A_K} = \bar{x}$$

$$\bar{y}_K = \frac{\sum_{j=1}^{K} \alpha_j y_j \eta_j}{A_K} = \bar{y}$$

and

$$A_K = \sum_{j=1}^{K} \alpha_j \eta_j^2$$

Show that the following algorithm will compute each of these quantities. Set $A_0 = 0$, $\sigma_0 = 0$, $\tau_0 = 0$, $\pi_0 = 0$, $\bar{x}_0 = 0$, $\bar{y}_0 = 0$. Then for k from 0 to $K - 1$, compute the quantities

$$A_{k+1} = A_k + \alpha_{k+1}\eta_{k+1}^2$$

$$\sigma_{k+1} = \sigma_k + \alpha_{k+1}(x_{k+1} - \bar{x}_k \eta_{k+1})^2 \frac{A_k}{A_{k+1}}$$

$$\tau_{k+1} = \tau_k + \alpha_{k+1}(y_{k+1} - \bar{y}_k \eta_{k+1})^2 \frac{A_k}{A_{k+1}}$$

$$\pi_{k+1} = \pi_k + \alpha_{k+1}(x_{k+1} - \bar{x}_k \eta_{k+1})(y_{k+1} - \bar{y}_k \eta_{k+1}) \frac{A_k}{A_{k+1}}$$

$$\bar{x}_{k+1} = \bar{x}_k + \alpha_{k+1}(x_{k+1} - \bar{x}_k \eta_{k+1}) \frac{\eta_{k+1}}{A_{k+1}}$$

$$\bar{y}_{k+1} = \bar{y}_k + \alpha_{k+1}(y_{k+1} - \bar{y}_k \eta_{k+1}) \frac{\eta_{k+1}}{A_{k+1}}.$$

Chapter 14

The Method of Steepest Descent and the Conjugate Gradient Method

In this chapter we consider a class of methods for solving linear systems of equations when the matrix of coefficients is both symmetric and positive definite. Although we are interested primarily in the application of these methods to the solution of difference schemes for elliptic equations, these methods can be applied to any symmetric and positive definite system. We begin by discussing the method of steepest descent and then discuss the conjugate gradient method, which can be regarded as an acceleration of the method of steepest descent. In Section 14.6 we discuss minimum residual methods, which can be applied to more general classes of equations. There have been many variations and extensions of the conjugate gradient method that cannot be discussed here. A good reference for these additional topics is the book by Hageman and Young [24].

14.1 The Method of Steepest Descent

We consider a system of linear equations

$$Ax = b \tag{14.1.1}$$

where matrix A is symmetric and positive definite. As in the previous chapter we will let K be the order of the matrix. Consider also the function $F(y)$ defined by

$$F(y) = \tfrac{1}{2}\left(y - x, A(y - x)\right) \tag{14.1.2}$$

where x is the solution to (14.1.1) and $(\cdot, \cdot)$ is the usual inner product on R^n. Obviously, the function F has a unique minimum at y equal to x, the solution of (14.1.1). Similarly, the function E given by

$$E(y) = F(y) - F(0) = \tfrac{1}{2}(y, Ay) - (y, b) \tag{14.1.3}$$

has a unique minimum at the solution of (14.1.1). Both the method of steepest descent and the conjugate gradient method are iterative methods that reduce the value of E at each step until a vector y is obtained for which $E(y)$ is minimal or nearly minimal. In many applications the function $E(y)$ represents a quantity of significance, such as the energy of the system. In these cases the solution of (14.1.1) is the state of minimum energy.

323

We first consider the method of steepest descent. The gradient of the function $E(y)$ is the vector

$$G(y) = Ay - b = -r \qquad (14.1.4)$$

where r is called the residual (see Exercise 14.1.1). Since the gradient of a function points in the direction of steepest ascent, to decrease the value of the function it is advantageous to go in the direction opposite of the gradient, which is the direction of steepest descent. The method of steepest descent, starting from an initial vector x_0, is given by

$$x^{k+1} = x^k + \alpha_k r^k \qquad (14.1.5)$$

where

$$r^k = b - Ax^k$$

and α_k is some parameter.

The notation we will use is that lowercase Roman letters will denote vectors and have superscripts and Greek letters will denote scalar quantities and have subscripts. The norm of a vector v will be denoted by $|v|$, where $|v| = (v, v)^{1/2}$.

The parameter α_k in (14.1.5) will be chosen so that $E(x^{k+1})$ is minimal. We have

$$
\begin{aligned}
E\left(x^{k+1}\right) &= E\left(x^k + \alpha_k r^k\right) \\
&= \tfrac{1}{2}\left(x^k, Ax^k\right) + \alpha_k\left(r^k, Ax^k\right) + \tfrac{1}{2}\alpha_k^2\left(r^k, Ar^k\right) - \left(x^k, b\right) - \alpha_k\left(r^k, b\right) \\
&= E\left(x^k\right) - \alpha_k\left(r^k, r^k\right) + \tfrac{1}{2}\alpha_k^2\left(r^k, Ar^k\right).
\end{aligned}
$$

Setting $\partial E/\partial \alpha_k = 0$, we find that α_k given by

$$\alpha_k = \frac{\left(r^k, r^k\right)}{\left(r^k, Ar^k\right)} = \frac{|r^k|^2}{\left(r^k, Ar^k\right)} \qquad (14.1.6)$$

is the value at which $E(x^{k+1})$ is minimal. From (14.1.5) we have that

$$r^{k+1} = r^k - \alpha_k Ar^k$$

and so from (14.1.6),

$$\left(r^{k+1}, r^k\right) = \left(r^k, r^k\right) - \alpha_k\left(r^k, Ar^k\right) = 0, \qquad (14.1.7)$$

showing that consecutive residuals are orthogonal. For this optimal choice of α_k we have

$$E\left(x^{k+1}\right) = E\left(x^k\right) - \frac{1}{2}\frac{|r^k|^4}{\left(r^k, Ar^k\right)} \qquad (14.1.8)$$

showing that $E(x^k)$ will decrease as k increases. Notice also from the definitions of $E\left(x^k\right)$ and r^k that

$$E\left(x^k\right) = \tfrac{1}{2}\left(A^{-1}r^k, r^k\right) + F(0)$$

and hence (14.1.8) is equivalent to

$$\left(A^{-1}r^{k+1}, r^{k+1}\right) = \left(A^{-1}r^k, r^k\right) - \frac{|r^k|^4}{(r^k, Ar^k)}. \tag{14.1.9}$$

We now collect the formulas for steepest descent:

$$x^{k+1} = x^k + \alpha_k r^k \tag{14.1.10a}$$

$$r^{k+1} = r^k - \alpha_k Ar^k \tag{14.1.10b}$$

$$\alpha_k = \frac{|r^k|^2}{(r_k, Ar^k)}. \tag{14.1.10c}$$

Notice that to implement the method, we need only one matrix multiplication per step; also, there is no necessity for storing A. Often A is quite sparse, as in solving elliptic systems, and we need only a means to generate Ar given r. Formula (14.1.10b) should be used instead of the formula $r^k = b - Ax^k$ to compute the residual vectors r^k. When using the finite precision of a computer, there is a loss of significant digits when the residual is computed as $b - Ax^k$, since the two vectors b and Ax^k will be nearly the same when k is not too small. The formula (14.1.10b) avoids this problem.

Although our derivation of the steepest descent method relied on matrix A being both symmetric and positive definite, we can apply the algorithm (14.1.10) in case A is not symmetric. The following theorem gives conditions on which the method will converge.

Theorem 14.1.1 *If A is a positive definite matrix for which $A^T A^{-1}$ is also positive definite, then the algorithm given by (14.1.10) converges to the unique solution of (14.1.1) for any initial iterate x_0.*

Proof First note that if A is positive definite, then A^{-1} is also positive definite, and if $A^T A^{-1}$ is positive definite, we have that there are constants c_0 and c_1 such that

$$c_0(x, A^{-1}x) \le (x, A^T A^{-1}x) \tag{14.1.11}$$

and

$$c_1(x, Ax) \le (x, x) \tag{14.1.12}$$

for all vectors x (see Exercise 14.1.2). We now consider $\left(r^{k+1}, A^{-1}r^{k+1}\right)$, where $r^0 = b - Ax^0$ and r^{k+1} depends on r^k by (14.1.10b). We have

$$\left(r^{k+1}, A^{-1}r^{k+1}\right) = \left(r^k, A^{-1}r^k\right) - \alpha_k\left(r^k, r^k\right) - \alpha_k\left(Ar^k, A^{-1}r^k\right) + \alpha_k^2\left(r^k, Ar^k\right)$$
$$= \left(r^k, A^{-1}r^k\right) - \alpha_k\left(r^k, A^T A^{-1}r^k\right)$$

by the definition of α_k. Now using (14.1.12) we have

$$\alpha_k = \frac{\left(r^k, r^k\right)}{(r^k, Ar^k)} \ge c_1$$

and thus, by (14.1.11),

$$\left(r^{k+1}, A^{-1}r^{k+1}\right) \le \left(r^k, A^{-1}r^k\right)(1 - c_0 c_1) \quad \text{for } k \ge 0. \tag{14.1.13}$$

Notice that $1 - c_0 c_1$ is nonnegative, since A^{-1} is positive definite. Therefore,

$$\left(r^k, A^{-1}r^k\right) \le \left(r^0, A^{-1}r^0\right)(1 - c_0 c_1)^k$$

and thus $\left(r^k, A^{-1}r^k\right)$ tends to zero.

But r^k, given by (14.1.10b), is $b - Ax^k$, as can be shown by induction. Since A^{-1} is positive definite, we have that the vectors r^k converge to zero, and because

$$x^k = A^{-1}(b - r^k)$$

it follows that the vectors x^k converge to $A^{-1}b$, which is the unique solution of (14.1.1). ∎

Corollary 14.1.2 *If A is symmetric and positive definite, then the steepest descent method converges.*

The estimate (14.1.13) shows that if the product $c_0 c_1$ can be taken to be close to 1 then the method of steepest descent will converge quite rapidly. As can be seen from Exercise 14.1.2, one way of having $c_0 c_1$ close to 1 is if A is close to being a multiple of the identity matrix. However, steepest descent can often be quite slow, and this usually occurs because the residuals oscillate. That is, in spite of (14.1.7), we can have r^{k+2} be in essentially the same direction as r^k or $-r^k$.

Because the method of steepest descent is often quite slow, we consider several means to accelerate it. One method that accelerates steepest descent is the conjugate gradient method, which is the subject of the next several sections. In Section 14.6 we consider the class of preconditioned minimum residual methods, which also are accelerations of the method of steepest descent.

EXERCISES 14.1

1. Using the relation

$$E(y + z) = E(y) + (z, Ay - b) + O(|z|^2)$$

for the function $E(y)$ given by (14.1.3), verify that the gradient of the function $E(y)$ is $G(y) = Ay - b$, as asserted in (14.1.4).

2. Show that the constants c_0 and c_1 of (14.1.11) and (14.1.12) can be taken to be

$$c_0 = \frac{\lambda_3}{\lambda_2}, \quad \text{and} \quad c_1 = \frac{1}{\lambda_1}$$

where $\lambda_1, \lambda_2,$ and λ_3 are the least eigenvalues of

$$\tfrac{1}{2}(A + A^T), \quad \tfrac{1}{2}(A^{-1} + A^{-T}), \quad \text{and} \quad \tfrac{1}{2}(A^{-1}A^T + AA^{-T}),$$

respectively.

3. Consider the matrix

$$A = \begin{pmatrix} 1 & b \\ 0 & 2 \end{pmatrix}$$

a. Show that A is positive definite if $|b| < 2\sqrt{2}$.

b. Show that $A^T A^{-1}$ is positive definite if $|b| < \frac{4}{3}$.

4. Show that if $|b| < 2$, then $|r^{k+2}| < |r^k|$ when the steepest descent algorithm is applied to the matrix of Exercise 3. Conclude that the method converges when $|b| < 2$. *Hint:* Show that if $r^k = \begin{pmatrix} x \\ y \end{pmatrix}$, then

$$r^{k+1} = \begin{pmatrix} y \\ -x \end{pmatrix} \frac{x(x - by)}{(x^2 + bxy + 2y^2)}.$$

5. Discuss the relationship between the example of Exercise 4 to Theorem 14.1.1 when $\frac{4}{3} \leq |b| < 2$.

6. Show that the method of steepest descent applied to the matrix of Exercise 3 does not converge for $|b| \geq 2$. *Hint:* Consider $r^0 = (\alpha, 1)^T$, where $\alpha^2 + \alpha - 1 = 0$.

7. Prove the Cauchy-Schwarz inequality

$$(x, Ay) \leq (x, Ax)^{1/2}(y, Ay)^{1/2}$$

for a positive definite matrix A. *Hint:* Consider $(\alpha x - \beta y, A(\alpha x - \beta y))$.

14.2 The Conjugate Gradient Method

The conjugate gradient method can be viewed as an acceleration of steepest descent. We begin our derivation of the method by writing

$$x^{k+1} = x^k + \alpha_k \left[r^k + \gamma_k (x^k - x^{k-1}) \right]$$

for some scalar parameters α_k and γ_k. This formula shows that the new change in position, $x^{k+1} - x^k$, is a linear combination of the steepest descent direction and the previous change in position $x^k - x^{k-1}$. We rewrite the preceding formula as

$$x^{k+1} = x^k + \alpha_k p^k$$

where

$$p^k = r^k + \gamma_k \left(x^k - x^{k-1} \right) = r^k + \gamma_k \alpha_{k-1} p^{k-1}$$
$$= r^k + \beta_{k-1} p^{k-1}.$$

Combining these formulas we have

$$x^{k+1} = x^k + \alpha_k p^k \qquad (14.2.1a)$$
$$r^{k+1} = r^k - \alpha_k A p^k \qquad (14.2.1b)$$
$$p^{k+1} = r^{k+1} + \beta_k p^k \qquad (14.2.1c)$$

where the parameters α_k and β_k are to be determined. The vector p^k is called the *search direction* to the kth iteration.

We now wish to determine the parameters α_k and β_k and also determine what p^0 should be so that (14.2.1) converges as rapidly as possible. As with steepest descent, we wish to choose x^{k+1} so that $E\left(x^{k+1}\right)$ is minimal. To begin we assume that p^k is known, and we choose α_k so that $E\left(x^{k+1}\right)$ is minimized. We have

$$E\left(x^{k+1}\right) = \tfrac{1}{2}\left(x^k, Ax^k\right) + \alpha_k\left(p^k, Ax^k\right) + \tfrac{1}{2}\alpha_k^2\left(p^k, Ap^k\right) - \left(x^k, b\right) - \alpha_k\left(p^k, b\right)$$
$$= E\left(x^k\right) - \alpha_k\left(p^k, r^k\right) + \tfrac{1}{2}\alpha_k^2\left(p^k, Ap^k\right).$$

By considering the derivative of $E(x^{k+1})$ with respect to α_k we obtain that

$$\alpha_k = \frac{\left(p^k, r^k\right)}{\left(p^k, Ap^k\right)} \quad \text{for } k \geq 0 \tag{14.2.2}$$

is the optimal value of α_k. Using this value of α_k we have

$$E\left(x^{k+1}\right) = E\left(x^k\right) - \frac{1}{2}\frac{\left(p^k, r^k\right)^2}{\left(p^k, Ap^k\right)}.$$

We first consider the case $k = 0$, where we have complete freedom to choose p^0. From this formula we see that r^0 is a good choice for p^0, since it will make $E\left(x^1\right)$ less $E\left(x^0\right)$. From now on we will assume $p^0 = r^0$; later on we will see other advantages to this choice. Next we use (14.2.2) with (14.2.1b) to give

$$\left(p^k, r^{k+1}\right) = \left(p^k, r^k\right) - \alpha_k\left(p^k, Ap^k\right) = 0. \tag{14.2.3}$$

Then using (14.2.3) with (14.2.1c), we have

$$\left(p^{k+1}, r^{k+1}\right) = \left(r^{k+1}, r^{k+1}\right) + \beta_k\left(p^k, r^{k+1}\right)$$
$$= |r^{k+1}|^2 \quad \text{for } k \geq 0.$$

Then by our choice of p^0 we have

$$\left(p^k, r^k\right) = |r^k|^2 \quad \text{for } k \geq 0. \tag{14.2.4}$$

This pattern of alternatively using (14.2.1b) and (14.2.1c) will be used repeatedly in our analysis of the conjugate gradient method.

With (14.2.4) and (14.2.2) we have that

$$\alpha_k = \frac{|r^k|^2}{\left(p^k, Ap^k\right)} \tag{14.2.5}$$

which is a convenient formula for computing α_k. We also have that

$$E\left(x^{k+1}\right) = E\left(x^k\right) - \frac{1}{2}\frac{|r^k|^4}{\left(p^k, Ap^k\right)}.$$

This formula shows that p^k should be chosen so that (p^k, Ap^k) is minimal, since that will minimize $E(x^{k+1})$ given x^k. By (14.2.1c) we see that β_{k-1} should be chosen to minimize (p^k, Ap^k) given p^{k-1}. We have

$$\left(p^k, Ap^k\right) = \left(r^k, Ar^k\right) + 2\beta_{k-1}\left(r^k, Ap^{k-1}\right) + \beta_{k-1}^2\left(p^{k-1}, Ap^{k-1}\right)$$

and so the optimal choice of β_{k-1} is

$$\beta_{k-1} = -\frac{\left(r^k, Ap^{k-1}\right)}{\left(p^{k-1}, Ap^{k-1}\right)} \quad \text{for } k \geq 1$$

or, equivalently,

$$\beta_k = -\frac{\left(r^{k+1}, Ap^k\right)}{\left(p^k, Ap^k\right)} \quad \text{for } k \geq 0. \tag{14.2.6}$$

Our first conclusion from this formula results from using this formula for β_k with (14.2.1c). We have

$$\left(p^{k+1}, Ap^k\right) = \left(r^{k+1}, Ap^k\right) + \beta_k\left(p^k, Ap^k\right) = 0$$

and so we obtain the important result that

$$\left(p^{k+1}, Ap^k\right) = 0 \quad \text{for } k \geq 0, \tag{14.2.7}$$

which we describe by saying that consecutive search directions are conjugate. Using (14.2.7) with (14.2.1c), we find

$$\begin{aligned}
\left(p^k, Ap^k\right) &= \left(r^k, Ap^k\right) + \beta_{k-1}\left(p^{k-1}, Ap^k\right) \\
&= \left(r^k, Ap^k\right),
\end{aligned}$$

which we use with (14.2.1b) and (14.2.5) to obtain

$$\begin{aligned}
\left(r^{k+1}, r^k\right) &= \left(r^k, r^k\right) - \alpha_k\left(Ap^k, r^k\right) \\
&= \left(r^k, r^k\right) - \alpha_k\left(p^k, Ap^k\right) \\
&= 0.
\end{aligned} \tag{14.2.8}$$

We now obtain a more convenient formula for β_k than (14.2.6). First, by (14.2.1b) and (14.2.8),

$$\begin{aligned}
\left(r^{k+1}, r^{k+1}\right) &= \left(r^{k+1}, r^k\right) - \alpha_k\left(r^{k+1}, Ap^k\right) \\
&= -\alpha_k\left(r^{k+1}, Ap^k\right),
\end{aligned}$$

so by (14.2.6) our formula for β_k is

$$\beta_k = \frac{1}{\alpha_k}\frac{|r^{k+1}|^2}{\left(p^k, Ap^k\right)} = \frac{|r^{k+1}|^2}{|r^k|^2}.$$

We now collect the formulas for the conjugate gradient method.

$$p^0 = r^0 = b - Ax^0 \tag{14.2.9a}$$

$$x^{k+1} = x^k + \alpha_k p^k \tag{14.2.9b}$$

$$r^{k+1} = r^k - \alpha_k A p^k \tag{14.2.9c}$$

$$p^{k+1} = r^{k+1} + \beta_k p^k \tag{14.2.9d}$$

$$\alpha_k = \frac{|r^k|^2}{(p^k, Ap^k)} \tag{14.2.9e}$$

$$\beta_k = \frac{|r^{k+1}|^2}{|r^k|^2} \tag{14.2.9f}$$

The implementation of these formulas in a computer program is discussed in the next section. We conclude this section with some basic observations about the algorithm.

We see from formulas (14.2.9) that if β_k is small, that is, if $|r^{k+1}|$ is much less that $|r^k|$, then p^{k+1} is essentially r^{k+1} and the conjugate gradient method is close to the steepest descent method. If $|r^{k+1}|$ is not much less than $|r^k|$, then the new search direction, p^{k+1}, will not be close to the local steepest descent direction, r^{k+1}. Notice that the vectors r^k as defined by (14.2.9c) are equal to the residual $b - Ax^k$ for all values of k; see Exercise 14.2.1.

Next we prove a very interesting and significant result about the residuals and search directions for the conjugate gradient method.

Theorem 14.2.1   *For the conjugate gradient method (14.2.9), the residuals and search directions satisfy the relations*

$$\left(r^k, r^j\right) = \left(p^k, Ap^j\right) = 0 \quad \text{for } k \neq j. \tag{14.2.10}$$

Proof   We prove this result by induction. First notice that

$$\left(r^0, r^1\right) = 0$$

and

$$\left(p^0, Ap^1\right) = 0$$

by (14.2.8) and (14.2.7).

Next, assume that

$$\left(r^\ell, r^j\right) = \left(p^\ell, Ap^j\right) = 0 \quad \text{for } 0 \leq j < \ell \leq k.$$

We wish to show that this holds for all j and ℓ with $0 \leq j < \ell \leq k+1$ as well. First, by (14.2.8) and (14.2.7), we take the case with j equal to k and ℓ equal to $k+1$:

$$\left(r^{k+1}, r^k\right) = \left(p^{k+1}, Ap^k\right) = 0.$$

Now assume that j is less than k. By (14.2.9c) and (14.2.9d) we have

$$\left(r^{k+1}, r^j\right) = \left(r^k, r^j\right) - \alpha_k \left(Ap^k, r^j\right)$$
$$= -\alpha_k \left(Ap^k, p^j - \beta_{j-1}p^{j-1}\right)$$
$$= 0$$

since $\left(p^\ell, Ap^j\right)$ and $\left(p^\ell, Ap^{j-1}\right)$ are zero by our induction hypothesis. Also, for j less than k

$$\left(p^{k+1}, Ap^j\right) = \left(r^{k+1}, Ap^j\right) + \beta_k \left(p^k, Ap^j\right)$$
$$= \left(r^{k+1}, r^j - r^{j+1}\right) \alpha_j^{-1}$$
$$= 0$$

by the result just proved. This completes the proof of the theorem. ∎

Theorem 14.2.1 has the following immediate corollary.

Corollary 14.2.2 *If the matrix A is a $K \times K$ symmetric positive definite matrix, then the conjugate gradient algorithm converges in at most K steps.*

Proof By Theorem 14.2.1 all the residuals are mutually orthogonal, by (14.2.10). Thus r^K is orthogonal to r^k for $k = 0, ..., K-1$. Since the dimension of the space is K, r^K must be zero, and so the method must be converged within K steps. ∎

This result is not often of practical importance, since for an elliptic difference equation on the square, e.g., the five-point Laplacian (12.5.1), with grid spacing $\Delta x = \Delta y = 1/N$ the vectors have dimension $K = (N-1)^2$. However, it does turn out that often the conjugate gradient method is essentially converged in far fewer than K steps. When viewed as an iterative method, it is very effective, the number of iteration steps being on the order on N (i.e., $K^{1/2}$) for elliptic difference equations. This is proved in the next section.

We have derived the conjugate gradient method by minimizing the quadratic functional $E(y)$ or $F(y)$. Notice that by (14.1.2)

$$F(y) = \tfrac{1}{2}\left(y - x, A(y - x)\right)$$
$$= \tfrac{1}{2}\left(-A^{-1}r, -r\right) = \tfrac{1}{2}\left(r, A^{-1}r\right). \tag{14.2.11}$$

Thus, the conjugate gradient method minimizes the functional $(r, A^{-1}r)$ at each step in the search direction.

Example 14.2.1 Table 14.2.1 displays the results of computations using both the S.O.R. and conjugate gradient methods to solve the five-point Laplacian on the unit square with Dirichlet boundary conditions. The exact solution that was calculated was $u = e^x \sin y$ for $0 \leq x, y \leq 1$. The finite difference grid used equal grid spacing in each direction. The three different grid spacings are displayed in the first column of the table.

Comparison of S.O.R. and Conjugate Gradient Methods

h	S.O.R.		Conjugate Gradient		
	Iterations	Error	Iterations	Error	Residual
0.100	31	5.52-5	27	5.51-5	1.91-8
0.050	64	1.38-5	54	1.39-5	3.19-8
0.025	122	3.21-6	107	3.48-6	2.59-8

Table 14.2.1

For both methods the initial iterate was the grid function that was equal to the exact solution on the boundary and was zero in the interior of the square. The S.O.R. method was terminated when the L^2 norm of the changes to the solution, given by

$$\omega \left(\sum_{\ell,m} |\tfrac{1}{4}(v_{\ell+1,m}^n + v_{\ell-1,m}^{n+1} + v_{\ell,m+1}^n + v_{\ell,m-1}^{n+1}) - v_{\ell,m}^n|^2 h^2 \right)^{1/2}$$

was less than the tolerance of 10^{-7}. The sum is for all interior grid points. The value for ω was $2(1 + \pi h)^{-1}$ for each case.

The conjugate gradient method was also terminated when the norm of the updates to the solution were less than the tolerance of 10^{-7}. The norm of the updates is given by $h\alpha_n|p^n|$. For each method the number of iterations and the norm of the error are given for the three values of h equal to $\frac{1}{10}$, $\frac{1}{20}$, and $\frac{1}{40}$. In addition, the norm of the residuals are displayed for the conjugate gradient method.

Table 14.2.1 clearly shows for both methods that the number of iterates is proportional to h^{-1}. The table also demonstrates the second-order accuracy of the five-point Laplacian finite difference scheme. Decreasing the tolerance from 10^{-7} to 10^{-8} and 10^{-9} decreased the residuals for the conjugate gradient method but did not decrease the errors. This shows that the error given is primarily due to the truncation error inherent in the finite difference scheme and is not the error due to the iterative method.

The error shown for h equal to 1/40 for the S.O.R. method actually increased as the tolerance was reduced from 10^{-7} to 10^{-8}. The error shown in the table is due to the fortuitous circumstance that the iterate at which the method was stopped was closer to the solution to the differential equation than it was to the true solution to the difference scheme. When the tolerance was reduced to 10^{-8}, the error was essentially that of the conjugate gradient method.

□

In doing computations to demonstrate the order of accuracy of schemes and the speed of iterative methods, we must be careful to distinguish between errors due to the use of finite difference schemes, i.e., truncation errors, and errors due to the iterative method. The results shown in Table 14.2.1 were done in double precision to remove the arithmetic errors due to the finite precision of the computer. Double-precision calculations are often not needed in practical computations because the arithmetic errors are usually much smaller than the uncertainty of the data.

Since the conjugate gradient method is more expensive per step than S.O.R. in terms of both storage and computation time, Table 14.2.1 shows that S.O.R. is more efficient than the conjugate gradient method for this problem. A major advantage of the conjugate gradient method is that it can be easily modified to a preconditioned conjugate gradient method, as is shown in Section 14.5. A second advantage of the conjugate gradient method is that it does not require the user to specify any parameters, such as the iteration parameter ω required by S.O.R. methods.

EXERCISES 14.2

1. Prove by induction that the vectors r^k as defined by (14.2.9) are equal to the residual $b - Ax^k$ for each k.

2. A skew matrix A is one for which $A^T = -A$. Show that the following algorithm converges when A is skew and nonsingular:

$$p_0 = -Ar^0$$
$$x^{k+1} = x^k + \alpha_k p^k$$
$$r^{k+1} = r^k = \alpha_k Ap^k$$
$$p^{k+1} = -Ar^{k+1} + \beta_k p^k$$
$$\alpha_k = |Ar^k|^2/|Ap^k|^2$$
$$\beta_k = |Ar^{k+1}|^2/|Ar^k|^2$$

Hint: Show that α_k and β_{k-1} minimize $|r^k|^2$ at each step. Also show that $\left(r^{k+1}, Ap^k\right) = \left(Ar^{k+1}, Ar^k\right) = 0$ for all k.

3. Show that if A is skew but singular, then with the algorithm given in Exercise 2, the vectors x^k converge to a vector x^* and the vectors r^k converge to r^*, such that

$$r^* = b - Ax^*$$

and r^* is a null vector of A. *Hint:* Show that $|r^k|$ converges and that $|Ar^k| \leq \|A\| \, |r^k - r^{k+1}|$ and $|r^{k+1} - r^k|^2 = |r^k|^2 - |r^{k+1}|^2$.

14.3 Implementing the Conjugate Gradient Method

We now discuss how to implement the conjugate gradient method using the five-point Laplacian on a uniform grid as an illustration. We begin by considering (14.2.9) and see that four vectors of dimension K are required. These are x^k, r^k, p^k, and an additional vector q^k, which is used to store the values of Ap^k.

We start with an initial iterate x^0 and then compute $r^0 = b - Ax^0$, $q^0 = Ar^0$, and α_0 with $p^0 = r^0$. Then (14.2.9) becomes

$$x^{k+1} = x^k + \alpha_k p^k \qquad (14.3.1a)$$

$$r^{k+1} = r^k - \alpha_k q^k \qquad (14.3.1b)$$

$$p^{k+1} = r^{k+1} + \beta_k p^k \qquad (14.3.1c)$$

$$q^{k+1} = A r^{k+1} + \beta_k q^k \qquad (14.3.1d)$$

$$\alpha_k = \frac{|r^k|^2}{(p^k, q^k)} \qquad (14.3.1e)$$

$$\beta_k = \frac{|r^{k+1}|^2}{|r^k|^2} \qquad (14.3.1f)$$

One can avoid using the vectors q^k if Ap^k is computed twice, once for (14.3.1b) and once for evaluating α^k.

We now show what these formulas become for the example of solving Poisson's equation on the unit square with equal spacing in both directions. The vectors will now be indexed by their grid point indices, and we denote the components of the vector x by the grid function $v_{\ell,m}$. The equations to solve are

$$-v_{\ell+1,m} - v_{\ell-1,m} - v_{\ell,m+1} - v_{\ell,m-1} + 4v_{\ell,m} = -h^2 f_{\ell,m} \qquad (14.3.2)$$

which forms the system of equations $Ax = b$. Notice that A is positive definite and symmetric and that the vector b contains both the values $h^2 f_{\ell,m}$ and the values of the solution on the boundary.

First, $v^0_{\ell,m}$ is given and then $r^0_{\ell,m}$ is computed in the interior as

$$
\begin{aligned}
r^0_{\ell,m} &= -h^2 f_{\ell,m} + v^0_{\ell+1,m} + v^0_{\ell-1,m} + v^0_{\ell,m+1} + v^0_{\ell,m-1} - 4v^0_{\ell,m} \\
p^0_{\ell,m} &= r^0_{\ell,m}
\end{aligned}
\qquad (14.3.3)
$$

with $|r^0|^2$ also being computed. Then $q^0_{\ell,m}$ is computed as

$$q^0_{\ell,m} = 4r^0_{\ell,m} - r^0_{\ell+1,m} - r^0_{\ell-1,m} - r^0_{\ell,m+1} - r^0_{\ell,m-1} \qquad (14.3.4)$$

and the inner product (p^0, q^0) is also computed to evaluate α_0 as $|r^0|^2/(p^0, q^0)$. Note that for Dirichlet boundary data, r^k, p^k, and q^k should be zero on the boundary.

Now begins the main computation loop. First v and r are updated by

$$
\begin{aligned}
v^{k+1}_{\ell,m} &= v^k_{\ell,m} + \alpha_k p^k_{\ell,m} \\
r^{k+1}_{\ell,m} &= r^k_{\ell,m} - \alpha_k q^k_{\ell,m}
\end{aligned}
\qquad (14.3.5)
$$

with $|r^{k+1}|^2$ also being computed. Using $|r^{k+1}|^2$, β_k is computed then p and q are updated by

$$
\begin{aligned}
p^{k+1}_{\ell,m} &= r^{k+1}_{\ell,m} + \beta_k p^k_{\ell,m} \\
q^{k+1}_{\ell,m} &= 4r^{k+1}_{\ell,m} - r^{k+1}_{\ell+1,m} - r^{k+1}_{\ell-1,m} - r^{k+1}_{\ell,m+1} - r^{k+1}_{\ell,m-1} + \beta_k q^k_{\ell,m}
\end{aligned}
\qquad (14.3.6)
$$

and the inner product (p^{k+1}, q^{k+1}) is computed by accumulating the products $p_{\ell,m}^{k+1} q_{\ell,m}^{k+1}$. Finally, α_{k+1} is computed as the ratio $|r^{k+1}|^2 / (p^{k+1}, q^{k+1})$ and k is incremented.

It is important to notice that in the computer code there is no need to use variables indexed by the iteration counter k. The values of α_k and β_k are not required beyond the kth iteration, and thus the implementation should use only variables α and β.

A trick can be used to reduce the code which initializes p^0 and q^0. After v^0 and r^0 have been computed, set β equal to zero and then use the the the code for formulas (14.3.6) to compute p^0 and q^0. This avoids using separate code for (14.3.4) and (14.3.6).

The conjugate gradient method is terminated when either $\alpha_k|p^k|$ or $|r^k|$ is sufficiently small. For most systems these two quantities are good indicators of how close the current iterate x^k is to the true solution. As with the general linear methods, e.g., S.O.R., the method should be continued until the error in the iteration is comparable to the truncation error in the numerical method. There is no reason to solve the linear system exactly when there is intrinsic truncation error due to using finite difference methods.

It should also be pointed out that it is not wise to compute the residual r^k as $b - Ax^k$, and the formula (14.3.1b) should be used instead. Although r^k is mathematically equivalent to $b - Ax^k$, when using the finite precision of a computer there is a loss of significant digits when the residual is computed as $b - Ax^k$, since the two vectors b and Ax^k will be nearly the same and much larger than r^k when k is not too small. The formula (14.3.1b) avoids this problem.

In those cases where the matrix A is ill conditioned, there will usually be a significant difference between the computed vector r^k and the true residual for large of values of k. Nonetheless, the method, as given by (14.3.1), will converge to machine precision even in the presence of these rounding errors. Of course, one must not set the convergence criteria smaller than what can be obtained with the machine arithmetic.

EXERCISES 14.3

1. Use the conjugate gradient method to solve Poisson's equation

$$u_{xx} + u_{yy} = -4\cos(x+y)\sin(x-y)$$

on the unit square. The boundary conditions and exact solution are given by the formula $u = \cos(x+y)\sin(x-y)$. Use the standard five-point difference scheme with $h = \Delta x = \Delta y = 0.1,\ 0.05,$ and 0.025. The initial iterate should be zero in the interior of the square. Comment on the accuracy of the scheme and the efficiency of the method. Stop the iterative method when the L^2 norm of the change is less than 10^{-6}.

2. Use the conjugate gradient method to solve Poisson's equation

$$u_{xx} + u_{yy} = -2\cos x \sin y$$

on the unit square. The boundary conditions and exact solution are given by the formula $u = \cos x \sin y$. Use the standard five-point difference scheme with $h = \Delta x = \Delta y = 0.1$, 0.05, and 0.025. The initial iterate should be zero in the interior of the square. Comment on the accuracy of the scheme and the efficiency of the method. Stop the iterative method when the L^2 norm of the change is less than 10^{-6}. Compare with the results of the S.O.R. method applied to this same equation (see Exercise 13.3.4).

14.4 A Convergence Estimate for the Conjugate Gradient Method

Theorem 14.2.1 shows that the conjugate gradient method will converge in at most K steps if A is a $K \times K$ matrix. However, we will now prove an estimate on the rate of convergence of the method that shows that the method is often essentially converged after far fewer than K steps.

Theorem 14.4.1   *If A is a symmetric positive definite matrix whose eigenvalues lie in the interval $[a, b]$, with $0 < a$, then the error vector e^k for the conjugate gradient method satisfies*

$$\left(e^k, Ae^k\right)^{1/2} \leq 2 \left(\frac{\sqrt{b} - \sqrt{a}}{\sqrt{b} + \sqrt{a}}\right)^k \left(e^0, Ae^0\right)^{1/2}. \tag{14.4.1}$$

Proof   We begin with the observation based on (14.2.9b) and (14.2.9c) that the residual after k steps of the conjugate gradient method can be expressed as a linear combination of the set of vectors $\{A^j r^0\}$ for j from 0 to k. We express this observation as

$$r^k = R_k(A)r^0 \tag{14.4.2}$$

where $R_k(\lambda)$ is a polynomial in λ of exact degree k (see Exercise 14.4.1). The coefficients of the polynomial $R_k(\lambda)$ depend on the initial residual r^0. We will also make use of the observation that

$$R_k(0) = 1 \tag{14.4.3}$$

for all nonnegative integers k.

The error e^k on the kth step of the conjugate gradient method is related to the residual by

$$r^k = Ae^k. \tag{14.4.4}$$

Since matrix A commutes with $R_k(A)$, a polynomial in A, we have by (14.4.3) that

$$A\left(e^k - R_k(A)e^0\right) = 0.$$

and since A is nonsingular we have

$$e^k = R_k(A)e^0. \tag{14.4.5}$$

We now use Theorem 14.2.1 to establish that

$$\left(e^k, Ae^k\right) = \left(Q_k(A)e^0, Ae^k\right) \tag{14.4.6}$$

for any polynomial $Q_k(\lambda)$ of degree k satisfying $Q_k(0) = 1$. Relation (14.4.6) is proved as follows. Using (14.4.5) and Theorem 14.2.1, we have

$$\left(e^k, Ae^k\right) = \left(e^k, r^k\right)$$

$$= \left(e^k + \sum_{j=0}^{k-1} \gamma_j r^j, \, r^k\right)$$

for any choice of the coefficients γ_j. But we then have, by (14.4.4) and (14.4.5), that

$$e^k + \sum_{j=0}^{k-1} \gamma_j r^j = \left[R_k(A) + \sum_{j=0}^{k-1} \gamma_j AR_j(A)\right]e^0$$

$$= Q_k(A)e^0$$

where it is easy to see that, by appropriate choice of the γ_j, $Q_k(\lambda)$ can be any polynomial of degree k satisfying $Q_k(0) = 1$. This establishes (14.4.6).

We now use the Cauchy-Schwarz inequality for positive definite matrices (see Exercise 14.1.7) to obtain

$$\left(e^k, Ae^k\right) = \left(Q_k(A)e^0, Ae^k\right)$$

$$\leq \left(Q_k(A)e^0, AQ_k(A)e^0\right)^{1/2} \left(e^k, Ae^k\right)^{1/2},$$

from which we obtain

$$\left(e^k, Ae^k\right) \leq \left(Q_k(A)e^0, AQ_k(A)e^0\right). \tag{14.4.7}$$

We now wish to choose $Q_k(A)$ so that the right-hand side of (14.4.7) is as small as possible, or nearly so. We will actually only estimate the minimum value of the right-hand side. We begin by using the spectral mapping theorem (see Appendix A). Since the eigenvalues of A are in the interval $[a, b]$, we have that

$$\left(Q_k(A)e^0, AQ_k(A)e^0\right) \leq \max_{a \leq \lambda \leq b} |Q_k(\lambda)|^2 \left(e^0, Ae^0\right). \tag{14.4.8}$$

We will choose the polynomial $Q_k(\lambda)$ so that $|Q_k(\lambda)|$ is quite small for λ in $[a, b]$. Recall that $Q_k(0)$ is 1. Based on an understanding of the properties of orthogonal polynomials, we choose

$$Q_k(\lambda) = \frac{T_k\left(\dfrac{b + a - 2\lambda}{b - a}\right)}{T_k\left(\dfrac{b + a}{b - a}\right)}$$

where $T_k(\mu)$ is the Tchebyshev polynomial of degree k given by

$$T_k(\mu) = \begin{cases} \cos(k\cos^{-1}\mu) & \text{if } |\mu| \leq 1 \\ [\text{sign}(\mu)]^k \cosh(k\cosh^{-1}\mu) & \text{if } |\mu| \geq 1. \end{cases} \tag{14.4.9}$$

See Exercise 14.4.2. Notice that $Q_k(0)$ is 1.

For λ in the interval $[a, b]$, the value of $|b + a - 2\lambda|/(b - a)$ is bounded by 1 and $|T_k(\mu)|$ for $\mu \in [-1, 1]$ is at most 1; therefore, we have

$$\max_{a \leq \lambda \leq b} |Q_k(\lambda)| \leq \left[T_k \left(\frac{b+a}{b-a} \right) \right]^{-1} = \left[\cosh \left(k \cosh^{-1} \left(\frac{b+a}{b-a} \right) \right) \right]^{-1}.$$

As k increases the value of $\cosh\{k\cosh^{-1}[(b+a)/(b-a)]\}$ also increases, showing that (e^k, Ae^k) decreases with k. To obtain a more useful estimate of this quantity, we set

$$\frac{b+a}{b-a} = \cosh\sigma = \frac{e^\sigma + e^{-\sigma}}{2}.$$

Solving this equation for e^σ, we have

$$e^\sigma = \frac{\sqrt{b} + \sqrt{a}}{\sqrt{b} - \sqrt{a}}.$$

(There should be no cause for confusion between e^σ, which is the exponential of σ, and e^k, which is the kth error vector.)

We then obtain

$$\cosh k\sigma = \frac{e^{k\sigma} + e^{-k\sigma}}{2} = \frac{1}{2} \left(\frac{\sqrt{b} + \sqrt{a}}{\sqrt{b} - \sqrt{a}} \right)^k \left[1 + \left(\frac{\sqrt{b} - \sqrt{a}}{\sqrt{b} + \sqrt{a}} \right)^{2k} \right]$$

$$\geq \frac{1}{2} \left(\frac{\sqrt{b} + \sqrt{a}}{\sqrt{b} - \sqrt{a}} \right)^k.$$

Thus we have

$$\max_{a \leq \lambda \leq b} |Q_k(\lambda)| \leq 2 \left(\frac{\sqrt{b} - \sqrt{a}}{\sqrt{b} + \sqrt{a}} \right)^k \tag{14.4.10}$$

This estimate with (14.4.8) gives (14.4.1), which proves Theorem 14.4.1. ∎

Theorem 14.4.1 shows that the conjugate gradient method converges faster when the eigenvalues of A are clustered together in the sense that a/b is close to 1. Notice also that the estimate (14.4.1) is independent of simple scaling of the matrix A, that is, the estimate is the same for $Ax = b$ and $\alpha Ax = \alpha b$ for any positive number α. For the five-point Laplacian on the unit square, the value of $\left(\sqrt{b} - \sqrt{a} \right) / \left(\sqrt{b} + \sqrt{a} \right)$ is $1 - O(h)$, as with S.O.R. and indeed the two methods are about equal in terms of the number of iterations required for a solution, as shown in Table 14.2.1 (see Exercise 14.4.3).

EXERCISES 14.4

1. Using induction on k, verify relation (14.4.2). You may wish to also show that p^k can be expressed as a polynomial in A multiplying r^0.

2. Verify that the Tchebyshev polynomials $T_k(\mu)$ given by (14.4.9) are indeed polynomials of degree k. *Hint:* Use the formula

$$\cos(k+1)\theta = -\cos(k-1)\theta + 2\cos k\theta \cos \theta$$

and a similar formula for $\cosh(k+1)\theta$ to establish a recurrence relation between the $T_k(\mu)$.

3. For the five-point Laplacian on the unit square with equal spacing in each direction, show that $\sqrt{a/b}$ is approximately $\frac{1}{2}\pi h$.

14.5 The Preconditioned Conjugate Gradient Method

A technique resulting in further acceleration of the conjugate gradient method is the preconditioned conjugate gradient method. We first discuss this method in some generality and then examine the particular case of preconditioning with S.S.O.R.

The basic idea of the preconditioned conjugate gradient method is to replace the system

$$Ax = b \tag{14.5.1}$$

by

$$B^{-1}AB^{-T}\left(B^T x\right) = B^{-1}b \tag{14.5.2}$$

where $B^{-1}AB^{-T}$ is a matrix for which the conjugate gradient method converges faster than it does with A itself. Matrix B is chosen so that computing $B^{-T}y$ and $B^{-1}y$ are easy operations to perform. We wish to have the eigenvalues of $B^{-1}AB^{-T}$ more clustered together than are those of A. Since A is symmetric and positive definite, there is a matrix C so that $A = CC^T$, and B is usually chosen to approximate C in some sense. Note that $B^{-1}AB^{-T}$ is symmetric and positive definite when A is. Note also that B need only approximate a multiple of C, so that $B^{-1}AB^{-T}$ is closer to being a multiple of the identity than is A itself.

Consider now the conjugate gradient method applied to

$$\tilde{A}\tilde{x} = \tilde{b} \tag{14.5.3}$$

where

$$\tilde{A} = B^{-1}AB^{-T}, \quad \tilde{x} = B^T x, \quad \tilde{b} = B^{-1}b.$$

We have from (14.2.9)

$$\tilde{x}^{k+1} = \tilde{x}^k + \alpha_k \tilde{p}^k$$
$$\tilde{r}^{k+1} = \tilde{r}^k - \alpha_k \tilde{A}\tilde{p}^k \qquad (14.5.4)$$
$$\tilde{p}^{k+1} = \tilde{r}^{k+1} + \beta_k \tilde{p}^k$$

where $\alpha_k = |\tilde{r}^k|^2/(\tilde{p}^k, \tilde{A}\tilde{p}^k)$ and $\beta_k = |\tilde{r}^{k+1}|^2/|\tilde{r}^k|^2$.

Now let us rewrite (14.5.4) in terms of the original variables x rather than $\tilde{x}$. Using $x^k = B^{-T}\tilde{x}^k$, $p^k = B^{-T}\tilde{p}^k$, and $r^k = B\tilde{r}^k$, we have

$$x^{k+1} = x^k + \alpha_k p^k$$
$$r^{k+1} = r^k - \alpha_k A p^k \qquad (14.5.5)$$
$$p^{k+1} = M^{-1}r^{k+1} + \beta_k p^k$$

where $M = BB^T$ and

$$\alpha_k = \frac{(r^k, M^{-1}r^k)}{(p^k, Ap^k)}, \quad \beta_k = \frac{(r^{k+1}, M^{-1}r^{k+1})}{(r^k, M^{-1}r^k)}.$$

We see that the effect of the preconditioning is to alter the equation for updating the search direction p^{k+1} and to alter the definitions of α_k and β_k. For the method to be effective, we must be easily able to solve

$$r = Mz = BB^T z$$

for z. A common choice of B is to take $B = \tilde{L}$, where $\tilde{L}$ is an approximate lower triangular factor of A in the sense that

$$A = \tilde{L}\tilde{L}^T + N$$

where N is small in some sense.

Preconditioning by S.S.O.R.

We consider now S.S.O.R. and show how it can be used as a preconditioning for the conjugate gradient method. We assume that A can be written in the form

$$A = I - L - L^T.$$

Notice that the matrix A in (14.3.2) is actually in the form $4(I - L - L^T)$, but the scalar multiple does not affect the conclusions. S.S.O.R. is a two-step process given by

$$v^{k+1/2} = v^k + \omega\left(Lv^{k+1/2} + L^T v^k - v^k + b\right)$$
$$v^{k+1} = v^{k+1/2} + \omega\left(Lv^{k+1/2} + L^T v^{k+1} - v^{k+1/2} + b\right). \qquad (14.5.6)$$

We wish to rewrite this in the form $M(v^{k+1} - v^k) = r^k$. Notice that we can express $v^{k+1} - v^k$ as a linear function of r^k in this way because the construction of v^{k+1} is linear and if r^k were zero, then the update $v^{k+1} - v^k$ would also be zero. It remains to determine the matrix M and to determine if it has the form $\tilde{B}\tilde{B}^T$.

We rewrite the first step as

$$v^{k+1/2} - v^k - \omega L\left(v^{k+1/2} - v^k\right) = \omega\left(Lv^k + L^T v^k - v^k + b\right)$$
$$= \omega r^k.$$

We can therefore write

$$v^{k+1/2} = v^k + (I - \omega L)^{-1} \omega r^k. \tag{14.5.7}$$

The second step of (14.5.6) can be rewritten as

$$\left(I - \omega L^T\right) v^{k+1} = \left(I(1 - \omega) + \omega L\right) v^{k+1/2} + \omega b$$

and substituting from (14.5.7) we have

$$\left(I - \omega L^T\right) v^{k+1} = [(1 - \omega)I + \omega L] v^k + [(1 - \omega)I + \omega L] (I - \omega L)^{-1} \omega r^k + \omega b$$

or

$$\left(I - \omega L^T\right) \left(v^{k+1} - v^k\right)$$
$$= \left(-\omega I + \omega L + \omega L^T\right) v^k + \omega b + [(1 - \omega)I + \omega L] (I - \omega L)^{-1} \omega r^k$$
$$= \omega r^k + [(1 - \omega)I + \omega L] (I - \omega L)^{-1} \omega r^k$$
$$= (I - \omega L)^{-1} [I - \omega L + (1 - \omega) I + \omega L] r^k$$
$$= (I - \omega L)^{-1} (2 - \omega) \omega r^k.$$

We thus have

$$\frac{1}{\omega(2 - \omega)} (I - \omega L) \left(I - \omega L^T\right) \left(v^{k+1} - v^k\right) = r^k. \tag{14.5.8}$$

If we compare expression (14.5.8) with the identity

$$A\left(v - v^k\right) = r^k,$$

we see that S.S.O.R. can be viewed as an iterative method, which approximates A by the matrix in (14.5.8). Since the matrix in (14.5.8) is in the form BB^T, it is natural to employ the preconditioned conjugate gradient method with $B = (\omega(2 - \omega))^{-1/2} (I - \omega L)$.

It is important to note that if we are going to use S.S.O.R. alone to solve the problem, we would use (14.5.6) with immediate replacement. Formula (14.5.8) is important only when using S.S.O.R. as a preconditioner.

We now apply this preconditioning matrix to Laplace's equation in a square. We have

$$x^{k+1} = x^k + \alpha_k p^k,$$
$$r^{k+1} = r^k - \alpha_k A p^k, \tag{14.5.9}$$

and

$$p^{k+1} = z^{k+1} + \beta_k p^k$$

where z^{k+1} is computed using (14.5.8). The computation of z^{k+1} is implemented as follows:

$$\tilde{z}_{\ell,m}^{k+1} = \tfrac{1}{4}\omega \left(\tilde{z}_{\ell,m-1}^{k+1} + \tilde{z}_{\ell-1,m}^{k+1} \right) + \omega\left(2 - \omega\right) r_{\ell,m}^{k+1}$$
$$z_{\ell,m}^{k+1} = \tfrac{1}{4}\omega \left(z_{\ell,m+1}^{k+1} + z_{\ell+1,m}^{k+1} \right) + \tilde{z}_{\ell,m}^{k+1} \tag{14.5.10}$$

for all interior points with $\tilde{z}$ and z being zero on the boundaries.

Notice that the quantities z and $\tilde{z}$ can occupy the same storage locations. The parameters for the preconditioned method are computed by the formulas

$$\alpha_k = \frac{\left(r^k, z^k\right)}{(p^k, A p^k)}$$
$$\beta_k = \frac{\left(r^{k+1}, z^{k+1}\right)}{\left(r^k, z^k\right)}.$$

The method of (14.5.10) is a method for solving

$$(I - \omega L)\,\tilde{z}^{k+1} = \omega\left(2 - \omega\right) r^{k+1}$$
$$\left(I - \omega L^T\right) z^{k+1} = \tilde{z}^{k+1}$$

Other ways of computing z^{k+1} can also be used. Notice that we have scaled $\tilde{z}$ to avoid taking the square root of $\omega(2 - \omega)$. We can also dispense with the factor $\omega(2 - \omega)$, since it represents only a scaling factor.

To implement the preconditioning requires two more loops than does the regular conjugate gradient method. The additional loops, given by (14.5.10), are very simple, and the slight extra effort is more than justified by the substantial increase in speed of the preconditioned method.

We now collect the formulas for implementing the preconditioned conjugate gradient method. To initialize the preconditioned conjugate gradient method, we use

$$p^0 = z^0 = M^{-1} r^0,$$

as we see from the relations between p^0, $\tilde{p}^0$, r^0, and $\tilde{r}^0$. The formulas are:

$$x^{k+1} = x^k + \alpha_k p^k \tag{14.5.11a}$$
$$r^{k+1} = r^k - \alpha_k q^k \tag{14.5.11b}$$
$$z^{k+1} = M^{-1} r^{k+1} \tag{14.5.11c}$$

$$p^{k+1} = z^{k+1} + \beta_k p^k \qquad\qquad (14.5.11\text{d})$$

$$q^{k+1} = A z^{k+1} + \beta_k q^k \qquad\qquad (14.5.11\text{e})$$

$$\alpha_k = \frac{(r^k, z^k)}{(p^k, q^k)} \qquad\qquad (14.5.11\text{f})$$

$$\beta_k = \frac{(r^{k+1}, z^{k+1})}{(r^k, z^k)} \qquad\qquad (14.5.11\text{g})$$

As with (14.3.1), we can avoid using the vectors q^k if Ap^k is computed twice, once for (14.5.11b) and once for evaluating α^k in (14.5.11f).

The preconditioned conjugate gradient method can be significantly faster than the conjugate gradient method. As we can see, it requires only minor modifications to a conjugate gradient method to implement a preconditioned conjugate gradient method. The choice of ω in the S.S.O.R. preconditioner is not as critical as it is in the S.S.O.R. method itself. The spectral radius for the preconditioned conjugate gradient method with the S.S.O.R. preconditioner is $1 - O\left(N^{-1/2}\right)$. This is illustrated in Table 14.5.1.

Example 14.5.1 Table 14.5.1 shows the results of solving Poisson's equation using the point S.O.R. method, the conjugate gradient method, and the preconditioned conjugate gradient method, with S.S.O.R. as the preconditioner. The exact solution that was calculated was $u = \cos x \sin y$ for $0 \le x, y \le 1$. The finite difference grid used equal grid spacing in each direction. The three different grid spacings are displayed in the first column of the table. The next columns show the number of iterations required to obtain a converged solution.

For each method the initial iterate was the grid function that was equal to the exact solution on the boundary and was zero in the interior of the square. Each method was terminated when the L^2 norm of the change in the solution was less than 10^{-7}. This convergence criterion was sufficient to produce results for which the error was primarily due to the truncation error. For both the S.O.R. method and the S.S.O.R. preconditioner, the value of ω was $2(1 + \pi h)^{-1}$. The table shows that the number of iterations for the first two methods is roughly proportional to h^{-1}, whereas for the preconditioned conjugate gradient method, the number of iterations is proportional to $h^{-1/2}$. These results are similar to those of Table 14.2.1.

Since the work in one iteration of the S.O.R. method is less than that in one iteration of the other two methods, it is not appropriate to judge the meth-

Comparison of the Speeds of S.O.R., the Conjugate Gradient Method, and the Preconditioned Conjugate Gradient Method

h	S.O.R.	C.G.	P.C.G.
0.100	33	26	12
0.050	60	52	16
0.025	115	103	22

Table 14.5.1

ods solely on the number of iterations. The conjugate gradient method involves roughly twice as much work per iteration as does point S.O.R., and the preconditioned conjugate gradient method involves three to four times as much work as S.O.R. Thus the preconditioned conjugate gradient method is faster than S.O.R. for h equal to $\frac{1}{40}$, but probably not for the grid spacing of $\frac{1}{10}$. Of course, for even smaller values of the grid spacing h, the preconditioned conjugate gradient method would be even faster relative to S.O.R. In terms of computer storage, the S.O.R. method requires much less storage than the other two methods, but this is not a significant concern in many scientific computations. $\square$

Formulas (14.5.11) show that five vectors are required to implement the preconditioned conjugate gradient method, as opposed to only four vectors for the conjugate gradient method. One way of using only four vectors for the preconditioned conjugate gradient method is to work with $\tilde{r} = B^{-1}r$ rather than r; see Eisenstat [13]. We then obtain the algorithm

$$x^{k+1} = x^k + \alpha_k p^k \qquad (14.5.12\text{a})$$

$$\tilde{r}^{k+1} = \tilde{r}^k - \alpha_k B^{-1} q^k \qquad (14.5.12\text{b})$$

$$p^{k+1} = B^{-T}\tilde{r}^{k+1} + \beta_k p^k \qquad (14.5.12\text{c})$$

$$q^{k+1} = A p^{k+1} \qquad (14.5.12\text{d})$$

$$\alpha_k = |\tilde{r}^k|^2 / (p^k, q^k) \qquad (14.5.12\text{e})$$

$$\beta_k = |\tilde{r}^{k+1}|^2 / |\tilde{r}^k|^2. \qquad (14.5.12\text{f})$$

The results of the calculations of the vectors $B^{-1}q^k$ and $B^{-T}\tilde{r}^{k+1}$ are stored in the vector q.

Preconditioning by Approximate Cholesky Factorization

Other preconditioning matrices for the conjugate gradient method can be obtained by approximating A as $\tilde{L}\tilde{L}^T$ for a convenient form of $\tilde{L}$. A factorization of a matrix as LL^T, where L is a lower triangular matrix, is called a Cholesky factorization; thus the product $\tilde{L}\tilde{L}^T$ is called an approximate Cholesky factorization of A. As an example we consider a matrix $\tilde{L}$ of the form

$$\left(\tilde{L}v\right)_{\ell,m} = av_{\ell,m} + bv_{\ell-1,m} + cv_{\ell,m-1} \qquad (14.5.13)$$

where a, b, and c are constants. It is easy to see then that

$$\left(\tilde{L}^T v\right)_{\ell,m} = av_{\ell,m} + bv_{\ell+1,m} + cv_{\ell,m+1} \qquad (14.5.14)$$

if we use the natural ordering of the components $v_{\ell,m}$ in the vector v. We then have, by (14.5.13) and (14.5.14),

$$
\begin{aligned}
\left(\tilde{L}\tilde{L}^T v\right)_{\ell,m} &= a\left(\tilde{L}^T v\right)_{\ell,m} + b\left(\tilde{L}^T v\right)_{\ell-1,m} + c\left(\tilde{L}^T v\right)_{\ell,m-1} \\
&= a\left(av_{\ell,m} + bv_{\ell+1,m} + cv_{\ell,m+1}\right) \\
&\quad + b\left(av_{\ell-1,m} + bv_{\ell,m} + cv_{\ell-1,m+1}\right) \\
&\quad + c\left(av_{\ell,m-1} + bv_{\ell+1,m-1} + cv_{\ell,m}\right) \\
&= \left(a^2 + b^2 + c^2\right) v_{\ell,m} + abv_{\ell+1,m} + acv_{\ell,m+1} \\
&\quad + abv_{\ell-1,m} + acv_{\ell,m-1} + bcv_{\ell-1,m+1} \\
&\quad + bcv_{\ell+1,m-1}.
\end{aligned}
$$

To have $\tilde{L}\tilde{L}^T$ approximate A, where A corresponds to the five-point Laplacian, we may set

$$
a^2 + b^2 + c^2 = 1
$$
$$
ab = ac = -\tfrac{1}{4}.
$$

Solving these equations we have

$$
a = \frac{\sqrt{2 + \sqrt{2}}}{2}
$$
$$
b = c = -\frac{1}{4a}.
$$

To implement this method it is often convenient to approximate A by $\tilde{L}D\tilde{L}^T$, where D is a diagonal matrix. For our particular choice of $\tilde{L}$, D is just a^2 times the identity. Using this choice of $\tilde{L}$ the preconditioned conjugate gradient method is (14.5.9) with (14.5.10) replaced by

$$
\begin{aligned}
\hat{z}_{\ell,m}^{k+1} &= \left(\hat{z}_{\ell,m-1}^{k+1} + \hat{z}_{\ell-1,m}^{k+1} + 4r_{\ell,m}^{k+1}\right) d \\
z_{\ell,m}^{k+1} &= \left(z_{\ell,m+1}^{k+1} + z_{\ell+1,m}^{k+1}\right) d + \hat{z}_{\ell,m}^{k+1}
\end{aligned}
\qquad (14.5.15)
$$

where

$$
d = \left(2 + \sqrt{2}\right)^{-1}.
$$

The temporary variable $\hat{z}$ is defined by

$$
\hat{z} = \frac{2}{\sqrt{2 + \sqrt{2}}} \tilde{L}^T z.
$$

We can try more sophisticated choices for the matrix $\tilde{L}$. For the discrete Laplacian on a square, the preceding methods all do quite well. For matrices arising from other problems we may have to work quite hard to get a good preconditioning matrix.

**Comparison of Three Preconditioning Methods
for the Nine-Point Laplacian**

h	None	Cholesky	5-point	9-point
0.100	28	16	18	16
0.050	57	28	25	23
0.025	112	52	34	32

Table 14.5.2

Example 14.5.2 To solve the difference equations for the fourth-order accurate Poisson's equation (12.5.6), we can use preconditioning based on the five-point Laplacian. This is a simple way to accelerate the solution procedure and it does not affect the accuracy of the scheme. In fact, using S.S.O.R. based on the nine-point Laplacian as the preconditioner with the nine-point Laplacian does not give a significant improvement over that using S.S.O.R. based on the five-point Laplacian as the preconditioner. This is illustrated in Table 14.5.2.

Table 14.5.2 displays the results of solving Laplace's equation using the nine-point Laplacian with the conjugate gradient method and with three different preconditioning methods. The three preconditioning methods are the approximate Cholesky factorization (14.5.15) for the five-point Laplacian, the S.S.O.R. preconditioning using the five-point Laplacian, and the S.S.O.R. preconditioning using the nine-point Laplacian. The exact solution that was calculated was $u = e^{3x}\sin 3y$ for $0 \le x, y \le 1$. The finite difference grid used equal grid spacing in each direction. The three different grid spacings are displayed in the first column of the table. The next columns show the number of iterations required to obtain a converged solution. For each method the initial iterate was the grid function that was equal to the exact solution on the boundary and was zero in the interior of the square.

Each method was terminated when the L^2 norm of the change in the solution was less than 10^{-10}. This convergence criterion was sufficient to produce results for which the error was primarily due to the truncation error, similar to the results shown in Table 12.5.1. For both of the S.S.O.R. preconditioners, the value of ω was $2(1 + \pi h)^{-1}$. The table shows that the number of iterations for the last two methods is roughly proportional to $h^{-1/2}$. There is not a significant difference between the last two methods, but the nine-point preconditioner is better as would be expected. The approximate Cholesky method based on the five-point scheme is not as good as the other two methods, but it still offers a significant improvement over the basic conjugate gradient method. $\square$

EXERCISES 14.5

1.   Repeat the calculations of Exercise 14.3.1 but using the preconditioned conjugate gradient method with the S.S.O.R. preconditioning. Comment on the efficiency of the method and observe that the number of iterations increases as $O(N^{1/2})$.

2. Repeat the calculations of Exercise 14.3.2 but using the preconditioned conjugate gradient method with the S.S.O.R. preconditioning. Comment on the efficiency of the method and observe that the number of iterations increases as $O(N^{1/2})$.

3. Repeat the calculations of Exercise 14.3.1 but using the preconditioned conjugate gradient method with the approximate Cholesky factorization as the preconditioning. Comment on the efficiency of the method and observe that the number of iterations increases as $O(N^{1/2})$.

4. Repeat the calculations of Exercise 14.3.2 but using the preconditioned conjugate gradient method with the approximate Cholesky factorization as the preconditioning. Comment on the efficiency of the method and observe that the number of iterations increases as $O(N^{1/2})$.

14.6 Minimum Residual Methods

A class of methods that are closely related to conjugate gradient methods are the methods called minimum residual methods. If we wish to solve

$$Ax = b \tag{14.6.1}$$

where A is nonsingular but not symmetric or positive definite we could modify the problem to be

$$A^T A x = A^T b \tag{14.6.2}$$

for which the matrix is symmetric and positive definite.

Using steepest descent or conjugate gradient methods on (14.6.2) will work, of course, but these methods will usually be quite slow. Steepest descent applied to (14.6.2) is called the *minimum residual method,* since it is minimizing the residual of (14.6.2) at each step.

These very slow methods can be improved by preconditioning the matrix A. That is, a minimum residual method is used on

$$B^{-1}Ax = B^{-1}b \tag{14.6.3}$$

or

$$AB^{-1}y = b \tag{14.6.4}$$

where $y = Bx$. The matrix B should be chosen to approximate A and yet be easily invertible. A common choice for B is an approximate LU factorization of A, that is,

$$B = LU = A + N$$

where N is small in some sense and L and U are lower and upper triangular matrices, respectively.

We now apply the steepest descent method (14.1.10) to (14.6.2). For the minimum residual method, we have

$$\tilde{r} = A^T b - A^T A x = A^T r$$

with $r = b - Ax$. Note also that

$$(\tilde{r}, (A^T A)^{-1} \tilde{r}) = (r, r).$$

From (14.1.10) we have that the minimum residual method applied to (14.6.1) is

$$x^{k+1} = x^k + \alpha_k p^k \qquad (14.6.5a)$$

$$r^{k+1} = r^k - \alpha_k A p^k \qquad (14.6.5b)$$

$$p^{k+1} = A^T r^{k+1} \qquad (14.6.5c)$$

$$\alpha_k = \frac{|A^T r^k|^2}{|A p^k|^2}. \qquad (14.6.5d)$$

Methods based on applying the conjugate gradient method to a minimum residual method are called *accelerated minimum residual methods*. There is a substantial literature on the many variations of these methods (see for example, Elman [14]), and we will not discuss the methods in much depth. The derivations of the basic methods are left as exercises.

Unfortunately there are no general rules on how to find a good preconditioning matrix B. Given a particular system, the literature should be consulted to find what others have done with similar problems. Several attempts may have to be made before a satisfactory preconditioning matrix is found.

For many problems the use of an accelerated method is not as crucial as finding a good preconditioning matrix; however, for some problems it is difficult to obtain a good preconditioning matrix and the use of an accelerated method is important.

The stopping criterion for a minimum residual method is usually based on the size of the residual. Note that if r^k is small but $\alpha_k p^k$ is much larger, then p^k is an approximate null vector of A, and changing x^k by $\alpha_k p^k$ need not give a much better solution. In these cases A is an ill-conditioned matrix, and the reader should refer to any of several references in numerical linear algebra for appropriate numerical methods for solution.

EXERCISES 14.6

1. Show that the conjugate gradient method applied to (14.6.2) may be expressed as

$$x^{k+1} = x^k + \alpha_k p^k$$

$$r^{k+1} = x^k - \alpha_k A p^k$$

$$p^{k+1} = A^T r^k + \beta_k p^k$$

$$\alpha_k = \frac{|A^T r^k|^2}{|A p^k|^2}$$

$$\beta_k = \frac{|A^T r^{k+1}|^2}{|A^T r^k|^2}$$

$$p^0 = A^T r^0.$$

2. Show that the conjugate gradient method applied to $AA^T y = b$ with $x = A^T y$ can be expressed as

$$x^{k+1} = x^k + \alpha_k p^k$$

$$r^{k+1} = r^k - \alpha_k A p^k$$

$$p^{k+1} = A^T r^{k+1} + \beta_k p^k$$

$$\alpha_k = \frac{|r^k|^2}{|p^k|^2}$$

$$\beta_k = \frac{|r^{k+1}|^2}{|r^k|^2}$$

$$p^0 = A^T r^0.$$

3. Show that using the conjugate gradient method on the system

$$\left(B^{-1} A\right)^T \left(B^{-1} A\right) x = \left(B^{-1} A\right)^T B^{-1} b$$

can be expressed as

$$x^{k+1} = x^k + \alpha_k p^k$$

$$r^{k+1} = r^k - \alpha_k A p^k$$

$$B B^T z^{k+1} = r^{k+1}$$

$$p^{k+1} = A^T z^{k+1} + \beta_k p^k$$

$$\alpha_k = \frac{|A^T z^k|^2}{\left(A p^k, (B B^T)^{-1} A p^k\right)}$$

$$\beta_k = \frac{|A^T z^{k+1}|^2}{|A^T z^k|^2}$$

$$p^0 = A^T r^0.$$

4. Write a computer program to test several methods discussed in this section. A set of $n \times n$ test matrices depending on four parameters, ρ_1, ρ_2, ρ_3, and ρ_4, can be generated as

$$A_{ij} = \begin{cases} 1 & \text{if } i = j \\ \dfrac{\cos(\rho_1 i)}{(i-j)^{\rho_2}} & \text{if } j < i \\ \rho_3 & \text{if } i < j = 1 + \lfloor n \sin^2(\rho_4 i) \rfloor \le n \\ 0 & \text{otherwise.} \end{cases}$$

(Here $\lfloor . \rfloor$ denotes the greatest integer function; $\lfloor x \rfloor$ is the greatest integer less than or equal to x.) These matrices are not symmetric and not positive definite for most values of the parameters. Use the lower triangular part of A as the preconditioning matrix, i.e.,

$$B_{ij} = \begin{cases} A_{ij} & \text{if } j \leq i \\ 0 & \text{if } j > i. \end{cases}$$

Investigate some of the methods discussed in this section and answer the following questions. Is an accelerated preconditioned minimum residual method necessarily much better than an unaccelerated preconditioned minimum residual method? Can you determine conditions when the acceleration is significantly better? When does the preconditioning as given here not give a significant improvement over the basic minimum residual method? *Hint:* To check your computer program, notice that when ρ_3 is zero, the preconditioned methods must converge on the first step.

Appendix A

Matrix and Vector Analysis

In this appendix we collect results about matrices and vectors that are used throughout the text. Since many of the applications of linear algebra in the text use vectors with complex components, we concern ourselves primarily with this case. We denote the set of complex numbers by C. The proofs of many of the results stated here are included for completeness.

A.1 Vector and Matrix Norms

We may consider a vector, v, as an element of C^M, that is, $v = (v_1, \ldots, v_M)$, where v_j, the jth component of v, is a complex number. Norms are real-valued functions on vector spaces that provide a notion of the *length* of a vector. There are three norms on C^M that we use. The most common norms are the ℓ^2 or Euclidean norm

$$|v|_2 = \left(\sum_{j=1}^M |v_j|^2 \right)^{1/2},$$

the ℓ^1 norm,

$$|v|_1 = \sum_{j=1}^M |v_j|,$$

and the ℓ^∞, or maximum, norm,

$$|v|_\infty = \max_{1 \le j \le M} |v_j|.$$

Each of these norms satisfy three important properties.

Proposition A.1 *Each of the norms just given satisfy the following three conditions.*

1. $|v| \ge 0$, *with equality if and only if* $v = 0$
2. $|v + w| \le |v| + |w|$
3. $|\alpha v| = |\alpha| \, |v|$ *for* $\alpha \in C$

The proof is easy and is omitted.

The three properties in Proposition A.1 are those that define a norm. In property 3 the expression $|\alpha|$ is the absolute value of the complex number α, and since the absolute value is a norm on C, the use of the same symbol for absolute value of a number and norm of a vector should cause no difficulty. We write expressions such as $(C^M, |\cdot|_1)$ when we wish to signify which norm is being considered.

The following relations between the norms given earlier are easily proved.

$$\begin{aligned} |v|_1 &\leq M^{1/2}|v|_2, \\ |v|_2 &\leq M^{1/2}|v|_\infty. \end{aligned} \tag{A.1}$$

We let e_j denote the vector whose components are all zero except for the jth component, which is 1.

Matrices and Matrix Norms

An $M \times N$ matrix may be defined as a linear map from C^N to C^M. The (i,j)th component of a matrix A will be written as A_{ij} or a_{ij}, where a_{ij} is defined as the ith component of Ae_j. The transpose of an $M \times N$ matrix A is the $N \times M$ matrix A^*, defined by

$$(A^*)_{ij} = \bar{A}_{ji}.$$

where the bar denotes the complex conjugate.

If we consider both C^N and C^M with norms, then we define the norm of an $M \times N$ matrix A by

$$\|A\| = \sup_{|v|=1} |Av| = \sup_{v \neq 0} \frac{|Av|}{|v|}, \tag{A.2}$$

where, of course, the expression $|Av|$ refers to the norm C^M and $|v|$ refers to the norm on C^N. The equivalence of the two expressions in (A.2) follows from the linearity of A and property 3 of Proposition A.1. The matrix norm defined in this way satisfies the properties of Proposition A.1 and thus is a norm on the vector space of $M \times N$ matrices. We collect the important properties of matrix norms in the following proposition.

Proposition A.2   *Let A and B be $M \times N$ matrices and let D be an $N \times P$ matrix. Then the following five conditions are satisfied.*
1. $\|A\| \geq 0$ *with equality if and only if $A = 0$*
2. $\|A + B\| \leq \|A\| + \|B\|$
3. $\|\alpha A\| \leq |\alpha| \, \|A\|$ *for $\alpha \in C$*
4. $|Av| \leq \|A\| \, |v|$ *for all $v \in C^N$*
5. $\|AD\| \leq \|A\| \, \|D\|$

The proofs of these results follow immediately from the definition of the matrix norm in (A.2).

An important consequence of inequality 5 in Proposition A.2 is that for a square matrix A, i.e., one for which $M = N$, we have

$$\|A^n\| \le \|A\|^n. \tag{A.3}$$

Scalar Products

The ℓ^2 norm has several useful properties not shared by the other two vector norms just given. These properties are a consequence of the ℓ^2 norm having an associated scalar product on C^M given by

$$\langle v, w \rangle = \sum_{j=1}^{M} \overline{v_j}\, w_j. \tag{A.4}$$

We have

$$|v|_2 = \langle v, v \rangle^{1/2}$$

and

$$4\,\mathrm{Re}\,\langle v, w \rangle = |v + w|_2^2 - |v - w|_2^2.$$

We also have

$$\langle v, Aw \rangle = \langle A^* v, w \rangle$$

for the transpose matrix of A. Vectors v and w are said to be *orthogonal* if

$$\langle v, w \rangle = 0.$$

There is a difference in terminology that should be pointed out here. The scalar product $\langle \cdot, \cdot \rangle$ is sometimes called a hermitian product, whereas the term scalar product is used to describe a product like (A.4) but without the conjugate on the v_j. Also the transpose is often called the conjugate transpose or adjoint.

Unitary Matrices

One of the most useful properties of the ℓ^2 norm is that there is a large class of matrices that leave the norm invariant.

Proposition A.3 *For a square $N \times N$ matrix U, the following statements are equivalent.*
1. $U^* U = I$
2. $|Uv|_2 = |v|_2$ *for all* $v \in C^N$

Matrices satisfying the conditions of Proposition A.3 are said to be *unitary*. Unitary matrices whose elements are all real numbers are called orthogonal matrices.

Proof of Proposition A.3   In terms of the components of the matrix U, condition 1 is

$$\sum_{i=1}^{N} \overline{u_{ij}}\, u_{ik} = \begin{cases} 1 & \text{if } j = k \\ 0 & \text{if } j \neq k. \end{cases}$$

This shows that the rows of U are vectors of unit norm that are orthogonal to each other. To prove condition 2 from condition 1, we have

$$|Uv|^2 = \sum_{i=1}^{N} \overline{\left(\sum_{j=1}^{N} u_{ij} v_j \right)} \left(\sum_{k=1}^{N} u_{ik} v_k \right)$$

$$= \sum_{j=1}^{N} \sum_{k=1}^{N} \overline{v_j} \left(\sum_{i=1}^{N} \overline{u_{ij}}\, u_{ij} \right) v_k$$

$$= \sum_{j=1}^{N} |v_j|^2 = |v|^2,$$

using the orthogonality of rows of U.

To show that condition 2 implies condition 1, we first take $v = e_j$, the vector whose only nonzero component is a 1 for the jth component. Then

$$1 = |e_j|^2 = |Ue_j|^2 = \sum_{i=1}^{N} \overline{u_{ij}}\, u_{ij}$$

for each j. Secondly, let $v = e_j + \alpha e_k$ for $j \neq k$ and α a complex number of absolute value 1; then

$$2 = |v|^2 = |Uv|^2 = \sum_{i=1}^{N} |u_{ij} + \alpha u_{jk}|^2$$

$$= 2 + 2\,\text{Re}\left(\alpha \sum_{i=1}^{N} \overline{u_{ij}}\, u_{ik} \right).$$

This implies that

$$\text{Re}\,\alpha \sum_{i=1}^{N} \overline{u_{ij}}\, u_{ik} = 0$$

for all values of α, which means that the complex number given by the summation must be zero. This proves that condition 1 follows from condition 2. ∎

For both the ℓ^1 and ℓ^∞ norms, the class of matrices leaving the norm invariant is much smaller.

Proposition A.4 *If P is a matrix such that*

$$|Pv| = |v|$$

for all vectors v and where the norm is either the ℓ^1 or ℓ^∞ norm, then P is a complex permutation matrix, that is, there is only one nonzero element in each row and column of P and each nonzero element has magnitude 1.

Proof We give the proof only for the ℓ^1 norm; the proof for the ℓ^∞ norm is similar. First, let $v = e_j$; then

$$1 = |Pe_j| = \sum_{i=1}^{N} |p_{ij}|,$$

so each column of P has norm 1. Next let

$$v = e_j + \alpha e_k$$

where $|\alpha| = 1$ and $j \neq k$. Then

$$|v| = 2 = |Pv| = \sum_{i=1}^{N} |p_{ij} + \alpha p_{ik}| \leq \sum_{i=1}^{N} |p_{ij}| + |p_{ik}| = 2.$$

Thus the preceding inequality must be an equality, that is, $|p_{ij} + \alpha p_{ik}| = |p_{ij}| + |p_{ik}|$ for each value of i. But this can be true for α equal to 1 and -1 only if either p_{ij} or p_{ik} is zero. Therefore, we conclude that $p_{ij} = 0$ if $p_{ik} \neq 0$, and vice versa. Since each column has norm 1, each column has at least one nonzero element, and the proposition is proved. ∎

The ℓ^2 norm is similar to the norm on the space $L^2(hZ)$ defined in Chapter 1. We use the notation L^2 to refer to norms in which the grid parameter h is used, and use the notation ℓ^2 when h is not used.

Eigenvalues

Associated with every square $N \times N$ matrix A are numbers called *eigenvalues*. An eigenvalue λ is characterized by having $A - \lambda I$ be a singular matrix. An eigenvector associated with the eigenvalue λ is a nontrivial vector v such that $(A - \lambda I)v = 0$.

A *generalized eigenvector* is a nonzero vector such that $(A - \lambda I)^k v = 0$, for some integer k. An eigenvalue λ is a *simple* eigenvalue if any two of its eigenvectors are multiples of each other. A eigenvalue λ is a *semisimple* eigenvalue if the only vectors satisfying $(A - \lambda I)^k v = 0$ are actual eigenvectors, i.e., satisfy $(A - \lambda I)v = 0$. We denote the set of eigenvalues of a matrix A by $\Lambda(A)$.

An important result using unitary matrices is Schur's lemma.

Proposition A.5 Schur's Lemma. *For each $N \times N$ matrix A, there exists a unitary matrix U such that*

$$U^* A U = T$$

is an upper triangular matrix, that is,

$$T_{ij} = 0 \quad \text{if } i > j.$$

Proof Let v_1 be an eigenvector of A with unit ℓ^2 norm and with eigenvalue t_{11}, i.e.,

$$Av_1 = t_{11}v_1.$$

The matrix

$$A^{(2)} = (I - v_1 v_1^*)A$$

maps the space of vectors orthogonal to v_1 into itself. By considering $A^{(2)}$ on the subspace of vectors orthogonal to v_1, we see that $A^{(2)}$ has an eigenvalue t_{22} and eigenvector v_2 of unit norm such that v_2 is orthogonal to v_1, that is,

$$A^{(2)}v_2 = t_{22}v_2$$

or

$$Av_2 = t_{22}v_2 + t_{12}v_1$$

where

$$t_{12} = v_1^* Av_2 = \langle v_1, Av_2 \rangle.$$

By setting

$$A^{(3)} = (I - v_2 v_2^*)A^{(2)}$$

we may continue the process, obtaining vectors v_j with

$$Av_j = \sum_{i=1}^{j} t_{ij}v_i.$$

Defining the matrix U as that whose ith column is the vector v_i, we have

$$AU = UT$$

where $T_{ij} = t_{ij}$, and so T is upper triangular and U is unitary. ∎

Formulas for Matrix Norms

We now prove some formulas for explicitly evaluating and estimating the matrix norms. First, we define the *spectral radius* of a square matrix A to be the largest of the magnitudes of the eigenvalues, i.e.,

$$\rho(A) = \max_{\lambda \in \Lambda(A)} |\lambda|.$$

The estimate $\rho(A) \le \|A\|$ holds for any matrix norm; see Exercise A.1.

Proposition A.6 *If A maps $(C^M, |\cdot|_p)$ to $(C^N, |\cdot|_p)$, then*

$$\|A\| = \max_{1 \le j \le M} \sum_{i=1}^{N} |a_{ij}|, \quad \text{if } p = 1,$$

$$\|A\| = \max_{1 \le i \le N} \sum_{j=1}^{M} |a_{ij}|, \quad \text{if } p = \infty,$$

and

$$\|A\| = \rho(A^*A)^{1/2}, \quad \text{if } p = 2.$$

Proof For p equal to 1, we have

$$|Av|_1 = \sum_{i=1}^{N} \left| \sum_{j=1}^{M} a_{ij} v_j \right| \leq \sum_{j=1}^{M} \sum_{i=1}^{N} |a_{ij}| \, |v_j|$$

$$\leq \max_j \sum_{i=1}^{N} |a_{ij}| \, |v|_1$$

This shows that $\|A\|$ is at most equal to the quantity given in the proposition. We can prove that equality holds by choosing $v = e_k$, where

$$\sum_{i=1}^{N} |a_{ik}| = \max_j \sum_{i=1}^{N} |a_{ij}|.$$

We see that

$$|Ae_k|_1 = \sum_{i=1}^{N} |a_{ik}|.$$

Thus the proposition is proved for p equal to 1.

For p infinite, we have

$$|Av|_\infty = \max_i \left| \sum_{j=1}^{M} a_{ij} v_j \right| \leq \max_i \sum_{j=1}^{M} |a_{ij}| \, |v_j|$$

$$\leq \left(\max_i \sum_{j=1}^{M} |a_{ij}| \right) \max_j |v_j|,$$

which shows that $\|A\|$ is bounded above by the expression in the proposition. To show that equality is obtained, we choose k such that

$$\sum_{j=1}^{M} |a_{kj}| = \max_i \sum_{j=1}^{M} |a_{ij}|$$

and set

$$v_j = \begin{cases} 0 & \text{if } a_{kj} = 0, \\ a_{kj}/|a_{kj}| & \text{otherwise.} \end{cases}$$

It is easy to check that

$$|Av| = \sum_{j=1}^{M} |a_{kj}| \, |v|,$$

which proves the proposition in this case.

For the case p equal to 2, we have

$$|Av|^2 = \langle Av, \, Av \rangle = \langle v, \, A^* Av \rangle$$

and by Schur's lemma there is a unitary matrix U such that

$$U^* A^* A U = D$$

is upper triangular. But $D^* = D$, and thus D is diagonal. Therefore,

$$0 \le |Av|^2 = \langle v,\ UDU^*v \rangle = \langle U^*v,\ DU^*v \rangle = \langle w,\ Dw \rangle$$

for all vectors w.

For a diagonal matrix with d_i being the ith element on the main diagonal, we have

$$\langle w,\ Dw \rangle = \sum d_i |w_i|^2$$

and so we see that each d_i is nonnegative; moreover

$$|Av|^2 \le \max_i\ d_i\ |w|^2$$

and since

$$|w| = |U^*v| = |v|$$

we have that

$$\|A\|^2 \le \max\ d_i.$$

The d_i are the eigenvalues of A^*A; moreover, by choosing w to be an eigenvector of D whose eigenvalue has maximum magnitude, the proposition is easily proved. ∎

A.2 Analytic Functions of Matrices

We also need to define analytic functions of square matrices. (See Appendix C.) For an analytic function with power series expansion

$$f(z) = \sum_{n=0}^{\infty} a_n (z - z_0)^n$$

around a point z_0 in the complex plane, we define $f(A)$ for a square matrix A as

$$f(A) = \sum_{n=0}^{\infty} a_n (A - z_0 I)^n.$$

In particular,

$$e^A = \sum_{n=0}^{\infty} \frac{1}{n!} A^n.$$

The convergence of this series is proved in a manner similar to proving that e^z exists for all complex numbers z. We have

$$\|e^A\| \le \sum_{n=0}^{\infty} \frac{1}{n!} \|A^n\| \le \sum_{n=0}^{\infty} \frac{1}{n!} \|A\|^n \le e^{\|A\|}.$$

Thus the exponential of a matrix is always defined.

We can also define e^{tA} as the unique solution to the matrix differential equation

$$\frac{dX}{dt} = AX, \quad X(0) = I. \tag{A.5}$$

This equation can also be viewed as a linear ordinary differential equation in the vector space of matrices. Because linear systems of ordinary differential equations have unique solutions, e^{tA} is the unique solution to (A.5) and to the equation

$$\frac{dX}{dt} = XA, \quad X(0) = I.$$

It is important to realize that in general

$$e^B e^A \neq e^A e^B \neq e^{A+B}.$$

If A and B commute, that is, $AB = BA$, then

$$e^A e^B = e^{A+B}.$$

Another useful formula is

$$e^{S^{-1}AS} = S^{-1} e^A S$$

for any invertible matrix S.

The Spectral Mapping Theorem

The spectral mapping theorem for matrices is the statement that if f is an analytic function defined on a set containing $\Lambda(A)$, then

$$f(\Lambda(A)) = \Lambda(f(A)). \tag{A.6}$$

This result is an immediate consequence of the observation that if λ is an eigenvalue of A, then $f(\lambda)$ is an eigenvalue of $f(A)$.

Square Roots of Matrices

In our discussion of boundary conditions for parabolic systems we need the following result.

Proposition A.7   Let B be an $N \times N$ matrix whose eigenvalues λ_ν, $\nu = 1, \ldots, N$, satisfy

$$\text{Re } \lambda_\nu > 0.$$

Then there exists a unique $N \times N$ matrix C such that

$$C^2 = B$$

and whose eigenvalues μ_ν, $\nu = 1, \ldots, N$, satisfy

$$\text{Re } \mu_\nu > 0.$$

Proof Let O be a unitary matrix such that $\tilde{B} = OBO^*$ is an upper triangular matrix with elements $(\tilde{b}_{ij})$. The upper triangular matrix $\tilde{C} = (\tilde{c}_{ij})$ is defined by

$$\tilde{C}^2 = \tilde{B}.$$

This means that the diagonal elements of $\tilde{C}$ satisfy

$$\tilde{c}_{ii}^2 = \tilde{b}_{ii},$$

and we choose $\tilde{c}_{ii}$ with real part positive. This is possible, since none of the $\tilde{b}_{ii}$ are negative real numbers. The off-diagonal elements for $j > i$ satisfy

$$\tilde{c}_{ij}(\tilde{c}_{ii} + \tilde{c}_{jj}) + \sum_{k=i+1}^{j-1} \tilde{c}_{ik}\tilde{c}_{kj} = \tilde{b}_{ij}.$$

These equations uniquely determine the $\tilde{c}_{ij}$, since $\tilde{c}_{ii} + \tilde{c}_{jj}$ is nonzero. Then

$$C = O^*\tilde{C}O$$

is the matrix whose existence is asserted in the proposition. ∎

Positive Definite, Hermitian, and Symmetric Matrices

We say a matrix A is positive semidefinite and write $A \geq 0$ if $\langle v, Av \rangle \geq 0$ for all vectors v. Using this notion, matrices can be given a partial ordering. We say $A \geq B$ if $A - B \geq 0$. The usual rules for an ordering relation hold for this ordering of matrices. For example, if $A \geq 0$, then $\alpha A \geq 0$ for any positive real number α, and $A \geq 0$ and $B \geq 0$ imply $A + B \geq 0$. We also define $A \leq B$ if $B \geq A$.

We say a matrix is positive definite and write $A > 0$ if $A \geq \varepsilon I$ for some positive number ε. A matrix A is said to be negative definite or negative semidefinite if $-A$ is positive definite or positive semidefinite, respectively.

An important class of matrices are those such that $A^* = A$, these matrices are called hermitian matrices. For any matrix A we define its real part Re A as $\frac{1}{2}(A^* + A)$. Re A is a hermitian matrix. If all the components of a hermitian matrix are real numbers, then the matrix is called a *symmetric matrix*.

Proposition A.8 *If* Re $A \leq cI$, *then* $\|e^{At}\|_2 \leq e^{ct}$.

Proof Let $Z(t) = e^{At}$. Then $\dfrac{dZ}{dt} = AZ$, and so

$$\frac{d}{dt}[Z^*(t)\,Z(t)] = \left(\frac{dZ}{dt}\right)^* Z + Z^* \frac{dZ}{dt} = Z^* A^* Z + Z^* AZ$$

$$\leq 2c\,Z^*(t)Z(t).$$

This implies

$$\frac{d}{dt}[e^{-2ct}Z^*(t)Z(t)] \leq 0.$$

By integrating this inequality, we obtain

$$e^{-2ct}Z^*(t)Z(t) - I \leq 0$$

or, equivalently,

$$Z^*(t)Z(t) \leq e^{2ct}I.$$

Therefore,

$$\|Z(t)\|_2 \leq e^{ct}. \quad \blacksquare$$

Proposition A.9 *If all the eigenvalues of a matrix A have positive real part, then there exists a matrix S such that*

$$\text{Re } SAS^{-1} \geq 0.$$

Proof By Schur's lemma,

$$U\,AU^* = T$$

is upper triangular for a suitable unitary matrix U. Let $D(\delta)$ be a diagonal matrix with $D_{ii} = \delta^i$ for $i = 1, \ldots, M$. Then $D^{-1}TD$ has elements

$$\delta^{-i}t_{ij}\delta^j = t_{ij}\delta^{j-i}.$$

Therefore, $\text{Re } \langle v, D^{-1}TDv \rangle = \text{Re } \sum_{i=1}^{M} t_{ii}|v_i|^2 + O(\delta)$, and for δ small enough

$$\text{Re } \langle v, D^{-1}TDv \rangle > 0$$

since each eigenvalue satisfies $\text{Re } t_{ii} > 0$. Then $S = D^{-1}U$ is the desired matrix. $\blacksquare$

Proposition A.10 *If the eigenvalues of A satisfy $\text{Re } \lambda(A) > 0$, then there are positive constants C_0 and ε such that*

$$\|e^{-tA}\| \leq C_0 e^{-\varepsilon t}.$$

Proof By Proposition A.9 there is a matrix S such that

$$\text{Re } SAS^{-1} > 0.$$

By Proposition A.8

$$\|e^{-t\tilde{A}}\| \leq e^{-\varepsilon t}.$$

Since $e^{-tA} = S^{-1}e^{-t\tilde{A}}S$, we have

$$\|e^{-tA}\| \leq \|S^{-1}\| \|S\| e^{-\varepsilon t}$$

which proves the proposition. $\blacksquare$

EXERCISES A

1. Show that

$$\rho(A) \le \|A\|$$

for a square matrix from $(C^N, |\cdot|)$ to itself for any vector norm.

2. If A is an $N \times M$ matrix considered as a map from $(C^N, |\cdot|_1)$ to $(C^M, |\cdot|_\infty)$, show that

$$\|A\| = \sup_{i,j} |a_{ij}|.$$

3. If B is an $N \times M$ matrix considered as a map from $(C^N, |\cdot|_\infty)$ to $(C^M, |\cdot|_1)$ show that

$$\|B\| \le \sum_{i=1}^M \sum_{j=1}^N |b_{ij}|.$$

Show that equality holds in this estimate only if

$$b_{ij} b_{k\ell} \overline{b_{i\ell} b_{kj}}$$

is nonnegative for all indices (i, j) and (k, ℓ).

4. Show that

$$e^{tA} e^{tB} = e^{t(A+B)}$$

for all t if and only if A and B commute. *Hint:* Take the second derivative of each side.

5. Show that

$$\sin \left[t \begin{pmatrix} 0 & 1 \\ -1 & 0 \end{pmatrix} \right] = \begin{pmatrix} 0 & 1 \\ -1 & 0 \end{pmatrix} \sinh t.$$

6. The trace of a square $N \times N$ matrix is defined by

$$\mathrm{Tr}(A) = \sum_{i=1}^N a_{ii}.$$

It is easy to show that

$$\mathrm{Tr}(CAC^{-1}) = \mathrm{Tr}(A)$$

for any invertible matrix C. Show that

$$\det e^A = e^{\mathrm{Tr}(A)},$$

and thus e^A is invertible for every matrix A. *Hint:* Use Schur's lemma.

7. Show that if S satisfies $S^* = -S$, then e^S is unitary.

8. Show that there are 2^N solutions to $X^2 = B$ if B is a nonsingular $N \times N$ matrix. Show that there are no solutions to $X^2 = \begin{pmatrix} 0 & 1 \\ 0 & 0 \end{pmatrix}$. Show there are infinitely many solutions to $X^2 = \begin{pmatrix} 0 & 0 \\ 0 & 0 \end{pmatrix}$.

9. Verify the matrix factorization formula

$$A^n - B^n = \sum_{\ell=0}^{n-1} A^{n-1-\ell}(A - B)B^\ell. \tag{A.7}$$

10. Show that if A is an $N \times N$ matrix and B is an $M \times M$ matrix with $\operatorname{Re} \lambda_i(A) + \operatorname{Re} \lambda_j(B) > 0$ for every $i = 1, \ldots, M$ and $j = 1, \ldots, N$, then the solution to

$$AX + XB = C$$

is given by

$$X = \int_0^\infty e^{-At} C e^{-Bt} \, dt.$$

11. Prove the spectral mapping theorem given by relation (A.6).

12. Use the relation $\rho(A^n) = \rho(A)^n$, derived from the spectral mapping theorem, to prove that

$$\lim_{n \to \infty} \|A^n\| = 0 \quad \text{if and only if} \quad \rho(A) < 1.$$

Appendix B

A Survey of Real Analysis

This appendix is a survey of some basic concepts of real analysis. The selection of topics is based upon the demands of the text and is not intended to be exhaustive.

B.1 Topological Concepts

One of the most basic concepts of analysis is that of an open set. A set O in C^n is an open set if for each point x_0 in O there is a positive real number ε such that the set $\{x : |x - x_0| < \varepsilon\}$ is contained in O. The norm $|\cdot|$ on C^n maybe any of the vector space norms discussed in Appendix A.

A set F is closed if its complement, written $\sim F$, is open. A compact set is any set K such that if K is contained in the union of a collection of open sets, then there is a finite subcollection of these open sets whose union contains K. In C^n compact sets are sets that are closed and bounded.

Several important properties of open sets are that the union of any collection of open sets is open, and the intersection of a finite number of open sets is also open. The empty set is open by definition.

A function f from C^n to C^m is continuous at a point x_0 if for each positive number ε there is a number δ such that $|f(x) - f(x_0)| < \varepsilon$ whenever $|x - x_0| < \delta$. A function is continuous if it is continuous at each point in its domain. A continuous function may also be characterized as one such that $f^{-1}(O)$ is an open set for each open set O in C^m, where $f^{-1}(O) = \{y : f(y) \in O\}$.

B.2 Measure Theory

If $\{f_n\}_{n=0}^\infty$ is a sequence of continuous functions on C^n such that for each x in C^n the sequence $\{f_n(x)\}_{n=0}^\infty$ converges, it need not be that the function f, given by $f(x) = \lim_{n\to\infty} f_n(x)$, is continuous. The function $f(x)$ is called the *pointwise limit* of the sequence $\{f_n\}_{n=0}^\infty$.

It is useful to consider a class of functions that contains the continuous functions but also contains pointwise limits of sequences from the class. A very useful class of functions that has this property is the class of measurable functions.

Before defining a measurable function we must define a measurable set. To do this we begin with the class of Borel sets. The collection of Borel sets is the collection of sets $\mathcal{B}$ containing all the open and closed sets and also containing any countable union or countable intersection of sets in $\mathcal{B}$. Note that if the sets A and B are in $\mathcal{B}$, then $A \backslash B$, which is $\{x : x \in A \text{ and } x \notin B\}$, is also in $\mathcal{B}$. The set of Borel sets is an example of a σ-algebra.

A measure is a function that assigns to sets a real number or infinity. The measure of a set generalizes the notion the length, area, or volume of the set. For convenience, we restrict our discussion at this point to the real line. On the real line a Borel measure is a function μ defined for each interval; the value of μ for an interval (a, b) will be written as $\mu(a, b)$. Except for trivial cases, a measure can not be defined for all subsets of the real line; it can, however, be defined for all Borel sets. The basic property satisfied by a measure is that it be *countably additive*. This means that if $\{M_i\}_{i=1}^{\infty}$ is a countable collection of disjoint Borel sets, then

$$\mu(\bigcup_{i=1}^{\infty} M_i) = \sum_{i=1}^{\infty} \mu(M_i). \tag{B.1}$$

As a consequence of the countable additivity (B.1), it follows that if $\{M_i\}_{i=1}^{\infty}$ is a collection of Borel sets that satisfy $M_{i+1} \subseteq M_i$ for each i, then the measure of the intersection $M = \bigcap_{i=1}^{\infty} M_i$ is given by

$$\mu(M) = \lim_{i \to \infty} \mu(M_i).$$

It can be shown that the countable additivity condition (B.1) completely determines the (Borel) measure if $\mu(a, b)$ is defined for each open interval (a, b).

The usual measure on the real line is defined by $\mu(a, b) = b - a$. Lebesgue measure is the completion of this Borel measure; the completion is that if Z is any subset of a Borel set A and $\mu(A)$ is zero, then $\mu(Z)$ is defined to be zero also. The σ-algebra formed from the Borel sets and these sets of measure zero is the collection of Lebesgue measurable sets. Unless we explicitly state otherwise, we restrict our discussion to Lebesgue measure in the rest of this appendix.

If F is a monotone increasing function on R, then one can define the measure μ_F by

$$\mu_F(a, b) = F(b) - F(a).$$

This is an example of a Stieltjes measure. If F is continuous and strictly monotone, then the completion of μ_F determines the same collection of measurable sets as does Lebesgue measure.

B.3 Measurable Functions

A measurable function on R is a function f such that $f^{-1}(a, b)$ is a measurable set for each open interval (a, b). This definition is easily seen to be an extension of the concept of a continuous function; in particular each continuous function is measurable. As with continuous functions, the sum and product of measurable functions is also measurable. Among the important properties of measurable functions is that pointwise limits of a sequence of measurable functions is measurable. That is, if $\{f_n\}_{n=1}^{\infty}$ is a sequence of measurable functions and f is the pointwise limit of the sequence, i.e.,

$$f(x) = \lim_{n \to \infty} f_n(x) \tag{B.2}$$

for each x, then f is also a measurable function. Similarly, the function $\sup_n f_n(x)$ is also measurable.

Measurable functions need be defined only to within sets of measure zero. If f and g are measurable functions, but they differ only on a set of measure zero, then they are equivalent for most purposes in the theory. Similarly, if the limit (B.2) holds for all x except for x in a set of measure zero, then the function f is still a measurable function. The convergence (B.2) is said to be convergence almost everywhere, written a.e., if it holds for all x except for those in a set of measure zero.

B.4 Lebesgue Integration

One of the most powerful uses of measurable functions is in the definition of Lebesgue integration. For any set A the characteristic function of A, χ_A, is defined by

$$\chi_A = \begin{cases} 1 & \text{if } x \in A \\ 0 & \text{if } x \notin A. \end{cases}$$

The function χ_A is a measurable function only if A is a measurable set. A simple function φ is one that can be represented as

$$\varphi = \sum_{i=1}^{N} \alpha_i \chi_{A_i} \tag{B.3}$$

for a finite number of measurable sets A_i and real numbers α_i. The representation is not unique. For each simple function φ represented as in (B.3), the integral of φ is defined by

$$\int \varphi = \sum_{i=1}^{N} \alpha_i \mu(A_i)$$

whenever the sum is defined. (The sum is not defined if there are sets A_i and A_j that have infinite measure and the corresponding α_i and α_j have opposite signs.) It is straightforward to show that the definition of the integral is independent of the representation of the simple function.

For any nonnegative measurable function f, the integral of f over R is defined by

$$\int f = \sup_{0 \le \varphi \le f} \int \varphi$$

where the supremum is over simple nonnegative functions. For any measurable function f, the integral is defined by

$$\int f = \int f_+ - \int f_-$$

where $f = f_+ - f_-$ and f_+ and f_- are nonnegative measurable functions. The integral of a measurable function f over measurable set A is defined by

$$\int_A f = \int f \chi_A.$$

A function f is said to be integrable if $\int f$ is defined.

This definition of the integral gives the same value as the Riemann integral when f is a continuous function and the set A is a finite interval; thus we may write

$$\int_{(a,b)} f = \int_a^b f(x)\, dx.$$

The choice of notation for the integral in formulas is arbitrary and will depend on the particular application.

The basic result relating the integral of a limit of a sequence of measurable function to the sequence of integrals is Fatou's lemma. Fatou's lemma is easily proved using the basic definitions.

Proposition B.1   Fatou's Lemma.   *If $\{f_n\}_{n=1}^\infty$ is a sequence of nonnegative integrable functions that converges almost everywhere to a measurable function f, then*

$$\int f \leq \liminf_{n \to \infty} \int f_n.$$

In Chapter 10 we require the Lebesgue dominated convergence theorem, which relies on Fatou's lemma.

Proposition B.2   Lebesgue Dominated Convergence Theorem.   *If $\{f_n\}_{n=1}^\infty$ is a sequence of integrable functions that converges almost everywhere to a function f, and if there is an integrable function F such that $|f_n| \leq F$ for all n, then*

$$\int f = \lim_{n \to \infty} \int f_n.$$

The proof depends on Fatou's lemma applied to the function sequences $\{F + f_n\}_{n=1}^\infty$ and $\{F - f_n\}_{n=1}^\infty$.

Functions that take on complex values are measurable if both the real and imaginary parts are measurable; a similar statement is true for the integrals of such functions.

On R^n, Lebesgue measure is defined by starting with Cartesian products of intervals and defining the measure as the usual volume of the region.

B.5 Function Spaces

One advantage of Lebesgue integration over Riemann integration, one that is very important in the application of this text, concerns the set of functions $L^2(R)$ and the Fourier transform. The space $L^2(R)$ consists of those functions such that

$$\|f\|_{L^2} = \left(\int |f|^2\right)^{1/2}$$

is finite. The quantity $\|f\|_{L^2}$ is a norm, which satisfies the properties of Proposition A.1, on the vector space $L^2(R)$. Actually, $L^2(R)$ is composed of equivalence classes of functions. Two functions f_1 and f_2 are equivalent if $\|f_1 - f_2\|$ is zero.

The Fourier transform of a function f in $L^2(R)$ is given by

$$\hat{f}(\omega) = \lim_{K \to \infty} \frac{1}{\sqrt{2\pi}} \int_{-K}^{K} e^{-i\omega x} f(x)\, dx.$$

The Fourier transform, as the pointwise limit of the continuous functions

$$\frac{1}{\sqrt{2\pi}} \int_{-K}^{K} e^{-i\omega x} f(x)\, dx,$$

is a measurable function and, moreover, is also in $L^2(R)$. By Parseval's relation and the Fourier inversion formula (see Chapter 2), the Fourier transform is a one-to-one and onto mapping of $L^2(R)$ to itself. This statement does not hold if we consider Riemann integration in place of Lebesgue integration.

Other spaces of functions of some interest in the text are $L^1(R)$ and $L^\infty(R)$. The norms are defined by

$$\|f\|_1 = \int |f|$$

for $L^1(R)$ and

$$\|f\|_\infty = \operatorname{ess\,sup}_x |f(x)|,$$

for $L^\infty(R)$. The essential supremum of $|f|$, written $\operatorname{ess\,sup}_x |f(x)|$, is the infimum of the supremum of $|g(x)|$ for all measurable functions g that are equal to f almost everywhere.

Appendix C

A Survey of Results from Complex Analysis

This appendix gives the basic concepts of complex analysis and a few of the principle results that we need in the text.

C.1 Basic Definitions

A function f is an analytic function in a domain Ω in the complex domain C if at each point of Ω, f has a power series expansion with a nonzero radius of convergence. An equivalent definition is that f has a derivative, defined by

$$f'(z) = \lim_{\varepsilon \to 0} \frac{f(z+\varepsilon) - f(z)}{\varepsilon}, \tag{C.1}$$

at each point z in Ω. The derivative defined by (C.1) must be independent of the way the complex parameter ε tends to zero. If f is written as $u + iv$, for real functions u and v, and if ε in (C.1) is taken alternatively to be real and pure imaginary, we conclude that f' is well defined if and only if u and v satisfy the Cauchy-Riemann equations

$$\begin{aligned} \frac{\partial u}{\partial x}(x, y) &= \frac{\partial v}{\partial y}(x, y) \\ \frac{\partial u}{\partial y}(x, y) &= -\frac{\partial v}{\partial x}(x, y) \end{aligned} \tag{C.2}$$

where $z = x + iy$. The Cauchy-Riemann equations imply that u and v are harmonic functions (see Chapter 12). Examples of analytic functions are polynomials, the trigonometric functions, the exponential function, and functions built up from them. For example, compositions of analytic functions are also analytic functions. Specific examples of analytic functions are the functions given by the expressions

$$\sin z, \quad \frac{\cos z}{1 + z^3}, \quad \ln(1 + 2e^{z^5}).$$

These functions are analytic functions in any region in which they are single valued and finite. In particular, since $\ln re^{i\theta} = \ln r + i\theta$, the logarithm is analytic only in regions that exclude the origin and for which the value of θ can be well defined. The formula $e^{iz} = \cos z + i \sin z$ relating the exponential function with the sine and cosine functions is a basic result of great significance.

C.2 Complex Integration

Integrals of analytic functions along a curve are defined using either Riemann sums or Lebesgue integration along the curve. The most important result concerning integrals of analytic functions is that if Γ is a closed curve in a domain Ω and f is analytic in Ω, then the integral of f along Γ is zero, that is,

$$\int_\Gamma f = 0. \tag{C.3}$$

This result is called Cauchy's theorem. An equivalent formulation of Cauchy's theorem is that if Γ_1 and Γ_2 are two curves with the same endpoints, then

$$\int_{\Gamma_1} f = \int_{\Gamma_2} f$$

if the function f is analytic in the region bounded by the two curves. In particular, for n not equal to -1, we have

$$\int_a^b z^n \, dz = \frac{b^{n+1} - a^{n+1}}{n+1}$$

for any two complex numbers a and b.

If f is analytic in a neighborhood of a point z_0, except at z_0 itself, and f can be expanded as

$$f(z) = \sum_{\ell=-L}^{\infty} a_\ell (z - z_0)^\ell \tag{C.4}$$

then the *residue* of f at z_0 is the coefficient a_{-1}. As a consequence of Cauchy's theorem, we have

$$\int_\Gamma f(z) \, dz = 2\pi i a_{-1} \tag{C.5}$$

for any curve Γ that winds once around z_0 in a counterclockwise direction. This result is proved by replacing Γ by a circle around z_0 with small radius. Using the power series of f, we may explicitly evaluate the integral.

In the special case that L in expansion (C.5) is 1, the residue is determined by

$$a_{-1} = \lim_{z \to z_0} (z - z_0) f(z). \tag{C.6}$$

In this case f is said to have a simple pole at z_0.

Formula (C.5) is the basis of the calculus of residues to evaluate integrals. The method is defined by the next proposition.

Proposition C.1 *If f is analytic in the domain Ω bounded by the simple closed curve Γ, except for a finite set of points $z_1, \ldots, z_N$ at which f has residues $r_1, \ldots, r_N$, then*

$$\int_\Gamma f(z) \, dz = 2\pi i \sum_{\ell=1}^{N} r_\ell,$$

where the curve Γ is taken in the counterclockwise direction.

Example C.1 As an example of Proposition C.1, we use it to compute the Fourier transform of the function given by $u(x) = (x^2 + 1)^{-1}$. By formula (2.1.1) the Fourier transform is

$$\hat{u}(\omega) = \frac{1}{\sqrt{2\pi}} \int_{-\infty}^{\infty} e^{-i\omega x} \frac{1}{x^2 + 1} \, dx.$$

To evaluate this integral, first note that the function $u(z) = (z^2 + 1)^{-1}$ is analytic in the whole complex plane except at the two points i and $-i$. We first evaluate $\hat{u}(\omega)$ for ω positive. We consider the family of curves Γ_R given by the interval $[-R, R]$ on the real axis and the arc in the lower half-plane given by $Re^{i\theta}$ for θ in the interval $[\pi, 2\pi]$. The residue of $e^{-i\omega z}(z^2 + 1)^{-1}$ at $-i$ is given by

$$\lim_{z \to -i} \frac{(z + i)e^{-i\omega z}}{(z^2 + 1)} = \lim_{z \to -i} \frac{e^{-i\omega z}}{(z - i)} = \frac{e^{-\omega}}{-2i}.$$

When R is larger than 1, then Proposition C.1 states that

$$\int_{\Gamma_R} \frac{e^{-i\omega z}}{z^2 + 1} \, dz = 2\pi i \frac{e^{-\omega}}{-2i} = -\pi e^{-\omega}.$$

Moreover, in the limit as R tends to infinity, the value of the integral over the arc tends to zero, as seen by the estimate

$$\left| \int_{-R}^{R} \frac{e^{-i\omega z}}{z^2 + 1} \, dz \right| \leq \int_{\pi}^{2\pi} \frac{e^{-\omega R |\sin \theta|}}{R^2 - 1} R \, d\theta.$$

Since the integrand is bounded and tends to zero pointwise as R tends to infinity, the Lebesgue dominated convergence theorem (see Appendix B) shows that in the limit the integral over the arc is zero. Therefore, we obtain

$$\int_{\infty}^{-\infty} \frac{e^{-i\omega z}}{z^2 + 1} \, dz = -\pi e^{-\omega}.$$

By reversing the direction of the integration on the real line and dividing by the factor of $\sqrt{2\pi}$, we obtain the Fourier transform for ω positive. A similar analysis, but using an arc in the upper half-plane, gives the value of $\hat{u}$ for negative values of ω. The final result is

$$\frac{1}{\sqrt{2\pi}} \int_{-\infty}^{\infty} e^{-i\omega x} \frac{1}{x^2 + 1} \, dx = \sqrt{\frac{\pi}{2}} e^{-|\omega|}.$$

See Exercise 2.1.2. □

A special case of Proposition C.1 is the Cauchy integral formula,

$$f(z) = \frac{1}{2\pi i} \int_\Gamma \frac{f(\zeta)}{\zeta - z} \, d\zeta \tag{C.7}$$

for any closed curve Γ winding once around the point z. If Γ is a circle of radius r, formula (C.7) is equivalent to the formula

$$f(z) = \frac{1}{2\pi} \int_0^{2\pi} f(z + re^{i\theta}) \, d\theta \tag{C.8}$$

From (C.8) we obtain the result

$$|f(z)| \le \max_{|z-\zeta|=r} |f(\zeta)|,$$

with equality only if f is a constant. This result can be easily extended to prove the following maximum principle.

Proposition C.2 The Maximum Principle. *If f is analytic in a bounded set Ω, then $|f|$ attains its maximum on the boundary of Ω.*

By applying Proposition C.2 to the analytic function $e^{f(z)}$, we can conclude that the real part of f must also attain its maximum value on the boundary. This leads to an alternate proof of Theorem 12.3.2 for the special case of Laplace's equation.

C.3 A Phragmen-Lindelöf Theorem

The next two results are needed in Chapter 6 to prove Theorem 6.3.1. The first of these is an example of a class of theorems called Phragmen-Lindelöf theorems. The proofs of these results are an excellent illustration of the power of the methods of complex analysis. A Phragmen-Lindelöf theorem states that if an analytic function satisfies a weak bound in some unbounded domain and a stronger bound on the boundary, then the function actually satisfies the stronger bound throughout the region.

Proposition C.3 *If f is an analytic function in the quadrant Q_1 given by $\operatorname{Re} z \ge 0$ and $\operatorname{Im} z \ge 0$ and there are constants K and d such that*

$$|f(z)| \le Ke^{d|z|} \quad \text{for } z \in Q_1$$

and

$$|f(z)| \le Ke^{-|z|^2} \quad \text{for both } \operatorname{Re} z = 0 \text{ and } \operatorname{Im} z = 0$$

then, in fact,

$$|f(z)| \le Ke^{-|z|^2} \quad \text{for all } z \in Q_1.$$

Proof We begin by considering the function

$$h(z) = \left(1 + \frac{z^2 e^{i\phi}}{n}\right)^n \exp\left[-\varepsilon \left(\frac{z}{\sqrt{i}}\right)^\alpha\right] f(z)$$

where ε is any positive number, α is between 1 and 2, ϕ is an arbitrary real number, and n is any positive integer. The square root of i is taken to be $(1 + i)/\sqrt{2}$. For the first part of the proof the parameters ε, ϕ, and n are fixed; later we will vary them as appropriate.

We first use the estimate

$$|h(z)| \leq \left(1 + \frac{|z|^2}{n}\right)^n \exp\left\{-\varepsilon |z|^\alpha \cos\left[\alpha\left(\theta - \frac{\pi}{4}\right)\right]\right\} |f(z)|$$

together with the estimate

$$\left(1 + \frac{x}{n}\right)^n \leq e^x$$

to conclude that on the boundary of Q_1

$$|h(z)| \leq e^{|z|^2} \exp\left[-\varepsilon |z|^\alpha \cos\left(\alpha\frac{\pi}{4}\right)\right] K e^{-|z|^2} \leq K.$$

and in the interior of Q_1

$$|h(z)| \leq C_n |z|^{2n} \exp\left\{-\varepsilon\left[|z|^\alpha \cos\left(\alpha\frac{\pi}{4}\right)\right]\right\} K e^{d|z|}$$

where C_n is some constant depending only on n. If $|z|$ is taken large enough, say $|z| = R$, then on this arc $|h(z)| \leq K$, since the first exponential factor ultimately suppresses the growth of the other factors.

Thus $h(z)$ is bounded by K on the boundary of the subdomain of Q_1, whose boundary consists of the real and imaginary axes and the circular arc $|z| = R$. By the maximum principle Proposition C.2, h is bounded by K in the interior as well. Moreover, since the value of R was arbitrary, h is bounded by K in all of Q_1.

We now fix the value of z and vary ε and n. We have

$$\left(1 + \frac{z^2 e^{i\phi}}{n}\right)^n f(z) = \exp\left[\varepsilon\left(\frac{z}{\sqrt{i}}\right)^\alpha\right] h(z)$$

and by the estimate on h

$$\left|\left(1 + \frac{z^2 e^{i\phi}}{n}\right)^n f(z)\right| \leq K \exp\left[\varepsilon |z|^\alpha \cos\left(\frac{\alpha\pi}{4}\right)\right].$$

Taking the limit as ε tends to zero, we obtain

$$\left|\left(1 + \frac{z^2 e^{i\phi}}{n}\right)^n f(z)\right| \leq K.$$

Next we take the limit as n tends to infinity, obtaining

$$\left|e^{z^2 e^{i\phi}} f(z)\right| \leq K,$$

or

$$|f(z)| \leq K e^{-\operatorname{Re}(z^2 e^{i\phi})}.$$

This estimate holds for all values of ϕ, and by choosing ϕ so that $\operatorname{Re} z^2 e^{i\phi}$ is equal to $|z|^2$, we have proved the proposition. ∎

C.4 A Result for Parabolic Systems

Proposition C.3 applied to parabolic systems of equations gives the next proposition about parabolic systems.

Proposition C.4 *If $u(t, x)$ is a solution to the parabolic system*

$$u_t = Bu_{xx} + Au_x + Cu$$

and both $u(0, x)$ and $u(T, x)$ are zero for $x > 0$, then $u(t, x)$ is identically zero.

Proof We begin by considering the Fourier transform of $u(0, x)$, which is

$$\hat{u}(0, \omega) = \frac{1}{\sqrt{2\pi}} \int_{-\infty}^{0} e^{-i\omega x} u(0, x) \, dx$$

since $u(0, x)$ is zero for x positive. If we set $\omega = \alpha + i\beta$, where α and β are real, we have

$$\hat{u}(0, \omega) = \frac{1}{\sqrt{2\pi}} \int_{-\infty}^{0} e^{-i\alpha x} e^{-|x|\beta} u(0, x) \, dx.$$

We see that each component of $\hat{u}(0, \omega)$ is a analytic function of ω for $\mathrm{Im}\, \omega > 0$.

Moreover, we can estimate the vector norm of $\hat{u}$ by

$$\|\hat{u}(0, \omega)\| \leq \frac{1}{\sqrt{2\pi}} \int_{-\infty}^{0} e^{-|x|\beta} \|u(0, x)\| \, dx$$

$$\leq \|u(0, \cdot)\| \frac{1}{\sqrt{2\pi}} \left(\int_{-\infty}^{0} e^{-2\beta|x|} \, dx \right)^{1/2}$$

$$= \|u(0, \cdot)\| \frac{1}{\sqrt{4\pi\beta}}$$

so $\hat{u}(0, \omega)$ is bounded for $\mathrm{Im}\, \omega = \beta \geq \beta_0 > 0$. Note that $\|\hat{u}(0, \omega)\|$ denotes the vector space norm of the function $\hat{u}$ evaluated at $(0, \omega)$, and $\|u(0, \cdot)\|$ denotes the L^2 norm of the function $u(0, x)$. By the assumptions of the theorem, an estimate of the same form as the preceding also applies to $\hat{u}(T, \omega)$.

We apply these estimates to the $\hat{u}(\frac{1}{2}T, \omega)$. We have

$$\begin{aligned}\hat{u}(\tfrac{1}{2}T, \omega) &= \exp\left((-\omega^2 B + i\omega A + C)\tfrac{1}{2}T\right) \hat{u}(0, \omega) \\ &= \exp\left(-(-\omega^2 B + i\omega A + C)\tfrac{1}{2}T\right) \hat{u}(T, \omega).\end{aligned} \tag{C.9}$$

From the first of these relations we conclude for $\omega = \alpha + i\beta_0$, that

$$\|\hat{u}(\tfrac{1}{2}T, \omega)\| \leq K_1 e^{-c_1 \alpha^2}$$

for some positive constants K_1 and c_1. Using the second representation for $\hat{u}(\frac{1}{2}T, \omega)$, with $\omega = i\beta$ for $\beta \geq \beta_0$, we have that

$$\|\hat{u}(\tfrac{1}{2}T, \omega)\| \leq K_2 e^{-c_2 \beta^2}$$

for some positive constants K_2 and c_2. Using both representations (C.9) shows that

$$\|\hat{u}(\tfrac{1}{2}T, \omega)\| \le K_3 e^{d|\omega|}$$

for some constants K_3 and d.

Proposition C.3, with some adjustment, shows that each component of $\hat{u}(\tfrac{1}{2}T, \omega)$ satisfies

$$|u_\ell(\tfrac{1}{2}T, \omega)| \le K e^{-c|\omega|^2}$$

for all ω with $\operatorname{Im} \omega \ge \beta_0$. We now use the Fourier inversion formula (2.1.2) and this estimate on $\hat{u}(\tfrac{1}{2}T, \omega)$ to show that $u(\tfrac{1}{2}T, x)$ is zero. We have

$$u(\tfrac{1}{2}T, x) = \frac{1}{\sqrt{2\pi}} \int_{-\infty+i\beta}^{\infty+i\beta} e^{i\omega x} \hat{u}(\tfrac{1}{2}T, \omega)\, d\omega$$

for any $\beta \ge \beta_0$. (We may replace the path of integration from the real line to the line given by $\operatorname{Im} z = \beta$ because of Cauchy's theorem.) Therefore,

$$\|u(\tfrac{1}{2}T, x)\| \le C \int_{-\infty}^{\infty} e^{\beta|x|} e^{-c(\alpha^2+\beta^2)}\, d\alpha$$

$$= C' e^{\beta|x|} e^{-c\beta^2}.$$

By taking β arbitrarily large, we conclude that $u(\tfrac{1}{2}T, x)$ is zero for all x, both positive and negative. By representations (C.9) we conclude that $u(0, x)$ is also zero, and hence that $u(t, x)$ is zero. ∎

EXERCISES C

1. Show that if $|f(z)|$ is bounded on the boundary of the quadrant Q_1, as defined in proposition C.3, and if $|f(z) \le C(1 + |z|^m)$ in the quadrant Q_1 for some value of m, then in fact $|f(z)|$ is bounded in Q_1.

2. Show that Proposition C.4 can be extended to R^n where $u(0, x)$ and $u(T, x)$ are zero for x in the half-space $x_1 \ge 0$.

3. Use the calculus of residues to verify the formulas given in Exercise 10.2.3. *Hint:* Consider the integral over the real line and the line $\operatorname{Im} z = \pi$.

4. Use the calculus of residues to show that

$$\int_0^\infty \frac{x^\alpha}{x^2 + 1}\, dx = \frac{\pi}{2\cos\tfrac{1}{2}\alpha\pi}$$

for $0 \le \alpha < 1$. *Hint:* Consider curves similar to those used in Example C.1 and use the relation $x^\alpha = e^{i\pi\alpha}|x|^\alpha$ for x negative when z^α is defined in the upper half-plane.

References

[1] Abarbanel, S., and D. Gottlieb. 1976. A note on the leap-frog scheme in two and three dimensions. *Journal of Computational Physics,* 21:351–5.

[2] Ahlfors, L.V. 1966. *Complex analysis,* 2nd ed. New York: McGraw-Hill.

[3] Apostol, T. 1964. *Mathematical analysis.* Reading, Mass.: Addison-Wesley.

[4] Beam, R.M., and R.F. Warming. 1980. Alternating direction implicit methods for parabolic equations with a mixed derivative. *SIAM Journal on Scientific and Statistical Computing,* 1:131–59.

[5] Brenner, P., V. Thomée, and L. Wahlbin. 1974. *Besov spaces and applications to difference methods for initial value problems.* New York: Springer-Verlag.

[6] Bube, K.P., and J.C. Strikwerda. 1983. Interior regularity estimates for elliptic systems of difference equations. *SIAM Journal on Numerical Analysis,* 20:653–70.

[7] Buck, R.C. 1965. *Advanced calculus.* New York: McGraw-Hill.

[8] Chazarain, J., and A. Piriou. 1982. *Introduction to the theory of linear partial differential equations.* New York: North-Holland.

[9] Courant, R., K.O. Friedrichs, and H. Lewy. 1928. Über die partiellen differenzengleichungen der mathematischen physik. *Mathematische Annalen,* 100:32–74.

[10] Crank, J., and P. Nicolson. 1947. A practical method for numerical integration of solutions of partial differential equations of heat-conduction type. *Proceedings of the Cambridge Philosophical Society,* 43:50–67.

[11] Douglas, J., and H.H. Rachford. 1956. On the numerical solution of heat conduction problems in two and three space variables. *Transactions of the American Mathematical Society,* 82:421–39.

[12] Douglis, A., and L. Nirenberg. 1955. Interior estimates for elliptic systems of partial differential equations. *Communications on Pure and Applied Mathematics,* 8:503–38.

[13] Eisenstat, S.C. 1981. Efficient implementation of a class of preconditioned conjugate gradient methods. *SIAM Journal on Scientific and Statistical Computing,* 2:1–4.

[14] Elman, H.C. 1982. Iterative methods for large, sparse, nonsymmetric, systems of linear equations. Ph.D. Dissertation, Yale University.

[15] Fairweather, G., and A.R. Mitchell. 1965. A high accuracy alternating direction method for the wave equation. *Journal of the Institute of Mathematics and Its Applications,* 1:309–16.

[16] Folland, G.B. 1976. *Introduction to partial differential equations.* Princeton, N.J.: Princeton University Press.

[17] Foquel, S.R. 1964. A counterexample to a problem of S. Nagy. *Proceedings of the American Mathematics Society,* 15:788–90.

[18] Frank, L.S. 1972. Algébra des opérateurs aux difference finies. *Israel Journal of Mathematics,* 13:24–55.

[19] Garabedian, P. 1956. Estimation of the relaxation factor for small mesh sizes. *Mathematical Tables and Other Aids to Computation,* 10:183–5.

[20] Garabedian, P. 1964. *Partial differential equations.* New York: John Wiley.

[21] Goldberg, R.R. 1965. *Fourier transforms.* New York: Cambridge University Press.

[22] Gottlieb, D. 1972. Strang type difference schemes for multidimensional problems. *SIAM Journal on Numerical Analysis,* 9:650–61.

[23] Gustafsson, B., H.-O. Kreiss, and A. Sundström. 1972. Stability theory of difference approximations for mixed initial-boundary value problems, II. *Mathematics of Computation,* 26:649–86.

[24] Hageman, L.A., and D.M. Young. 1981. *Applied iterative methods.* New York: Academic Press.

[25] James, K.R. 1973. Convergence of matrix iterations subject to diagonal dominance. *SIAM Journal on Numerical Analysis,* 10:478–84.

[26] Kreiss, H.-O. 1962. Über die stabilitätsdefinition für differenzengleichungen die partielle differentialgleichungen approximieren. *Nordisk Tidskrift for Informationsbehandling (BIT),* 2:153–81.

[27] Kreiss, H.-O. 1963. Über sachgemässe cauchyprobleme. *Mathematica Scandinavica,* 13:109–28.

[28] Kreiss, H.-O. 1970. Initial boundary value problems for hyperbolic systems. *Communications on Pure and Applied Mathematics,* 23:277–98.

[29] Kreiss, H.-O. 1974. "Boundary conditions for hyperbolic differential equations." In *Conference on Numerical Solution of Differential Equations,* Eds. A. Dodd and B. Eckman. 64–74. Lecture Notes in Mathematics, 363. New York: Springer-Verlag.

[30] Lax, P.D., and L. Nirenberg. 1966. On stability of difference schemes; a sharp form of Gårding's inequality. *Communications on Pure and Applied Mathematics,* 19:473–92.

[31] Lax, P.D., and B. Wendroff. 1960. Systems of conservation laws. *Communications on Pure and Applied Mathematics,* 13:217–37.

[32] LeVeque, R.J., and J. Oliger 1983. Numerical methods based on additive splittings for hyperbolic partial differential equations. *Mathematics of Computation*, 40:469–97.

[33] MacCormack, R.W. 1971. Numerical solution of the interaction of a shock wave with a laminar boundary layer. In *Proceedings of the Second International Conference on Numerical Methods in Fluid Dynamics*, Ed. M. Holt. 151-63. Lecture Notes in Physics, 8. New York: Springer-Verlag.

[34] Michelson, D., 1983. Stability theory of difference approximations for multi-dimensional initial-boundary value problems. *Mathematics of Computation*, 40:1–45.

[35] Miller, J.J.H. 1971. On the location of zeros of certain classes of polynomials with applications to numerical analysis. *Journal of the Institute of Mathematics and Its Applications*, 8:397–406.

[36] Mitchell, A.R., and G. Fairweather. 1964. Improved forms of the alternating direction methods of Douglas, Peaceman and Rachford for solving parabolic and elliptic equations. *Numerische Mathematik*, 6:285–92.

[37] Morton, K.W., and S. Schecter. 1965. On the stability of finite difference matrices. *SIAM Journal on Numerical Analysis, Series B*, 2:119–28.

[38] Oliger, J., and A. Sundström. 1978. Theoretical and practical aspects of some initial-boundary value problems in fluid dynamics. *SIAM Journal on Applied Mathematics*, 35:419–46.

[39] Osher, S. 1969. Stability of difference approximations of dissipative type for mixed initial-boundary value problems, I. *Mathematics of Computation*, 23:335–40.

[40] Osher, S. 1969. Systems of difference equations with general homogeneous boundary conditions. *Transactions of the American Mathematics Society*, 137:177–201.

[41] Peaceman, D.W., and H.H. Rachford. 1955. The numerical solution of parabolic and elliptic differential equations. *Journal of the Society for Industrial and Applied Mathematics*, 3:28–41.

[42] Pearcy, C. 1966. An elementary proof of the power inequality for the numerical radius. *Michigan Mathematics Journal*, 13:289–91.

[43] Peetre, J., and V. Thomée. 1967. On the rate of convergence for discrete initial-value problems. *Mathematica Scandinavica*, 21:159–76.

[44] Richtmyer, R.D., and K.W. Morton. 1967. *Difference methods for initial-value problems*, 2nd ed. New York: Wiley Interscience.

[45] Shintani, H., and K. Toemeda. 1977. Stability of difference schemes for nonsymmetric linear hyperbolic systems with variable coefficients. *Hiroshima Mathematical Journal*, 7:309–78.

[46] Strang, G. 1968. On the construction and comparison of difference schemes. *SIAM Journal on Numerical Analysis,* 5:506–17.

[47] Strikwerda, J.C., and B.A. Wade. 1988. An extension of the Kreiss matrix theorem. *SIAM Journal on Numerical Analysis,* 25:1272–78.

[48] Tadmor, E. 1981. The equivalence of L-stability, the resolvent condition, and strict H-stability. *Linear Algebra and Its Applications,* 41:151–9.

[49] Taylor, M.E. 1984. *Pseudodifferential operators.* Princeton, N.J.: Princeton University Press.

[50] Titchmarsh, E.C. 1962. *Introduction to the theory of Fourier integrals.* Oxford: Clarendon Press.

[51] Trefethen, L.N. 1982. Group velocity in finite difference schemes. *SIAM Review,* 24:113–36.

[52] Trefethen, L.N. 1984. Instability of difference models for hyperbolic initial boundary value problems. *Communications on Pure and Applied Mathematics,* 37:329–67.

[53] Varga, R.S. 1962. *Matrix iterative analysis.* Englewood Cliffs, N.J.: Prentice-Hall.

[54] Vichnevetsky, R., and J. Bowles. 1982. *Fourier analysis of numerical approximations of hyperbolic equations.* Philadelphia, Penn.: SIAM.

[55] Wachpress, E.L. 1966. *Iterative solution of elliptic systems and application to the neutron diffusion equations of reactor physics.* Englewood Cliffs, N.J.: Prentice-Hall.

[56] Wade, B.A. 1987. Stability and sharp convergence estimates for symmetrizable difference operators. Ph.D. Dissertation, University of Wisconsin.

[57] Weinberger, H.F. 1965. *A first course in partial differential equations.* New York: John Wiley.

[58] West, D.H.D. 1979. Updating mean and variance estimates: an improved method. *Communications of the ACM,* 22:532–5.

[59] Yamaguti, M., and T. Nogi. 1967. An algebra of pseudo difference schemes and its applications. *Publications of the Research Institute of Mathematics, Kyoto University, Series A,* 3:151–66.

[60] Yanenko, N.N. 1971. *The method of fractional steps.* English translation edited by M. Holt. New York: Springer-Verlag.

[61] Young, D.M. 1971. *Iterative solution of large linear systems.* New York: Academic Press.

Index